HANDBOOK OF MEASUREMENT AND ASSESSMENT IN BEHAVIORAL SCIENCES

Edited by
DEAN K. WHITLA, *Harvard University*

HANDBOOK OF MEASUREMENT AND ASSESSMENT IN BEHAVIORAL SCIENCES

ADDISON-WESLEY PUBLISHING COMPANY
READING, MASSACHUSETTS · MENLO PARK, CALIFORNIA · LONDON · DON MILLS, ONTARIO

INTRODUCTION

This compilation of chapters is intended to serve the true function of a handbook and to be a ready and comprehensive reference on some diverse and intriguing measurement problems that are intrinsic to research in the behavioral sciences. To assist in this effort, an extensive summary of the chapters is here presented. This rather unusual approach is meant to be an introductory guide to the content of the chapters which can later serve as a précis and as a reminder of the wealth of ideas presented in the volume itself. For the chapters in Part I, on Measurement Statistics, this summary also provides a nonmathematical appraisal of the content.

The chapters have been organized into two domains: Part I covers many areas of statistics appropriate for the behavioral sciences, and Part II contains chapters covering a wide range of application of measurement and assessment techniques. While there is variation in sophistication among the chapters, primarily along mathematical dimensions, the exposition is intended to be at a professional level.

The first chapter, Tatsuoka's article on mathematical models, is set in the perspective of model-building as an intellectual style which has long been effectively used in the physical sciences but which is a relatively new development in the behavioral sciences. Tatsuoka begins by developing a general rubric, namely a classification system of figurative and analogue models, and from this point presents interrelationships of these styles with mathematical models.

Against this background, the author proceeds to explicate the stimulus-sampling models of learning, linear-operator models, Luce's beta model, an urn model, a single-element conditioning model, Markov-chain models, and an information-processing model. He develops in a highly lucid style the essence of the mathematical properties, the unique qualities of the model, and the effectiveness that has been demonstrated through experimental trials for each of the systems.

In summary, this chapter takes one rapidly through the short but productive history of mathematical model-building in the behavioral sciences. As Tatsuoka points out, this form of articulation has been a powerful means of closing the gap between, for example, the contiguity and reinforcement views of learning. Models have also helped to clarify the degree to which the dynamics of group behavior can be explained by means of principles of individual psychology alone without the introduction of concepts of social interaction, group cohesiveness, social pressure, and so forth. The general rubrics developed for the presentation of these ideas plus the restatement of the mathematical bases of each of the models contribute to the effectiveness of this chapter.

In many delightful ways the Rulon and Brooks chapter is a tour de force, a rare (and in this instance a productive) method of statistical presentation.* In their chapter for this handbook, Rulon and Brooks show with particular elegance the interrelations among the t-test, the F-test, Hotelling's T^2, Mahalanobis' D^2 and Wilks's Λ. The comparisons are worth making because these are topics seldom covered by statistical texts and consequently are left untouched in the experimental literature of the behavioral sciences. Using essentially algebraic manipulations and numerical examples, the authors demonstrate convincingly the relative power of these several statistics. Wilks's Λ is demonstrated as applicable to any case for which t, F, T^2, or D^2 might be employed.

The particular form in which the material is presented and the way in which the argument is developed are provocative and contribute to the significance of this work. The guileless reader should be cautioned that the neatness of the examples and their accuracy as developed to four places are due in large part to the extreme degree in which these data fit the properties of the Gaussian model; Rulon and Brooks are as fallible as any of us when required to manipulate ordinary data.

In Chapter 3, Bock and Haggard record the remarkable advances in multivariate analysis in recent years, particularly in the generalization of analysis of variance. The principles of univariate experimental design are applicable to the multivariate case when it is appropriate to assume independence among the variables; however, when this is not true there is a need for a multivariate test which takes into account the correlations between variables and the nature of the sampling distributions. To illustrate the similarity between the multivariate and the univariate design, the authors consistently compare these statistics. It is interesting to note the value of the multivariate results, which give not only an evaluation of the several hypotheses but also useful data for the interpretation of the interaction effect.

Bock and Haggard, after developing the mathematics and illustrative materials for such cases, proceed to show the power of multivariate generalization for the analysis of covariance. Since designs with disproportional numbers of cases are common in behavioral research, this treatment receives special attention. The authors present criteria for selecting statistical tests, among them some that are the subject of the Rulon and Brooks chapter; however, their primary interest is in the step-down F-statistic. They also develop the multivariate regression model, canonical correlation, the stepwise regression analysis, and the test for homogeneity of regression. One particular strength of this chapter is the consistent terminology

---

* If the reader wishes to expand his knowledge in further enjoyable ways, he should delve into an article by the senior author entitled "The Stanine and the Septile," a fable published in the *Journal of Personnel Psychology*.

which Bock and Haggard use in discussing a great range of multivariate tests. This sophisticated presentation, effectively punctuated with appropriate examples, ends with some brief comments on special uses of multivariate statistics, trend analysis, and scaling problems.

Harman presents a comprehensive view of factor analysis which is less mathematically oriented than his usual treatises. Through abandoning some of their mathematical elegance, he has substituted effective prose which makes it possible for him to retain the power of his presentation. Specifically, he starts with the historical problems (many of us yet bear the scars of hand calculator computations!), and gives us a sense of the place of factor analysis in the domain of statistics—specifically, within the analysis of interdependence. He then provides an understanding of the alternatives available among the direct or factor solutions; he contrasts the derived or rotated solutions, and provides information about an additional form of output—the factor score. As he weaves his way through a simple computational example, he illustrates the alternatives among which the factor analyst can, must, and in fact, does decide (whether or not he knows it). Harman explains the bases for these decisions, and does so in such a manner that factor analysts will no longer need to allow such decisions to be made by default, by the universal all-knowing computer program.

Stevens' chapter on scaling provides both a view of Fechner's work on just noticeable differences (jnd) and Thurstone's indirect methods of scaling on the one hand, and a summary of the current trends, procedures, and findings on the other. He makes the point that the formal models of measurement emphasizing the logical and mathematical procedures presented in the preceding chapters have little or no importance until they are tied to empirical observations.

The author clearly documents the interrelationships among continua scaled by magnitude estimation, category, and number of jnds. The universality of these relationships when applied to prothetic (intensive) continua approaches a psychological law. Ekman proved that the relationship between the Thurstonian indirect methods of scaling and direct procedures of ratio and magnitude estimation is logarithmic. Stevens feels that this work, which empirically established the generality of this power function on subjective continua, should be known as Ekman's law. He reviews studies on attitude statements, preference for wristwatches, esthetic value of handwriting, drawings, and music, the importance of Swedish monarchs, occupational preferences, pleasantness of odors, liberal-conservative attitudes, seriousness of offenses, and other similar continua that show there is a remarkable convergence of evidence supporting this power relationship. On many continua, this power law cannot be directly confirmed, since a number of these stimuli can be measured only by comparing results obtained using various scaling procedures. In such cases, the same power function remains invariate when the comparison is made between the forms of the scale. The consistency of this relationship indicates an essential unity among the principles that govern quantitative relations. As Stevens ends his chapter, he states that "for those who must build their science on some consensus of human judgment, a way now seems open for effective quantification."

Peaker, in his discussion of sampling, emphasizes the contrast between importance and significance in the context of sampling statistics. In his remarks about sampling error he reminds us of his Scotch heritage with his illustration that error in the context of sampling does not mean "mistake" but "wandering," as in knight errantry. With simplicity and power he develops the effects of stratification, stage sampling, and replication, and shows most parsimoniously the importance and reasons for such forms of sampling, their relative power, and the size of sample necessary. He also provides a judicious choice of formulas useful in making sampling decisions. His Table I summarizes the effects of stage sampling and illustrates why confidence limits are often greatly understated.

Peaker's methods of simulation, of approximating significance, and of evaluating an experimental design are wise and functional suggestions for improving the conduct of research.

In Guilford's comprehensive article on the structure of intellect, this important thinker has presented a review of his own work as well as some critical commentary on the field of intelligence testing. He opens by discussing some traditional views of the nature of intelligence and notes the passing in the United States of the concept of a unitary intelligence and of a meaningful g or general factor. He then goes on to provide a concise overview of his structure-of-intellect model, which is, in brief, a classification of intellectual abilities demonstrated by factor analysis. He acknowledges that the abilities defined by his model do not represent "functions that operate separately in behavior," and that there are "many intricate kinds of mutual involvements of abilities in everyday life."

Recognizing these interdependencies, he has arrived at five categories of factors: cognition, memory, divergent production, convergent production, and evaluation. He points out, quite rightly, the stimulus value of findings from factor analysis for theoretical thinking. For example, his structure-of-intellect model is based on a view of the reacting organism where information is the crucial concept. The organism is an information processor, the type of processing differing in accordance with the type of information being processed. It is this interaction of processor and processed data that produces the distinguishable abilities found in the S.I. model. In Guilford's view his model offers hope for understanding the important human faculties of thinking, reasoning, and imagination.

Guilford sees Piaget's genetic approach to the structure of intellect (which he considers briefly in the article) as complementary to his own; the models should serve to supplement each other as ways of considering intelligence. He does note that one of the significant differences between his efforts and those of Piaget is that the latter ". . . has given more attention to the development of *particular* products than to generic *types* of products."

In his discussion of the implications of his work for education, Guilford is particularly hopeful. His model provides a systematic taxonomy of intellectual skills; the value of such a taxonomy to curriculum developers is discussed at length. Guilford also stresses the limitations which he feels exist in the current crop of intelligence tests, such as their stress on semantic and cognitive abilities, with little or no sampling of divergent production abilities and symbolic or behavioral abilities.

Guilford is somewhat at odds with Frank Barron's work in a later chapter in his attitude toward the growing tendency to use "creativity" batteries, for he fears that stress on such batteries would result in continued neglect of many other and equally important abilities. He feels that more fruitful work will be done in the area of behavioral categories, and he cites the relatively untapped problem areas of sense-modality: auditory, kinesthetic, and tactual information.

Special problems of factor analysis in his work on intellect are covered by Guilford in the last section of this chapter.

The chapter entitled "Measurement of Aptitude and Achievement" contains a review of some of the basic concepts in testing and provides a straightforward introduction to the field, accompanied by numerous examples. Seibel discusses many of the pitfalls into which the amateur can fall. Taking behavior as the means of measuring intellectual powers and characteristics, he focuses the chapter on paper-and-pencil tests as measures of behavior.

Seibel defines the problems of assessing behavior in terms of aptitude and achievement as (1) accuracy or consistency of observation, that is, test reliability; (2) validity of a test; (3) the meaning of a test score. While he distinguishes among three types of tests—aptitude, achievement, and intelligence—he stresses their similarities, in that all measure learned skills and abilities. He points out that if we looked at a test item without knowing its source, we would find it difficult to specify the type of test from which it was taken.

Seibel then discusses problems of reliability and ways of testing items, and furnishes the initiate to the field with a sound, easy-to-read discussion of statistics fundamental to test analysis, such as the correlation coefficient, the standard deviation, and the standard error of measurement. In his section on norms he discusses problems of reference groups, and derived scores or standard scores. He provides many practical examples of application.

The author also discusses validity in its various guises—content or face validity, concurrent validity, and predictive validity—and devotes a section to standardized tests, individual and group tests, and objective and essay tests. In his appendices he has given the reader information on sources of test catalogs, as well as a descriptive list of selected standardized tests.

Wing treats with élan and wit the elusive dimensions of human personality, and the diversity of approaches to the measurement of this tantalizing subject. His chapter focuses on three approaches to personality assessment: clinical observation, experimental manipulation, and statistical manipulation.

His discussions of these three styles bring out the salient features of each method. I note as an example his comments on clinical method: its focus on the individual, its emphasis on global assessment and on theoretical considerations. He describes the virtue of flexibility in the clinical approach and makes the valuable point that the clinician in a very real sense uses himself as a measuring instrument.

Wing asserts that all approaches to measuring personality use inference about what is going on inside the person in order to classify, describe, or communicate characteristics or patterns. He points to the value of eclectic use of various approaches, to fit the situation at hand.

The common thrust to the diverse work in this field is an interest in establishing "the relationship between dependent and independent variables." From this standpoint, Wing discusses statistical manipulation of data, noting that this approach involves the concern with the whole personality that is typical of clinical work, along with the conditions of "rigorous, quantitative measurement" typical of experimental assessment. He notes the *a posteriori* method of hypothesizing in the statistical method, compared to the *a priori* hypothesizing of the clinical and experimental approaches, and points out that in contrast to the clinician, the statistical researcher is concerned with the normal rather than the abnormal case, with representative populations rather than single individuals.

This article then goes on to consider some of the techniques of measurement and their problems, starting with the practical and pervasive consideration of economy. This the author mentions to point up the fundamental considerations that the measurer, whatever his style, must be selective in his techniques.

As does Seibel, Wing considers the importance of reliability and validity in assessment, and reduces to two crucial categories the types of assessment that one can employ: "what the individual tells you about himself, whether through interviews, paper-and-pencil tests, projective tests, or reports of dreams; and what can be observed about him by others, whether in controlled or laboratory situations or in real-life situations." He goes on to review projective techniques, self-evaluating techniques, and observations of behavior.

In conclusion, Wing puts forth his suggestion that a key to improving the predictive efficiency, or empirical validity, of many personality measures "lies in developing conformity between the measurement environment and the criterion environment." He hypothesizes that the greater the similarity between the two environments, the greater the chances of achieving high empirical validity, and he reports on studies that point in this direction.

Barron brings to "The Measurement of Creativity" his special and engaging blend of artistry and scientific investigation. He notes that "a first criterion for an original response is that it should have a certain stated uncommonness in the particular group being studied." Yet he is cognizant of the difficult human predicament of radical originality: if an idea is too far ahead of its time, it may be considered bizarre or delusional. Even more fundamentally, the original response "must correspond to some extent, or be adaptive to, reality."

Barron provides examples of all kinds of verbal originality. As we know, tests to measure creativity put great reliance on verbal fluency and usage; he rightly points to the need for measures of originality in nonverbal constructions, and mentions Guilford's development of a variety of nonverbal tests of creativity.

The author goes on to introduce us to the Psychodiagnostic. He discusses at some length Rorschach's work on inkblots, enjoining us to be wary of the problems of evaluation of the Psychodiagnostic, which depends more than any other test he reviews on consensual verification. "If the examiner himself cannot 'see' the form the examinee 'sees,' he must try to find someone else who *can* see it. If after a reasonable effort in searching, the form still proves elusive, it is considered not to be 'there.' " The scoring scheme, he notes, is as ambiguous as the blots themselves are; and being complex, it does not lend itself well to isolation of variables and correlation among components.

Barron explores questionnaire and preference inventories, such as the Strong Vocational Interest Blank and the Minnesota Multiphasic Personality Inventory, as examples of tests that can be scored by machine and that depend "not on sampling in miniature certain kinds of creative abilities but rather on searching widely for the attitudes, preferences, and motives that are known to stimulate an individual to create." One of Barron's studies using data from the Strong Blank is described.

From other studies he has undertaken, the author suggests that the original person is "forceful, self-assertive, fond of conflict and even combat, perhaps a bit self-dramatizing or exhibitionistic, and with a flair for individualistic and distinctive statement." Again, however, his tests in the reported research were, in general, tests that tapped verbal expression, and Barron concedes readily that this is only one aspect of creativity. As an attempt to tap other aspects of creativity, he and G. S. Welsh have constructed a nonverbal preference inventory of line drawings that are meant to discriminate between artists and nonartists. The essential variable of separation appears to be a preference for what Barron calls "complex dynamic asymmetry" as opposed to "simple static symmetry."

Discussing measurement of creativity in children, Barron notes that tests similar to the adult tests have long been in use.

As he considers suggestions for creativity testing, Barron points out the limitations of presently existing tests: their superficiality, their attempts to measure creativity or creative ability in fragments, and their abortion of the creative process by their shortness. He closes with an acknowledgment of the criterion problem in this complex and elusive area.

Berdie and Campbell begin their well-wrought chapter with the statement that the concept of interest, "like many other concepts in psychology, is a convenient but not a necessary construct." They choose to stress the heuristic value of such concepts and the facility of communication between investigators that common terminology helps to secure.

The authors see the number of possible interests as limited only by the number of possible experiences within the environment. Interest measurement, however, has tended to group interest into a dichotomy of vocational or recreational—work or play—interests. Research over the past 25 years is covered in this review, including the well-known constructs of Donald Super, who has identified four interpretations of interest: expressed interest, manifest interest, tested interest and inventoried interest. Almost all research, the authors note, has been conducted on inventoried interests, and almost all interest inventories cover vocational interests. In this chapter, therefore, they choose to focus on the problems of these vocational-interest inventories.

It was E. K. Strong who originally utilized the benefits of a men-in-general sampling as a base for comparing criterion groups on interests. The definition of groups proved to be an important problem in determining scales. Berdie and Campbell write about the Strong Vocational Interest Blank and the Minnesota Multiphasic Personality Inventory in considerable detail. In their discussion of scaling, they note that scales based on differences in responses of criterion groups and a reference group of men-in-general have several advantages: they are easily understood, simple to develop, and demonstrably effective. The problems of level of reference group and similarity of various professions are considered through the work of Strong and Dunnette. The empirically derived scales of the SVIB and the homogeneous scales of the Kuder Preference Record, Vocational, are then given as interesting examples of the value of two different approaches to interest measurement. The problem of scale validity is cogently presented as a problem of item format and item content.

Many special problems of faking, reliability, and individual resistance to testing are parsimoniously treated. Under the area of item content the authors cover useful information for evaluation using Strong's four standards: unfamiliarity, ambiguity, differentiation between criterion groups and men-in-general, and number of scales scored on. The methods of weighting of items are also sufficiently reviewed.

As in Seibel's chapter, these authors discuss the various types of validity, summarizing their conclusions in the statement that "a large number of research studies leave little question but that interest inventories can provide descriptive psychological information characterizing groups in a way conforming to reasonable expectations."

Howells, in making the distinction between measurement in other fields and measurement in anthropology, notes that the latter evaluates—from the standpoint of genetics, race, or evolution—variation rather than qualities; in other words, rather than assessing performance, the physical anthropologist studies the organism itself.

Physical anthropology, with its biological basis, stresses the point of view of genetics and function. Howells presents the growth of this field over the past 100 years as a growth in methodological tools (measurement of traits, etc.) and in theory (particularly progress of evolutionary theory), and of important interactions between the two.

In his discussion of the long history of attempts to assess variation in human beings by body type, he points out that the body-constitution method has always been an attempt to classify man's whole nature—temper as well as form. He then goes on to review the work of Viola, Kretschmer, and Sheldon, and distinguishes Sheldon from others working earlier in the field especially by his use of scaling. Sheldon's types are "not primary categories, as in previous systems, but rather intervals in a continuous three-dimensional space." While Sheldon's attempts to use his work as a system for constitutional psychology have largely fallen into contempt because of his methods of presenting results, such researchers as the Gluecks have found associations between body type and delinquency. On the whole, body typing has not been extended much beyond the relation of body form to disease.

The use of factor analysis in working with components of body shape has yielded some interesting work, including that of Sheldon, as well as of Howells himself. This method permits differentiations of the principal modes of individuals. Results from this work have revealed factors approximating the endomorphic and ectomorphic types, although a factor representing mesomorphy directly has not been found.

Analysis of body composition should, as Howells points up, be a complementary process to the synthetic approach of physical typing. Little work has been done, however, combining these two approaches.

Howells, as his second major area of discussion, covers work in practical anthropometry, or assessing growth. In studying growth, workers at the simplest level have provided tables of expected heights and weights. The research into basic growth processes has emphasized longitudinal observation. In this area, constitution and body type are areas of special interest, as are the biochemical aspects of body development.

Howells distinguishes R. A. Fisher as the coordinator of the measuring and genetic study phases of anthropology. Fisher's background in statistics and theoretical genetics especially suited him to this task, which he handled with brilliance, developing a theory of population genetics that considered the structure of populations in genetic terms.

Howells has provided his own excellent definition of anthropometry: "the measurement of human variables generally . . . the study of man in many of his most important aspects." This intrepid researcher sees this field as the avenue to eventual analysis of multifactorial genetics and as the way to study the responses of individuals and groups to different environments or diets and to arrive at some general predictions of disease susceptibility. Of interest to educators particularly is his view that anthropometry is an approach that will be useful to an understanding of native intelligence.

At the end of his article, Howells points to directions of anthropometrical development, stressing as important areas the identification of external causes of variation in human traits and research into genetic factors. He closes with an emphasis on the ever-broadening possibilities for statistical analysis, especially factor analytic techniques, and reviews several relevant and intriguing studies. In summary, he points to the gains for human understanding that may emerge from the anthropologist's use of methods from other fields to explore the basic factors in the underlying genetic and biological nature of man.

Starting with the issues underlying the old and largely unresolved question, "What do we do after making our predictions?" Tiedeman and Field present their view of the guidance process. Viewing guidance as the "science of purposeful action applied through education," they separate the guidance function from that of teaching in terms of a useful dichotomy of "inside" and "outside" information. The guidance function is to make the former type of information available to the student in the decision process.

The concept of purposeful action gives rise to a general paradigm based on expected performance leading to differentiation, feedback, and integration. The development of this paradigm involves the origins and evaluation of an individual's expected performance using the concepts of cognitive dissonance, and dissonance and discontinuity, as they affect personality development. It also serves as a model useful in developing a statement about measurement needs.

Tiedeman and Field show that the trait model of measurement does not adequately meet the requirements of the paradigm. They stress the contrast between information relevant for a particular individual making his own decisions and information useful for making decisions about others. They propose that their dynamic prediction model has within it more capacity for incorporating the steps of exploration, crystallization, choice, and clarification fundamental in personal decisions. To meet the requirements of this theoretical position, they posit that a series of statistical methods must be developed. It might not be inappropriate to mention that Tiedeman recently received a sizable research grant to explore and develop such a model; we can look forward to some exciting research.

The college admissions process provides a good opportunity for examining the decision process through a number of psychological, sociological, and statistical models. The advantages are that this process cycles annually, providing automatic replication, that it is a dynamic, reality-oriented function which meets a highly significant institutional need—the selection of new members of the social system—and that in the course of this decision-making process, many data are collected. The chapter starts at a rather simple level of exposition on the topic of the regression equation, a device that has been widely used for the prediction of grades in college admissions. Examples of the effectiveness of this procedure are given in both tabular and correlation form. Explanations of the meaning and power of correlation, and ways the components of the regression equation might be evaluated have been included. There is a discussion of the oscillating beta function that arises under cyclic conditions such as occur in admissions, and that can markedly change the interpretation of regression equation findings. The "regressive" qualities of these equations are discussed in the context of Galton's data, which formed the original basis for the concept of regression. The effect of restriction in range of variables on correlation and on prediction are discussed along with some new work on the evaluation of Pearson's restriction-in-range formulas.

The chapter contains a report on an extensive study of Harvard College admissions practices. Using the information collected on 21 variables during the admissions decisions, the author presents a variety of analyses to document the nature of the decision process. These analyses began with correlations and tabulations, and continued through factor analyses and associated rotations. The results are presented for two reasons: first, the opportunity to see a problem of a social system explored continuously for the period of a decade provides analyses of the decision process that in themselves are interesting; second, the sequential nature of the analyses brings to the fore a number of methodological problems of factor analysis that were explored as part of the search for adequate interpretation of the results. Multiple correlations showed that the decision process was a highly predictable one and that there existed over the period of ten years a marked shift in the basis of the decisions.

The chapter ends with some explorations into validation, some discussion of the problems of experimental design in this setting, and a citation of statistics—some of which invite comparisons, some that are provocative (students with lower scores graduate on schedule more frequently than do those with higher scores), some that are preliminary (it is impossible to predict grades in "life")—interspersed with hypotheses which are in need of validation. The chapter provides a detailed illustration of the application of statistical techniques to one domain of social inquiry.

In retrospect, these chapters range widely over the theoretical and applied areas of measurement and assessment. They represent an effort to come to grips with salient problems in the behavioral sciences and, in the process, to advance the science of measurement.

May the reader find their perusal an adventure in learning.

Cambridge, Mass.   D.K.W.
November 1967

ACKNOWLEDGMENTS

Correct computational techniques; accurate mathematical analysis; the development of criteria and abstract concepts related to aims and choice, in terms of which the analysis may be unified; and the beginnings of an operational inductive logic, have each required exposition and exemplification, sometimes not unattended by controversy. In each of these fields there is still much to be done.*

R. A. Fisher's words put perspective on the fourteen chapters that follow, for these chapters represent fourteen styles of work and illustrate the range and power of measurement in addressing problems of evaluation in today's world.

Words cannot adequately convey my indebtedness to the authors; I want to thank them in measure corresponding to their patience with and understanding of a neophyte editor. I also wish to acknowledge the assistance I have received from many who read and commented on the chapters: Charles C. McArthur, Frederick Mosteller, John Whiteley, Humphrey Doermann, Jane Knitzer, Fred L. Glimp, Irving L. Broudy, Martin Schatzoff, and especially Janet P. Hanley. I would also like to thank Miss Elizabeth Gibb and Mrs. Carole Edwards for their invaluable services in the preparation of the manuscript.

---

* R. A. FISHER, *Contributions to Mathematical Statistics,* New York, John Wiley and Sons, 1950.

CONTENTS

xix

Part 1   MEASUREMENT STATISTICS

CHAPTER 1

MATHEMATICAL MODELS
IN THE BEHAVIORAL AND SOCIAL SCIENCES*

MAURICE M. TATSUOKA, *University of Illinois*

I. INTRODUCTION

Not long ago Arrow could correctly say of the social sciences that ". . . outside the realm of economics, very little use has been made of mathematical and symbolic methods" (Arrow, 1951, p. 130). Although he was writing of the social sciences in a narrower sense, referring to the policy sciences, his remark would have been equally true if he had included psychology. Today, however, the use of models, with varying degrees of mathematical and symbolic machinery, has become something of a fad in the social-science area—particularly in psychology. It is seldom that one picks up an article on psychological research that does not refer to a model in some way or another; often the reference is to a mathematical model.

While this proliferation of model-building has been hailed by many as a sign of the maturing of psychology as a science, it has not been without its critics. Most of the criticisms have come, quite naturally, from psychologists who hold the view that human behavior cannot be described mathematically. However, some objections have been raised even by quantitatively oriented psychologists. A noteworthy example is this declamation by McNemar in his Presidential Address at the Western Psychological Association's 1959 convention: "In a sense, this model business is nothing more than a new name for old hat stuff . . . One suspects that such [model-] building rests on a foundation of mathematical quicksand and psychological bog" (McNemar, 1960, p. 300). There may be some justification for such complaints; for, as the philosopher of science Max Black says, "When used unemphatically, 'model' in such contexts [i.e., in statements by some social scientists] is often no more than a pretentious substitute for 'theory' or 'mathematical treatment' " (Black, 1962, p. 233). Nevertheless, it would be purblind of anyone to deny that a great deal of the model-building activity of psychologists over the past decade represents a significant contribution to the science of human behavior.

At any rate, regardless of what attitude we may take toward mathematical models, it is certain that they are "here to stay," and that the future will see their increasing use and development. It behooves us, therefore, to gain an understanding of the nature of models, a knowledge of their relationship to other kinds of theoriz-

* Partial support for preparation of this chapter has been received from the National Science Foundation (Grant NSF–G 10679). The author is indebted to J. A. Easley, Jr. for helpful comments on an earlier draft of this chapter.

3

ing and to experimentation, and an appreciation of their advantages and limitations. Only then can we view them in a proper perspective and avoid the two extremes of going completely overboard for them or of refusing to see any merit in them.

The purpose of this chapter is to provide the interested but uninitiated reader with a brief introduction to the field and with a frame of reference that may help him in reading and appraising the literature related to mathematical models in psychology. It is hoped that the chapter will also provide a guide to this literature, although the bibliography is far from being exhaustive. The reader is especially urged to thumb through articles appearing in the *Journal of Mathematical Psychology,* which began publication in 1964, to get an idea of the vigorous activity currently going on in this field.

II. VARIOUS KINDS OF MODELS AND MODEL-BUILDING: SOME CLASSIFICATIONS

Although this chapter is concerned primarily with mathematical models, I shall begin with a discussion of the general notion of models in science. Ever since the dawn of science, investigators have been engaging in what we would now call "model-building," even though the model-builder himself may have thought that he was describing physical phenomena or entities as they really were. Consider, for example, the Ptolemaic (geocentric) and Copernican (heliocentric) "models" of the solar system. In all likelihood, Ptolemy and Copernicus each thought that he was giving a true account of the universe. But now we view these as two alternative theories or models, one more fruitful than the other, but neither one providing an accurate or factual account.

It is difficult to ascertain just when and by whom the term "model" was first explicitly used to indicate the scientist's recognition that he was thinking and speaking in an "as though" language, that he was conjuring up a mental imagery to facilitate reasoning. But the use of the word in this sense dates at least as far back as the early teens of this century, when Bohr spoke of the "planetary model of the atom" developed by Rutherford and himself.

Interestingly enough, critical analyses of the role of models in scientific development have antedated the actual use of the word "model" by the theory-builder himself. Such analyses have long been undertaken by philosophers of science as well as by scientists of philosophical bent, among whom there seems to exist a wide variety of views as to the nature and worth of models. Part of the diversity stems from differences in the use of the word "model"—these differences, in turn, being partly idiosyncratic and partly a function of varying emphases in different periods.

Pierre Duhem, a French physicist of the nineteenth century, is often cited as one of the foremost opponents of the use of models. He objected vehemently to Faraday's lines-of-force model of the electrostatic field: ". . . the English physicist materializes these [abstract lines of force] and thickens them to the dimensions of a tube which he will fill with vulcanized rubber" (Duhem, 1954, p. 70).

This objection may be regarded as directed either at the *ontological commitment* (i.e., the attribution of material existence to the electrical field) implied by the model, or at the very use of such a model in scientific theorizing. If the former were the case, most modern scientists would agree with Duhem's position. But other passages in Duhem's writings show that he regarded the sheer use of models, with or without ontological commitment, as a debasement of scientific rigor—a crutch for obtuse minds.

Carnap (1955, pp. 209–210) seems to share Duhem's critical view of models. He writes (italics mine):

When abstract, nonintuitive formulas, as, e.g., Maxwell's equations of electromagnetism, were proposed as new axioms, physicists endeavored to make them 'intuitive' by constructing a 'model,' i.e., a way of representing electromagnetic micro-processes by an analogy to known macro-processes, e.g., movements of visible things. Many attempts were made in this direction, but without satisfactory results. It is important to realize that the discovery of a model has no more than an aesthetic or didactic *or at best a heuristic value,* but is not at all essential for a successful application of the physical theory.*

Such a view obviously relegates the heuristic phase of scientific activity to a secondary position, and assigns prime or sole value to the completed theory or system. Carnap chooses to ignore the vital role played by Faraday's intuitive picture of "real actions going on in the medium"—which preceded and led to Maxwell's equations—and thus gives the impression that the only models related to electromagnetic theory were those developed *after* Maxwell's equations. It is true that models constructed after the development of a formal theory (such as those purporting to explain abstract concepts like the "curl" or "rotation" of a magnetic field by analogy with whirls in flowing water) have only aesthetic or didactic value. But to lump such *ex post facto* models together with those which play an essential heuristic role *prior to* a formal theory seems an unwarranted generalization.

A viewpoint opposing those of Duhem and Carnap is expressed by Black, ". . . that models are sometimes not epiphenomena of research, but play a distinctive and irreplaceable part in scientific investigation" (Black, 1962, p. 236). Comparing models with metaphors, Black argues that thinking metaphorically is "a distinctive mode of achieving insight." In much the same way, he continues, the use of a model in scientific research may "help us to notice what otherwise would be overlooked, to shift the relative emphasis attached to details—in short, *to see new connections*" (1962, p. 237).

Figurative Models

The foregoing discussion, besides pointing out two diametrically opposed views on the value of models, allows us to discern at least two different kinds of models. The first is what we might call a *figurative model,* suggesting a figure of speech. This is exemplified by Faraday's lines-of-force model of the field between two electric conductors, in which he spoke of expansions and contractions of an elastic medium.

---

* R. Carnap, "Foundations of logic and mathematics," in *International Encyclopedia of Unified Science.* (Chicago: The University of Chicago Press, 1955, © 1955 by The University of Chicago Press.) Quoted by permission of the publisher.

It was this sort of model-building that came under violent attack from Duhem. Yet, talking and thinking in terms of this model gave Faraday new insights and led him to "see new connections"; it ultimately enabled him to arrive at a satisfactory explanation of most electrostatic phenomena, and some electromagnetic ones as well.

The second kind of model we saw exemplified above, in Maxwell's translation of Faraday's ideas into equations, is the *mathematical model.* More will be said about this later, but it should be mentioned here that the essential function of a mathematical model is to provide a system of *rules of inference,* or a *calculus,* for deriving testable statements (equations) from a set of basic postulates. Thus, for example, Maxwell's field equations (the basic postulates, arrived at by mathematizing Faraday's figurative model) led to, among other things, the prediction that electromagnetic waves are propagated with the very speed at which it had been shown that light traveled.

To summarize the foregoing analysis, we may say that Maxwell developed a mathematical model for Faraday's figurative model of certain electrical phenomena. Of course, this is an oversimplified characterization of what was actually involved in the development of the Faraday-Maxwell theory of electromagnetism. For one thing, it is clear from Maxwell's writings that he, too, engaged in a great deal of figurative model-building to "sharpen" and further extend Faraday's picture before he finally developed his mathematical model. Nevertheless, this stylized description will help us keep in mind two fairly distinct phases of scientific activity: an initial informal theorizing, and a subsequent formalization thereof.

The entire history of psychology abounds in examples of figurative models. From the ancient concept of "a man within a man," through the postulation of a *psyche* by the Greeks, the "machine" or "clockwork" models of the seventeenth century, the hydraulic and "energy dynamics" models of Freud, to the "reflex arc" model and its more modern variants, as well as the opposing "cognitive map" model—all these (and many more) can be regarded as figurative models of human behavior, sometimes with, and sometimes without, ontological commitment. Until the present century, however, these figurative models have only rarely been followed by any formalization to speak of.

Analogue Models

Let us now consider another class of models which I shall, following Black, call *analogue models.** A well-known example of such a model is found in the kinetic theory of gases, developed by Joule, among others. In this model, the molecules of a gas in a container are imagined to be perfectly elastic spheres ("idealized" billiard balls) of minute size that are undergoing random motion and incessantly colliding with each other and with the walls of the container. The laws of Newtonian mechanics governing elastic collisions are then applied to the system of gas molecules, and empirically testable consequences (such as Boyle's law) are deduced.

---

* The extension of my use of this term, however, may not coincide exactly with Black's. He may classify as a *theoretical* model much of what I would subsume under the class of analogue models.

The identifying feature of analogue model-building is that it involves an application of the laws of an already well-established theory in some other domain. The prototypic domain and the new domain for which the analogue model is being built may, in some cases, be closely akin, e.g., the domain of macroscopic physical objects (for which Newtonian mechanics was known to hold) and the domain of gas molecules (for which the kinetic-theory model was built). In other cases, the two domains may be vastly different from each other, e.g., the domain of electrical or electronic communication systems (for which the Weaver-Shannon information theory was known to be fruitful) and that of certain psychological phenomena (for which information-theoretic models have been built with varying degrees of success —see the discussion in Section III, below).

When the prototypic and new domains are closely contiguous, analogue model-building may, after the fact, seem to be little more than a routine application of the established theory to slightly different phenomena. Yet, there is a definite "creative leap" in, for example, Joule's thinking of treating gas molecules as though they were minute elastic spheres whose motions might be governed by the laws of Newtonian mechanics.

On the other hand, when the two domains are far apart, it may sometimes be difficult to distinguish an analogue model from a figurative model. When, for instance, the stimulus-organism-response sequence in a psychological experiment is likened to the transmitter-channel-receiver sequence in a communication system, the model-building activity may seem more closely to resemble Faraday's imagining lines of force in a magnetic field than it does Joule's treating gas molecules as minia-ture billiard balls. A distinction can be made, however; it lies, as noted earlier, in the use (or the attempted use) of an established theory in the prototypic domain for drawing inferences concerning the new domain. For this to be possible, the model-builder has to establish a one-to-one correspondence between certain features or elements of the new domain and those in the prototypic domain. Furthermore, suitable rules of translation must be developed so that *relationships* among elements in the new domain correspond to relationships among the counterpart elements in the prototypic domain. If these correspondences can successfully be established, we say that the two domains are *isomorphic* to each other.

Thus another way of characterizing an analogue model is to say that it pre-sumes some sort of isomorphism between the domain of interest and another domain for which an established theory exists. As in other forms of reasoning by analogy, however, it should be clearly recognized that there is no *a priori* guarantee that the isomorphism will continue to hold beyond the correspondences deliberately established by the model-builder. Consequently, analogue models do not, of them-selves, generate laws or theorems for the new domain, but merely furnish the in-vestigator with plausible hypotheses to test.

Mathematical Models

We now come to the type of model that is our primary concern in this chapter, mathematical models, of which one example was cited earlier. Often a mathematical model is described as though it were an abstract analogue model of some kind. For example, Bush and Mosteller, in the introduction to their *Stochastic Models for Learning,* make the following series of statements (p. 1):

First, there must be a mathematical theory or system . . . The elements of the system are not operationally defined, for they are abstract concepts which acquire meaning only through their relationships with one another. Nevertheless, the empirical phenomena for which one hopes to build a model may suggest an appropriate mathematical system to use as a framework . . . The second step in the development of a mathematical model is to state the general correspondence between elements in the mathematical system and empirical phenomena.*

In particular, the last sentence quoted seems to suggest that a direct correspondence is established between elements of an abstract mathematical system (such as set theory, Boolean algebra, probability calculus, or the like) and elements of the domain of interest. We would then have an analogue model for the domain of interest (e.g., learning phenomena), with a domain of such abstract concepts as sets, statements, or probability measures as the prototypic domain. A theorem in the mathematical system (concerning, say, probability measures) would, then, by a suitable rule of translation, generate a hypothesis concerning some empirical phenomenon.

The preceding characterization does not seem entirely correct to me.† It obscures the important fact that there must already exist an informal theory or a figurative model for the domain of interest before one can even start to build a mathematical model for that domain. Maxwell's equations did not "model" a set of electromagnetic phenomena by establishing correspondences between them and elements in the theory of partial differential equations. Rather, they *formalized* Faraday's figurative model—an informal theory—of these phenomena. Similarly, as we shall see below, a mathematical model in the social sciences is a formalization of some preexisting informal theory, or perhaps of a class of informal theories. Unless this fact is kept in mind, there is danger of attributing to mathematical models an "autonomous" status independent of the informal theory on which it is, however remotely, based.

It was in protest against the tendency they saw in model-builders to forget the fact mentioned above that Galanter and Miller asserted: "The stochastic models of human behavior that are currently available rely heavily—and in ways seldom made explicit—upon a particular kind of psychological theory." (1960, p. 277). One need not agree with their further suggestion that this theory is "incorrect" in order to recognize that any limitations which may be present in the underlying informal theory will be reflected in any mathematical model based on it. A mathematical model, as pointed out earlier (in connection with Maxwell's equations), serves

---

* R. R. Bush and F. Mosteller, *Stochastic Models for Learning* (New York: John Wiley & Sons, 1955). Quoted by permission of the publisher.
† Nor do Bush and Mosteller necessarily endorse this characterization. However, statements such as those quoted from their book convey the impression that the process of developing a mathematical model might be somewhat as I have described.

essentially as a calculus; it offers powerful machinery for drawing a chain (or several chains) of inferences from a set of basic postulates. Predictions from a mathematical model, therefore, are really (with qualifications noted below) "predictions"* from the basic postulates, and the latter are mathematical translations (or, better, *explications*) of the postulates that are implicit in the underlying informal theory. The informal theory may sometimes be relatively specific, as, for example, a certain brand of reinforcement theory of learning or, alternatively, a contiguity theory. At other times it may be so broad and so loosely defined as to amount to little more than a general way of thinking about the domain of interest. It may then be preferable to regard the model-builder as having taken over, from a certain school of thought, a figurative model which he then proceeds to "sharpen" to a point where mathematization is possible. In such a case, it may be more correct to speak of the mathematical model as possessing a "historically related," rather than an "underlying," informal theory.

Some qualifications must now be made in identifying predictions from a mathematical model with "predictions" from the underlying or historically related theory. Often, certain *simplifying assumptions* are made at some stage for the sake of mathematical tractability. (See, e.g., the *independence-of-path* assumption usually made in stochastic learning models, as described in Section IV, below.) It may happen that these assumptions are in conflict with some notion inherent in the related informal theory. If so, predictions from the mathematical model will, of course, differ from those potentially possible from the informal theory. More often, however, the simplifying assumptions refer to matters about which there is no commitment, one way or the other, in the informal theory. In such cases, we cannot tell whether the predictions would be at variance with those that might conceivably have been made from the informal theory.

Another point at which a mathematical model may deviate from the intent of the informal theory that it models is in the very process of translating the basic postulates into mathematical form. It must not be thought that the process of translation is a mechanical one. A considerable amount of "sharpening" of the original, informally stated postulates is usually necessary. In addition, the model-builder must often engage in some prior figurative modeling before he can begin to render the basic postulates suitable for mathematization. There is no *a priori* way of guaranteeing that a particular mode of translation is "correct." Only experimental tests of the deduced predictions can decide whether or not the mathematical rendition was correct—or, more properly speaking, *fruitful*.

One of the main advantages of mathematical models can be seen from the foregoing discussion, which showed how they are related to an informal theory, but nevertheless may lead to somewhat variant predictions. It is generally recognized that a scientific theory, to be worthy of its name, must be *potentially falsifiable*. Karl Popper (1959), in discussing the asymmetry between *verifiability* and *falsi-*

---

* I use quotation marks for the second occurrence of the term "predictions," because it refers to predictions that are in some vague sense implied by, but cannot *actually* be made from, the basic postulates themselves without the aid of the mathematical model.

fiability, adopts the latter as the criterion for "demarking" statements acceptable as empirical ones. Obviously, a statement which cannot possibly be falsified (refuted) by experiment or observation is inadmissible as an empirical statement.

The establishment of a mathematical model, by giving precise form to basic postulates and auxiliary assumptions, and by permitting unequivocal quantitative predictions via its calculus, increases the chances that the postulates, if untenable, will be refuted by experimental evidence. To borrow from the terminology of statistical hypothesis-testing, we may say that a mathematical model *increases the power* of experimental tests.

That the advantage cited above is not a trivial one can readily be recognized when we consider that many of the older psychological theories persisted as long as they did just because their testable consequences were vague and equivocal. If a theory can, in the face of what its critics would view as adverse empirical evidence, be "saved" by means of subtle changes in interpretation of its predictions, then we cannot accord it much scientific status. The elimination of such equivocality (or at least its reduction) which is effected by mathematical models must, then, be regarded as an essential scientific advance.

Another way in which mathematical models enhance the scientific enterprise, one closely related to the above, is this: When a prediction fails to be supported by experiment, it is much easier to locate the source of trouble if the postulates and assumptions are mathematically stated than it is otherwise. The restrictions embodied in the simplifying assumptions can be successively liberalized or removed. (This will inevitably make the mathematical deduction of testable predictions more difficult, or even impossible, by exact analytic methods. But with modern high-speed electronic computers available, an approximate numerical solution is very often feasible.) Thus the possibility of remedying the situation—not by subtle changes in interpretation, but by explicit changes in assumptions—is greatly increased. In short, mathematical models inherently have a "self-corrective" mechanism that is essential to scientific progress.

Other Classification Schemes in Recent Literature

In developing the foregoing classification of models, I have not attempted to be very rigorous. The "categories" are not necessarily mutually exclusive, nor do they exhaust all conceivable types of models. I have merely provided convenient labels which are plausible, at least in certain pure cases, and which will facilitate subsequent discussions in this chapter. Readers who are interested in more systematic classifications and more general discussions of models may consult the several papers described briefly below.

Max Black's (1962) paper, "Models and Archetypes," already referred to, presents a philosophical analysis of "the presuppositions and the implications" of the various uses of models by scientists. He classifies models into "analogue models," and "theoretical models." The main difference between Black's classification system and mine lies in his treating under the single category of "theoretical models" what I have felt convenient to distinguish as the products of two distinct activities: figurative and mathematical model-building. Consequently, Black's class of "mathematical models" is a subset of mine, excluding the mathematical aspect of "theoretical models." One gets the impression that this "residual" class of mathematical models is, for Black, a rather trivial type. (Perhaps this is because his essay was written in 1958, and Professor Black had not yet had a chance to examine the then very recent developments of mathematical models in the social and behavioral sciences.)

In a paper entitled "The Model in Theory Construction," Lachman (1960) distinguishes four functions of models: (a) providing modes of representation, (b) serving as rules of inference, (c) supplying interpretations, and (d) providing pictorial vizualization. He illustrates these functions in the context of the Hull-Spence r_g (fractional anticipatory responses theory), and with reference to Estes' statistical learning theory. Toulmin's (1953) criteria for evaluating a model (*deployability, scope,* and *precision*) are also discussed in connection with these theories.

The September 1960 issue of *Synthese* is devoted to a symposium on "The Concept and the Role of the Model in Mathematics and Natural and Social Sciences." Among the papers found there, two should be of special interest to psychologists: the paper by Atkinson ("The Use of Models in Experimental Psychology") and that by Suppes ("A Comparison of the Meaning and Uses of Models in Mathematics and the Empirical Sciences"). Atkinson illustrates the axiomatic approach in constructing a mathematical model by showing in detail the developments in connection with a particular learning experiment in which monetary gain or loss was at stake on each trial. Suppes, after examining a number of quotations involving the word "model," taken from books in the physical and the social science areas (as well as one from mathematical logic), asserts that "the meaning of the concept of model is the same in mathematics and the empirical sciences" (Suppes, 1960, p. 289). Yet, he himself endorses the generally acknowledged contrast between a model as a linguistic (e.g., mathematical) entity in the empirical sciences and a model as a nonlinguistic entity (e.g., the set of positive integers) which satisfies a given theory in pure mathematics. Suppes's assertion is therefore a bold one. The way in which he reconciles these two apparently conflicting views on the unity or duality of the concept of model is to draw a distinction between *meaning* and *use*. His thesis is that there is interdisciplinary "constancy of meaning [but] difference of use."

In a paper entitled "Two Views about the Function of Models in Empirical Theories" Götlind (1961) identifies four different uses of the term "model" in the literature, and proposes a definition that would explicate the more important of these uses. By his definition, a model is a step or a series of steps in "the correlation procedure of a mathematized theory for empirical phenomena."

III. SOME ANALOGUE MODELS IN PSYCHOLOGY

The line between figurative models and analogue models is, as noted earlier, sometimes difficult to draw. If one includes such notions as conditioning (in learning theory), which is based on an analogy with the physiological concept of conditioned reflex, then the history of psychology may be said to replete with analogue models. In this section, however, we shall consider only two classes of models which bear a distinct mark of their analogue status (in that they seek to apply well-established theories from other fields to psychological phenomena), and which are also quantitative in nature.

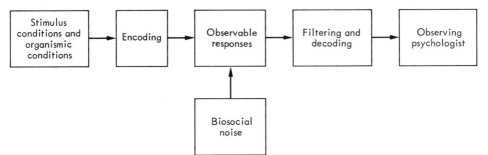

Fig. 1. Communications-system model for a psychological experiment. [From D. A. Grant, "The discrimination of sequences in stimulus events and the transmission of information." *Amer. Psychologist* **9,** 62–68 (1954). Reproduced by permission of the publisher.]

Information-Theory Models

The possibility of developing analogue models for psychology that are based on the mathematical theory of communication (or "information theory") was recognized soon after Shannon published his now classic paper in that field in 1948. Miller and Frick (1949) are generally acknowledged as the earliest pioneers in this development, which reached its peak in the mid-1950's.

One way of establishing an isomorphism between the sequence of events in a communication system and that in a psychological experiment was presented by Grant (1954), as shown in Fig. 1. The three basic components of a communication system—the *source* of messages, the *communication channel,* and the *destination*—are here put into correspondence, respectively, with the *stimulus* (and organismic) conditions, the *responses,* and the *observing psychologist.* The intervening components, *encoder* and *decoder* (e.g., a telephone transmitter which changes sound waves into electrical pulses, and a receiver which does the opposite), may have different sorts of counterparts, depending on the kind of psychological experiment to be analyzed. Encoding may, for instance, be made to correspond to the organism's perception of the stimulus condition; decoding may involve various measuring instruments as well as the psychologist's interpretation of the observable responses. Finally, *noise* is identified with any and all irrelevant stimuli that may affect the responses in unpredictable ways.

Having established correspondences between elements in a communication system and those in a psychological experiment, the analogue modelist would proceed to "translate" one or more theorems of information theory into psychological terms, thereby obtaining quantitative predictions that can be subjected to experimental test.

One of the fundamental theorems of information theory states a mathematical relationship between channel capacity (the maximum number of different signals that can be transmitted over the channel per unit time), the statistical structure of the message source (i.e., the probability distribution over the different signal *elements* or symbols), and the average rate of transmission of symbols. To state this theorem precisely, some preliminary definitions and units of measurement are needed.

The basic unit for measuring the amount of information contained in a message is the *bit* (a contraction of "binary digit"). A signal which cuts down the uncertainty on the part of its recipient by a factor of ½ is said to convey one bit of information. For example, if a message recipient has no prior knowledge of whether a certain person who is the subject of the message is a male or a female, then a signal indicating the sex of this person conveys to the recipient one bit of information. Next, if the recipient is also totally ignorant as to which of eight districts of the country this person is from, then a signal specifying the district conveys to him three bits of information—since it has *halved* the number of alternatives *three* successive times ($8 \times \frac{1}{2} \times \frac{1}{2} \times \frac{1}{2} = 1$). In general, if a signal identifies for the recipient one out of n *a priori* equally probable alternatives, it conveys to him $\log_2 n$ bits of information.

Next, the statistical structure of the message source must be precisely defined. Suppose that n symbols are available from which signals are constructed. Then in the simplest case, when the selection of symbols is independent, the source is statistically *completely* characterized once the probabilities

$$p_1, p_2, p_3, \ldots, p_n,$$

with which these symbols are selected have been specified. If a single quantity is desired which will give a *partial* statistical characterization of the source, it is natural to ask for some sort of *average* amount of information transmitted per symbol. Shannon showed that a theoretically fruitful measure of such an average is given by the quantity

$$H = \sum p_i \log_2 p_i,$$

which he called the *entropy* of the source. Its unit is "bits per *symbol.*"

In terms of the foregoing concepts, one way of stating the fundamental theorem of *noiseless* systems is as follows: The channel capacity C is given by

$$C = H \cdot R_{\max},$$

where $R_{\max}$ is the maximum rate (in *symbols* per second) at which symbols can be transmitted, using the most efficient coding device. Since the entropy H is measured in bits per symbol and $R_{\max}$ is in symbols per second, it follows that the unit for measuring channel capacity is (bits/symbol) × (symbols/second), or "bits per second."

It is intuitively plausible that this theorem might be applicable in predicting the information-handling capacity of human beings under specified conditions. Its relevance to military and industrial psychology, as well as to basic studies of re-action time, is evident.

Licklider and Miller (1951) and Jacobson (1951), among others, have conducted experiments on capacities with respect to auditory and visual signals. Unfortunately, such experimental results do not seem either to confirm or disconfirm the theoretical predictions unequivocally. One reason for this is that experimental estimates typically yield upper bounds on channel capacity, while use of the theorem from information theory yields lower bounds.

Somewhat closer agreement with theoretical lower bounds (which range from 10 to 100 bits per second) have been obtained in experiments using more complicated "signals," such as language (Miller, 1951), music notes, and mental arithmetic problems (Quastler and Wulff, 1955). From their own data and from a survey of other experimenters' results, Quastler and Wulff conclude that 25 bits per second is the maximum channel capacity of human information transfer in these types of experiments.

The discussion above centered around but one use of the information-theory model in psychology—that which draws upon the theorem on channel capacity. Another and possibly more prevalent use involves laws relating to noise in communication channels. The psychological analogue of noise may be anything which hinders a perfect correlation between stimulus and response. Thus stated, the concept of noise would apply universally to all fields of psychology. In practice, however, *bona fide* psychological applications of the theory of noisy communication have been confined primarily to the fields of psychophysics and psychometric scaling. For example, the classic problem of having subjects judge the scale values, along some continuum, of stimuli such as sound, light, or taste has been treated as a problem of information transfer under conditions of noise or equivocation.

A third type of application utilizes information-theoretic concepts and methods of analysis for describing sequential dependencies in psychological data. Examples of this type are found in the voluminous literature on verbal learning experiments. The well-known fact that meaningful material is easier to learn (and to recall) than, say, nonsense syllables can be explained in terms of the higher sequential dependencies among the stimulus elements in the former. Another way of putting this is to say that meaningful material contains a high degree of redundancy due to "contextual constraint," and is thus easier to learn than material that is low in this property.

A survey and interpretation of experiments involving the concepts of noise and of sequential dependencies was presented by Miller (1956). A more extensive survey of various behavioral applications of information theory can be found in the second part of a monograph-length article by Luce (1960), the first part of which is devoted to an exposition of the mathematical theory of "selective information" itself.

In concluding our brief discussion of information-theory models in psychology, an overall evaluation of the current status should be made. It is probably true, as

Luce (1960, pp. 51–52) suggests, that an initial enthusiasm for what appeared to be a powerful new tool with almost unlimited potential has given way to a more balanced view, one which recognizes that there are serious limitations as well. Thus, while it cannot be denied that the quantitative measurement of information offered a new approach to studying some age-old problems in psychology, the actual application of theorems of information theory to psychological data has proved less satisfactory than initially expected. The difficulty in connection with the fundamental theorem on channel capacity has already been pointed out. Attempts to apply the theory of noisy channels to psychological experiments have likewise yielded rather equivocal results.

Such limitations are probably inherent in the use of analogue models for which the prototypic domain is as remote from the domain of application as electrical communication systems are from psychology. The analogy and correspondences established in such cases tend to be rather tenuous; the various ways in which they may break down have been discussed by Cronbach (1955) and by Hake (1955). For example, Cronbach points out that Shannon's entropy measure as applied to noisy systems is designed to deal with indefinitely long messages and delays. But in psychological experiments we are invariably concerned with finite messages and delays. Hake, admonishing against an earlier hope on the part of many psychologists that channel capacity may turn out to be an invariant of human behavior, points out that there are various physiological limits to human information-handling capacity for which there are no analogues in communication systems.

Game-Theory Models

The theory of games has the distinction of being the first completely mathematical theory that was developed specifically in the context of a social science, namely, economics. Although several mathematicians had done earlier work in this field, the now classic book, *Theory of Games and Economic Behavior,* by von Neumann and Morgenstern (1944), was the first comprehensive treatise on the subject.

Another distinguishing feature of game theory is that it is *normative* instead of *descriptive*. It was originally formulated to recommend, rather than to describe or predict, behavior. To state it otherwise, we might say that game theory is descriptive only of the behavior of hypothetical, idealized "rational men" in situations of economic competition. Nevertheless, it has inspired the hope in many behavioral scientists that it could serve also to predict how an intelligent subject would actually behave under certain well-defined conditions involving gain or loss.

Used in this way, game theory becomes an analogue model. The analogy is between the behavior of the hypothetical rational man and that of an actual, intelligent human being. The extent to which predictions from this model agree with observations would depend, then, on two conditions: first, how closely the "intelligence" of the real subject approximates that of the rational man; and second, how nearly his set of values coincides with that attributed to the rational man through the postulates of game theory.

Let us examine game theory in terms of the simplest case, that of *zero-sum**
two-person games. Consider such a game with the *payoff matrix*

$$
\begin{array}{c c}
 & \begin{array}{c c} B_1 & B_2 \end{array} \\
\begin{array}{c} A_1 \\ A_2 \end{array} & \begin{bmatrix} 1 & 3 \\ -2 & -4 \end{bmatrix},
\end{array}
$$

which expresses the following rules of the game. On each play, Player A chooses one of two options, A_1 or A_2. His opponent, player B, chooses either B_1 or B_2. If A_1 and B_1 are chosen, A gains \$1 and B loses this amount; if A_2 and B_1 are chosen, A loses \$2 and B gains this amount; and so on. In other words, the elements of the matrix specify the amounts which A *receives* from B—his receiving a negative amount being interpreted as his *paying B*. More generally, if m options are available to A, and n options to B, the payoff matrix would have m rows and n columns.

The optimal strategy for each player in the above game is prescribed by von Neumann's famous *minimax* principle. The idea is that each player should choose that option which minimizes his maximum possible loss (or, what amounts to the same thing, maximizes his minimum possible gain). For Player A, option A_1 is obviously the better choice: his maximum "loss" under A_1 is a gain of \$1, whereas his maximum loss under A_2 is an actual loss of \$4. Thus A_1 minimizes his maximum loss.† For Player B, option B_1 leads to a maximum loss of \$1, while B_2 leads to a maximum loss of \$3. His maximum loss is, therefore, minimized if he chooses B_1.

In the example just given, the maximum of the minimum possible gain for A and the minimum of the maximum possible loss for B were both equal to \$1, as given by the (A_1, B_1)-element of the payoff matrix. In such a case, neither player can do better, in repeated plays of the game, than to consistently choose that option which satisfies the minimax principle for him. The (A_1, B_1) combination of options in the present example is therefore called a *pure* minimax strategy.

There would be very little to game theory if pure minimax strategies always existed. But this is not the case. For example, there is no pure minimax strategy for a game with the payoff matrix

$$
\begin{array}{c c}
 & \begin{array}{c c} B_1 & B_2 \end{array} \\
\begin{array}{c} A_1 \\ A_2 \end{array} & \begin{bmatrix} -3 & 2 \\ 1 & -1 \end{bmatrix}.
\end{array}
$$

Here, the maximum of the minimum possible "gain" for A is

$$-\$1, \qquad \text{the } (A_2, B_2)\text{-element},$$

---

* In "zero-sum" games, whatever amount one player gains, the other player loses.
† Actually, A's choice of A_1 satisfies the intuitively appealing "sure-thing" principle. For, no matter which option B chooses, A is better off under A_1 than under A_2. Note, however, that the sure-thing principle is not available to Player B.

while the minimum of the maximum possible loss for B is

$$\$1, \qquad \text{the } (A_2, B_1)\text{-element.}$$

In such a case, neither player can persistently choose a fixed one of his options in repeated plays without his opponent's capitalizing on this fact to the latter's advantage. Rather, the optimal strategy for each player is to use a "probability mixture" of the options he can choose from. Suitable choices of the probabilities with which each player selects the particular option on a given play yield what is called a mixed minimax strategy. One of the fundamental theorems of game theory, established by von Neumann, shows that there always exists a *mixed* minimax strategy for any zero-sum two-person game with a finite number of alternatives available to each player.

The foregoing discussion of the simplest case of game theory, sketchy as it is, suffices to make evident two quite independent facets of the theory. One of these was explicitly illustrated above: the problem of choosing among several possible strategies. This is a *decision problem*. The other facet was glossed over by using a monetary unit for the elements of the payoff matrix. But what if the "payoffs"— the "gains" or "losses" resulting from various possible outcomes of a "game"— were not measurable in dollars and cents? The elements of the payoff matrix would then have to be specified on some other value scale, which might involve the fun of playing, the thrill of gambling, and so forth. What the appropriate value scale is (if any) in a given gamelike situation is a problem of *utility theory*.

In their book, von Neumann and Morgenstern were primarily concerned with the choice-of-strategy or decision-making aspect of games. With respect to utility, they advanced plausible arguments for assuming that it could be treated as a linear function of monetary value. In psychological applications of game-theoretical models, however, the utility-scale aspect is just as important (or interesting) as the decision-making aspect. In fact, one could, with only slight risk of oversimplification, classify psychological studies inspired by game theory into two categories: (a) those which assume an *a priori* utility scale and inquire how "rationally" or "irrationally" people behave in choice situations, as gauged by the minimax rule or some other decision-making principle (such as maximizing expected utility); (b) those which give the benefit of the doubt that people *are* rational, and seek to determine what sort of utility scale they must possess in order that their choice behavior be regarded as rational. An early experiment by Mosteller and Nogee (1951) to determine nonlinear utility curves for money in a simple gambling situation is a good example of the latter category.

An elementary exposition of game theory and other principles of decision-making was given by Edwards (1954) together with an extensive survey of experimental studies in this field. A collection of papers under the editorship of Thrall, Coombs, and Davis (1954), entitled *Decision Processes,* is an important source book of theoretical and experimental work done in the field in the early 1950's.

More recently, a series of papers by Siegel and his coworkers (Siegel, 1959, 1961; Siegel and Goldstein, 1959) describes some ingenious experiments and quantitative models which combine the decision-making and utility-measuring aspects noted above. A further distinguishing feature of these studies is that they focus attention on the relationship between decision-making and learning. For example, one paper of this series (Siegel, 1961) concerns the so-called "probability-matching" behavior (cf. p. 45, below) often observed in two-choice learning experiments. Briefly stated, this means that in learning experiments where two possible responses (such as pushing the left or right button) are reinforced with fixed probabilities (e.g., "left" reinforced on 75% and "right" on 25% of the trials), the subject eventually "learns" to make the two alternative responses with relative frequencies approximately equal to the respective reinforcement probabilities. Siegel presents experimental evidence to show that this is not a general law, but is contingent on the utility of the reward relative to the utility of varying one's responses. For, by experimentally manipulating this relative utility, he was able to change the subjects' response proportions from probability-matching to almost complete fixation on the more favorable response.

Another recent study of the relationship between game-theoretical decision-making and learning processes is described by Suppes and Atkinson (1960) in their book entitled *Markov Learning Models for Multiperson Interactions*. Departing from an original intention (stated in their introduction) of arranging a "competition between game theory and learning theory in their relative ability to predict behavior" (p. 2), they developed an elaborate program of experiments to see "how far learning theory can be extended to predict behavior in situations that correspond ever more closely to real games" (p. 2). The situations they deal with are those which involve social interaction, and one major purpose of their study is to demonstrate that a large class of these situations can be successfully analyzed without introducing such typically sociopsychological concepts as group cohesiveness, group pressure, etc. Consequently, this book may stimulate a considerable amount of controversy among social psychologists.

Although our purpose in this section has been to illustrate some analogue models in psychology, it can be said that the last two instances described above were game-theoretical only in setting. Methodologically they might better be regarded as cases of independent mathematical model-building with relatively little technical application of game theory as such. They are, therefore, "transition cases" which possess some features of the class of analogue models and some of the class of mathematical models.

IV. MATHEMATICAL MODELS IN PSYCHOLOGY

Now that he has seen some examples of quantitative analogue models in psychology, we hope that the reader has a better idea of the delineation of that class of models referred to as mathematical models in this chapter. Characterized negatively, these are the quantitative models that do *not* depend primarily on the existence of well-established mathematical theories in other domains with which an analogy may be drawn. Stated positively, these are the outcomes of that variety of model-building activity which starts from the formalization of a group of axioms inherent in a preexisting informal theory and then applies suitable mathematical machinery (sometimes inventing new techniques) for developing empirically testable consequences of the axioms.

In a sense, then, mathematical modelists may be regarded as merely carrying out to their logical conclusions the programs initiated by earlier behavioristic psychologists such as Thorndike, Guthrie, Hull, and others. For the enduring contributions of these pioneers lie not so much in their creation of specific "brands" of learning theory as in their developing a set of basic concepts in a scientifically precise manner, and specifying just how these concepts are to function in the theories embodying them. (These two types of activity are, of course, the first steps toward establishing a set of formal axioms.) · What most of the earlier workers lacked was an inclination to state their basic postulates in mathematical language. Or, even when they did so state them (as in Hull's case), the particular mathematical formulation they adopted (or the particular concepts they chose to represent mathematically) turned out to be unamenable to further mathematical treatment for deducing essentially new quantitative predictions. It was against this historical background that the first paper describing a mathematical model in psychology* (in the sense used in this chapter) appeared in 1950: Estes' "Toward a Statistical Theory of Learning." The starting point in Estes' system is a set of axioms about the sampling and conditioning of stimulus elements. In essence, these axioms formalize the basic postulates of Guthrie's contiguity theory of learning.

To avoid any misunderstanding, it should be mentioned that even apart from the exceptions cited in our last footnote, Estes' paper was by no means the first to apply mathematical methods to a psychological problem—nor, indeed, to learning phenomena. Thurstone (1930) was probably the first to derive a learning curve based on "rational" (as against empirical) considerations. Relatively simple psychological assumptions enabled him to write a differential equation which, upon integration, yielded what he called "the learning function." This was an important advance over the earlier *ad hoc* empirical curve-fitting approach used by Ebbinghaus and others. Nevertheless, the predictions that could be made as a result of Thurstone's innovation were restricted to those which followed from the learning curve itself (e.g., the relationship between learning time and amount of learning material). His basic psychological assumptions, formulated in precise mathematical terms though they were, lacked the structure for enabling one to make a variety of deductions about the finer details of learning phenomena such as became possible with later mathematical models.

---

* We arbitrarily exclude the field of psychophysics when we make this statement, for mathematical models have been used in that field since the time of Weber and Fechner (i.e., the midnineteenth century). Also, some readers may object that factor analysis, which antedated by far the advent of mathematical learning theory, should surely be included in the class of mathematical models in psychology. Reasons for excluding these two fields are given in Section V, at the end of this chapter.

Soon after the appearance of Estes' paper, a somewhat different approach to the developing of mathematical models for learning was announced by Bush and Mosteller (1951). Central to their approach is the idea of *linear operators*. They postulate that the response probabilities on each trial of a learning experiment can be expressed as linear functions of the response probabilities on the immediately preceding trial. Thus their starting point is more abstract than that of Estes' system. Hence their model is, in a sense, noncommittal as to whether association or reinforcement is the mechanism underlying the successive changes in response probabilities. The interesting point (and perhaps a theoretically significant one) is that at least in certain cases, both the Estes and Bush-Mosteller models lead to identical predictions, as we shall see below.

Since the bulk of this section is devoted to an exposition of mathematical models of learning which stem from the programs initiated by Estes and by Bush and Mosteller, we will first briefly survey mathematical models in branches of psychology other than the theory of learning.

Small-Group Behavior

It was only a few years ago that Coleman remarked, ". . . in this branch of social science it seems that mathematical developments have lagged even farther behind empirical work than one might expect" (1960, p. 8). Today, however, among well-defined fields of psychology the study of small groups is second only to learning theory in the abundance of mathematical models.

Simon (1952) was one of the first to develop a mathematical model for small-group behavior, his work being a formalization of an informal theory described by Homans in *The Human Group* (1950). For example, he translated into mathematical form such verbally stated generalizations (postulates) as the following sequence:

i) *Sentiments of friendliness* tend to develop among any group of people who come into sustained interaction.

ii) These feelings increase both the *amount of interaction* in the group and the *amount of group activity*.

iii) The increases stated in (ii) in turn increase the friendliness, and so on, in a circular fashion.

iv) A certain *amount of environmentally imposed activity* initially characterizes a group.

It is evident, even before performing any mathematical operation, that without some restriction postulate (iii) would imply, over time, an unbounded increase in friendliness, interaction, and activity. To set limits on these increases, Simon postulates that a reversal takes place in the direction of change of the three variables when they reach certain values, called "appropriate levels." The introduction of these equilibrium-restoring conditions is an example of how some assumptions not explicitly stated in the postulates of an informal theory may have to be added in the process of formalization (or in the prior step of sharpening the informal postulates). In Simon's treatment, the additions do not distort Homans' original theory, which must have tacitly assumed such added restrictions; otherwise the absurd implication of an infinite friendliness, interaction, and activity is inescapable.

We shall not review here Simon's mathematical translation of the postulates stated above, nor his process of deriving deductions from them.* Instead, we shall merely cite two of the propositions that Simon deduces from his mathematical model, at least one of which could probably not have been deduced by verbal arguments from the informal postulates themselves:

1) As the amount of *environmentally imposed* group activity is decreased below some critical value (say E_0), the level of friendliness, and eventually also the amount of *actual* group activity, will drop to zero—i.e., the group will dissolve.

2) The amount of environmentally imposed group activity necessary to form a group in the first place is *greater* than the critical value E_0 required to prevent the group, once formed, from dissolving.

To be sure, these deductions (and two others which Simon presents) do not tell a great deal about group behavior. But this is because Homans' original postulates themselves were rather weak ones. Simon's work has been discussed here at some length, primarily because it well exemplifies a "pure case" of a mathematical model as a formalization of a preexisting informal theory.

Other applications, made in the early 1950's, of mathematical methods in the study of small groups include the works of Stephan and Mishler (1952), Lorge and Solomon (1955), and Simon and Guetzkow (1955). The work of Rapoport (1951, 1953a,b) and other mathematical biophysicists dealing with "random neural nets" is also applicable to communication and sociometric choice in human groups, as the titles of Rapoport's 1953 papers indicate.

Stephan and Mishler's mathematical treatment of social interaction in discussion groups represents the opposite extreme from Simon's work, in terms of the specificity of the informal theory which it formalizes. It may be regarded as a case in which the "informal theory" is merely a general way of looking at the phenomena in question. (See discussion pp. 6–7, above.) The problem they treated was one of determining a functional relationship between the frequency of an individual's participation and his rank-in-group in frequency of participation. The same problem had earlier been studied by Bales *et al.* (1951), who attempted (without great success) to fit a harmonic progression† to their data. Stephan and Mishler used

---

* The interested reader may find Coleman's exposition, in the paper cited above, easier to follow than the original article by Simon. Coleman fills in several gaps in Simon's rather abbreviated development, and adds many explanatory remarks.
† More specifically, $f_i = C/i$, where f_i is the theoretical participation frequency of the member ranking ith in frequency of participation, and C is a constant such that Σf_i equals the total number of interactive participations by all members of the group. This equation, incidentally, is the same as that for an empirical law found by Zipf (1949) to hold for the frequencies of usage of various words in a language.

Bales's data and similar ones of their own, and found that the frequencies of participation for successive members could be expressed as a geometric progression* with much better fit than Bales had achieved with his harmonic progression.

So far, Stephan and Mishler's treatment is simply an *ad hoc* curve-fitting venture. However, they went a step further and attempted to give a theoretical explanation for their quantitative empirical generalization. They postulated that each member of a discussion group has a "verbal participation potential," and that the observed regularity can be explained in terms of interindividual variability in this quantity. However, it turned out that their experiments, conducted to test their hypothesis, yielded disconfirmatory results. Consequently, their verbally stated postulates never received a formal mathematical translation.

Lorge and Solomon (1955) considered group problem-solving with an orientation similar to that of Suppes and Atkinson (noted toward the end of the previous section), namely, that many group phenomena may be explained without introducing special "group effects." While they accepted the empirical generalization (repeatedly confirmed since Shaw's early work, 1932) that groups perform better than individuals in solving certain problems, Lorge and Solomon sought to explain this effect without postulating any special benefit from group interaction. Toward this end, they proposed two alternative models, both based on individual problem-solving abilities (or probabilities) of the group members. The first, and simpler, of these models is an elementary probability calculation showing that, given a group of individuals all of whom have the same probability for solving a problem single-handed, it follows that there will be a greater probability for *at least one* member (and hence the group) to solve the problem. For example, if each person has a probability 0.14 (estimated from Shaw's data for one of three problems she used), then the probability that a group of four people will solve the problem is

$$1 - (1 - 0.14)^4 = 0.46.$$

Since this value falls short of the group probability, 0.60 in Shaw's results, Lorge and Solomon proposed a more complicated model, assuming a multistage problem-solving process. The essential idea here is that different individuals may be able to solve different stages of the problem, so that by complementing one another they may, as a group, solve the problem even if no one member can do so alone. However, no conclusive test of this model was possible, because of the difficulty of identifying the stages of the problem and the subjects' abilities on each of them.

Toward the late 1950's one observes a sharp rise in the degree of mathematical sophistication in treating small-group processes. The change lies not so much in the elaborateness of the mathematical techniques used as in the concept of what constitutes a mathematical model. Thus, for example, Lorge and Solomon (1959, 1960) treat much the same problem (though with additional variables) as in their

---

* That is, $f_i = ar^{i-1}$, where r is the ratio of the frequencies of participation by members of adjacent ranks (found to be nearly constant for all adjacent pairs), and a is a parameter determined from the data.

1955 paper, but a sharpening of their basic postulates and the deductive structure of their model is greatly in evidence.

On the empirical side of the picture, Hoppe (1962) carried out an experiment comparing individual and group learning of nonsense-syllable lists and found "no evidence to reject" the Lorge-Solomon models for explaining the superiority of group over individual performance. The agreement between predicted and observed results, however, was only fair.

Striving for better reality-correspondence, yet continuing to wield Occam's razor in seeking to "delay the entry of such variables" as conformity, roles, and interaction, Restle (1962) supplements the Lorge-Solomon postulate of "pooling of ability" with considerations from the theory of "waiting times."* The result is a mathematical model whose wealth of statistical predictions shows good agreement with data from "two memorizing experiments and two experiments on the solution of verbal problems" (1962, p. 262).

One of the most ubiquitous and, at the same time, least fully analyzed concepts of social psychology has been that of interaction. An important step toward clarifying this notation was taken by Sidowski, Wyckoff, and Tabory (1956) when they explicated it at least for what they called a "minimal social situation." Interaction in such a context, according to their definition, consists in the impact of one group member's responses on the nature (or merely the occurrence probabilities) of the reinforcing events for other members. Burke (1962) generalized this concept of interaction somewhat to include the possibility that one member's responses may affect the stimuli as well as the reinforcements for other members of the group. With this definition of interaction, he developed mathematical models for two classes of simple two-person interactive learning experiments. Predictions from these models have yet to be subjected to experimental testing.

Other small-group phenomena for which mathematical models have been developed include social conformity, division of labor, and dominance structure ("pecking order"). Expositions of typical works in these areas and references to relevant literature may be found in Coleman's survey cited earlier, and in a recent collection of papers entitled *Mathematical Methods in Small Group Processes,* edited by Criswell, Solomon, and Suppes (1962).

Individual Choice Behavior

At first glance, the phrase "choice behavior" may suggest a rather narrow, specific topic of study. A little reflection tells us, however, that it is the central theme of a large part of psychology, including branches that are concerned with perception, motivation, utility, and simple learning. To describe mathematically this "common core" of many psychological fields was the purpose of Luce's (1959) widely quoted book, *Individual Choice Behavior: A Theoretical Analysis.*

---

* This is a study of the probability distribution of the trial number on which the first success is observed in a sequence of binomial trials.

The power and wide applicability of Luce's mathematical theory derive largely from his having come to grips with an age-old problem concerning the relationship between pairwise choices and more general ones. Traditional solutions to this problem (when they were attempted at all) usually involved the assumption of transitivity of choices—that is, the assumption that if a person chooses A over B, and also B over C, then he will choose A over C when these alternatives are offered. It takes no profound analysis to see that this assumption cannot be expected to hold except in choice situations which permit perfect discrimination or, in other words, where all the pairwise choice probabilities involved are equal to 1 or 0.

What Luce did was to replace this transitivity postulate with a weaker one (hence a more general one) stated in terms of choice probabilities over elements of a finite set of alternatives. This is his celebrated "Axiom 1," which implies the transitivity postulate in the special case of perfect discrimination. To state this axiom, the following notation is needed:

Let T be a finite set of alternatives, and S and R be any pair of successively subsumed subsets thereof ($R \subset S \subset T$). Denote by $P_T(S)$ the probability that, when a choice must be made from the elements of T, the chosen element lies in the subset S. Similar interpretations hold for $P_S(R)$, etc.

With this notation, Luce's Axiom 1, which has two parts, may be stated as follows:

i) If T contains *no* pair of elements for which perfect discrimination holds, then

$$P_T(R) = P_T(S)P_S(R).$$

ii) If T does contain a pair of elements for which perfect discrimination holds, and if T^* and S^* denote the "remainder sets" after the *never*-chosen member of this pair is removed from T and S, respectively, then

$$P_T(S) = P_{T^*}(S^*).$$

The second part simply states that if some element x of T is *never* chosen over some other element, then x may be deleted when choices from T are being considered. This seems quite a reasonable assumption, and its repeated use allows us to reduce the set of alternatives to one containing no perfectly discriminable pair; then part (i) can be applied.

The intuitive meaning of part (i) may be seen by imagining a choice to be made in two steps: first, grouping the alternatives into several categories and choosing one of them; second, choosing a particular alternative out of the chosen category. Part (i) of the axiom then asserts that the final outcome does not depend on the particular category grouping made in the first step. This assumption is not quite so plausible as that of part (ii). In fact, one could readily imagine complex choice situations in which the particular grouping used would make a big difference. As Luce says, ". . . we cannot expect the axiom to be valid except for simple decisions" (p. 7). The interesting point is that for most applications, it turns out to be sufficient to assume Axiom 1 to hold for sets of only three alternatives—choices among which would certainly seem to qualify as "simple decisions."

At any rate, Luce proceeds to show that *if Axiom 1 holds,* then several important consequences follow. An especially striking result is that all choice probabilities are completely determined by the pairwise probabilities (Theorem 1).

Another consequence of Axiom 1 is that in a set of three alternatives $\{x, y, z\}$, the probability of observing the intransitivity $x > y > z > x$ (where the symbol '$>$' means "is chosen over") is equal to the probability of the *reverse* intransitivity, $x > z > y > x$ (Theorem 2).

A third consequence is that for any finite set of pairwise nonperfectly discriminable alternatives, there exists a ratio scale which measures what might be called the degree of preference for each alternative; and the choice probability of each alternative is proportional to its value on this scale (Theorem 3). This in itself is not of great practical significance, since all it gives us is a collection of fragmentary, local scales, each one applicable only within a given subset of nonperfectly discriminable alternatives. However, Luce shows that, provided the total set of alternatives satisfies two further conditions (called "finite connectedness" and "strong stochastic transitivity"), these local scales can all be connected together to yield a single ratio scale for the entire set (Theorem 4).

In essence, the foregoing constitutes all of the basic theory. The bulk of Luce's book is devoted to applications of this axiomatic theory of choice to three fields of psychology: psychophysics, utility theory, and learning theory. Of course, in each particular field of application, additional axioms of substantive nature are introduced that impart to each field its distinctive qualities.

Independently of Luce's work, and almost simultaneously with it, Audley (1960) proposed a stochastic model for individual choice behavior. This model, being partly an outgrowth of investigations by Audley and others of the so-called "urn model" for learning (see p. 37), deals with choice situations somewhat narrower in scope than obtain in Luce's theory. It is couched in terms which suggest that its applicability lies primarily (although not exclusively) in choice behavior in learning experiments.

Central to Audley's model is the concept of "implicit response." While this concept is left undefined, its role in the model is specified by two basic axioms, the gist of which is as follows:

i) "For given stimulus and organismic conditions," the probability of occurrence of each kind of implicit response during a small time interval is proportional to the duration of the interval.

ii) "A final choice response is made when a run of K implicit responses of a given kind appears."

From these axioms, we can see how the emphasis in Audley's formulation of the choice problem differs from that in Luce's theory. Audley is concerned primarily with the sequential and temporal aspects of choice behavior. For example, it is not difficult to see, even without carrying out mathematical transformations, that his basic axioms relate the choice time to two quantities: first, the proportionality constant (i.e., the rate parameter) entering into axiom (i); and second, the length

(K) of the run of implicit responses of a given kind required before a final choice of the corresponding kind takes place.

On the basis of these axioms, Audley derives mathematical expressions for quantities like these: the probability that the final choice will be of a given kind; the mean latencies for various final choices; and the mean number of vicarious trial-and-error responses (i.e., the "implicit responses" of the model) preceding any final choice.

Stimulus-Sampling Models of Learning

As mentioned earlier, the idea central to Estes' (1950) statistical learning theory is that on each trial of a learning experiment, the subject "draws a sample" from a population of stimulus elements. This sample constitutes the "effective stimulus" —i.e., that part of the total stimulus situation which the subject "perceives"—on that trial. It is then assumed that all stimulus elements in this effective set become (or remain) "conditioned" or "connected" to the particular response elicited on that trial. This means that any of the *sampled* elements which were already conditioned to that response remain so, whereas those which were not yet conditioned to it (i.e., which were conditioned to *other* responses) now become so conditioned, and their connections with other responses are automatically broken. This is the gist of Estes' conditioning axiom.

Let us illustrate this idea concretely for the simplest case, when only two types of response are distinguished: the response R which the experimenter records as "positive," and the residual class of all other responses, designated non-R. Imagine the total stimulus population to be represented by a bagful of beads, say S in number. These beads are of two colors, red and white. The red ones stand for those stimulus elements that are conditioned to response R, and the white ones for those not so conditioned, i.e., those which are conditioned to non-R.

Imagine further that on each trial, the subject mixes the beads well and scoops out a ladleful of beads, say s in number; this represents the effective stimulus for that trial. If, on a given trial, the subject makes response R, then all the white beads among the s he has scooped out *suddenly turn red,* and the red beads remain red. Similarly, if he makes response non-R on that trial, the red beads among the s drawn turn white, and the white ones remain white. After each trial, the subject puts the s beads back into the bag; thus there will always be S beads to sample from, although the color ratio will (in general) have changed.

So far, nothing has been said explicitly about how the subject's *propensity* for making one response or another depends on the state of the stimulus population at a given time, although it has certainly been implied in speaking of stimulus elements' being "conditioned to" one response or another. The relationship between stimulus and response is specified in another key axiom of Estes' system, called the response axiom. It asserts that the *probability* that a given response will occur on any trial is equal to the fraction, say $X/S,$ of stimulus elements "conditioned to" that particular response *prior to* that trial. Thus in our red-and-white-beads analogy, if the successive color changes *through* the nth trial have resulted in, say, 60% of the S beads in the bag being red, then the probability that response R will be elicited on the $(n + 1)$th trial is equal to 0.60 (and, of course, the probability of response non-R is 0.40).

From the two axioms discussed above (and a further assumption that the ratio of red to white beads in the sample of s beads is equal to that in the total population), it is possible to derive relations between response probabilities on adjacent trials. Let us retrace such a derivation with the aid of our bag-of-beads analogy.

Suppose that when the subject is about to make his trial-n response, there are X red beads (and hence $S - X$ white ones) among the S in the bag. Then, according to the response axiom, the probability p_n that his response will be R on that trial is given by

$$p_n = X/S. \tag{1}$$

The "effective stimulus" of s beads will, by the homogeneity assumption, consist of $s(X/S)$ red ones and $s[(S - X)/S] = s(1 - X/S)$ white ones.

Now, if the subject in fact makes response R on trial n, then—by the conditioning axiom—the $s(1 - X/S)$ white beads will turn red, and the red ones will remain red. Thus when the s beads are replaced in the bag after trial n, there will be an increase of $s(1 - X/S)$ in the number of red beads, bringing the total to $X + s(1 - X/S)$. Consequently, on the next trial, the probability of response R will be equal to

$$\begin{aligned} p_{n+1} &= [X + s(1 - X/S)]/S \\ &= X/S + (s/S)(1 - X/S) \\ &= p_n + (s/S)(1 - p_n), \end{aligned} \tag{2}$$

where, in the last step, X/S has been replaced by using Eq. (1).

On the other hand, if the subject makes response non-R on trial n, similar arguments show that the number of red beads will have decreased from X to $X - s(X/S)$ by the time he is ready for trial $n + 1$. Hence, in this case, the next probability of response R will be

$$\begin{aligned} p_{n+1} &= [X - s(X/S)]/S \\ &= p_n - (s/S)p_n. \end{aligned} \tag{3}$$

In a subsequent paper by Estes and Burke (1953) the symbol θ is introduced in place of s/S for the "sampling ratio." Using this notation, and regrouping the terms in the last members of Eqs. (2) and (3), we rewrite these equations for later reference as follows:

$$\begin{aligned} p_{n+1} &= (1 - \theta)p_n + \theta, && \text{if } R \text{ on trial } n; \\ p_{n+1} &= (1 - \theta)p_n, && \text{if non-}R \text{ on trial } n. \end{aligned} \tag{4}$$

Once these *recursion relations* for the probability of response R on successive trials have been obtained, it becomes possible mathematically to derive various testable predictions from the model.* For example, the expected number of trials required for perfect learning of response R, the expected number of non-R responses, and so forth, can be expressed as mathematical functions of θ and the initial probability, p_0, of response R. The two quantities θ and p_0 are called the *parameters* of the model, and their values are estimated from experimental data. (It might be wondered how the sampling ratio θ can possibly be estimated, but Estes and Burke showed that this was also a measure of the *rate of learning*, and hence could be tied in with observation.)

What we described in the foregoing is the simplest of the stimulus-sampling models. A number of generalizations and modifications have been made by Estes and his coworkers since this first model was announced. Thus Estes and Burke (1953) considered the case when the various stimulus elements had different probabilities—θ_i for the ith element—of being sampled on any trial, instead of each having the same probability θ ($= s/S$). This generalization, however, led to the need for assuming specific distributions for the θ_i's before the model could function adequately. To avoid this difficulty, Burke, Estes, and Hellyer (1954) introduced the simplifying assumption that the θ_i's could take only two distinct values, θ_L and $\theta_{\bar{L}}$, associated with elements in two identifiable subsets S_L and $S_{\bar{L}}$, respectively, of the total stimulus population. In their experimental test of the resulting model, θ_L could be manipulated by varying the size of S_L, which consisted of the experimentally relevant stimulus elements, while $S_{\bar{L}}$ was the complementary subset of all other stimulus elements. The observed learning rates increased proportionally with the size of S_L, thus confirming their predictions from the model.

Further modifications of the basic stimulus-sampling model include those developed to account for the phenomena of spontaneous recovery (Estes, 1955), for discrimination learning (Restle, 1955a,b; Atkinson, 1958), and learning in two-person gamelike situations (Atkinson and Suppes, 1958, 1959).

Linear-Operator Models of Learning

Bush and Mosteller (1951a, 1955) used only a very general psychological assumption to introduce their linear-operator model. They assumed that each time a response occurs, there is some "outcome" which affects the probabilities associated with the various classes of responses in some way (including no alterations at all). Since an outcome may be identified with either a reinforcing event or a change in the stimulus situation, their assumption makes no commitment as to whether reinforcement or association is the mechanism responsible for learning.

Another assumption they make is what they call the *independence-of-path* assumption. This says that the way in which the set of response probabilities is altered on a given trial is determined solely by the response-outcome pair on that

---

* It should be mentioned that Estes did not, in his 1950 paper, utilize these recursion relations. Rather, he derived from his axioms several differential equations and other mathematical relations applicable to specific types of experimental situations, and thereby obtained many quantitative predictions. It was apparently realized only later that his axioms also lead to linear relations between response probabilities on adjacent trials.

trial, and is independent of earlier events in the learning process. For instance, if $p_n = 0.40$ for a certain response on trial n, then the value of p_{n+1} will be uniquely determined by the actual response on trial n and its outcome, regardless of what "path" (in the learning sequence) the subject took in arriving at the value $p_n = 0.40$. This is a simplifying assumption (cf. discussion in Section II, above) needed in order to justify expressing the probabilities on trial $(n + 1)$ as functions of the probabilities on trial n but not of those on trials $n - 1$, $n - 2$, etc.

With the foregoing assumptions, Bush and Mosteller proceed to write the trial-$(n + 1)$ probabilities as *linear* functions of the trial-n probabilities. Thus, for the simplest case of just two response classes (like R and non-R), with probabilities p_n and q_n ($= 1 - p_n$) on trial n, they write

$$p_{n+1} = u_i p_n + v_i q_n,$$
$$q_{n+1} = u_i' p_n + v_i' q_n, \tag{5}$$

where u_i, v_i, u_i', and v_i' are constants which depend on the particular response-outcome pair occurring on trial n. These four constants are not all independent, however, since we must have

$$q_{n+1} = 1 - p_{n+1}.$$

In fact, because the two probabilities are mutually complementary on each and every trial, it is necessary to trace the successive transformations of only one of them, say p. Therefore, we will henceforth consider only the first of the pair of equations (5), replacing q_n with $1 - p_n$ to write it as

$$
\begin{aligned}
p_{n+1} &= u_i p_n + v_i(1 - p_n) \\
&= v_i + (u_i - v_i)p_n \\
&= v_i + w_i p_n,
\end{aligned} \tag{6}
$$

where w_i is simply a new symbol for $u_i - v_i$.

When the basic equation is written in this form, the linearity restriction of the Bush-Mosteller models will perhaps not seem quite so arbitrary as it must have originally. For if p_{n+1} is expressible as any function $f(p_n)$ of p_n (as postulated in the two assumptions described earlier), and if this function can be expanded as a power series (as many commonly encountered functions can be), then we would have

$$
\begin{aligned}
p_{n+1} &= f(p_n) \\
&= c_0 + c_1 p_n + c_2 p_n^2 + c_3 p_n^3 + \cdots
\end{aligned}
$$

Equation (6) may then be regarded as an approximation to this series, in which only the first two terms are used. This is not to say that the linearity assumption is not a stringent one, but only that it is a rather natural one. After all, it is adopted purely for mathematical convenience, as Bush and Mosteller are the first to admit (1951a, p. 314).

Returning now to Eq. (6), let us rewrite it in two alternative forms, each having certain interpretative advantages. First, it may be rewritten as

$$p_{n+1} = p_n + a_i(1 - p_n) - b_i p_n, \tag{7}$$

where a_i is simply a new symbol for v_i, and $b_i = 1 - v_i - w_i$. From the requirement that the p's, being probabilities, must always have values between 0 and 1 (inclusive), it can be shown that both a_i and b_i are similarly restricted:

$$0 \leq a_i \leq 1 \quad \text{and} \quad 0 \leq b_i \leq 1.$$

In particular, since these constants are nonnegative, Eq. (7) tells us that the change from p_n to p_{n+1} can be analyzed into two parts: a *gain* proportional to $1 - p_n$ and a *loss* proportional to p_n. For this reason, Bush and Mosteller call Eq. (7) the *gain-loss form* of their basic linear equation.

A second alternative form of Eq. (6) is obtained by rewriting w_i as α_i and v_i as $(1 - \alpha_i)\lambda_i$. We then have

$$p_{n+1} = \alpha_i p_n + (1 - \alpha_i)\lambda_i, \tag{8}$$

which is called the *fixed-point* form. The constants are again subject to the restrictions

$$0 \leq \alpha_i \leq 1 \quad \text{and} \quad 0 \leq \lambda_i \leq 1.$$

Equation (8) is the form used in most of Bush and Mosteller's mathematical developments, and the reason for its being called the "fixed-point" form is this: if, on any trial, p_n takes the value λ_i, then the value of p_{n+1} will, according to Eq. (8), also be λ_i. (Furthermore, λ_i is the *only* value of p_n such that $p_{n+1} = p_n$, except when $\alpha_i = 1$.) What Eq. (8) tells us, then, is that each time a response probability is changed in accordance with that equation, the new probability value is a *weighted average* of the previous value and the fixed-point value λ_i. Since the weights are α_i and $(1 - \alpha_i)$, respectively, it follows that the smaller α_i is, the closer the new probability value is to λ_i and the farther it is from the previous probability value. Thus α_i is a parameter that is negatively related to learning rate—the larger α_i is, the slower the learning process.

Having written the recursion relation between response probabilities on adjacent trials as Eq. (8), Bush and Mosteller have established their basic (or general) model. Their next step is to *specialize* the equation to adapt it to specific types of experimental situations. Recall that the subscript i was introduced originally in the u_i, v_i, etc., of Eq. (5) to indicate that these constants depend on the particular response-outcome pair. This meaning of i of course carries over to the α_i and λ_i of Eq. (8). Thus in applying the model to a given experiment there will usually be two or more parameter pairs (α_1, λ_1), (α_2, λ_2), etc., each pair yielding a separate instance of Eq. (8).

For example, if in a T-maze experiment a left turn (response L) is always rewarded and a right turn (response R) never is, there will be just two (α, λ) pairs, and hence two equations of the form of (8):

$$p_{n+1} = \alpha_1 p_n + (1 - \alpha_1)\lambda_1, \quad \text{if } L \text{ is chosen on trial } n;$$
$$p_{n+1} = \alpha_2 p_n + (1 - \alpha_2)\lambda_2, \quad \text{if } R \text{ is chosen on trial } n.$$

On the other hand, if turns to each side of the maze are rewarded a certain predetermined percent of the time (partial reinforcement), we will need four equations:

$$p_{n+1} = \alpha_1 p_n + (1 - \alpha_1)\lambda_1, \quad \text{if } L \text{ is chosen and is rewarded on trial } n;$$
$$p_{n+1} = \alpha_2 p_n + (1 - \alpha_2)\lambda_2, \quad \text{if } L \text{ is chosen and is unrewarded on trial } n;$$
$$p_{n+1} = \alpha_3 p_n + (1 - \alpha_3)\lambda_3, \quad \text{if } R \text{ is chosen and is rewarded on trial } n;$$
$$p_{n+1} = \alpha_4 p_n + (1 - \alpha_4)\lambda_4, \quad \text{if } R \text{ is chosen and is unrewarded on trial } n.$$

(As noted earlier, the probabilities p_n and p_{n+1} always refer to one of the two alternative responses, say R.) Finally, there are experiments in which the outcome on each trial is completely predetermined by the experimenter, and is independent of the subject's response. An example of this type is a "prediction experiment," in which on each trial the subject guesses which of two lights will come on, and the lighting schedule is prearranged by the experimenter. Here again, two equations will suffice:

$$p_{n+1} = \alpha_1 p_n + (1 - \alpha_1)\lambda_1, \quad \text{if light 1 flashes on trial } n;$$
$$p_{n+1} = \alpha_2 p_n + (1 - \alpha_2)\lambda_2, \quad \text{if light 2 flashes on trial } n;$$

where the probabilities are those of the subject's predicting that light 1, for instance, will come on.

Note that although the probability-changes for both the first and third examples above were described by two equations, there is a difference between the two cases with regard to what it is that determines which of the two equations applies on a given trial. In the first case, the subject's response completely determines the applicable equation. It is redundant to speak of the "response-outcome pair" in such a case, for a particular outcome always follows a particular response. In the third example, on the other hand, the subject's response has no bearing on the outcome, i.e., whether light 1 or light 2 flashes; hence neither is it relevant to the decision as to which of the two probability-changing equations holds on a given trial. That decision is, in this case, determined solely by the prearranged schedule of outcomes.

The partial-reinforcement T-maze experiment, requiring four equations, exemplifies the only type of those cited above in which a genuine response-outcome *pair* determines the particular equation to be applied on each trial.

Considerations like these led Bush and Mosteller to distinguish three classes of learning experiments, depending on what type of event (response, outcome, or response-outcome pair) determines which one of the two or more probability-changing equations is to be applied after a given trial. Their categories consist of experiments that involve (a) subject-controlled events (e.g., consistent-reinforcement T-maze experiments), (b) experimenter-controlled events (e.g., two-choice prediction experiments), and (c) experimenter-subject-controlled events (e.g., partial-reinforcement T-maze experiments).

In principle, once we have determined which of the three classes a given experiment belongs to, and have decided what will constitute the responses and the outcomes, we are in a position to apply the appropriate type of linear model, leaving the determination of the α_i and λ_i values to experimental estimation. However, it is usually possible to exercise greater economy by making further *a priori* restrictions on one or more of the parameters (i.e., over and above the universal ones that $0 \leq \alpha_i, \lambda_i \leq 1$). Such restrictions are arrived at (or postulated) on the basis of one's familiarity, from past experience, with certain features of experiments like the one to be analyzed. We illustrate this process with reference to the class of experiments involving two subject-controlled events.

At this point, we introduce a slight change in notation. Instead of writing Eq. (8) in the recursion-relation style as we have been doing up to now, we shall use the *operator* notation. (This is, in fact, what Bush and Mosteller use throughout, and what gives rise to the name "linear-operator model.") This notation means that we conceptualize the change from p_n to p_{n+1} as an *operation* on the earlier p giving rise to the new p. Letting Q denote the operator, we symbolize "the result of operating on p by Q" as Qp. (This symbol should not be construed as the product "Q times p.") Thus Eq. (8) is written as

$$Q_ip = \alpha_ip + (1 - \alpha_i)\lambda_i, \tag{9}$$

where we no longer use the subscript n on p. It is to be understood that no matter what the trial number is on which a certain response probability has the value p, if event i occurs on *that* trial, then the corresponding probability on the *next* trial is $Q_i\,p$. The advantages of the operator notation will become apparent in the discussion below.

Let us return now to the class of experiments with two subject-controlled events. The general pair of operators for this class is:

$$Q_1p = \alpha_1p + (1 - \alpha_1)\lambda_1,$$
$$Q_2p = \alpha_2p + (1 - \alpha_2)\lambda_2. \tag{10}$$

Note that the qualifying clauses, "if event 1 occurs" and "if event 2 occurs," are no longer needed, for they are already implied by the subscripts on Q; Q_1 is applied when event 1 occurs, and Q_2 is applied when event 2 occurs. (This is one advantage, although a minor one, of the operator notation.)

For many simple learning experiments where only two responses are distinguished, and just one of them is rewarded as "correct," it is reasonable to assume that the subject eventually learns always to make the correct response. Also, it is a plausible assumption that on each trial, regardless of whether the correct or incorrect response is made, the subject's propensity for making the correct response is increased.

Translated into the language of linear-operator models, with p denoting the probability of the correct response, these assumptions become as follows: (i) as n increases without bound, p_n tends to the limiting value 1; and (ii) both Q_1 and Q_2 act on p so as to increase it. We have already seen that each λ_i ($i = 1, 2$) is the fixed point of the associated operator Q_i. An extension of this argument shows that

λ_i is also the *limiting point* toward which any p ($\neq 0$) is moved as Q_i is repeatedly applied. Hence assumptions (i) and (ii) together imply that $\lambda_1 = \lambda_2 = 1$. Consequently, when applied to experiments for which these assumptions are valid, Eqs. (10) reduce to the simpler ones,

$$Q_1 p = \alpha_1 p + (1 - \alpha_1),$$
$$Q_2 p = \alpha_2 p + (1 - \alpha_2), \tag{11}$$

with only three parameters: the two α's and the initial value of p.

There are other two-alternative learning experiments, however, in which both responses are in some sense rewarded. In such cases, we expect that making either response on any trial would increase the probability for *that* response on the next trial. In the model, if p is identified with the probability of response 1 (following which Q_1 is applied), we now expect Q_1 to increase p, but Q_2 to decrease p (since the occurrence of response 2 increases $q = 1 - p$). It is reasonable to assume in this situation that $\lambda_1 = 1$ and $\lambda_2 = 0$. Hence Eqs. (10) reduce this time to

$$Q_1 p = \alpha_1 p + (1 - \alpha_1),$$
$$Q_2 p = \alpha_2 p. \tag{12}$$

The two examples discussed above should suffice to illustrate the kind of reasoning one engages in to specialize the general operators (10) to simpler ones like (11) and (12), applicable under particular experimental conditions. It is of interest, however, to consider a further specialization of Eqs. (12) when the experiment to which the model is to be applied possesses a certain symmetry. If the occurrence of response 1 has the same effect on p as does the occurrence of response 2 on q ($= 1 - p$), then we may set $\alpha_1 = \alpha_2 = \alpha$ ("equal-alpha condition") in the equations.* The result is:

$$Q_1 p = \alpha p + (1 - \alpha),$$
$$Q_2 p = \alpha p.$$

When we compare these equations with those for the simplest case of Estes' stimulus-sampling model [Eqs. (4)], we see that the two pairs of equations become identical as soon as we make a notational change by writing α as $1 - \theta$ (and hence $1 - \alpha$ as θ). Thus we find that although Estes' model and the Bush-Mosteller model are based on apparently rather different psychological assumptions, their consequences are identical for this special case, at least. Many other points of correspondence between the two model systems have been noted by a number of authors, and their logical foundations have been systematically investigated by Estes and Suppes (1959). In view of the many similarities between the two systems of models, it has become customary to refer to them collectively as "linear models," except when attention is to be focused on the stimulus-sampling rationale of the system developed primarily by Estes and his coworkers.

---

* The symmetry-of-effects condition does not, in general, require that $\lambda_1 = 1$ and $\lambda_2 = 0$, but only that $\lambda_1 + \lambda_2 = 1$.

We have now seen how the general linear-operator model is developed, and how it is then specialized to three classes, and further "tailored" to fit particular experimental conditions. Our final task is to take a brief glimpse at some of the mathematical machinery used in deducing testable predictions from these models.

One commonly used approach is to first derive a *functional equation* satisfied by the quantity we are interested in, such as the mean number of "errors," the mean length of runs (unbroken series of occurrences) of one response, etc. Then this equation is solved by various methods, including the use of difference equations or differential equations which approximate them, power-series expansions, and so forth. We illustrate the procedure with reference to the model specified by Eqs. (11).

The operators for the model under consideration may be further simplified by identifying p with the probability of the *unrewarded* response (or "error"), rather than with that of the rewarded response as was done in Eqs. (11). With this new meaning of p, the limiting-point values λ_1 and λ_2 both become 0, and Eqs. (11) are replaced by the simpler ones,

$$Q_1 p = \alpha_1 p,$$
$$Q_2 p = \alpha_2 p, \tag{13}$$

which serve exactly the same purpose.

Using Eqs. (13) as their starting point, Tatsuoka and Mosteller (1959) obtained a functional equation satisfied by the distribution of the total number of errors predicted by the model. Briefly, their derivation was as follows.

Denote by $f(m; p)$ the probability that the total number of errors is equal to m, given the initial probability p. (Of course, $f(m; p)$ also depends on α_1 and α_2, but we omit these to simplify the notation.)

Imagine that we have a large population of subjects, all with initial error probability p, going through a learning process described by Eqs. (13). Then $f(m; p)$ is the proportion of subjects who make exactly m errors in the entire sequence of trials. These subjects can be divided into two subclasses: those who make an error on trial 1 and make exactly $m - 1$ errors subsequently; and those who do *not* make an error on trial 1 but make exactly m errors later.

By definition of p, subjects of the first subclass constitute a proportion of p of the entire population; and, by the second of Eqs. (13), their error probability on trial 2 is $\alpha_2 p$. Hence a proportion $f(m - 1; \alpha_2 p)$ of these subjects make $m - 1$ errors *counting from trial 2* (treated as though it were the initial trial with error probability $\alpha_2 p$). Therefore, $pf(m - 1; \alpha_2 p)$ is the contribution of the first subclass to the proportion $f(m; p)$. Similar arguments show that $(1 - p)f(m; \alpha_1 p)$ is the contribution of the second subclass to $f(m; p)$. Hence we obtain

$$f(m; p) = pf(m - 1; \alpha_2 p) + (1 - p)f(m; \alpha_1 p) \tag{14}$$

as a functional equation which must be satisfied by $f(m; p)$.

Having obtained this functional equation, Tatsuoka and Mosteller use it as a basis for deriving two further functional equations that are satisfied by the mean and variance, respectively, of the total number of errors. Letting $\mu(p)$ denote the mean number of errors made by a population of subjects with initial error probability p, we have by definition,

$$\mu(p) = \sum_{m=0}^{\infty} m f(m; p).$$

For the $f(m; p)$ in the summand on the right, we substitute the right-hand member of Eq. (14), and after some algebraic manipulation we get

$$\mu(p) = p[\mu(\alpha_2 p) + 1] + (1 - p)\mu(\alpha_1 p). \tag{15}$$

This equation, and a similar one derived for the variance, were solved by the method of power-series expansions, and numerical results were tabulated for various pairs of (α_1, α_2)-values with p varying from 0.1 to 1.0 in steps of 0.1.

To compare these results with observation, data from an experiment on avoidance training (Solomon and Wynne, 1953) were used. In this experiment, 30 dogs learned to avoid an electric shock by jumping over a barrier within 10 seconds after onset of the conditioned stimulus. Failure to jump in time resulted in the shock, and constituted an "error." The three parameters of the model had already been estimated by Bush and Mosteller (1955, pp. 241–246), who obtained $\alpha_1 = 0.80$, $\alpha_2 = 0.92$, and $p = 1$ (very nearly). With these parameter values, the mean and variance of the number of errors found from the Tatsuoka-Mosteller table were $\mu = 8.22$ and $\sigma^2 = 6.52$, respectively. The corresponding values calculated from the experimental data were $m = 7.80$ and $s^2 = 6.36$, respectively. The agreement is seen to be quite good, especially when we consider that μ would be expected to be somewhat larger than m, since the model postulates an infinite number of trials, whereas in the experiment this number is of course finite.

In order to avoid giving the impression that the power-series method referred to above is always feasible, we point out a mathematical problem arising from the other case of two subject-controlled events that was described earlier, namely, the case in which both responses are "rewarded" and the operators are given by Eqs. (12). In this situation, where there are two "attractive goals" so to speak, we do not expect all subjects eventually to "fixate" on a particular one of the two alternatives. Rather, the ultimate outcome of a long series of such trials will be that a certain percentage of the population of subjects will fixate on alternative 1, and the rest will fixate on alternative 2. Hence the problem here is to determine the proportion $P(p; \alpha_1, \alpha_2)$ of subjects who eventually fixate on alternative 1, among a population with initial probability p for that alternative and with rate parameters α_1, α_2.

A functional equation for this proportion is

$$P(p) = pP(\alpha_1 p + 1 - \alpha_1) + (1 - p)P(\alpha_2 p), \tag{16}$$

where the secondary arguments α_1, α_2 of $P(p; \alpha_1, \alpha_2)$ have been omitted. This equation was derived by Bellman and Shapiro (in Harris, Bellman, and Shapiro, 1952) and by Karlin (1953), all of whom have discovered many interesting properties of the function $P(p)$. However, except for special cases when the two α's are equal or when one of them is either 1 or 0, Eq. (16) long defied even a numerical solution which offered sufficient accuracy with a reasonable amount of labor. In particular, the power-series method is of no avail here except when $|\alpha_1 - \alpha_2|$ is very small. Mosteller and Tatsuoka (1960) described a method for approximating the solution by any number of grid-point values $P_1, P_2, \ldots, P_n$ for which an approximate set of n linear equations can be written. (With a high-speed computer, n can be taken quite large, and very close approximations can be achieved.) They also derived a differential equation whose solution approximates $P(p)$, although less closely than does the set of linear equations.

In the foregoing discussion of linear-operator models, we have confined ourselves to those dealing with simple learning. Extensions and modifications of the basic model have been made to handle stimulus generalization and discrimination learning (Bush and Mosteller, 1951b), the development of secondary drives (Bush and Wilson, 1956), group decision-making (Hays and Bush, 1954), and two-person interactive learning (Burke, 1959, 1960).

An interesting modification proposed by Sternberg (1959a,b) was to relax the independence-of-path assumption to permit dependence of response probabilities on a single step of the path. His "one-trial perseveration model" for the case of two subject-controlled events ("error" and "success") with equal alphas (symmetry of effects) takes the following form:

$$
\begin{aligned}
Q_1 p &= \alpha p, & &\text{(success and success)}, \\
Q_2 p &= \alpha p + \beta, & &\text{(success and error)}, \\
Q_3 p &= \alpha p - \beta, & &\text{(error and success)}, \\
Q_4 p &= \alpha p + (1 - \alpha)\beta, & &\text{(error and error)}.
\end{aligned}
$$

In these equations β is a new parameter, a measure of the strength of perseveration, and p is the error probability. Each of the four operators applies when the pair of responses for the preceding and current trials, respectively, is as specified in the parentheses following its equation. Note that when $\beta = 0$ (i.e., when there is no perseveration of the preceding response) $Q_1 p$ and $Q_2 p$, as well as $Q_3 p$ and $Q_4 p$, will reduce, as expected, to special cases of Eqs. (13) with $\alpha_1 = \alpha_2$.

Sternberg derived the mean and variance of the number of errors, the expected number of error runs of given length, and several other testable predictions from his model. These results showed closer agreement with data from a two-choice learning experiment with human subjects than did the corresponding predictions from each of three path-independent linear models.

Other Mathematical Models for Learning and Related Phenomena

We conclude this section with a brief survey of other mathematical models for learning, concept formation, and problem-solving. These models have varying degrees of affinity with the linear models described in the two preceding subsections. In particular, one of the classes discussed below (that of Markov-chain models) may today be regarded as comprising the linear models cast into an alternative form for certain mathematical advantages, rather than being a separate system of models *per se*. Nevertheless, its origin was historically independent of those of the linear models, and so we discuss this class separately.

Luce's beta model. As mentioned earlier, learning theory was one of the fields to which Luce (1959) applied his axiomatic theory of choice behavior. The main additional assumption which he introduced in this connection was that the ratio scale for degree of preference (whose existence was proved in his Theorem 4) could, in this context, be interpreted as a scale for *response strength*.

The notion of strength or intensity of a response has, in traditional learning theory, been distinguished from the observed relative frequency of that response. When the developers of linear models for learning chose response *probability* as their basic dependent variable, they in effect tossed out the concept of response *strength* from their theoretical paraphernalia. What Luce did was to "resurrect" the latter concept and relate it to response probability (construed as an instance of choice probability) in accordance with his Theorem 4, as follows.

Let T be identified with the set $\{R_1, R_2, \ldots, R_k\}$ of alternative responses available to a subject in a learning experiment, and denote by v_i the scale value (i.e., by assumption, the strength) of the ith response on a given trial. Then, provided all the conditions of Theorem 4 are satisfied, we have

$$P_T(R_i) = \frac{v_i}{\sum_{j=1}^{k} v_j} \qquad (i = 1, 2, \ldots, k) \qquad (17)$$

as the probability that response R_i will be "chosen" out of set T, on the trial in question.

Taking v_i as the basic variable to describe learning processes, Luce considers three different possibilities for the form of the operator which changes v_i from one trial to the next. (The three forms are derived from different sets of axioms, but we shall not discuss them here.) One possibility leads to the general linear-operator model described in the previous subsection, which Luce designates as the "alpha model." The second possibility gives rise to the "beta model," and the third generates a model ("gamma") different from the second in that it restricts response strength to finite values, whereas the beta model does not.

The distinguishing feature of the beta model is that it postulates the strength v_i of response R_i on a given trial to be determinable uniquely from the previous value of v_i, without regard to what the strength v_j of any other response R_j may have been. This postulate is called the "irrelevance-of-irrelevant-alternatives assumption," and together with three other postulates (which are common to both the alpha and beta models) it leads to strength-changing operators whose general form is

$$Q_i^* v_i = \beta_i v_i \qquad (i = 1, 2, \ldots, k). \qquad (18)$$

The parameters β_i depend, of course, on the event (i.e., the response-outcome pair) occurring on the trial in question; so a more complete notation would require another subscript for specifying the particular event. The β's are restricted to positive values, but (unlike the α's in the linear model) they may exceed 1. Clearly, Eq. (18) implies that the strength of R_i decreases, remains unchanged, or increases depending on whether $\beta_i < 1$, $\beta_i = 1$, or $\beta_i > 1$.

To see how the response probabilities change from trial to trial in the beta model, let us consider the case of two subject-controlled events. Letting p and q ($= 1 - p$) denote the probabilities of R_1 and R_2, respectively, we have, by Eq. (17),

$$p = v_1/(v_1 + v_2) \quad \text{and} \quad q = v_2/(v_1 + v_2) \tag{19}$$

on any given trial.

The chosen response uniquely determines the outcome, so there will be four operators for changing the two response strengths:

$$
\begin{aligned}
Q_{11}^* v_1 &= \beta_{11} v_1 &&\text{and} & Q_{21}^* v_2 &= \beta_{21} v_2, &&\text{if } R_1 \text{ occurs;} \\
Q_{12}^* v_2 &= \beta_{12} v_1 &&\text{and} & Q_{22}^* v_2 &= \beta_{22} v_2, &&\text{if } R_2 \text{ occurs.}
\end{aligned} \tag{20}
$$

The number of parameters can be reduced, however, when we note that the expressions for p and q [Eqs. (19)] can be written as

$$p = \frac{v_1/v_2}{v_1/v_2 + 1} \quad \text{and} \quad q = \frac{1}{v_1/v_2 + 1}, \tag{21}$$

which are functions only of the ratio of the two response strengths. Accordingly, we define a new variable $r = v_1/v_2$, whose transformation rules are, from Eqs. (20),

$$
\begin{aligned}
Q_1^* r &= (\beta_{11}/\beta_{21})r, &&\text{if } R_1 \text{ occurs;} \\
Q_2^* r &= (\beta_{12}/\beta_{22})r, &&\text{if } R_2 \text{ occurs.}
\end{aligned}
$$

When β_1 is written for β_{11}/β_{21} and β_2 for β_{12}/β_{22}, these equations become

$$Q_i^* r = \beta_i r \quad (i = 1, 2), \tag{22}$$

where each Q_i^* is applied when the corresponsing R_i occurs on the trial in question.

Expressing r in terms of p from the first of equations (21), we have

$$r = p/(1 - p).$$

Consequently, when r is operated on by the Q_i^* of equation (22), the new p becomes

$$\frac{\beta_i r}{\beta_i r + 1} = \frac{\beta_i[p/(1 - p)]}{\beta_i[p/(1 - p)] + 1},$$

which simplifies to

$$\frac{\beta_i p}{1 + (\beta_i - 1)p}.$$

We thus see that in the beta model the response probability p (of R_1) undergoes a *nonlinear* change in accordance with the operators

$$Q_i p = \frac{\beta_i p}{1 + (\beta_i - 1)p} \quad (i = 1, 2). \tag{23}$$

This nonlinearity makes the derivation of testable consequences from this model a far more formidable task than it is in the case of linear models.

Experimental tests of predictions from the beta model are scarce, due to the difficulty mentioned above. Bush, Galanter, and Luce (1959) compared the relative adequacy of the alpha and beta models in describing data from two experiments, one in avoidance learning, and the other in retraining after overlearning. The alpha model showed somewhat better agreement for the first experiment, but the beta model was decidedly superior for the second.

Fey (1961) compared the alpha and beta models with respect to the property of *parameter invariance,* that is, the extent to which parameter values estimated from data for one experiment suffice in describing those for a slightly different experiment. He used data from a simple T-maze experiment (left, always rewarded; right, never) to estimate the parameters of the two models, and then used these values to predict from each model various statistics for a partial-reinforcement experiment (left, rewarded with probability 0.75; right, rewarded with probability 0.25). He found about the same amounts of discrepancy between the cross-validation data statistics and the predictions from both models, although each had shown very close agreement with the original data.

Mathematical properties of the beta model for two alternatives have been studied by Bush (1960), Lamperti and Suppes (1960), and Kanal (1962a,b). Bush presents exact formulas for several statistics in special cases (i.e., when one or both of the β's have special values, or the two are equal), and approximate formulas or expressions for upper and lower bounds in the general case. Lamperti and Suppes deal mainly with the conditions under which the probability of one alternative tends to 1 or 0 (or neither) as the number of trials increases without bound. Kanal gives general solutions to functional equations for various statistics, for both the alpha and the beta models. Unfortunately, many of the expressions are rather unwieldy from the practical computational standpoint.

Extensions of the beta model to situations other than simple learning (e.g., stimulus generalization, discrimination learning, etc.), such as exist for linear models, have not to my knowledge been reported in the literature. In an unpublished paper, Tatsuoka and Abe (1961) describe an attempt to develop a beta model for discrimination learning which met with limited success in a special case.

An urn model. A two-alternative model proposed by Audley and Jonckheere (1956), which resorts to an urn-and-ball scheme to describe the probability changes, is worthy of brief mention, at least to dispel the incorrect idea sometimes held, that it is similar in nature to the stimulus-sampling model. The resemblance is illusory.

In the stimulus-sampling model, if one wishes to imagine a bag of beads to draw from (as we have done for expository purposes), the beads represent stimulus elements, and the sample drawn is the perceived part of the total stimulus population. In the urn model, on the other hand, the drawing of a ball and the subsequent changes made in the contents of the urn are mathematical fictions intended only as aids in computing the successive response probabilities. If any psychological meaning is to be attached to the balls, it should be that the relative number of balls of the two colors measures the relative *strength* of the two responses. Changing the composition of the urn after each trial corresponds, then, to transforming the response strengths. Consequently, it is clear that the urn model actually resembles Luce's beta model more than it does the stimulus-sampling model. We will see below that it indeed does generate something akin to the beta model as a special case.

The scheme of the general urn model is as follows.

Initially, an urn contains r red balls and $N - r$ black ones. On each trial, one ball is drawn at random, its color noted, and the ball replaced in the urn. Furthermore, several new balls are added to the urn in accordance with the following rules:

> If a red ball was drawn, add a red balls and $c_1 - a$ black balls.
> If a black ball was drawn, add b red balls and $c_2 - b$ black balls.

Now suppose that among the first n trials, red balls were drawn k times, and black ones, $n - k$ times. Then, from the rules given above, it follows that the probability of drawing a red ball on the $(n + 1)$th trial is given by:

$$P_{n+1}(R \mid k) = \frac{r + ka + (n - k)b}{N + kc_1 + (n - k)c_2}$$
$$= \frac{\rho + k\alpha + (n - k)\beta}{1 + k\gamma_1 + (n - k)\gamma_2}, \tag{24}$$

where $\rho = r/N$, $\alpha = a/N$, $\beta = b/N$, $\gamma_i = c_i/N$ $(i = 1, 2)$.

If we interpret the drawing of a red ball on any trial as the making of the "correct" response on that trial, Eq. (24) tells us the probability of a correct response on trial $n + 1$, given that there were exactly k correct responses earlier. Suitable restrictions must be placed on the parameters, of course, to ensure that this expression is a nonnegative, increasing function of k which does not exceed 1.

For making comparisons with the beta model, it is convenient to derive recursion formulas expressing the probability p_{n+1} of a correct response on trial $n + 1$ (regardless of the number of earlier correct responses) as functions of p_n. The formula for each of the two cases (depending on whether the correct or incorrect response occurs on trial n) can be obtained by eliminating k between Eq. (24) and a similar equation for $P_n (R \mid k - 1)$ or $p_n (R \mid k)$, respectively. For the first case, Audley and Jonckheere give the equation

$$p_{n+1} = \frac{a + (b + cn)p_n}{(d + cn) + ep_n}, \qquad \text{if } R \text{ occurs on trial } n, \tag{25}$$

where a, b, c, d, e, represent rather lengthy expressions involving α, β, γ_1, γ_2, and ρ.

Comparing Eq. (25) with the first of Eqs. (23), we see that the two become similar in form if we impose the conditions that

$$a = 0 \qquad \text{and} \qquad e = b - d, \tag{26}$$

for under these conditions Eq. (25) reduces to

$$p_{n+1} = \frac{[(b + cn)/(d + cn)]p_n}{1 + [(b + cn)/(d + cn) - 1]p_n}.$$

However, this is not identical with Eq. (23), because there the β_1 is a constant, whereas the quantity $(b + cn)/(d + cn)$ depends on the trial number n. (This dependency cannot be eliminated by imposing the further condition $c = 0$, for it turns out that if this condition is added to the previous two, the whole model collapses.)

We thus see that even with special restrictions on the parameters, the urn model generates a response-probability recursion rule more complicated than that for the beta model; the operator itself changes from trial to trial. We might say that the urn model corresponds to a "nonstationary beta model," as it were, under the restrictions (26), which in terms of the original parameters, require that $\alpha = \beta = \gamma_1/2$.

Audley and Jonckheere also present a modified urn model in which the total number of balls is held constant throughout the sequence of trials. This is done by removing as many balls of one color as there are balls of the other color added. The color of the balls added on each trial coincides with that of the ball which was drawn and replaced. With this modification, linear operators similar to those in the Bush-Mosteller system are obtained.

Single-element conditioning model. An interesting variation of the stimulus-sampling model is the single-element, or "all-or-none," conditioning model. Applicable in situations where only one relevant stimulus element (or stimulus pattern) and a specific, correct response to it are identified on each trial, the underlying assumptions of this model are as follows:

i) On each trial the single stimulus, which is always "sampled," is either conditioned or unconditioned to the correct response.

ii) Until the stimulus is conditioned, there is a *constant probability p* (<1) that the correct response will be elicited.

iii) As soon as the stimulus is conditioned, the probability of the correct response (from the next trial onward) becomes unity and remains so.

iv) On each trial there is a constant probability c that the stimulus, if not yet conditioned, will become conditioned.

This type of model was first proposed by Estes (1959a), as an extreme case of what he called *pattern models,* involving few stimulus elements, in contrast to his earlier *component models,* which (as we have seen) assume large populations of stimulus elements. Independently, a model mathematically equivalent to this (although not framed in stimulus-sampling terms) was considered by Bush and Mosteller (1959) as a possible formalization of the notion that learning takes place by sudden insight. An extensive study of the properties of single-element models was made by Bower (1961) in connection with applications to paired-associate learning. Some of these properties can be discussed without going into a great deal of mathematics; they are noted below.

First, it is reasonable, in experiments of the paired-associate type, to assume that the constant preconditioning success probability p is equal to $1/N$, where N is the number of response items in the list. Hence in such cases there is only one parameter, the conditioning probability c, to be estimated from observed data. Second, the assumption that the success probability prior to conditioning is a constant implies that the total number of errors *preceding* the last error (not counting the last one itself) follows a binomial distribution. That is to say, the probability that this number will be k is given by

$$\binom{n-1}{k} p^{n-1-k}(1-p)^k, \qquad (k \leq n-1),$$

where n is the trial number of the last error. Knowing this distribution enables us, in turn, to study many sequential properties of the preconditioning responses, and Bower has derived numerous formulas for such properties.

Suppes and Ginsberg (1962, 1963) applied the all-or-none model to the analysis of a series of experiments on concept formation in young children. Since this is a relatively novel application of learning models, we discuss in some detail one of these experiments, in which the concept to be formed was that of binary notation for numbers.

In one part of this experiment, children five to six years of age were required to learn binary numerals for the numbers 4 and 5. To preclude rote memorization of specific symbols, however, three different and unfamiliar pairs of symbols (Γ and $*$; λ and π; $\leftrightarrow$ and Σ) were used in place of '1' and '0' in the standard binary numerals '100' and '101.' The resulting six stimulus patterns ($\Gamma**$, $\leftrightarrow\Sigma\leftrightarrow$, etc.) were presented one at a time in random order for 16 blocks (96 trials in all), and the subjects responded by indicating each time whether the pattern stood for 4 or for 5. They were told on each trial whether their response was right or wrong, and were required to correct themselves overtly in the latter event.

The conditions of the experiment make it fairly plausible that the axioms of the model are satisfied. The binary-numeral pattern presented on each trial constitutes the single stimulus to be conditioned to the appropriate response. Once the children "catch on" (i.e., achieve the concept), they will respond correctly with probability close to 1; until then they will be guessing and their probability of being correct will, in this case, be $p = \frac{1}{2}$.

Unfortunately, the task was apparently a little too difficult for such young children. Only half of the subjects actually learned the general concept, as evidenced by responses to four test trials with two other different symbol pairs for '1' and '0'. (The rest were, it seems, still in the process of "acquiring the six individual S-R associations.")

Despite this circumstance, predictions from the model were in quite close agreement with observation. The observed mean number of errors per item per subject

(4.32) was used for estimating the value of the single parameter c to be 0.088. Using this value in formulas derived from the model, Suppes and Ginsberg computed 13 other statistics to be compared with the corresponding observed statistics. These included such quantities as the standard deviation of number of errors, mean number of error runs, mean number of alternations of success and failure, and so forth. With one statistic excluded (whose error was small in absolute magnitude but large in percentage), the average error in the predicted values was about 9%, with seven values showing less than 5% error.

Markov-chain models. If a coin is tossed over and over again, the record of outcomes (a long chain of H's and T's) will normally be sequentially independent. That is, the probability of an H at any place in the sequence will not in any way depend on whether an H or a T occurred in the previous position (or anywhere else), and likewise for the probability of a T at any place.

We can easily design a "rigged" coin-tossing "experiment," however, in which such sequential independence does not hold. Suppose that we have two coins, A and B. Coin A is loaded in favor of heads, the probability of its showing heads being $P_A(H) = \frac{3}{5}$, say (and hence $P_A(T) = \frac{2}{5}$). Coin B is biased the other way, with $P_B(H) = \frac{3}{7}$ and $P_B(T) = \frac{4}{7}$. In making our sequence of tosses, we adopt the following rules: Each time we get an H, we use coin A for the next toss; each time we get a T we use coin B for the next toss.

The record of outcomes generated in this manner will show a definite sequential dependency. If there is an H in a certain position of the sequence, say the nth, then the probabilities of finding an H or a T in the $(n + 1)$th position are $\frac{3}{5}$ and $\frac{2}{5}$, respectively, whereas if the nth entry is a T, the two probabilities for the $(n + 1)$th entry are $\frac{3}{7}$ and $\frac{4}{7}$. Note, however, that these conditional probabilities,

$$P(H \text{ in } (n + 1)\text{th} \mid H \text{ in } n\text{th}) = \tfrac{3}{5}, \text{ etc.},$$

hold true regardless of *how* the nth entry came to be what it is—that is, whether it, in turn, was preceded by an H or a T.

The sequence of H's and T's just described exemplifies a simple *Markov chain* involving two *states*. The fundamental property of a two-state Markov chain is that it is completely described by four *transition probabilities* like the $P(H \mid H) = \frac{3}{5}$, $P(T \mid H) = \frac{2}{5}$, $P(H \mid T) = \frac{3}{7}$, and $P(T \mid T) = \frac{4}{7}$ in the example above. [In this context, a conditional probability symbol, e.g., $P(T \mid H)$, should be read, "probability of state T at one step, given state H at the preceding step," or, more briefly, "probability of going (in one step) from state H to state T."]

A convenient way of listing these probabilities is to arrange them in a matrix, called the *transition matrix,* as follows:

$$\begin{array}{c} \\ H \\ T \end{array} \begin{array}{cc} H & T \end{array} \\ \begin{bmatrix} 3/5 & 2/5 \\ 3/7 & 4/7 \end{bmatrix},$$

where the rows refer to states before the transition, and the columns, to those after the transition. Thus if we call H the first state and T the second state, the element in the ith row and jth column of this matrix is the probability of going from the ith state to the jth state in one step ($i = 1, 2; j = 1, 2$). We therefore introduce the shorter notation p_{ij} for this transition probability, in place of $P(H \mid H)$, $P(T \mid H)$, etc. Note that $p_{11} + p_{12} = p_{21} + p_{22} = 1$; that is, the elements of each row necessarily add up to 1, because whichever state we start from, we must, after the transition, be either in that state or in the other one.

The extension of the above notation to cases in which any one of s (> 2) states may exist at each step of a chain is immediate. There will then be s^2 transition probabilities p_{ij} ($i = 1, 2, \ldots, s; j = 1, 2, \ldots, s$); the transition matrix will have s rows and s columns:

$$\begin{bmatrix} p_{11} & p_{12} & \cdots & p_{1s} \\ p_{21} & p_{22} & \cdots & p_{2s} \\ \vdots & & & \vdots \\ p_{s1} & p_{s2} & \cdots & p_{ss} \end{bmatrix},$$

and the sum of the elements in each row will be 1.

Although its transition matrix completely describes any Markov *chain*, we need certain other probabilities in order fully to specify the *process* which generates the chain. These are the *initial probabilities* with which we enter the chain, and they are denoted $p_1^{(0)}, p_2^{(0)}, \ldots, p_s^{(0)}$. For instance, in the experiment using coins A and B, we might arbitrarily decide to start the process by tossing coin A. This is the same as fixing the initial state "deterministically" at H (or state 1), and our initial probabilities are then $p_1^{(0)} = 1$, $p_2^{(0)} = 0$. Another way to start the process might be to toss an unbiased coin and use coin A or B for the first toss counted in the chain, depending on whether the unbiased coin lands heads or tails. In this case, we would be entering the chain with initial probabilities $p_1^{(0)} = \frac{1}{2}$, $p_2^{(0)} = \frac{1}{2}$.

Once the initial probabilities as well as the transition probabilities have been specified, we can successively compute the probabilities for the several states in the first step, second step, and so forth. These computations, based on elementary principles of probability theory, are compactly represented by matrix multiplication.* Thus, for our illustrative example, if we use the second set of initial probabilities given above, we obtain

$$[p_1^{(1)}, p_2^{(1)}] = [\tfrac{1}{2}, \tfrac{1}{2}] \begin{bmatrix} \tfrac{3}{5} & \tfrac{2}{5} \\ \tfrac{3}{7} & \tfrac{4}{7} \end{bmatrix} = [\tfrac{17}{35}, \tfrac{18}{35}]$$

as the vector of state probabilities for the first step in the chain (i.e., the outcome of the first toss of coin A or B, whichever was chosen by the unbiased coin). In

---

* The product **AB** of two matrices (defined only when the number of columns in **A** is equal to the number of rows in **B**) is a matrix with as many rows as **A** and as many columns as **B**, its (i, j)-element being given by $\Sigma_{k=1}^n a_{ik} b_{kj}$. In particular, an n-dimensional row vector (i.e., a one-row, n-column matrix) $\mathbf{p} = [p_1, p_2, \ldots, p_n]$ *times* a square matrix **Q** with n rows and n columns gives another n-dimensional vector whose ith element is equal to $\Sigma_{k=1}^n p_k q_{ki}$.

general, if we denote the vector of state probabilities for step n by $\mathbf{p}^{(n)}$, and the transition matrix by $\mathbf{Q}$, we have

$$
\begin{aligned}
\mathbf{p}^{(1)} &= \mathbf{p}^{(0)}\mathbf{Q}, \\
\mathbf{p}^{(2)} &= \mathbf{p}^{(1)}\mathbf{Q} = (\mathbf{p}^{(0)}\mathbf{Q})\mathbf{Q} = \mathbf{p}^{(0)}\mathbf{Q}^2, \\
&\vdots \\
\mathbf{p}^{(n)} &= \mathbf{p}^{(0)}\mathbf{Q}^n.
\end{aligned}
\tag{27}
$$

This equation, expressing how a Markov process is determined from the initial probabilities and the transition matrix, is one of the basic theorems in the theory of Markov chains. Numerous other theorems have been established which describe various properties of Markov chains in great detail and provide useful computational formulas.

Miller and Frick (1949), in the same paper in which they first introduced information theory to the psychological literature, also showed the potential fruitfulness of Markov-chain theory for the analysis of sequential properties of behavioral data. Although applications to learning phenomena as such were ruled out in that paper, Miller and McGill (1952) utilized several results from Markov-chain theory in making deductions from their model for free-recall verbal learning and compared them with experimental data. This model was probably the first seriously constructed "Markov learning model," though the authors did not call it that. In an earlier paper, Miller (1952) had been more explicit in advocating the use of Markov models in psychology.

Bush and Mosteller (1955) indicate at several points in their book that the processes generated by their linear-operator model can, in certain cases, be profitably regarded as Markov processes. However, they do not make very extensive use of results derived directly from Markov-chain theory. The reason is that for all but the simplest special cases, a recasting of their linear models into Markov models requires identifying the possible values of a response probability p as the states of the Markov process,* and since p can usually take any value between 0 and 1, there results an infinite number of states.

Stimulus-sampling models have an advantage over linear-operator models in this respect. Since they explicitly assume a finite number of stimulus elements, it becomes possible (and sufficient), in two-response situations, to define Markov states in terms of the number of stimulus elements (or patterns) that are conditioned to one of the responses at a given moment. Thus if there are S stimulus elements, it suffices to identify $S + 1$ states, depending on whether $0, 1, 2, \ldots,$ or S elements are connected to response R_1 at a given step of the Markov chain. For this reason, most of the Markov-chain interpretations of linear learning models have been made by researchers who use the stimulus-sampling approach. In particular, Atkinson and Suppes have done much to stimulate the increasing use of Markov

---

* Note that this identification is permissible only because of the independence-of-path assumption, whereby the conditional probability $P(p_{n+1}|p_n)$ is independent of the value of p_{n-1}, etc.

models, most of their work cited in this chapter having made extensive use of Markov-chain theory. Credit is due also to Kemeny and Snell (1957) who compared the Markov processes resulting from the linear-operator and the stimulus-sampling models, respectively.

Estes (1959a), in the paper in which he first made the distinction between component and pattern models, systematically investigated the results of Markovian formulations for various subclasses of stimulus-sampling models. Here we will only take a glimpse at the simplest case: that of two experimenter-controlled events for which a single-pattern stimulus model is applicable.

As an example, Estes considers a prediction experiment in which the subject guesses whether the ball will stop on red or black in a series of spins of a roulette wheel. The "ready" signal and all the background cues constitute the single stimulus pattern perceived by the subject at the onset of each trial. His response is either R_1 (guessing "red") or R_2 (guessing "black"). The wheel is so constructed that the probability of red (reinforcing event E_1) and that of black (E_2) are π and $1 - \pi$, respectively, on each spin.

Since only one stimulus pattern is assumed, there are two states in the Markov process: (1) if the stimulus is conditioned to response R_1; (2) if it is conditioned to R_2. The state at the beginning of each trial (or, equivalently, at the end of the preceding trial) uniquely determines the response on that trial. Next, let c denote the probability that the single stimulus pattern, if not conditioned to R_i on a given trial, will become conditioned to R_i if the corresponding event E_i occurs on that trial.

Consider now the probability p_{12} of a transition from state 1 on one trial to state 2 on the next. This transition can take place only if E_2 occurs on the earlier trial, which it does with probability $1 - \pi$; and given E_2, the probability that the stimulus will then become conditioned to R_2 is c. Therefore, $p_{12} = (1 - \pi)c$. Consequently, $p_{11} = 1 - (1 - \pi)c$, for the state must either change to 2 or remain as 1. By similar arguments, we find $p_{21} = \pi c$, and hence $p_{22} = 1 - \pi c$. Collecting the four transition probabilities, we get the transition matrix

$$\mathbf{Q} = \begin{bmatrix} 1 - c + \pi c & (1 - \pi)c \\ \pi c & 1 - \pi c \end{bmatrix}. \tag{28}$$

One question of interest in experiments of the kind under consideration is this: After a very long series of trials, what will be the subject's ultimate probabilities for the two responses R_1 and R_2? Recalling that the probability of R_i on any trial is, by assumption, equal to the probability that state i exists at the end of the *preceding* trial, we obtain the answer by finding $\mathbf{p}^{(n)} = [p_1^{(n)}, p_2^{(n)}]$ and letting n tend to infinity. From the general relation (27), we know that to determine $\mathbf{p}^{(n)}$ we need $\mathbf{Q}^n$. It can be shown that for the particular $\mathbf{Q}$ given by Eq. (28), the nth power is

$$\mathbf{Q}^n = \begin{bmatrix} \pi + (1 - \pi)(1 - c)^n & (1 - \pi)[1 - (1 - c)^n] \\ \pi[1 - (1 - c)^n] & 1 - \pi[1 - (1 - c)^n] \end{bmatrix}.$$

Since c is a probability value, $0 < 1 - c < 1$, and $(1 - c)^n$ tends to 0 as n increases without bound; so we obtain

$$\lim_{n \to \infty} \mathbf{Q}^n = \begin{bmatrix} \pi & 1 - \pi \\ \pi & 1 - \pi \end{bmatrix}.$$

Consequently,

$$\lim_{n \to \infty} \mathbf{p}^{(n)} = [p_1^{(0)}, p_2^{(0)}] \begin{bmatrix} \pi & 1 - \pi \\ \pi & 1 - \pi \end{bmatrix} = [\pi, 1 - \pi],$$

because $p_1^{(0)} + p_2^{(0)} = 1$.

We thus find the interesting result that according to the model, the limiting values of the two response probabilities do not depend on what the initial response probabilities may have been. Rather, they are respectively equal to the experimenter-determined probabilities, π and $1 - \pi$, for stops on red and on black. This is what Estes calls the "probability-matching rule," whose conflict with game-theoretic predictions we have noted earlier (see p. 16).

An information-processing model of problem-solving. Finally, let us briefly consider a kind of model quite different from any we have discussed in the foregoing—a model developed by Newell, Shaw, and Simon (1958, 1960), which is based on programs for information-processing systems like high-speed digital computers. It should be pointed out right away that this is *not* an analogue model in which the human brain is compared to computer structures, and synapses to electrical relays. It is the *program,* rather than the computer itself, that plays the central role in this model, a role which is functionally analogous to that played by a set of equations in a mathematical model. The computer, in executing a program, is in effect logically deducing some testable consequences from the program. If these consequences (simulations of human problem-solving behavior) are in agreement with observation (actual human problem-solving behavior), the model is deemed successful. If not, the program is modified, much as equations are modified in mathematical models, and testable consequences are again deduced.

The basic "ingredients" of the information-processing model of these authors are:

1) A control system consisting of a number of *memories,* which contain symbolized information and are interconnected by various ordering relations . . .

2) A number of *primitive information processes,* which operate on the information in the memories . . .

3) A perfectly definite set of rules for combining these processes into whole *programs* of processing . . . (Newell, Shaw, and Simon, 1958, p. 151)

In their 1958 paper, Newell and his co-workers describe a series of experiments involving a program, called the "Logic Theorist" (LT), capable of proving theorems in elementary symbolic logic. Although a detailed discussion of the program would take us too far afield, some of its salient features should be noted so that the very idea of comparing the computer's execution of the program with the behavior of human subjects facing the task of proving the same theorems will not seem ludicrous. Corresponding to the three basic ingredients of the model which were cited above, LT has the following elements built into it.

1) A list of axioms of sentential calculus (specifically, that given in Whitehead and Russell's *Principia Mathematica*) to be stored in the computer's memory.

2) Four rules of inference in symbolic logic: (a) *substitution* (of a new variable or expression for all occurrences of some variable in a true expression); (b) *replacement* (of a connective by its definition in terms of other connectives); (c) *detachment* (to get "*B*" from a combination of "*A* implies *B*" and "*A*"); (d) *chaining* (to get "*A* implies *C*" from "*A* implies *B*" and "*B* implies *C*").

3) A set of rules that specifies a heuristic strategy for finding proofs. In essence, the strategy involves two aspects: (a) breaking the problem down into component subproblems (hierarchical structuring); (b) a "reducing-the-gap" principle which allows the pursuing of any line of attack only if at each step the "gap" between the expression to be proved and the expression at hand is reduced, as judged by a *similarity test*. More will be said about LT's strategy when we compare its behavior with human problem-solving behavior below.

In the initial experiment, LT was given the task of proving the first 52 theorems in Chapter 2 of *Principia,* in the order in which they occur there. Each theorem proved was stored in the memory, along with the axioms, and was available for use in proving subsequent theorems. Under these conditions, LT was able to prove 38 (73%) of the 52 theorems. (The program stipulated that if for any theorem a proof could not be found within 45 minutes, attempts to prove that theorem would be terminated.) Of these 38 theorems, about half were proved in less than a minute each; most of the rest took between one and five minutes each, and a few took more than 15 minutes.

In the second experiment, after the memory had been cleared of all the theorems proved in the first one, LT was given Theorem 12 to prove. This time, it failed to find a proof even though it had found one for the same theorem in about 10 seconds when Theorems 1 through 11 were held in memory.

The third experiment was intermediate between the first two. Theorem 3 was stored in memory, along with the axioms. Now LT was able to prove Theorem 12 in about 15 minutes, taking three steps for the proof, whereas in the first experiment, with all preceding theorems available, only one step had been required.

Even the gross outcomes of the experiments, summarily described above, show "humanoid" qualities. LT found some theorems easy to prove, other difficult or impossible (within the allotted time limit). It was unable to prove a relatively easy theorem when prerequisite knowledge was "forgotten", but it did succeed when given a "hint." But the resemblances become far more striking when detailed "protocols" are examined after requiring LT to "think aloud" while it works—i.e., to print out its intermediate steps and lines of attack, both successful and unsuccessful. We describe only a few of these resemblances below.

It was already indicated, in the brief description of LT's strategy, that it does *not* go about searching for a proof of a given expression by *blind* trial-and-error (i.e., by trying all possible sequences of expressions permitted by the four rules of inference). It uses a much more "insightful" kind of trial-and-error. For instance, in attempting a step by the substitution method, it works backward to restrict its trials to only those types of substitution which satisfy certain necessary conditions. Furthermore, in searching for already proven expressions in which to make the substitution, it considers only "likely candidates" by a similarity criterion. (This usually cuts down the scope of search to about 10% of the total list of axioms and previously proved theorems.) These two modes of attack exemplify the problem-subproblem hierarchy referred to earlier. The actual use of the similarity criterion involves a further breakdown into "sub-subproblems" such as finding the number of levels in the expression, the number of distinct variables, and so on.

The *selective* trial-and-error process just described in connection with the substitution method is continued by LT as long as the "gap" is reduced at each step. Lacking this reduction, similar processes are undertaken, using (in this order) the detachment method, and then the chaining method, of which there are two variants, forward and backward chaining.

After having read all this, one may be inclined to ask, "What's so remarkable about the fact that LT's problem-solving behavior resembles that of humans? Wasn't it just programmed to behave this way?" Certainly, but the point is that a program *was* written which "incorporates a *sufficient* set of elementary processes arranged in a sufficiently effective strategy to produce this result" (Newell, Shaw, and Simon, 1958, p. 155). This is why the author's claim is justified: that the *program* (not the computer) constitutes a model for human problem-solving behavior in much the same sense as does a set of equations in a mathematical model. To be sure, the "predictions" from the program, which we sampled above, were largely qualitative rather than quantitative. But the *relative* times required to prove various theorems offer a quantitative prediction which can be checked against data for human subjects. Furthermore, if detailed protocols were obtained showing the sequence in which various attempts are made by human subjects, these would enable an investigator to make more than just qualitative tests of predictions from the model.

It should be mentioned in closing that the information-processing model was, in large measure, responsible for inspiring Miller, Galanter, and Pribram (1960) to conceive of their "TOTE (Test-Operate-Test-Exist) model" of human behavior. (Actually, "TOTE" is the name they give to the feedback loop which they propose as the *unit* of analysis, to replace the "reflex," for describing behavior in general.) The *test* phase of TOTE corresponds closely to the "reducing-the-gap" principle in LT, and the *operational* phase may consist of a hierarchy of TOTE units (subproblems). Implications of adopting this descriptive unit for explaining the "plans and the structure of behavior" are discussed at length in their interesting and provocative book. It remains to be seen to what extent *their* plans will structure a rigorously and quantitatively testable theory of human behavior.

V. SUMMARY AND EVALUATION

In this chapter a survey was made of mathematical models that have been developed in several fields of psychology and (to some extent) of social psychology since about 1950. The main emphasis was on mathematical models for learning; other fields briefly touched upon included those of small-group behavior, individual choice behavior, and concept formation. Quantitative models derived from information theory and game theory were also discussed, but these were distinguished from "mathematical models" as such, for reasons discussed in Section II and summarized below.

Two other areas of psychological research rich in mathematical models—factor analysis and psychophysics—were not considered here, partly because they are treated separately in other chapters of this handbook (Chapters 4 and 5). Also, these branches are concerned primarily with the static and structural aspects of psychology, whereas those considered in this chapter deal with the dynamic and "process-oriented" aspects. Consequently, there are wide differences between the mathematical constitutions of the models used in these two fields and those of the models discussed in this chapter. This is not to say that the models described in these pages show any unity of mathematical form. But at least they share, with a few exceptions, the property of being *stochastic,* i.e., of being based largely on probability considerations in which temporal changes in probability play a major role.

While the survey and exposition were confined to mathematical models (and, as just noted, mainly to the narrower subclass of stochastic models), I have attempted to place these in a broader context by first discussing the nature and functions of various kinds of models and model-building in science. Thus, in Section II, three types of models were distinguished: figurative models, analogue models, and mathematical models. The first two types were examined primarily in their relationships to the third, and it was seen that these relationships were quite different.

The distinctive feature of analogue models is that they seek to establish some kind of isomorphism between a domain of interest and a prototypic domain for which a well-established theory already exists, and thence to apply some of the laws of this theory to the new domain. If this theory is a mathematical one, the analogue model will also assume a mathematical form. It will then be indistinguishable *on the surface* from what we have called a mathematical model; rather, the distinction is in the approach used in its inception.

On the other hand, figurative models, insofar as they are related at all to mathematical models, may be regarded as "preludes" to the latter. They comprise figurative or metaphorical ways of speaking and thinking of a domain of interest which often enable the scientist to see patterns of interrelationship among the phenomena he is studying. Sometimes figurative models may constitute all that exists in the way of an informal theory for the particular domain. At other times, an informal theory stemming from figurative models may be relatively well developed, and may include many "laws" (or generalizations) stated verbally, or even semiquantitatively.

In either case, a mathematical model-builder goes about his business by formalizing the essential ideas contained in such figurative models—whether they form the basic postulates of a fairly well-developed informal theory, or exist merely as general ways of thinking of the phenomena in question. Often, he himself has to engage in a considerable amount of figurative modeling in order to sharpen the basic postulates before they can be expressed in mathematical form. Almost invariably, certain simplifying assumptions are introduced at this stage. Once the basic postulates have been mathematically stated as formal axioms, it becomes possible (in principle, at least) to deduce many testable predictions by mathematical derivations from the axioms.

There can hardly be any disagreement concerning the last assertion made above; it merely states the main function of mathematical models. With regard to my description of the "genesis" of a mathematical model, however, it may be objected that rarely does a model-builder actually operate in this way. What, for instance, is the "figurative model" which Bush and Mosteller supposedly formalized in developing their linear-operator model? It is true that, in comparison with Estes' stimulus-sampling notion, the figurative model underpinning the Bush-Mosteller system seems virtually to fade out of existence. But this is because they chose to adopt, as their starting point, an assumption which they believed to be "not inconsistent with most current learning theories." To put it crudely, they pared several prevalent figurative models down to the bones, until a common core was revealed in the postulate that *something* happens after each trial which affects response probabilities!

To pursue the critic's role further, it may be pointed out that even in the case of Estes' mathematical model, for which a definite figurative model can be exhibited, the builder did not have from the outset a blueprint for formalizing this model. Rather, his starting point consisted of some acquisition curves plotted from data for a particular experiment on operant conditioning. These showed such intriguing regularities that Estes was led to seek some quantitative treatment other than *ad hoc* curve-fitting. He went about his quest guided by the experimenter's disciplined intuition, as well as by his knowledge of existing theories of learning—speculating, trying out hunches, and even drawing an analogy from chemistry—as he recounts in an article (1959b) included in a monumental, multivolume collection entitled *Psychology: A Study of a Science*. Only gradually did it emerge that the quantitative description he was developing for those learning curves was tantamount to a formalization of the notion of learning by association. Once this was evident— but only then—was the task of formalizing the basic postulates undertaken in earnest.

Thus it must be conceded that the purported description given above of how a mathematical model-builder goes about his business may not apply to a pioneer in a new field, except as a *rational reconstruction* of his travail. Nevertheless, such a rationally reconstructed "description" may serve as a methodological guide for later workers in the field. Moreover, it is only by explicitly recognizing that a mathematical model "models" an informal theory that implications can be drawn from investigations of the model to the underlying theory or general orientation.

The point just made may be illustrated with reference to the finding (in Section IV) that the stimulus-sampling and linear-operator models often yield closely similar, if not identical, predictions. This circumstance leads one to suspect that the traditional controversy between the contiguity and the reinforcement views of learning may be due, in large measure, to semantic differences. It seems that in many situations the cause of parsimony is best served, as Estes holds, by regarding "the term *reinforcement* . . . simply as a convenient label for procedures which serve to evoke responses in the presence of new stimuli and to protect newly formed associations by removing the stimuli before interfering responses can occur" (Estes, 1959b, p. 403). In other cases, reinforcement terminology may provide the more parsimonious conceptualization of what constitutes the stimuli which become "associated by contiguity" with the reinforced response.

Another controversy which mathematical models may help to settle (or at least to clarify) is whether the dynamics of group behavior can be explained by means of principles of individual psychology alone—that is, without introducing concepts peculiar to social psychology, such as social interaction, group cohesiveness, social pressure, and so forth. The question boils down, essentially, to whether these latter concepts can be explicated in terms of the more elementary concepts that occur in individual psychology.

With a few exceptions, those who developed the mathematical models for small-group processes referred to in this chapter were seen to espouse the reductionist viewpoint. It should be mentioned, however, that many of these attempts have come under considerable criticism. For instance, Moore and Anderson present strong arguments, from the nonreductionist standpoint, for maintaining that the reason Suppes and Atkinson (1960) were successful in using Markov learning models for analysis of their experiments on multiperson interactions was that these experiments "did not involve social interaction in the sense meant by most sociologists and social psychologists" (Moore and Anderson, 1962, p. 200).

If this is so, then it must be conceded that mathematical models successful in describing individual learning have not been proved adequate where genuine social phenomena are involved. But even this negative conclusion (if accepted) represents an advance which the use of mathematical models has helped to make. In using them, we are forced to state precisely and formally the denotations of the basic concepts involved. So if these are at variance with accepted usage in competing theories, the discrepancy is readily discernible.

Bush (1962) expresses the view that current stochastic models are inadequate for describing interactive behavior. His recommendation is that a "clean experimental paradigm" be found for phenomena of genuine sociopsychological interest before attempting to develop mathematical models for them. This may be interpreted, it seems to me, as saying that some prior figurative modeling is needed in order to sharpen concepts like social interaction to a point where mathematization can be effected, without at the same time divesting them of the essential meaning they have for social psychologists.

Finally, there is the well-known cleavage between the trial-and-error (or "continuist") and the "insight" (or "discontinuist") viewpoints of learning. The concept of vicarious trial and error was introduced into psychological theorizing some twenty years ago, largely as an attempt to reconcile these two opposing views, but the controversy has continued with little abatement.

Estes, in putting forth the idea of pattern models, was in effect attempting to account for insightful learning within the general framework of stimulus-sampling theory. A special case of these models—the single-element model—was used by Suppes and Ginsberg to describe data from experiments on concept formation in young children, and considerable success was achieved, at least for group data. However, when individual differences in rate of conditioning are taken into consideration, predictions from the model show much poorer agreement with data based on observation.*

The unsatisfactory state of affairs with regard to the continuist-discontinuist controversy can be partly traced, it seems to me, to the lack of an unambiguous conceptualization of what constitutes vicarious trial and error. If this concept is explicated by something like the selective trial-and-error process used by LT (which is unobservable without a detailed "protocol") in the Newell-Shaw-Simon model, much clarification may result. Bush's recommendation, cited in connection with the problem of social interaction, is equally relevant here. His further suggestion that a model involving strategies or "plans" may be needed would seem to apply with even more force in this case.

Thus, although it is still premature to judge whether such a proposal as that by Miller, Galanter, and Pribram (to adopt TOTE as the unit of analysis) will lead to a tractable mathematical model, it certainly appears that an innovation of that order of magnitude is needed for the next "breakthrough" of mathematical models. Only with renewed and extensive prior figurative modeling can we hope to develop mathematical models that will be successful in areas of behavior involving the "higher mental processes"—if by "success" we mean something comparable to the achievements by mathematical models in describing relatively simple learning processes. It would, therefore, be a mistake to shrug off proposals like the one just cited by regarding them as nonsubstantive "methodological advice" uttered by "demurrers to the currently dominant lines of theoretical development," as Estes (1962, p. 142) seems inclined to do. For, as Mosteller says, "Progress can best be made if we are willing to consider and then destroy a great many of our mathematical efforts" (1958, p. 59).

---

* Suppes considers a modification of the model to include two stimulus elements, only one of which is sampled at each trial, and the preconditioning guessing probability depends on which one is sampled. This model produces better qualitative agreement with data, but detailed analyses have yet to be made.

REFERENCES

ARROW, K. J., "Mathematical models in the social sciences," in D. Lerner and H. D. Lasswell (eds.), *The Policy Sciences*. Stanford: Stanford University Press, 1951, pp. 129–154

ATKINSON, R. C., "A Markov model for discrimination learning." *Psychometrika* **23,** 309–322 (1958)

ATKINSON, R. C., "The use of models in experimental psychology." *Synthese* **12,** 162–171 (1960)

ATKINSON, R. C., and P. SUPPES, "An analysis of two-person game situations in terms of statistical learning theory." *J. Exp. Psychol.* **55,** 369–378 (1958)

ATKINSON, R. C., and P. SUPPES, "Applications of a Markov model to two-person non-cooperative games," in R. R. Bush and W. K. Estes (eds.), *Studies in Mathematical Learning Theory*. Stanford: Stanford University Press, 1959, pp. 65–75

AUDLEY, R. J., "A stochastic model for individual choice behavior." *Psychol. Rev.* **67,** 1–15 (1960)

AUDLEY, R. J., and A. R. JONCKHEERE, "The statistical analysis of the learning process." *Brit. J. Stat. Psychol.* **9,** 12–20 (1956)

BALES, R. F., F. L. STRODTBECK, T. M. MILLS, and MARY E. ROSEBOROUGH, "Channels of communication in small groups." *Amer. Soc. Rev.* **16,** 461–468 (1951)

BLACK, M., "Models and archetypes," in M. Black, *Models and Metaphors*. Ithaca: Cornell University Press, 1962, pp. 219–243

BOWER, G. H., "Application of a model to paired-associate learning." *Psychometrika* **26,** 255–280 (1961)

BURKE, C. J., "Applications of a linear model to two-person interactions," in R. R. Bush and W. K. Estes (eds.), *Studies in Mathematical Learning Theory*. Stanford: Stanford University Press, 1959, pp. 180–203

BURKE, C. J., "Some two-person interactions," in K. J. Arrow, S. Karlin, and P. Suppes (eds.), *Mathematical Methods in the Social Sciences, 1959*. Stanford: Stanford University Press, 1960, pp. 242–253

BURKE, C. J., "Two-person interactive learning: A progress report," in Joan H. Criswell, H. Solomon, and P. Suppes (eds.), *Mathematical Methods in Small Group Processes*. Stanford: Stanford University Press, 1962, pp. 49–68

BURKE, C. J., and W. K. ESTES, "A component model for stimulus variables in discrimination learning." *Psychometrika* **22,** 133–145 (1957)

BURKE, C. J., W. K. ESTES, and S. HELLYER, "Rate of verbal conditioning in relation to stimulus variability." *J. Exp. Psychol.* **48,** 153–161 (1954)

BUSH, R. R., "Some properties of Luce's beta model for learning," in K. J. Arrow, S. Karlin, and P. Suppes (eds.), *Mathematical Methods in the Social Sciences, 1959*. Stanford: Stanford University Press, 1960, pp. 254–264

BUSH, R. R., "The application of learning models to interactive behavior," in Joan H. Criswell, H. Solomon, and P. Suppes (eds.), *Mathematical Methods in Small Group Processes*. Stanford: Stanford University Press, 1962, pp. 69–73

BUSH, R. R., E. GALANTER, and R. D. LUCE, "Tests of the 'beta model,' " in R. R. Bush and W. K. Estes (eds.), *Studies in Mathematical Learning Theory*. Stanford: Stanford University Press, 1959, pp. 381–399

BUSH, R. R., and F. MOSTELLER, "A mathematical model for simple learning." *Psychol. Rev.* **58**, 313–323 (1951a)

BUSH, R. R., and F. MOSTELLER, "A model for stimulus generalization and discrimination." *Psychol. Rev.* **58**, 413–423 (1951b)

BUSH, R. R., and F. MOSTELLER, *Stochastic Models for Learning*. New York: John Wiley & Sons, 1955

BUSH, R. R., and F. MOSTELLER, "A comparison of eight models," in R. R. Bush and W. K. Estes (eds.), *Studies in Mathematical Learning Theory*. Stanford: Stanford University Press, 1959, pp. 293–307

BUSH, R. R., and T. R. WILSON, "Two-choice behavior of paradise fish." *J. Exp. Psychol.* **51**, 315–322 (1956)

CARNAP, R., "Foundations of logic and mathematics," in *International Encyclopedia of Unified Science (Vol. 1)*. Chicago: University of Chicago Press, 1955

COLEMAN, J. S., "The mathematical study of small groups," in H. Solomon (ed.), *Mathematical Thinking in the Measurement of Behavior*. Glencoe, Illinois: The Free Press, 1960, pp. 7–149

CRISWELL, JOAN H., H. SOLOMON, and P. SUPPES (eds.), *Mathematical Methods in Small Group Processes*. Stanford: Stanford University Press, 1962

CRONBACH, L. J., "On the non-rational application of information measures in psychology," in H. Quastler (ed.), *Information Theory in Psychology*. Glencoe, Illinois: The Free Press, 1955, pp. 14–26

DUHEM, P., *The Aim and Structure of Physical Theory*. Princeton: Princeton University Press, 1954

EDWARDS, W., "The theory of decision making." *Psychol. Bull.* **51**, 380–417 (1954)

ESTES, W. K., "Toward a statistical theory of learning." *Psychol. Rev.* **57**, 94–107 (1950)

ESTES, W. K., "Statistical theory of spontaneous recovery and regression." *Psychol. Rev.* **62**, 145–154 (1955)

ESTES, W. K., "Component and pattern models with Markovian interpretations," in R. R. Bush and W. K. Estes (eds.), *Studies in Mathematical Learning Theory*. Stanford: Stanford University Press, 1959a, pp. 9–52

ESTES, W. K., "The statistical approach to learning theory," in S. Koch (ed.), *Psychology: A Study of a Science (Vol. II)*. New York: McGraw-Hill, 1959b, pp. 383–491

ESTES, W. K., "Learning theory." *Annu. Rev. Psychol.* **13**, 107–144 (1962)

ESTES, W. K., and C. J. BURKE, "A theory of stimulus variability in learning." *Psychol. Rev.* **60**, 276–286 (1953)

ESTES, W. K., and C. J. BURKE, "Application of a statistical model to simple discrimination learning in human subjects." *J. Exp. Psychol.* **50**, 81–88 (1955)

ESTES, W. K., and P. SUPPES, "Foundations of linear models," in R. R. Bush and W. K. Estes (eds.), *Studies in Mathematical Learning Theory*. Stanford: Stanford University Press, 1959, pp. 137–179

FEY, C. F., "An investigation of some mathematical models for learning." *J. Exp. Psychol.* **61**, 455–461 (1961)

GALANTER, E., and G. A. MILLER, "Some comments on stochastic models and psychological theories," in K. J. Arrow, S. Karlin, and P. Suppes (eds.), *Mathematical Methods in the Social Sciences, 1959.* Stanford: Stanford University Press, 1960, pp. 277–297

GÖTLIND, E., "Two views about the function of models in empirical theories." *Theoria* **27**, 58–69 (1961)

GRANT, D. A., "The discrimination of sequences in stimulus events and the transmission of information." *Amer. Psychologist* **9**, 62–68 (1954)

HAKE, H. W., "A note on the concept of 'channel capacity' in psychology," in H. Quastler (ed.), *Information Theory in Psychology.* Glencoe, Illinois: The Free Press, 1955, pp. 248–253

HARRIS, T., R. BELLMAN, and H. N. Shapiro, *Studies on Functional Equations Occurring in Decision Processes.* RM 878, RAND Corporation, 1952

HAYS, D. G., and R. R. BUSH, "A study of group action." *Amer. Soc. Rev.* **19**, 693–701 (1954)

HOMANS, G. C., *The Human Group.* New York: Harcourt, Brace & World, 1950

HOPPE, R. A., "Memorizing by individuals and groups." *J. Abnorm. Soc. Psychol.* **65**, 64–67 (1962)

JACOBSON, H., "The informational capacity of the human eye." *Science* **113**, 292–293 (1951)

KANAL, L., "A functional equation analysis of two learning models." *Psychometrika* **27**, 89–104 (1962a)

KANAL, L., "The asymptotic distribution for the two-absorbing-barrier beta model." *Psychometrika* **27**, 105–109 (1962b)

KARLIN, S., "Some random walks arising in learning models I." *Pacific J. Math.* **3**, 725–756 (1953)

KEMENY, J. G., and J. L. SNELL, "Markov processes in learning theory." *Psychometrika* **22**, 221–230 (1957)

LACHMAN, R., "The model in theory construction." *Psychol. Rev.* **67**, 113–129 (1960)

LAMPERTI, J., and P. SUPPES, "Some asymptotic properties of Luce's beta learning model," *Psychometrika* **25**, 233–241 (1960)

LICKLIDER, J. C. R., and G. A. MILLER, "The perception of speech," in S. S. Stevens (ed.), *Handbook of Experimental Psychology.* New York: John Wiley & Sons, 1951, pp. 1040–1074

LORGE, I., and H. SOLOMON, "Two models of group behavior in the solution of eureka-type problems." *Psychometrika* **20**, 139–148 (1955)

LORGE, I., and H. SOLOMON, "Individual performance and group performance in problem solving related to group size and previous exposure to the problem." *J. Soc. Psychol.* **48**, 107–114 (1959)

LORGE, I., and H. SOLOMON, "Group and individual performance in problem solving related to previous exposure to problem, level of aspiration, and group size." *Behav. Sci.* **5(1)**, 28–38 (1960)

LUCE, R. D., *Individual Choice Behavior: A Theoretical Analysis.* New York: John Wiley & Sons, 1959

LUCE, R. D., "The theory of selective information and some of its behavioral applications," in R. D. Luce (ed.), *Development in Mathematical Psychology.* Glencoe, Illinois: The Free Press, 1960, pp. 5–119

LUCE, R. D., R. R. BUSH, and E. GALANTER (eds.), *Handbook of Mathematical Psychology (Vol. II).* New York: John Wiley & Sons, 1963

McNEMAR, Q., "At random: Sense and nonsense." *Amer. Psychologist* **15,** 295–300 (1960)

MILLER, G. A., "Speech and language," in S. S. Stevens (ed.), *Handbook of Experimental Psychology.* New York: John Wiley & Sons, 1951, pp. 789–810

MILLER, G. A., "Finite Markov processes in psychology." *Psychometrika* **17,** 149–167 (1952)

MILLER, G. A., "The magical number seven, plus or minus two: Some limits on our capacity for processing information." *Psychol. Rev.* **63,** 81–97 (1956)

MILLER, G. A., and F. C. FRICK, "Statistical behavioristics and sequences of responses." *Psychol. Rev.* **56,** 311–324 (1949)

MILLER, G. A., E. GALANTER, and K. H. PRIBRAM, *Plans and the Structure of Behavior.* New York: Holt, Rinehart and Winston, 1960

MILLER, G. A., and W. J. McGILL, "A statistical description of verbal learning." *Psychometrika* **17,** 369–396 (1952)

MOORE, O. K., and A. R. ANDERSON, "Some puzzling aspects of social interaction," in Joan H. Criswell, H. Solomon, and P. Suppes (eds.), *Mathematical Methods in Small Group Processes.* Stanford: Stanford University Press, 1962, pp. 232–249

MOSTELLER, F., "Stochastic models for the learning process." *Proc. Amer. Philos. Soc.* **102,** 53–59 (1958)

MOSTELLER, F., and P. NOGEE, "An experimental measurement of utility." *J. Polit. Econ.* **59,** 371–404 (1951)

MOSTELLER, F., and M. TATSUOKA, "Ultimate choice between two attractive goals: Predictions from a model." *Psychometrika* **25,** 1–17 (1960)

NEWELL, A., J. C. SHAW, and H. A. SIMON, "Elements of a theory of human problem solving." *Psychol. Rev.* **65,** 151–166 (1958)

NEWELL, A., J. C. SHAW, and H. A. SIMON, "Report on a general problem-solving program," in *Proceedings of the International Conference on Information Processing.* Paris: UNESCO, 1960, pp. 256–264

POPPER, K. R., *The Logic of Scientific Discovery.* New York: Basic Books, 1959

QUASTLER, H., and V. J. WULFF, *Human Performance in Information Transmission.* Control Systems Laboratory Report No. 62, University of Illinois, 1955

RAPOPORT, A., "Nets with distance bias." *Bull. Math. Biophysics* **13,** 85–91 (1951)

RAPOPORT, A., "Spread of information through a population with socio-structural bias. I. Assumption of transitivity." *Bull. Math. Biophysics* **15,** 523–533 (1953a)

RAPOPORT, A., "Spread of information through a population with socio-structural bias. II. Various models with partial transitivity." *Bull. Math. Biophysics* **15,** 535–546 (1953b)

RESTLE, F., "A theory of discrimination learning." *Psychol. Rev.* **62,** 11–19 (1955a)

RESTLE, F., "Axioms of a theory of discrimination learning." *Psychometrika* **20,** 201–208 (1955b)

RESTLE, F., "A survey and classification of learning models," in R. R. Bush and W. K. Estes (eds.), *Studies in Mathematical Learning Theory*. Stanford: Stanford University Press, 1959, pp. 415–427

RESTLE, F., "Speed and accuracy of cognitive achievement in small groups," in Joan H. Criswell, H. Solomon, and P. Suppes (eds.), *Mathematical Methods in Small Group Processes*. Stanford: Stanford University Press, 1962, pp. 250–262

SHANNON, C. E., "A mathematical theory of communication." *Bell System Tech. J.* **27,** 379–423; 623–656 (1948)

SHAW, M. E., "A comparison of individuals and small groups in the rational solution of complex problems." *Amer. J. Psychol.* **44,** 491–504 (1932)

SIDOWSKI, J. B., L. B. WYCKOFF, and L. TABORY, "The influence of reinforcement and punishment in a minimal social situation." *J. Abnorm. Soc. Psychol.* **52,** 115–119 (1956)

SIEGEL, S., "Theoretical models of choice and strategy behavior: Stable state behavior in the two-choice uncertain outcome situation." *Psychometrika* **24,** 303–316 (1959)

SIEGEL, S., "Decision making and learning under varying conditions of reinforcement." *Ann. N. Y. Acad. Sci.* **89,** 766–783 (1961)

SIEGEL, S., and D. A. GOLDSTEIN, "Decision-making behavior in a two-choice uncertain outcome situation." *J. Exp. Psychol.* **57,** 37–42 (1959)

SIMON, H. A., "A formal theory of interaction of social groups." *Amer. Soc. Rev.* **17,** 202–211 (1952)

SIMON, H. A., and H. GUETZKOW, "A model of short- and long-run mechanisms involved in pressures toward uniformity in groups." *Psychol. Rev.* **62,** 56–58 (1955)

SOLOMON, R. L., and L. C. WYNNE, "Traumatic avoidance learning: Acquisition in normal dogs." *Psychol. Monogr.* **67,** No. 4 (Whole No. 354) (1953)

STEPHAN, F., and E. G. MISHLER, "The distribution of participation in small groups: An exponential approximation." *Amer. Soc. Rev.* **17,** 598–608 (1952)

STERNBERG, S. H., "A path-dependent linear model," in R. R. Bush and W. K. Estes (eds.), *Studies in Mathematical Learning Theory*. Stanford: Stanford University Press, 1959a, pp. 308–339

STERNBERG, S. H., "Application of four models to sequential dependence in human learning," in R. R. Bush and W. K. Estes (eds.), *Studies in Mathematical Learning Theory*. Stanford: Stanford University Press, 1959b, pp. 340–380

SUPPES, P., "A comparison of the meaning and uses of models in mathematics and the empirical sciences." *Synthese* **12,** 287–301 (1960)

SUPPES, P., and R. C. ATKINSON, *Markov Learning Models for Multiperson Interactions*. Stanford: Stanford University Press, 1960

SUPPES, P., and ROSE GINSBERG, "Applications of a stimulus sampling model to children's concept formation with and without overt correction responses." *J. Exp. Psychol.* **63,** 330–336 (1962)

SUPPES, P., and ROSE GINSBERG, "A fundamental property of all-or-none models, binomial distribution of responses prior to conditioning, with application to concept formation in children." *Psychol. Rev.* **70,** 139–161 (1963)

TATSUOKA, M., and CAROL ABE, *Beta Models for Discrimination Learning.* University of Hawaii Psychological Research Center Memorandum HC-2, 1961

TATSUOKA, M., and F. MOSTELLER, "A commuting-operator model," in R. R. Bush and W. K. Estes (eds.), *Studies in Mathematical Learning Theory.* Stanford: Stanford University Press, 1959, pp. 228–247

THRALL, R. M., C. H. COOMBS, and R. L. DAVIS (eds.), *Decision Processes.* New York: John Wiley & Sons, 1954

THURSTONE, L., "The learning function." *J. Gen. Psychol.* **3,** 469–491 (1930)

TOULMIN, S. E., *The Philosophy of Science.* London: Hutchinson's University Library, 1953

VON NEUMANN, J., and O. MORGENSTERN, *Theory of Games and Economic Behavior.* Princeton: Princeton University Press, 1944

ZIPF, G. K., *Human Behavior and the Principle of Least Effort.* Reading, Mass.: Addison-Wesley, 1949

CHAPTER 2

ON STATISTICAL TESTS
OF GROUP DIFFERENCES*

P. J. RULON, *Professor of Education Emeritus, Harvard University*
Educational Research Corporation
W. D. BROOKS, *International Business Machines, Inc.*

This expository paper was prepared after a study of the statistical texts, manuals, and handbooks most commonly consulted by research workers in education and psychology. An overwhelming majority of these manuals terminate their treatment of group differences with the F-test and make no mention of Hotelling's T^2, of Mahalanobis' D^2, or of Wilks's Λ. Accordingly, the experimental literature in psychology and education frequently reports studies in which parallel groups are evaluated on two bases, say speed and accuracy, with the difference in speed tested with the t-test or the F-test, and the difference in accuracy tested also, but separately, without any multivariate test of the significance of the two differences simultaneously, as by means of T^2, D^2, or Λ.

In these same texts and manuals the treatment of covariance is still less complete. Seldom is the t-test shown with adjustment for covariance variables. Instead, covariance is developed with the F-test, and the student is encouraged to obtain t by taking the square root. The case of more than two groups and more than one covariance variable is infrequently treated, and no mention is made of T^2 with adjustment by covariance, or of D^2 or Λ.

A further unsatisfactory feature of the most used texts is the variation in terminology, especially in the analysis of covariance. If two methods of teaching typing are evaluated by a parallel group experiment, the tests given the learners before the instructional period may be called matching tests, control tests, or pretests. The tests for speed, accuracy, etc., used to assess typing proficiency during and after the instructional periods may be called end tests, posttests, or criterion tests. The most general names for these two sets of variables, and therefore probably the best, are those proposed by Rao, who calls them "original variables" and "additional variables," so that the end tests in the typing experiment would be addi-

---

* The work on this manuscript was supported in part by the United States Navy, under Contract No. N61339–294, with the Communications Psychology Division of the Training Device Center in Port Washington, New York. This paper may be reproduced in whole or in part for any purpose of the United States Government.

tional to the original pretests, for example. Because many of the readers of this paper might not appreciate the generality of the Rao nomenclature, we have used throughout the expression "test variables" for the ones tested after the adjustment by covariance, and "covariance variables" for the ones whose effect on the group differences is removed by the covariance adjustment. Our covariance variables are the original variables, and our test variables are the additional variables.

ANALYSIS OF VARIANCE

Case IA: Two Groups, One Test Variable

Skill-level scores were collected for 630 members of military detachment S and 509 members of military detachment D. For each detachment the mean skill-level score and the "Fisherian" sum of squares are given in Table 1. As may be seen by inspection, detachment S has a slightly higher mean score than detachment D.

Table 1   Data for Case IA

	N	M	$\sum (X - M)^2$
Detachment S	630	4.7683	508.8409
Detachment D	509	4.0177	322.1651

1. The t-test.   The statistical significance of the difference between such means may be evaluated by the t-test, written

$$t = \frac{M_S - M_D}{\left[\dfrac{\sum x_S^2 + \sum x_D^2}{N_S + N_D - 2} \left(\dfrac{1}{N_S} + \dfrac{1}{N_D} \right) \right]^{1/2}},$$

wherein $\sum x^2 = \sum (X - M)^2$.*
  For our data,

$$t = \frac{4.7683 - 4.0177}{\left[\dfrac{508.8409 + 322.1651}{630 + 509 - 2} \left(\dfrac{1}{630} + \dfrac{1}{509} \right) \right]^{1/2}}$$
$$= 14.73125.$$

Reference to the t-table with 1137 degrees of freedom indicates that a t-value of 14.7 is significant far beyond the 0.001 level. Thus the difference 0.7506 between the mean skill-level scores is statistically quite significant.

---

* This formula is a rearrangement of R. A. Fisher's expression for t, which may be found in any of the several editions of his *Statistical Methods for Research Workers,* Edinburgh: Oliver and Boyd, Section 24.1. For a statement of t which more obviously resembles the present one, see E. F. Lindquist, *Statistical Analysis in Educational Research,* Boston: Houghton Mifflin, 1940, p. 57.

2. The F-test.[*]   The significance of this difference may be tested just as well with the F-test, employing the usual analysis of variance, as in Table 2. The ratio of mean squares gives $F = 158.6060/0.730876 = 217.01$. Reference to the F-table with 1 and 1137 degrees of freedom shows that an F-value of 217.01 is significant far beyond the 0.001 level of significance.

Table 2   Analysis of variance for Case IA

Source of variation	Sum of squares	Number of degrees of freedom	Mean square
Between groups	158.6060	1	158.6060
Within groups	831.0060	1137	0.730876
Total	989.6120	1138	

Of course this F is exactly as significant as is the t from the same data. The t-tables do not give significance levels for values as large as 14.7, and the F-tables do not go as far as $F = 217$ with our numbers of degrees of freedom. The identity of the two approaches may be established either algebraically[†] or by comparing entries in the two tables. The algebraic relationship between the two tests is illustrated by the fact that the entries in Table 2, from which F was computed, can be derived from the data in Table 1, which were used in the computation of t. The 158.6060 in Table 2 comes from

$$(4.7683 - 4.0177)^2 (630)(509)/(630 + 509)$$

in Table 1. The 831.0060 in Table 2 comes from adding 508.8409 and 322.1651 from Table 1. And the 1137 in Table 2 comes from subtracting 2 from $630 + 509$ in Table 1, giving $N_1 + N_2 - 2$. It is to be noted that this same $N_1 + N_2 - 2$ appears in the formula for t, following Table 1.

Correspondence of the significance levels in the tables of t and F may be checked by noting that, for example, the 5% level of F with 1 and 20 degrees of freedom is 4.35, which is just the square of 2.086, the 5% level of t with 20 degrees of freedom.

To end this excursus, we will remark that the $F = 217.01$ that we derived from Table 2 is just the square of $t = 14.7315$ that we obtained from the same data.

---

[*] The F-test was proposed by G. W. Snedecor in *Calculation and Interpretation of Analysis of Variance and Covariance*, Ames, Iowa: Collegiate Press, 1934, pp. 15, 89. He named the statistic F in honor of R. A. Fisher, who had proposed a z-statistic for the same application. See R. A. Fisher, "On a distribution yielding the error functions of several well-known statistics." *Proceedings of the International Mathematical Congress*, Toronto, 1924, pp. 805–813. The relationship between F and z is

$$F = e^{2z}, \quad \text{or} \quad z = \tfrac{1}{2} \ln F.$$

[†] See, for example, P. J. Rulon, "Fisher's t-test as a special case of his z-test." *J. Exp. Educ.* **11**, 245–249 (1943).

3. The T^2-test. Hotelling's T^2-test applies to two groups, any number of test variables.* T^2 is given by

$$T^2 = \frac{N_1 N_2 (N_1 + N_2 - 2)}{N_1 + N_2} d' W^{-1} d.$$

N_1 and N_2 are the numbers of cases in the groups. For our one-test-variable case, $d' = d$ and is the difference between the group means, while W^{-1} is the reciprocal of W, the within-groups sum of squares. We have, therefore,

$$T^2 = \frac{(630)(509)(630 + 509 - 2)}{630 + 509} (0.750572) \frac{1}{831.0060} (0.750572)^{\dagger}$$

$$= 217.01.$$

This is just the value we obtained for F from the same data. Thus we see that in the case of one test variable, Hotelling's T^2 is simply F. It is to be referred to the F-table with 1 and 1137 degrees of freedom, as before.

4. The D^2-test.‡ Mahalanobis' D^2 may be written in the notation of the preceding section:

$$D^2 = d' \left(\frac{W}{N_1 + N_2 - 2} \right)^{-1} d.$$

For our one-test-variable case we will have

$$D^2 = (0.750572) \left(\frac{831.0060}{630 + 509 - 2} \right)^{-1} (0.750572) = 0.770799.$$

The F-transformation is to be written

$$F = \frac{N_1 N_2}{N_1 + N_2} D^2.$$

Substituting our numbers of cases, we have

$$F = \frac{(630)(509)}{630 + 509} (0.770799) = 217.01.$$

This is the same value of F as obtained from these data in earlier sections and is to be referred to the F-table with 1 and 1137 degrees of freedom, as before.

A comparison of the formulas for D^2 and T^2 in this and the preceding section shows that a simple relationship exists between the two. It is

$$D^2 = \frac{N_1 + N_2}{N_1 N_2} T^2.$$

---

* See H. Hotelling, "The generalization of Student's ratio." *Ann. Math. Stat.* **2**, 360–378 (1931).
† This difference, 0.750572, is copied from earlier computations, before the means were rounded to four decimals as in Table 1.
‡ P. C. Mahalanobis, "On the generalized distance in statistics." *Proceedings of the National Institute of Science (India)* **12**, 49 (1936).

Thus Mahalanobis' "generalized distance" may be easily computed from Hotelling's statistical test of the differences between groups.

5. The Λ-test. Wilks's Λ is applicable to any number of groups, any number of test variables.* We apply it to our two-group, one-test-variable problem by reading from Table 2:

$$\text{Within-groups sum of squares} = 831.0060 = W,$$
$$\text{Total sum of squares} = 989.6120 = T.$$

Then, in this case,

$$\Lambda = \frac{W}{T} = \frac{831.0060}{989.6120} = 0.8397291.$$

For our example, this is to be evaluated by computing

$$F = \frac{1 - \Lambda}{\Lambda} (N_1 + N_2 - 2)$$
$$= \frac{1 - 0.8397291}{0.8397291} (630 + 509 - 2) = 217.01.$$

This is the same value for F as obtained from the same data in earlier sections, and is to be referred to the F-table with 1 and 1137 degrees of freedom as before.

In the cases to which the F-test applies—namely, with any number of groups, one test variable—the F-transformation of Λ can be shown to be a simple algebraic identity with F itself. In our present case, we have two groups and one test variable. Going back to Table 2, from which we computed the value of F from our data, we note that our computation of F employed a ratio of mean squares. The mean square between groups was

$$\frac{158.6060}{1} = 158.6060,$$

while the mean square within groups was

$$\frac{831.0060}{1137} = 0.730876.$$

To obtain F, we divided 158.6060 by 0.730876, getting $F = 217.01$.

We could have worked with sums of squares and the numbers of degrees of freedom, to compute

$$F = \frac{158.6060/1}{831.0060/1137} = 217.01,$$

or we could have written

$$F = \frac{158.6060}{831.0060} \frac{1137}{1} = 217.01,$$

---

* See S. S. Wilks, "Certain generalizations in the analysis of variance." *Biometrika,* **24,** 471–494 (1932).

which may also be written

$$F = \frac{B}{W}(N_1 + N_2 - 2),$$

where B is the between-groups sum of squares and W is the within-groups sum of squares. As before, $N_1 + N_2 - 2$ is 1137.

Now, from Table 2 it is clear that $B + W = T$, where T is the total sum of squares. Then $B = T - W$. Therefore,

$$F = \frac{B}{W}(N_1 + N_2 - 2)$$

becomes

$$F = \frac{T - W}{W}(N_1 + N_2 - 2) = \left(\frac{T}{W} - 1\right)(N_1 + N_2 - 2)$$

$$= \frac{T}{W}\left(1 - \frac{W}{T}\right)(N_1 + N_2 - 2) = \frac{1 - W/T}{W/T}(N_1 + N_2 - 2)$$

$$= \frac{1 - \Lambda}{\Lambda}(N_1 + N_2 - 2).$$

Case IB: Any Number of Groups, One Test Variable

1. The F-test. The F-test is applicable to testing the differences among any number of groups, as regards one test variable. A typical table showing the analysis of variance will be like Table 3.

In this case, k is the number of groups and N is the total number of cases, or $N_1 + N_2 + \cdots + N_k$. It will be seen that A in this case replaces B in the preceding section, since with more than two groups, "between groups" becomes "among groups." If in Table 3 we put "between $= B$" for "among $= A$," and set $k = 2$, then we have exactly the form of Table 2, which dealt with two groups.

Table 3 Analysis of variance for k groups

Source of variation	Sum of squares	Number of degrees of freedom	Mean square
Among groups	A	$k - 1$	$A/(k - 1)$
Within groups	W	$N - k$	$W/(N - k)$
Total	T	$N - 1$	

From Table 3, the F-ratio is computed as the ratio of among-groups mean square to between-groups mean square. That is,

$$F = \frac{A/(k - 1)}{W/(N - k)} = \frac{A}{W}\frac{N - k}{k - 1}.$$

The obtained value of F is to be referred to the F-table with $k - 1$ and $N - k$ degrees of freedom.

Since this form of F is applicable to any number of groups, it is applicable to $k = 2$ groups. Setting $k = 2$ we have

$$F = \frac{A}{W} \frac{N-2}{2-1} = \frac{A}{W} \frac{N-2}{1}.$$

Now, for two groups, writing B for "between" instead of A for "among," and writing $N_1 + N_2$ for N, we have

$$F = \frac{B}{W} (N_1 + N_2 - 2),$$

as in the preceding section for the Case IA, 5.

2. The Λ-test. We pointed out in the preceding section that in the two-group case, the F-transformation of Λ can be shown to be algebraically identical to F itself. This is true also in the present case of k groups. We have observed from Table 3 that

$$W + A = T, \qquad A = T - W,$$

so that

$$F = \frac{A}{W} \frac{N-k}{k-1}$$

from the preceding section, Case IB, 1 becomes

$$F = \frac{T-W}{W} \frac{N-k}{k-1}.$$

Dividing numerator and denominator by T, we have

$$F = \frac{1 - W/T}{W/T} \frac{N-k}{k-1} = \frac{1 - \Lambda}{\Lambda} \frac{N-k}{k-1}.$$

Thus we see that the Λ-test, which is applicable to any number of groups, any number of test variables, reduces to the F-test when applied to data to which the F-test is applicable—namely, to any number k of groups, compared by means of one test variable.

Since this Λ-test is applicable to any number k of groups, it is applicable to $k = 2$ groups. Setting $k = 2$, we have

$$F = \frac{1 - \Lambda}{\Lambda} \frac{N-2}{2-1} = \frac{1 - \Lambda}{\Lambda} (N_1 + N_2 - 2),$$

as in the preceding section, Case IA, 5.

Case IC: Two Groups, Any Number of Test Variables

The members of our two military detachments were given effectiveness ratings by their supervisors. Detachment S appeared to excel detachment D in these ratings, as it did in the skill-level scores. The means for both these variables are shown in Table 4.

Table 4   Data for Case IC

	N	Mean skill-level score	Mean effectiveness rating
Detachment S	630	4.7683	3.9286
Detachment D	509	4.0177	3.5324

We have already tested the statistical significance of the difference between the two skill-level means. We could similarly test the difference 0.3962 between the effectiveness rating means. Instead, we shall test both differences simultaneously.

For this purpose we employ the within-groups sum of squares for the skill-level score, as before, and now also the within-groups sum of squares for effectiveness rating and the within-groups sum of cross products between skill-level score and effectiveness rating.* We present these values in the form of a matrix as follows:

$$\mathbf{W} = \begin{bmatrix} 831.0060 & 255.7797 \\ 255.7797 & 952.5008 \end{bmatrix}.$$

The within-groups sum of squares for skill-level scores appears in the upper left-hand corner, and the within-groups sum of squares for effectiveness rating appears in the lower right-hand corner. The sum of cross products between the two variables appears at the upper right and again at the lower left.

The total sum of squares and cross products is similarly arranged in a matrix as follows:

$$\mathbf{T} = \begin{bmatrix} 989.6120 & 339.4925 \\ 339.4925 & 996.6845 \end{bmatrix}.$$

1. The T^2-test.   We have seen that Hotelling's T^2 is written

$$T^2 = \frac{N_1 N_2 (N_1 + N_2 - 2)}{N_1 + N_2} d' W^{-1} d.$$

When there is more than one test variable, $\mathbf{d}$ is a column vector of mean differences between the two groups, $\mathbf{d}'$ is its transpose, and $\mathbf{W}^{-1}$ is the inverse of the $\mathbf{W}$-matrix.† For our data

$$\mathbf{d} = \begin{bmatrix} 4.7683 - 4.0177 \\ 3.9286 - 3.5324 \end{bmatrix} = \begin{bmatrix} 0.750572 \\ 0.396155 \end{bmatrix}.‡$$

---

* The computational procedure for obtaining such sums of squares and cross products is given in, for example, J. E. Wert, C. O. Neidt, and J. D. Ahmann, *Statistical Methods in Educational and Psychological Research,* New York: Appleton-Century-Crofts, 1954, p. 345.
† The elementary matrix operations employed for this work are set forth in the early chapters of texts on matrix algebra. See, for example, R. A. Frazer, W. J. Duncan, and A. R. Collar, *Elementary Matrices,* Cambridge: Cambridge University Press, 1955.
‡ These differences are copied from earlier computations, before the means were rounded as shown in Table 4.

We have already presented the **W**-matrix. Its inverse is

$$\mathbf{W}^{-1} = 10^{-4}\begin{bmatrix} 13.117847 & -3.522599 \\ -3.522599 & 11.444614 \end{bmatrix}.$$

Hence

$$\mathbf{d'W}^{-1}\mathbf{d} = 10^{-4}(0.750572, 0.396155)\begin{bmatrix} 13.117847 & -3.522599 \\ -3.522599 & 11.444614 \end{bmatrix}\begin{bmatrix} 0.750572 \\ 0.396155 \end{bmatrix} = 0.000709131,$$

and

$$T^2 = \frac{(630)(509)(630 + 509 - 2)}{630 + 509}\,0.000709131 = 226.998.$$

In the case of two test variables, the significance of T^2 is tested by writing

$$F = \frac{N_1 + N_2 - 3}{2(N_1 + N_2 - 2)}\,T^2.$$

Hence for our example

$$F = \frac{630 + 509 - 3}{2(630 + 509 - 2)} \cdot 226.998 = 113.399.$$

This is to be referred to the F-table with 2 and $N_1 + N_2 - 3$ degrees of freedom. So we have $F = 113.4$ with 2 and 1136 degrees of freedom.

Although we have used only two test variables in our example, the procedure and notation are directly applicable to the case of any number of test variables. For three or more test variables the **W**-matrix will be 3×3 or larger and the column vector **d** of mean differences will contain three or more differences between pairs of means. The value of T^2 will be computed by the same formula we have employed for our example.

But in the general case of any number t of test variables, the significance of the obtained T^2 is to be tested by writing

$$F = \frac{N_1 + N_2 - t - 1}{t(N_1 + N_2 - 2)}\,T^2,$$

and referring the obtained value to the F-table with t and $N_1 + N_2 - t - 1$ degrees of freedom.

If $t = 2$ is substituted in the expression just above for the general case, it reduces to the form we used for F in our two-test-variable example.

2. The D^2-test. We have seen that Mahalanobis' D^2 is written

$$D^2 = \mathbf{d'}\left(\frac{\mathbf{W}}{N_1 + N_2 - 2}\right)^{-1}\mathbf{d},$$

where **d** and **W** are defined as in the preceding section, Case IC, 1.

We have already presented the **W**-matrix for our example. Dividing it by $N_1 + N_2 - 2 = 1137$, we obtain

$$\frac{\mathbf{W}}{1137} = \begin{bmatrix} 0.730876 & 0.224960 \\ 0.224960 & 0.837732 \end{bmatrix}.$$

This matrix is sometimes called the within-groups dispersion matrix. The 0.730876 in the upper left-hand corner is exactly the mean square within groups on the first test variable, first reported in Table 2, for Case IA, 2. The inverse of this matrix is

$$\begin{bmatrix} 1.491500 & -0.400519 \\ -0.400519 & 1.301253 \end{bmatrix}.$$

Hence

$$D^2 = (0.750572, 0.396155) \begin{bmatrix} 1.491500 & -0.400519 \\ -0.400519 & 1.301253 \end{bmatrix} \begin{bmatrix} 0.750572 \\ 0.396155 \end{bmatrix} = 0.806284.$$

The significance of this D^2 is to be evaluated by writing

$$F = \frac{N_1 N_2 (N_1 + N_2 - 3)}{2(N_1 + N_2)(N_1 + N_2 - 2)} D^2$$

$$= \frac{(630)(509)(1136)}{2(1139)(1137)} \cdot 0.806284 = 113.399.$$

This value is to be referred to the F-table with 2 and 1136 degrees of freedom. Note that we have the same value of F and the same numbers of degrees of freedom as were obtained in the preceding section dealing with the T^2-test.

It is clear that, beginning with the original data from any problem, the D^2-test is somewhat more laborious to compute than is the T^2-test. In the computation of D^2, the **W**-matrix is first divided by the number of degrees of freedom within groups. This has the effect of multiplying $\mathbf{W}^{-1}$ by the same number of degrees of freedom. Then in the calculation of F, this same number of degrees of freedom appears in the denominator, so that it is divided back out again. In the calculation of T^2, one proceeds from the **W**-matrix directly without this division, with its effect of multiplication of the inverse; in other words, there is no dividing again to undo the inverse division. The D^2-test is therefore commonly used only when one is presented with the within-groups dispersion matrix and the differences between means, and is not presented with the original **W**-matrix.

We have remarked the simple relation between D^2 and T^2. It is

$$D^2 = \frac{N_1 + N_2}{N_1 N_2} T^2.$$

For our example, we obtained $T^2 = 226.998$. From this we could have computed D^2 as

$$D^2 = \frac{630 + 509}{(630)(509)} \cdot 226.998 = 0.806283,$$

which differs from our earlier value 0.806284 only by a rounding error in the last place.

Although we applied the D^2-test with only two test variables, it is directly applicable, with the same notation, to the case of any number of test variables. With three or more test variables, the matrix **W** will be 3×3 or larger, and the column vector **d** will contain three or more differences between pairs of test means. The value of D^2 will be computed by the same formula we have used, but the F-test of its significance will be accomplished by writing

$$F = \frac{N_1 N_2 (N_1 + N_2 - t - 1)}{t(N_1 + N_2)(N_1 + N_2 - 2)} D^2,$$

where t is the number of test variables. This is to be referred to the F-table with t and $N_1 + N_2 - t - 1$ degrees of freedom. This will, of course, produce the same value of F, with the same number of degrees of freedom, as would be obtained by applying the T^2-test.

If $t = 2$ is substituted in the expression for the F-test above, the expression reduces to the form we used for the case of two test variables.

3. The Λ-test. Wilks's Λ for this case is defined in terms of determinants, namely,

$$\Lambda = \frac{|\mathbf{W}|}{|\mathbf{T}|}.$$

Here

$$|\mathbf{W}| = (831.0060)(952.5008) - (255.7797)^2 = 726{,}110.6,$$

while

$$|\mathbf{T}| = 871{,}075.8,$$

so that

$$\Lambda = \frac{726{,}110.6}{871{,}075.8} = 0.833579.$$

This value is to be used in

$$F = \frac{1 - \Lambda}{\Lambda} \frac{N - 3}{2}$$
$$= \frac{1 - 0.833579}{0.833579} \frac{1139 - 3}{2} = 113.399.$$

This quantity is to be referred to the F-table with 2 and 1136 degrees of freedom. The value of F and the numbers of degrees of freedom are identical to those obtained by the applications of the D^2-test and the T^2-test.

We have applied the Λ-test to the case of two test variables. The calculation of Λ for any number of test variables will still proceed by the evaluation of the ratio of the determinants of $\mathbf{W}$ and $\mathbf{T}$. When there are three or more test variables, $\mathbf{W}$ and $\mathbf{T}$ will each be 3×3 or larger. The significance of the computed Λ for two groups will be evaluated by computing

$$F = \frac{1 - \Lambda}{\Lambda} \frac{N - t - 1}{t},$$

where t is the number of test variables. This will be referred to the F-table with t and $N - t - 1$ degrees of freedom.

It will be seen that if $t = 2$ is substituted in the expression for F just above, the expression reduces to the form we used in the two-test-variable case.

Case ID: Three Groups, Any Number of Test Variables

For this case, only the Λ-test is applicable. For t test variables, the matrices $\mathbf{W}$ and $\mathbf{T}$ will each be of the order of $t \times t$ and Λ will be computed as the ratio between the determinants of $\mathbf{W}$ and $\mathbf{T}$ as before. The significance of Λ will be evaluated by computing

$$F = \frac{1 - \sqrt{\Lambda}}{\sqrt{\Lambda}} \frac{N - t - 2}{t},$$

which will be referred to the F-table with $2t$ and $2(N - t - 2)$ degrees of freedom.

Since this procedure applies to the case of three groups, any number of test variables, it applies to the case of three groups, one test variable, as discussed in Case IB above. In that section we computed Λ as always, but evaluated it by writing

$$F = \frac{1 - \Lambda}{\Lambda} \frac{N - k}{k - 1},$$

to be evaluated by reference to the F-table with $k - 1$ and $N - k$ degrees of freedom.

For $k = 3$, this becomes

$$F = \frac{1 - \Lambda}{\Lambda} \frac{N - 3}{2},$$

whereas the expression at the opening of this section gives, upon setting $t = 1$,

$$F = \frac{1 - \sqrt{\Lambda}}{\sqrt{\Lambda}} \frac{N - 3}{1}.$$

It is a fact of the F-distribution that for any Λ, the last two expressions above will yield the same significance level, or probability, P. This cannot very well be seen in our numerical example, and it is not the purpose of the present discussion to explore the mathematics of the F-distribution. But a suitable numerical example may not be amiss.

Suppose that from a total of $N_1 + N_2 + N_3 = 28$ cases, we had computed $\Lambda = 0.78715$ and then computed

$$F = \frac{1 - \Lambda}{\Lambda} \frac{N - 3}{2} = \frac{1 - 0.78715}{0.78715} \frac{28 - 3}{2} = 3.38,$$

to be referred to the F-table with 2 and 25 degrees of freedom. In column 2, in row 25 of the table, we would find 3.38 precisely at the 0.05 level, indicating that our 3.38 is just barely significant at the 0.05 level.

If now we use the alternative calculation, we will have

$$F = \frac{1 - \sqrt{\Lambda}}{\sqrt{\Lambda}} \frac{N - 3}{1} = \frac{1 - 0.88721}{0.88721} \cdot 25 = 3.19,$$

to be referred to the F-table and with 2 and 50 degrees of freedom. In column 2 and row 50, we find the 0.05 level of F to be 3.18, which differs from our 3.19 by a rounding error only, so that our Λ is again just barely significant at the 0.05 level.

Thus the Λ-value, 0.78715, from three groups, one test variable, may be evaluated either by setting $k = 3$ for the Case IB, any number of groups, one test variable, or by setting $t = 1$ for the Case ID at hand, three groups, any number of test variables.

Case IE: Any Number of Groups, Two Test Variables

For this case, only the Λ-test is applicable. Since there are only two test variables, **W** and **T** will each be a 2×2 matrix, and the evaluation of the determinants will be quite easy. Having computed Λ as the ratio between the determinants of **W** and **T**, we evaluate its significance by writing

$$F = \frac{1 - \sqrt{\Lambda}}{\sqrt{\Lambda}} \frac{N - k - 1}{k - 1},$$

where k is the number of groups and N is the total number of cases. This value is to be referred to the F-table with $2(k - 1)$ and $2(N - k - 1)$ degrees of freedom.

Since this test applies to the case of any number of groups, two test variables, it applies to the case of two groups, two test variables, discussed in Case IC, 3, the Λ-test.

Putting $k = 2$ in the above expression yields

$$F = \frac{1 - \sqrt{\Lambda}}{\sqrt{\Lambda}} \frac{N - 3}{1},$$

to be referred to the F-table with 2 and $2(N - 3)$ degrees of freedom, whereas in Case IC, 3, we had for the same case of two groups, two test variables,

$$F = \frac{1 - \Lambda}{\Lambda} \frac{N - 3}{2},$$

to be referred to the F-table with 2 and $N - 3$ degrees of freedom.

We have remarked in the preceding section that these apparently different tests yield the same significance level for Λ. So the case of two groups, two test variables, may be treated as a special case of either Case IE, any number of groups, two test variables, or Case IC, two groups, any number of test variables.

Case IF: Any Number of Groups, Any Number of Test Variables

In this case only the Λ-test is applicable. We have dealt with the case of any number of groups, one test variable, Case IB; with a case of two groups, any number of test variables, Case IC; with a case of three groups, any number of test variables, Case ID; and with the case of any number of groups, two test variables, Case IE. We therefore need only to consider the general case of more than three groups, more than two test variables. For this general case, we may make use of an excellent approximation suggested by C. R. Rao.* In the use of this approxima-

---

* C. R. Rao proposed this approximation at the International Statistical Conference, India, 1951. We have been unable to gain access to a copy of the proceedings of this conference. However, Rao himself describes this approximation in his *Advanced Statistical Methods in Biometric Research,* New York: John Wiley & Sons, 1952, pp. 261–262.

tion, Λ is computed as always, as the ratio of the determinants of W and T. To evaluate the significance of the attained Λ we write

$$F = \frac{1 - \Lambda^{1/s}}{\Lambda^{1/s}} \frac{ms - v}{t(k - 1)},$$

where t and k as before are the number of test variables and the number of groups, while

$$m = \frac{2N - t - k - 2}{2}, \qquad s = \sqrt{\frac{t^2(k - 1)^2 - 4}{t^2 + (k - 1)^2 - 5}}, \qquad \text{and} \qquad v = \frac{t(k - 1) - 2}{2}.$$

The calculated value of F is to be referred to the F-table with $t(k - 1)$ and $ms - v$ degrees of freedom. It is not necessary that $ms - v$ be a whole number.

The calculation of F by this approximation appears quite complicated, but of course we need it only for rather complicated and infrequent applications where it will be worth the trouble. It is a very powerful approximation, the error involved being on the order of $1/m^4$ in terms of the probability from the F-table.*

Another approximation for interpreting the significance of the Λ in the general case, employing the χ^2-distribution, has been suggested by Bartlett.† It appears to be a somewhat less powerful approximation.

Some idea of the accuracy of the Rao approximation may be gained from the fact that when appropriate t's and k's are substituted in it, it reduces not approximately, but exactly, to the tests we have discussed in earlier sections.

Consider, for example, Case IA, two groups, one test variable. Then

$$m = \frac{2N - t - k - 2}{2}$$

becomes

$$m = \frac{2N - 1 - 2 - 2}{2} = \frac{2N - 5}{2},$$

while

$$s = \sqrt{\frac{t^2(k - 1)^2 - 4}{t^2 + (k - 1)^2 - 5}}$$

becomes

$$s = \sqrt{\frac{1(2 - 1)^2 - 4}{1 + (2 - 1)^2 - 5}} = \sqrt{\frac{1 - 4}{2 - 5}} = 1,$$

and

$$v = \frac{t(k - 1) - 2}{2}$$

---

* This feature of the approximation was reported by Rao to the senior author in a personal communication dated 18 February 1960.
† See M. S. Bartlett, "Multivariate analysis." *J. Roy. Stat. Soc. Supp.* **9,** 76 (1947). That this is a somewhat less powerful approximation has been reported to the senior author by Prof. Bartlett in a personal communication dated 17 February 1960.

becomes

$$v = \frac{1(2 - 1) - 2}{2} = -\frac{1}{2}.$$

Therefore,

$$F = \frac{1 - \Lambda^{1/s}}{\Lambda^{1/s}} \frac{ms - v}{t(k - 1)}$$

becomes

$$F = \frac{1 - \Lambda}{\Lambda} \frac{\dfrac{2N - 5}{2} \cdot 1 - \left(-\dfrac{1}{2}\right)}{1(2 - 1)} = \frac{1 - \Lambda}{\Lambda} \frac{N - 2}{1},$$

to be referred to the F-table with 1 and $N - 2$ degrees of freedom.

This is just the form we used in Case IA, 5, two groups, one test variable, the case to which Fisher's t-test is usually applied.

Or consider Case IB, any number of groups, one test variable. Then

$$m = \frac{2N - 1 - k - 2}{2} = \frac{2N - k - 3}{2},$$

$$s = \sqrt{\frac{1^2(k - 1)^2 - 4}{1^2 + (k - 1)^2 - 5}} = \sqrt{\frac{(k - 1)^2 - 4}{(k - 1)^2 - 4}} = 1,^*$$

$$v = \frac{1(k - 1) - 2}{2} = \frac{k - 3}{2}.$$

Therefore,

$$F = \frac{1 - \Lambda}{\Lambda} \frac{\dfrac{2N - k - 3}{2} \cdot 1 - \dfrac{k - 3}{2}}{1(k - 1)} = \frac{1 - \Lambda}{\Lambda} \frac{N - k}{k - 1},$$

to be referred to the F-table with $k - 1$ and $N - k$ degrees of freedom. This is just the form we arrived at in Case IB, 2, the case of any number of groups, one test variable.

Consider next, Case IC, two groups, any number of test variables. In this case

$$m = \frac{2N - t - 2 - 2}{2} = \frac{2N - t - 4}{2},$$

$$s = \sqrt{\frac{t^2(2 - 1)^2 - 4}{t^2 + (2 - 1)^2 - 5}} = \sqrt{\frac{t^2 - 4}{t^2 - 4}} = 1,^\dagger$$

$$v = \frac{t(2 - 1) - 2}{2} = \frac{t - 2}{2}.$$

---

* When $k = 3$ it appears that $s = \sqrt{0/0}$, indeterminate. However, we still say $s = 1$. See next footnote.
† Mathematical purists who question whether $s = 1$ when $t = 2$ are referred to L'Hôpital's Rule and reminded that although F-tables contain only integral values of the parameters, the F-distribution, in terms of Γ-functions, is, in fact, continuous.

Then

$$F = \frac{1 - \Lambda}{\Lambda} \frac{\frac{2N - t - 4}{2} \cdot 1 - \frac{t - 2}{2}}{t(2 - 1)} = \frac{1 - \Lambda}{\Lambda} \frac{N - t - 1}{t},$$

to be referred to the F-table with t and $N - t - 1$ degrees of freedom. This is just the test we arrived at in Case IC, 3, two groups, any number of test variables.

Now consider Case ID, three groups, any number of test variables. We will have

$$m = \frac{2N - t - 3 - 2}{2} = \frac{2N - t - 5}{2},$$

$$s = \sqrt{\frac{t^2(3 - 1)^2 - 4}{t^2 + (3 - 1)^2 - 5}} = \sqrt{\frac{4t^2 - 4}{t^2 - 1}} = 2,^*$$

$$v = \frac{t(3 - 1) - 2}{2} = t - 1.$$

Then

$$F = \frac{1 - \Lambda^{1/2}}{\Lambda^{1/2}} \frac{\frac{2N - t - 5}{2} \cdot 2 - (t - 1)}{t(3 - 1)} = \frac{1 - \sqrt{\Lambda}}{\sqrt{\Lambda}} \frac{2(N - t - 2)}{2t},$$

to be referred to the F-table with $2t$ and $2(N - t - 2)$ degrees of freedom. This is just the form we introduced in Case ID, which dealt with three groups, any number of test variables.

Finally, consider Case IE, any number of groups, two test variables. For this case $k = k$, $t = 2$, so that

$$m = \frac{2N - 2 - k - 2}{2} = \frac{2N - k - 4}{2},$$

$$s = \sqrt{\frac{2^2(k - 1)^2 - 4}{2^2 + (k - 1)^2 - 5}} = \sqrt{\frac{4(k - 1)^2 - 4}{(k - 1)^2 - 1}} = 2,^\dagger$$

$$v = \frac{2(k - 1) - 2}{2} = k - 2.$$

Then

$$F = \frac{1 - \Lambda^{1/2}}{\Lambda^{1/2}} \frac{\frac{2N - k - 4}{2} \cdot 2 - (k - 2)}{2(k - 1)} = \frac{1 - \sqrt{\Lambda}}{\sqrt{\Lambda}} \frac{2(N - k - 1)}{2(k - 1)},$$

to be referred to the F-table with $2(k - 1)$ and $2(N - k - 1)$ degrees of freedom. This is just the form we presented in Case IE, any number of groups, two test variables.

---

* In the case $t = 1$, we apply L'Hôpital's Rule.
† In the case $k = 2$, we adduce L'Hôpital's Rule.

Thus we see that the Rao approximation for the F-test of Wilks's Λ is completely general, reducing to Fisher's t-test, Snedecor's F, Hotelling's T^2, and Mahalanobis' D^2-test when the appropriate k and t are substituted, and reducing also to the exact distribution of Wilks's Λ wherever that distribution is known.

ANALYSIS OF COVARIANCE

Sometimes the k groups that were tested on t test variables were also tested on one or more covariance variables. The members of our detachment S and our detachment D were pretested on mechanical aptitude.

Case IIA: Two Groups, One Test Variable, One Covariance Variable

We will begin by asking whether the group differences in mechanical aptitude can explain the apparent superiority of detachment S over detachment D in skill level. Perhaps the detachment S members were superior in mechanical aptitude and this would explain their apparent superiority in skill level. The relevant N's and M's are given in Table 5. From this table it appears that the members of detachment S were not superior in mechanical aptitude to the members of detachment D, and we cannot expect the superior skill level of detachment S to be explained by superior mechanical aptitude. Covariance analysis will show just this: that with covariance adjustment for the difference in mechanical aptitude, detachment S will appear more significantly superior than it did in the analysis of skill-level scores without covariance adjustment.

In the analysis of covariance, the test variable is ordinarily denoted by y, and the covariance variable by x. In our example, x will be the score on the covariance variable, mechanical aptitude, and y the score on the test variable, skill level. In this notation the data for the members of our detachments S and D are as in Table 6.

1. The t-test. At the very beginning of this discussion, in Case IA, 1 (*the t-test*), we presented t as follows:

$$t = \frac{M_S - M_D}{\left[\dfrac{\sum x_S^2 + \sum x_D^2}{N_S + N_D - 2}\left(\dfrac{1}{N_S} + \dfrac{1}{N_D}\right)\right]^{1/2}}.$$

When one covariance adjustment is applied, the adjusted t becomes

$$t = \frac{(\text{Adj } \overline{Y}_S) - (\text{Adj } \overline{Y}_D)}{\left[\dfrac{(\text{Adj } WSy^2)}{N_S + N_D - 3}\left(\dfrac{1}{N_S} + \dfrac{1}{N_D} + \dfrac{(\overline{X}_S - \overline{X}_D)^2}{WSx^2}\right)\right]^{1/2}},$$

where $(\text{Adj } \overline{Y}_S)$ is the adjusted mean of detachment S on the test variable, skill level. For detachment D, $(\text{Adj } \overline{Y}_D)$ has the corresponding meaning. In the de-

Table 5 Data for Case IIA

	N	$\bar{Y}$ Mean skill level	$\bar{X}$ Mean mechanical aptitude
Detachment S	630	4.768254	5.660317
Detachment D	509	4.017682	5.764243
Total	1139	4.432836	5.706760
Difference (S − D)		0.750572	−0.103926

Table 6 Sums of squares and cross products for Case IIA

Source of variation	$\sum y^2$	$\sum x^2$	$\sum xy$
Total	989.6120	2468.0581	232.5673
Within groups	831.0060	2465.0171	254.5281
Between groups	158.6060	3.0410	−21.9608

nominator, (Adj WSy^2) is the adjusted within-groups sum of squares of the test variable, skill level. It is to be observed that the number of degrees of freedom by which this is divided is here $N_S + N_D - 3$, smaller by one than the $N_S + N_D - 2$ in the t-test without covariance correction. In the added term under the square root sign in the denominator, $\bar{X}_S$ and $\bar{X}_D$ are the group means on the covariance variable, mechanical aptitude, and WSx^2 is the within-groups sum of squares of this same variable.*

The adjusted means in the numerator are computed as follows:

$$(\text{Adj } \bar{Y}_S) = \bar{Y}_S - b(\bar{X}_S - \bar{X}_T),$$

$$(\text{Adj } \bar{Y}_D) = \bar{Y}_D - b(\bar{X}_D - \bar{X}_T),\dagger$$

where $\bar{Y}_S$ and $\bar{Y}_D$ are the test-variable means of the two groups before adjustment, b is the within-groups regression coefficient, $\bar{X}_S$ and $\bar{X}_D$ are covariance-variable means for the two groups, and $\bar{X}_T$ is the combined mean over both groups, on the covariance variable.

In the above expressions for the adjusted test-variable means, $\bar{Y}_S$ and $\bar{Y}_D$ may be obtained from the "skill level" column of Table 5, and $\bar{X}_S$ and $\bar{X}_D$ may be read from the last column of Table 5, as may $\bar{X}_T$.

---

* This adjustment is given in, for example, W. G. Cochran and Gertrude M. Cox, *Experimental Designs (2nd ed.)*, New York: John Wiley & Sons, 1957, p. 87.
† The calculation of such adjusted test-score means is explained in, for example, Wert, Neidt, and Ahmann, *op. cit.*, p. 352.

The calculation of b employs information given in Table 6, second line. We write

$$b = \frac{\sum xy}{\sum x^2} = \frac{254.5281}{2465.0171} = 0.103256.$$

Then

$$(\text{Adj } \bar{Y}_S) = 4.768254 - (0.103256)(5.660317 - 5.706760)$$
$$= 4.768254 + 0.004796 = 4.773050,$$

$$(\text{Adj } \bar{Y}_D) = 4.017682 - (0.103256)(5.764243 - 5.706760)$$
$$= 4.017682 - 0.005935 = 4.011747.$$

It will be observed that the test-score mean for detachment S was adjusted upward, while that for detachment D was adjusted downward, so that we now have a greater difference between means than we had originally. This reflects the fact that detachment S "started out behind and wound up ahead," and its test variable superiority is enhanced by taking into account the fact that it started under a handicap.

In the denominator of t, the adjusted sum of squares is computed from information given in the second line of Table 6. We write*

$$(\text{Adj } WS^2 y) = \sum{}^2 y - \frac{(\sum xy)^2}{\sum x^2}$$

$$= 831.0060 - \frac{(254.5281)^2}{2465.0171} = 804.7244.$$

Then

$$t = \frac{4.773050 - 4.011747}{\sqrt{(804.7244/1136)[1/630 + 1/509 + (-0.103926)^2/2465.0171]}}$$

$$= \frac{0.761303}{\sqrt{0.0025192}} = 15.168.$$

This is larger than the 14.73 we obtained for t from the test variable without adjustment, and is to be referred to the t-table with almost the same number of degrees of freedom: 1136 instead of 1137. So the superiority of detachment S in skill level is statistically still more significant after covariance adjustment for initial difference in mechanical aptitude.

2. The F-test. In Case IA, 2, above, we pointed out that the F-test could be employed in the two-group case, and that it led to the same result, in terms of statistical significance, as the application of the t-test. To apply the F-test in the present case, we need the adjusted total sum of squares, in addition to the adjusted sum of

---

* See Wert, Neidt, and Ahmann, *op. cit.*, p. 351.

squares within groups. The adjusted total sum of squares is computed from information given in the "total" line of Table 6. We write

$$(\text{Adj } TS^2 y) = \sum^2 y - \frac{(\sum xy)^2}{\sum x^2}$$

$$= 989.6120 - \frac{(232.5673)^2}{2468.058} = 967.6970.$$

We have already seen that the adjusted sum of squares within groups is 804.7244. We are now prepared to write an analysis-of-variance table analogous to Table 2 in Case IA, 2. We will obtain the between-groups sum of squares by subtraction, as shown in Table 7.

Table 7   Analysis of variance of residuals, Case IIA

Source of variation	Number of degrees of freedom	Sum of squares	Mean square
Total	1137	967.6970	
Within groups	1136	804.7244	0.708384
Between groups	1	162.9726	162.9726

As in Case IA, 2, we compute F as the ratio of the between-groups mean square to the within-groups mean square. Thus

$$F = \frac{162.9726}{0.708383} = 230.06.$$

Reference to the F-table with 1 and 1136 degrees of freedom shows this value of F to be significant far beyond the 0.001 level. In fact, this $F = 230.06$ with 1 and 1136 degrees of freedom is more significant than is the $F = 217.01$ with 1 and 1137 degrees of freedom, that resulted from the analysis of skill-level scores without adjustment by covariance. This is, of course, what we expected when we noticed that detachment S was below detachment D on the covariance variable, mechanical aptitude.

The square root of 230.06 is 15.168, which is the value we obtained for t in the preceding section. Thus the F-test is equivalent to the t-test in this situation, and since the F-test is applicable in the case of more than two groups, it is frequently the only test suggested for covariance analysis. If the adjusted means are desired, they will be computed as before, from the information given in Tables 5 and 6.

3. The T^2-test.   We have already seen (Case IA, 3) that T^2 without covariance is written

$$T^2 = \frac{N_1 N_2 (N_1 + N_2 - 2)}{N_1 + N_2} d' W^{-1} d.$$

To see how this is to be adjusted for one covariance variable, we divide numerator and denominator by $N_1 N_2$, getting

$$T^2 = \frac{N_1 + N_2 - 2}{1/N_1 + 1/N_2} d'W^{-1}d.$$

Next we make the same kind of revisions we made on t, two sections back. $N_1 + N_2 - 2$ will become $N_S + N_D - 3$, an additional term will be added to the denominator, and we will have

$$T^2 = \frac{N_S + N_D - 3}{1/N_S + 1/N_D + (\bar{X}_S - \bar{X}_D)^2/WS x^2} d'W^{-1}d.$$

The difference between group means, $d' = d$, will become the difference between the adjusted group means. The W will be the within-groups sum of squares of residuals, as in Table 7. Therefore, in the present case we will have

$$T^2 = \frac{630 + 509 - 3}{1/630 + 1/509 + (-0.103926)^2/2465.0171} (0.761303) \frac{1}{804.7244} (0.761303)$$
$$= 230.06.$$

This is just what we obtained for F in the preceding section. It is to be referred to the F-table with 1 and $(N_1 + N_2 - 3) = 1136$ degrees of freedom. Also, this 230.06 is the square of 15.168, which is the value we obtained for t in section IIA, 1.

4. The D^2-test. In the notation of the preceding section, D^2 with adjustment for one covariance variable is written

$$D^2 = d' \left(\frac{W}{N_1 + N_2 - 3} \right)^{-1} d,$$

wherein d and W are adjusted values, so that in the present case

$$D^2 = (0.761303) \left(\frac{804.7244}{1136} \right)^{-1} (0.761303) = 0.818176.$$

Without covariance, D^2 for one test variable is evaluated by computing

$$F = \frac{N_1 N_2}{N_1 + N_2} D^2.$$

To see the analogy with earlier tests, we divide numerator and denominator by $N_1 N_2$, getting

$$F = \frac{D^2}{1/N_1 + 1/N_2}.$$

Next we revise the denominator for adjustment by one covariance variable, as we did for t and for T^2:

$$F = \frac{D^2}{1/N_S + 1/N_D + (\bar{X}_S - \bar{X}_D)^2/WS x^2}.$$

Then for our example,

$$F = \frac{0.818176}{1/630 + 1/509 + (-0.103926)^2/2465.0171}$$

$$= \frac{0.818176}{0.00355632} = 230.06.$$

This is just the value we obtained for the F equivalent of T^2 in the preceding section. It is to be referred to the F-table with 1 and $N_1 + N_2 - 3 = 1136$ degrees of freedom, as before.

5. The Λ-test. From the same data, Wilks's Λ is computed as the ratio between the two adjusted sums of squares in Table 7:

$$\Lambda = \frac{W}{T} = \frac{804.7244}{967.6970} = 0.831586.$$

This is to be evaluated by writing

$$F = \frac{1 - \Lambda}{\Lambda} (N_1 + N_2 - 3),$$

which is just like the F in Case IA, 5, except that we have reduced the number of degrees of freedom by 1, as we did in the sections just above. We have

$$F = \frac{1 - 0.831586}{0.831586} (1136) = 230.06.$$

This is exactly the value we obtained in Case IIA, 2, where we applied the F-test directly. It is to be referred to the F-table with 1 and $N_1 + N_2 - 3 = 1136$ degrees of freedom, as before.

6. Discussion. All five of the statistics we have employed in the five preceding sections have yielded the same interpretation of the data, and the choice among the five would seem to hinge upon directness and ease of computational procedure. In this connection one can hardly fail to be impressed by the greater elegance of the F- and Λ-tests, as compared to any of the others.

Case IIB: Two Groups, One Test Variable, Any Number of Covariance Variables

Besides being pretested on mechanical aptitude, our detachments S and D were pretested on technical aptitude. Their mean scores are given in Table 8, wherein, for convenience, we have repeated the skill-level means and the mechanical-aptitude means.

When, as in this case, there are two or more covariance variables, they are commonly distinguished with subscripts, as in Table 9, wherein y is the test variable, skill level; x_1 is the covariance variable, mechanical aptitude; and x_2 is the covariance variable, technical aptitude.

Table 8 Data for Case IIB

	N	$\bar{Y}$ Mean skill level	$\bar{X}_1$ Mean mechanical aptitude	$\bar{X}_2$ Mean technical aptitude
Detachment S	630	4.768254	5.660317	4.849206
Detachment D	509	4.017682	5.764243	4.968566
Total	1139	4.432836	5.706760	4.902546
Difference (S − D)		0.750572	−0.103926	−0.119360

Table 9 Sums of squares and cross products for Case IIB

Source of variation	$\sum y^2$	$\sum x_1^2$	$\sum x_2^2$	$\sum x_1 y$	$\sum x_2 y$	$\sum x_1 x_2$
Total	989.6120	2468.0581	3596.1826	232.5673	225.0448	2157.4504
Within groups	831.0060	2465.0171	3592.1716	254.5281	250.2670	2153.9580
Between groups	158.6060	3.0410	4.0110	−21.9608	−25.2222	3.4924

1. The *t*-test. For two covariance variables, t is written

$$t = \frac{(\text{Adj } \bar{Y}_S) - (\text{Adj } \bar{Y}_D)}{\left[\dfrac{\text{Adj } WSy^2}{N_S + N_D - 4} \left(\dfrac{1}{N_S} + \dfrac{1}{N_D} + \mathbf{d}_x' \mathbf{W}_x^{-1} \mathbf{d}_x \right) \right]},$$

where all the terms are the same as in section IIA, 1, above, except that $\mathbf{d}_x$ is a column vector of differences between group means on the two covariance variables, $\mathbf{d}'$ is its transpose, and $\mathbf{W}$ is the 2×2 matrix of within-groups sums of squares and cross products of the covariance variables.

For the adjusted group means we write

$$(\text{Adj } \bar{Y}_S) = \bar{Y}_S - b_1(\bar{X}_{S1} - \bar{X}_{T1}) - b_2(\bar{X}_{S2} - \bar{X}_{T2}),$$
$$(\text{Adj } \bar{Y}_D) = \bar{Y}_D - b_1(\bar{X}_{D1} - \bar{X}_{T1}) - b_2(\bar{X}_{D2} - \bar{X}_{T2}).*$$

The values of b_1 and b_2 are determined by solving the normal equations

$$\sum x_1 y = b_1 \sum x_1^2 + b_2 \sum x_1 x_2,$$
$$\sum x_2 y = b_1 \sum x_1 x_2 + b_2 \sum x_2^2,$$

wherein the sums are "within groups."

---

* This procedure is set forth in a slightly different notation in Wert, Neidt, and Ahmann, *op. cit.,* p. 348. The notation we use is strictly analogous with that in our section IIA, 1.

For our data we will use the "within-groups" line of Table 9 to write

$$254.5281 = 2465.0171b_1 + 2153.9580b_2,$$
$$250.2670 = 2153.9580b_1 + 3592.1716b_2,$$

from which

$$b_1 = 0.0890210, \qquad b_2 = 0.0162908.$$

So then

$$(\text{Adj } \bar{Y}_S) = 4.768254 - (0.0890210)(5.660317 - 5.706760)$$
$$- (0.0162908)(4.849206 - 4.902546)$$
$$= 4.768254 + 0.005003 = 4.773257$$

$$(\text{Adj } \bar{Y}_D) = 4.017682 - (0.0890210)(5.764243 - 5.706760)$$
$$- (0.0162908)(4.968566 - 4.902546)$$
$$= 4.017682 - 0.006193 = 4.011489.$$

It will be observed that the test-variable mean for detachment S has been adjusted upward, and the mean for detachment D has been adjusted downward, so that detachment S exhibits a larger superiority after the adjustment of the means than it did before. This reflects the fact that it "started out behind," on each of the covariance variables, with a lower mean on each than detachment D had.

The surprising part is that the adjustment for two covariance variables turned out to be so little different from the adjustment for only one. For Case IIA above, we found the adjusted means to be 4.7731 and 4.0118, as compared to the 4.7733 and 4.0115 just obtained. The change is only 0.0002 for detachment S and -0.0003 for detachment D. Apparently very little is gained by adding the second covariance variable, when treating these particular data.

For the denominator of t we need the adjusted within-groups sum of squares. It is given by*

$$(\text{Adj } WSy^2) = \sum y^2 - b_1 \sum x_1 y - b_2 \sum x_2 y$$
$$= 831.0060 - (0.0890210)(254.5281)$$
$$- (0.0162908)(250.2670)$$
$$= 804.2706.$$

For our data,

$$\mathbf{d}_x = \begin{bmatrix} -0.103926 \\ -0.119360 \end{bmatrix}$$

and

$$\mathbf{W}_x = \begin{bmatrix} 2465.0171 & 2153.9580 \\ 2153.9580 & 3592.1716 \end{bmatrix}.$$

---

* Compare Wert, Neidt, and Ahmann, *op. cit.*, p. 346.

Then

$$\mathbf{W}_x^{-1} = 10^{-4}\begin{bmatrix} 8.521888 & -5.109942 \\ -5.109942 & 5.847883 \end{bmatrix},$$

so that

$$\mathbf{d}_x'\mathbf{W}_x^{-1}\mathbf{d}_x = [-0.103926, -0.119360]10^{-4}\begin{bmatrix} 8.521888 & -5.109942 \\ -5.109942 & 5.847883 \end{bmatrix}\mathbf{d}_x$$

$$= 10^{-4}[-0.275723, -0.166947]\begin{bmatrix} -0.103926 \\ -0.119360 \end{bmatrix}$$

$$= 0.00000485816.$$

Then

$$t = \frac{4.773257 - 4.011489}{\left[\dfrac{804.2706}{1135}\left(\dfrac{1}{630} + \dfrac{1}{509} + 0.00000486\right)\right]^{1/2}}$$

$$= \frac{0.761768}{\sqrt{(0.708608)(0.00355680)}} = 15.174.$$

This is to be referred to the t-table with 1135 degrees of freedom.

This value, $t = 15.174$, is only slightly larger than the value $t = 15.168$ that we obtained in Case IIA, 1, where we used only one covariance variable. As we noticed in connection with the adjusted means, it appears that the addition of the second covariance variable brought about very little improvement in the case of these particular data.

The numerical example in this section employed only two covariance variables. However, the procedure is easily extended to any number of covariance variables. If there are three covariance variables, the adjusted means will be given by

$$(\text{Adj } \bar{Y}_\text{S}) = \bar{Y}_\text{S} - b_1(\bar{X}_{\text{S}1} - \bar{X}_{\text{T}1}) - b_2(\bar{X}_{\text{S}2} - \bar{X}_{\text{T}2}) - b_3(\bar{X}_{\text{S}3} - \bar{X}_{\text{T}3}),$$

$$(\text{Adj } \bar{Y}_\text{D}) = \bar{Y}_\text{D} - b_1(\bar{X}_{\text{D}1} - \bar{X}_{\text{T}1}) - b_2(\bar{X}_{\text{D}2} - \bar{X}_{\text{T}2}) - b_3(\bar{X}_{\text{D}3} - \bar{X}_{\text{T}3}),$$

wherein the notation is analogous to that previously employed. A fourth covariance variable would simply add a fourth subtraction term to each equation.

For three covariance variables the b's would be obtained by solving the three normal equations

$$\sum x_1 y = b_1 \sum x_1^2 + b_2 \sum x_1 x_2 + b_3 \sum x_1 x_3,$$

$$\sum x_2 y = b_1 \sum x_1 x_2 + b_2 \sum x_2^2 + b_3 \sum x_2 x_3,$$

$$\sum x_3 y = b_1 \sum x_1 x_3 + b_2 \sum x_2 x_3 + b_3 \sum x_3^2,$$

wherein all the sums of squares and cross products are to be "within groups." There is a clear sequence of subscripts on both sides of these equations, so it would be easy to write the equations for four covariance variables. There would be four of them, and each would have four terms on the right-hand side.

The adjusted sum of squares within groups is similarly dealt with in the case of three covariance variables. For three covariance variables we would have

$$(\text{Adj } WSy^2) = \sum y^2 - b_1 \sum x_1 y - b_2 \sum x_2 y - b_3 \sum x_3 y,$$

wherein of course the sums on the right are to come from the "within-groups" line of a table like Table 9. The sequence of subscripts on the right of the above equation makes it clear how a fourth covariance variable would be added.

The number of degrees of freedom by which the adjusted sum of squares is divided in the denominator of t would in general be

$$\text{ndf} = N_1 + N_2 - c - 2,$$

where c is the number of covariance variables.

For three or more covariance variables $\mathbf{d}_x$ will be a column vector of three or more differences between group means and $\mathbf{W}_x$ will be 3×3 or larger.

In the general case of two groups, one test variable, any number of covariance variables, we have, therefore,

$$t = \frac{(\text{Adj } \bar{Y}_1) - (\text{Adj } \bar{Y}_2)}{\left[\dfrac{(\text{Adj } WSy^2)}{N_1 + N_2 - c - 2} \left(\dfrac{1}{N_1} + \dfrac{1}{N_2} + \mathbf{d}_x' \mathbf{W}_x^{-1} \mathbf{d}_x \right) \right]^{1/2}},$$

to be referred to the t-table with $N_1 + N_2 - c - 2$ degrees of freedom.

2. The F-test. We have already seen that the F-test for the two-group case with covariance is computed more directly than is the t-test. This will appear even more clearly in the present section. We need only a ratio of two adjusted mean squares, one between groups and the other within groups. We have already found that the adjusted sum of squares within groups in our numerical example is 804.2706. The adjusted sum of squares between groups is obtained by subtraction, as it was in Table 7 in the preceding Case IIA, 2. Following the procedure we employed for the adjusted within-groups sum of squares, we write for adjusted total sum of squares

$$(\text{Adj } TSy^2) = \sum y^2 - b_1 \sum x_1 y - b_2 \sum x_2 y,$$

where the sums on the right-hand side come from the "total" line of Table 9, and the b's are obtained by solving the normal equations

$$\sum x_1 y = b_1 \sum x_1^2 + b_2 \sum x_1 x_2,$$
$$\sum x_2 y = b_1 \sum x_1 x_2 + b_2 \sum x_2^2,$$

where all sums come from the "total" line of Table 9. We will have

$$232.5673 = 2468.0581 b_1 + 2157.4504 b_2,$$
$$225.0448 = 2157.4504 b_1 + 3596.1826 b_2,$$

which yield

$$b_1 = 0.0831158, \qquad b_2 = 0.0127153,$$

whence the adjusted total sum of squares is

$$(\text{Adj } TSy^2) = 989.6120 - (0.0831158)(232.5673) - (0.127153)(225.0448)$$
$$= 967.4205.$$

We are now prepared to write a table of the analysis of variance of residuals, as we did in Table 7 of the preceding section IIA, 2. This we do in Table 10, wherein the adjusted sum of squares between groups is obtained by subtraction. From Table 10 we compute

$$F = \frac{163.1499}{0.708608} = 230.24,$$

to be referred to the F-table with 1 and 1135 degrees of freedom.

Table 10   Analysis of variance of residuals, Case IIB

Source of variation	Number of degrees of freedom	Sum of squares	Mean square
Total	1136	967.4205	
Within groups	1135	804.2706	0.708608
Between groups	1	163.1499	163.1499

This value, $F = 230.24$, is slightly larger than the $F = 230.06$ that we obtained in Case IIA, 2, where we dealt with only one covariance variable. The increase is so small, however, that the employment of a second covariance variable seems to have added very little to the interpretation of the data in this case. This is just what we found in the preceding section, using the t-test. If we take the square root of $F = 230.24$, we get $t = 15.174$, to be referred to the t-table with 1135 degrees of freedom. This is just the value we obtained in the preceding section.

We have dealt with a numerical example in which there were only two covariance variables, but the procedure for three or more is a direct extension of the procedure we have used. We will need an adjusted total sum of squares, an adjusted within-groups sum of squares, and a revised number of degrees of freedom. We have already seen in the preceding section how to compute the adjusted within-groups sum of squares. The adjusted total sum of squares will be computed in an exactly analogous manner, using the "total" line of a table like Table 9. For three covariance variables we will have

$$(\text{Adj } TSy^2) = \sum y^2 - b_1 \sum x_1 y - b_2 \sum x_2 y - b_3 \sum x_3 y,$$

in which the sums on the right-hand side come from the "total" line of a table like Table 9. For a fourth covariance variable, there would be a fourth subtraction term, written by extending the subscript system.

The b's for this adjustment will be obtained by solving the normal equations

$$\sum x_1 y = b_1 \sum x_1^2 + b_2 \sum x_1 x_2 + b_3 \sum x_1 x_3,$$

$$\sum x_2 y = b_1 \sum x_1 x_2 + b_2 \sum x_2^2 + b_3 \sum x_2 x_3,$$

$$\sum x_3 y = b_1 \sum x_1 x_3 + b_2 \sum x_2 x_3 + b_3 \sum x_3^2,$$

wherein all sums on both sides of the equation come from the "total" line of a table like Table 9. There is a clearly visible sequence of subscripts on both sides of these equations, so that the system can be extended to four or more covariance variables.

The adjusted sum of squares between groups will be obtained by subtracting the adjusted sum of squares within groups from the adjusted total sum of squares, as in Table 7.

The number of degrees of freedom between two groups is always 1. Within groups, the number of degrees of freedom will be given by $N_1 + N_2 - c - 2$, where c is the number of covariance variables. We have seen this in the preceding section, Case IIB, 1.

In the general case of two groups, one test variable, any number of covariance variables, we will have for the analysis of variance of residuals a table like Table 11.

Table 11 Analysis of variance of residuals for the case of two groups, one test variable, any number of covariance variables

Source of variation	Number of degrees of freedom	Sum of squares	Mean square
Total	$N_1 + N_2 - c - 1$	(Adj TSy^2)	
Within groups	$N_1 + N_2 - c - 2$	(Adj WSy^2)	(Adj WSy^2)/$(N_1 + N_2 - c - 2)$
Between groups	1	(Adj BSy^2)	(Adj BSy^2)/1

From the information in such a table, F will be computed as

$$F = \frac{(\text{Adj } BSy^2)}{(\text{Adj } WSy^2)} (N_1 + N_2 - c - 2),$$

to be referred to the F-table with 1 and $N_1 + N_2 - c - 2$ degrees of freedom.

3. The T^2-test. For the present case of one test variable, two covariance variables, T^2 is written

$$T^2 = \frac{N_1 + N_2 - 4}{1/N_1 + 1/N_2 + \mathbf{d}_z' \mathbf{W}_z^{-1} \mathbf{d}_z} d_y' W_y^{-1} d_y,$$

wherein $d'_y = d_y =$ the difference between the adjusted test variable means for the two groups, and W_y is the adjusted within-groups sum of squares. In the denominator, $\mathbf{d}_x$ is a two-element column vector of differences between group means on the two covariance variables and $\mathbf{W}_x$ is a 2×2 matrix of within-groups sums of squares and cross products of the covariance variables. We have already computed the adjusted mean difference, the adjusted within-groups sum of squares, and the entire denominator, in connection with the t-test, in Case IIB, 1. Thus the application of the T^2-test to our data gives

$$T^2 = \frac{1135}{1/630 + 1/509 + 0.00000486} \, 0.761768 \, \frac{1}{804.2706} \, 0.761768$$

$$= \frac{1}{0.00355680} \, \frac{(0.761768)^2}{0.708608} = \frac{0.580290}{0.00252038} = 230.24.$$

This is to be evaluated by referring it to the F-table with 1 and 1135 degrees of freedom. It is the same value of F, with the same numbers of degrees of freedom, as we obtained in the preceding section where we applied the F-test directly.

We have dealt with a numerical example in which there were only two covariance variables. However, the procedure can be extended immediately to the case of two groups, one test variable, any number of covariance variables. We need the difference between the adjusted test variable means, an adjusted sum of squares within groups, a revised number of degrees of freedom, and a revised denominator.

We have seen in the preceding section, Case IIB, 1, how to compute the adjusted test-variable means in the case of any number of covariance variables, and how to compute the adjusted within-groups sum of squares. For c covariance variables, the number of degrees of freedom for the adjusted within-groups sum of squares is $N_1 + N_2 - c - 2$. In general, then, for two groups, one test variable, any number of covariance variables, we will have

$$T^2 = \frac{N_1 + N_2 - c - 2}{1/N_1 + 1/N_2 + \mathbf{d}_x' \mathbf{W}_x^{-1} \mathbf{d}_x} \, d_y' W_y^{-1} d_y,$$

wherein $d'_y = d_y =$ the difference between the adjusted test-variable means; W_y^{-1} is the reciprocal of the adjusted within-groups sum of squares on the test variable; $\mathbf{d}_x$ is a column vector of differences between group means on the covariance variables; and $\mathbf{W}_x$ is the matrix of sums of squares and cross products on the covariance variables. For three or more covariance variables $\mathbf{d}_x$ will contain three or more differences between group means, and $\mathbf{W}_x$ will be a 3×3 matrix or larger.

This is to be evaluated by referring it to the F-table with 1 and $N_1 + N_2 - c - 2$ degrees of freedom.

4. The D^2-test. In our numerical example dealing with two groups, one test variable, two covariance variables, D^2 is written

$$D^2 = d_y' \left(\frac{W_y}{N_1 + N_2 - 4} \right)^{-1} d_y,$$

where $d'_y = d_y =$ the difference between the adjusted test-variable means, and W is the adjusted within-groups sum of squares. For our numerical example we will have

$$D^2 = (0.761768) \left(\frac{804.2706}{1135}\right)^{-1} (0.761768)$$

$$= \frac{0.580290}{0.708608} = 0.818915.$$

This is to be evaluated by computing

$$F = \frac{D^2}{1/N_1 + 1/N_2 + \mathbf{d}'_x\mathbf{W}_x^{-1}\mathbf{d}_x} = \frac{0.818915}{0.00355680} = 230.24.$$

This is to be referred to the F-table with 1 and 1135 degrees of freedom. It is the same value of F, with the same numbers of degrees of freedom, that we obtained in the preceding section from the application of the T^2-test.

We have dealt with a numerical example in which there were only two co-variance variables. However, the procedure can be extended easily to the case of two groups, one test variable, any number of covariance variables. In such a case we will write

$$D^2 = d'_y \left(\frac{W_y}{N_1 + N_2 - c - 2}\right)^{-1} d_y,$$

where $d'_y = d_y =$ the difference between the adjusted test variable means, W_y is the adjusted sum of squares within groups, and c is the number of covariance variables.

The obtained value of D^2 is to be evaluated by writing

$$F = \frac{D^2}{1/N_1 + 1/N_2 + \mathbf{d}'_x\mathbf{W}_x^{-1}\mathbf{d}_x},$$

where $\mathbf{d}_x$ is a column vector of the differences between the groups on the c co-variance variables, and $\mathbf{W}_x$ is a $c \times c$ matrix of the within-groups sums of squares and cross products of the covariance variables. This quantity is to be referred to the F-table with 1 and $N_1 + N_2 - c - 2$ degrees of freedom.

5. The Λ-test.   For our numerical example, Λ is to be computed from the quantities given in Table 10: $\Lambda = W/T$, where W is the adjusted sum of squares within groups, and T is the adjusted total sum of squares, so that

$$\Lambda = \frac{804.2706}{967.4205} = 0.831356.$$

This is to be evaluated by writing

$$F = \frac{1 - \Lambda}{\Lambda}(N_1 + N_2 - 4) = \frac{1 - 0.831356}{0.831356}(1135) = 230.24.$$

This is to be referred to the F-table with 1 and 1135 degrees of freedom. It is just the value of F, with the same numbers of degrees of freedom, that we obtained in the earlier section IIB, 2, where we applied the F-test directly.

When the Λ-test is applied to a case of two groups, one test variable, any number of covariance variables, the expression $\Lambda = W/T$ will employ for W the within-groups sum of squares adjusted for the number c of control variables as explained in Case IIB, 1; and for T the total sum of squares adjusted for the number c of covariance variables as explained in Case IIB, 2. The obtained value of Λ will be evaluated by writing

$$F = \frac{1 - \Lambda}{\Lambda} (N_1 + N_2 - c - 2),$$

where c is the number of covariance variables. This is to be referred to the F-table with 1 and $N_1 + N_2 - c - 2$ degrees of freedom.

Case IIC: Any Number of Groups, One Test Variable, Any Number of Covariance Variables

For this case, only the F-test and the Λ-test are applicable.

1. The F-test. For any number k of groups, the F-test with covariance adjustment is written

$$F = \frac{\text{Adj } ASy^2/(k - 1)}{\text{Adj } WSy^2/(N - k - c)}$$

$$= \frac{\text{Adj } ASy^2}{\text{Adj } WSy^2} \frac{N - k - c}{k - 1},$$

where Adj ASy^2 is the adjusted among-groups sum of squares of the test variable, computed by subtraction as in Case IIB, 2; Adj WSy^2 is the adjusted within-groups sum of squares of the test variable, computed as in Case IIB, 1; N is the total number of cases in all groups, and c is the number of covariance variables.

The analysis of variance of residuals will be arranged in a table like Table 12, in which the mean squares entering into F are shown in the last column. The

Table 12 Analysis of variance of residuals, k groups, one test variable, c covariance variables

Source of variation	Sum of squares	Number of degrees of freedom	Mean square
Total	Adj TSy^2	$N - c - 1$	
Within groups	Adj WSy^2	$N - k - c$	$\dfrac{\text{Adj } WSy^2}{N - k - c}$
Among groups	Adj ASy^2	$k - 1$	$\dfrac{\text{Adj } ASy^2}{k - 1}$

obtained value of F is to be referred to the F-table with $k - 1$ and $N - k - c$ degrees of freedom.

2. The Λ-test. In the case of k groups, one test variable, any number c of covariance variables, Λ is written

$$\Lambda = \frac{W_{y.x}}{T_{y.x}} = \frac{\text{Adj } WSy^2}{\text{Adj } TSy^2},$$

wherein $W_{y.x}$ and $T_{y.x}$ are the adjusted within-groups and total sums of squares of the test variable y. The adjusted values will be computed in accordance with the procedure used in Cases IIB, 1, and IIB, 2, above. The obtained Λ will be evaluated by writing

$$F = \frac{1 - \Lambda}{\Lambda} \frac{N - k - c}{k - 1}$$

and referring the result to the F-table with $k - 1$ and $N - k - c$ degrees of freedom.

Case IID: Two Groups, Any Number of Test Variables, Any Number of Covariance Variables

For this case the t-test and the F-test apply only when the number t of test variables is 1. This special case was treated in Case IIB. In this section we will analyze the data from two groups, for each of which we have two test variables and two covariance variables. We will test whether the two test variables in combination, after adjustment for the two covariance variables in combination, distinguish significantly between the two groups. For our two groups the means of the two test variables have already been given in Table 4, Case IC, and the means of the two covariance variables have been given in Table 8, Case IIB.

Table 13 Within-groups sums of squares and cross products for Case IID

		y_1	y_2	x_1	x_2
	y_1	831.0060	255.7797	254.5281	250.2670
	y_2	255.7797	952.5008	209.6043	253.7330
$W =$					
	x_1	254.5281	209.6043	2465.0171	2153.9580
	x_2	250.2670	253.7330	2153.9580	3592.1716

For any of the statistical tests in this section we will need the within-groups sums of squares and cross products of the test variables y and the covariance variables x. Some of these have been given before, in Table 9, Case IIB. It will be convenient here to repeat these and add the ones not yet presented. Table 13 shows a matrix made up of all the within-groups sums of squares and cross products. The dotted lines partition the matrix into four submatrices which may be denoted

$$\mathbf{W} = \begin{bmatrix} \mathbf{W}_{yy} & \mathbf{W}_{yx} \\ \mathbf{W}_{xy} & \mathbf{W}_{xx} \end{bmatrix}.$$

1. The T^2-test. The calculation of T^2 for this case with covariance adjustment follows very closely the method used in Case IIB, 3, wherein there was only one test variable. We will use here an expression very similar to the one in Case IIB, 3:

$$T^2 = \frac{N_1 + N_2 - c - 2}{1/N_1 + 1/N_2 + \mathbf{d}_x' \mathbf{W}_{xx}^{-1} \mathbf{d}_x} \mathbf{d}_{y.x}' \mathbf{W}_{y.x}^{-1} \mathbf{d}_{y.x}.$$

In our numerical example, we have $t = 2$ test variables and $c = 2$ covariance variables. N_1 and N_1 are as before. In the denominator, $\mathbf{d}_x$ is a column vector of differences between group means on the two covariance variables. From the bottom line of Table 8 we have

$$\mathbf{d}_x = \begin{bmatrix} -0.103926 \\ -0.119360 \end{bmatrix}.$$

We have already seen this vector in Case IIB, 1, which dealt with the t-test adjusted for these same covariance variables. In fact, the entire denominator of our present T^2 was evaluated in that section, and found to be 0.00355680.

In the case of two test variables, $\mathbf{d}_{y.x}$ is a two-element column vector of differences between adjusted test variable means. Also, $\mathbf{W}_{y.x}$ is an adjusted 2×2 matrix of within-group sums of squares and cross products of the two test variables.

We have already seen in Case IIB, 1, that the difference between the adjusted group means of the first test variable y_1 is 0.761768. The same procedure as there employed yields 0.406171 for the difference between the adjusted means on the second test variable y_2. Then

$$\mathbf{d}_{y.x} = \begin{bmatrix} 0.761768 \\ 0.406171 \end{bmatrix}.$$

For the matrix $\mathbf{W}_{y.x}$ of adjusted within-groups sums of squares and cross products, we will adopt the notation for the submatrices indicated in Table 13:

$$\mathbf{W} = \begin{bmatrix} \mathbf{W}_{yy} & \mathbf{W}_{yx} \\ \hline \mathbf{W}_{xy} & \mathbf{W}_{xx} \end{bmatrix}.$$

We want $\mathbf{W}_{yy}$ adjusted for covariance. It is given by

$$\mathbf{W}_{y.x} = \mathbf{W}_{yy} - \mathbf{W}_{yx} \mathbf{W}_{xx}^{-1} \mathbf{W}_{xy}.*$$

In Case IIB, 1, we computed the inverse of $\mathbf{W}_{xx}$. It is

$$\mathbf{W}_{xx}^{-1} = 10^{-4} \begin{bmatrix} 8.521888 & -5.109942 \\ -5.109942 & 5.847883 \end{bmatrix}.$$

---

* This is given in a different notation by Rao, *op. cit.*, p. 266.

Then

$$\mathbf{W}_{y.x} = \begin{bmatrix} 831.0060 & 255.7797 \\ 255.7797 & 952.5008 \end{bmatrix}$$

$$- \begin{bmatrix} 254.5281 & 250.2670 \\ 209.6043 & 253.7330 \end{bmatrix} 10^{-4} \begin{bmatrix} 8.521888 & -5.109942 \\ -5.109942 & 5.847883 \end{bmatrix} \begin{bmatrix} 254.5281 & 209.6043 \\ 250.2670 & 253.7330 \end{bmatrix}$$

$$= \begin{bmatrix} 831.0060 & 255.7797 \\ 255.7797 & 952.5008 \end{bmatrix} - \begin{bmatrix} 26.735396 & 22.792708 \\ 22.792708 & 20.736007 \end{bmatrix}$$

$$= \begin{bmatrix} 804.270604 & 232.986992 \\ 232.986992 & 931.764793 \end{bmatrix},$$

a 2×2 matrix. The inverse of this is

$$\mathbf{W}_{y.x}^{-1} = 10^{-4} \begin{bmatrix} 13.404603 & -3.351809 \\ -3.351809 & 11.570439 \end{bmatrix},$$

so that

$$\mathbf{d}_{y.x} \mathbf{W}_{y.x}^{-1} \mathbf{d}_{y.x} = [0.761768, 0.406171] W_{y.x}^{-1} \begin{bmatrix} 0.761768 \\ 0.406171 \end{bmatrix}$$

$$= 7.613242 \cdot 10^{-4}.$$

Therefore,

$$T^2 = \frac{630 + 509 - 2 - 2}{0.00355680} \cdot 7.613242 \cdot 10^{-4} = 242.94.$$

This is to be evaluated by computing

$$F = \frac{N_1 + N_2 - 5}{2(N_1 + N_2 - 4)} T^2 = \frac{1134}{2270} \cdot 242.94 = 121.36,$$

to be referred to the F-table with 2 and 1134 degrees of freedom.

We have dealt with the case of two test variables and two covariance variables. However, the procedure can be extended to any number of test variables with any number of covariance variables. The procedure for adjusting the test-variable means for any number of covariance variables has been given in Case IIB, 1. With more than two test variables, the matrix $\mathbf{W}_{yy}$ will be 3×3 or larger, in general $t \times t$; and with more than two covariance variables, the matrix $\mathbf{W}_{xx}$ will be 3×3 or larger, in general $c \times c$. But the matrix of adjusted within-groups sums of squares and cross products will be computed with the same matrix equation we used for $\mathbf{W}_{y.x}$. T^2 will be computed by the formula we presented at the beginning of this section. The obtained T^2 will be evaluated by writing

$$F = \frac{(N_1 + N_2 - t - c - 1)}{t(N_1 + N_2 - c - 2)} T^2,$$

to be referred to the F-table with t and $N_1 + N_2 - t - c - 1$ degrees of freedom.

2. The D^2-test. With adjustment for any number c of covariance variables, Mahalanobis' D^2 is written, in the notation of the preceding section,

$$D^2 = \mathbf{d}'_{y.x} \left(\frac{\mathbf{W}_{y.x}}{N_1 + N_2 - c - 2)} \right)^{-1} \mathbf{d}_{y.x},$$

and is evaluated by writing

$$F = \frac{(N_1 + N_2 - c - t - 1)D^2}{t(1/N_1 + 1/N_2 + \mathbf{d}'_x \mathbf{W}_{xx}^{-1} \mathbf{d}_x)(N_1 + N_2 - c - 2)},$$

and referring the obtained value of F to the F-table with t and $N_1 + N_2 - c - t - 1$ degrees of freedom.

For our numerical example the entries in these expressions have been computed in earlier sections. We will compute the adjusted dispersion matrix by dividing $\mathbf{W}_{y.x}$ by $N_1 + N_2 - c - 2 = 1135$, getting

$$\frac{\mathbf{W}_{y.x}}{1135} = \begin{bmatrix} 0.708611 & 0.205276 \\ 0.205276 & 0.820941 \end{bmatrix}.$$

The inverse of this is

$$\begin{bmatrix} 1.521422 & -0.380430 \\ -0.380430 & 1.313245 \end{bmatrix},$$

so that

$$D^2 = [0.761768, 0406171] \begin{bmatrix} 1.521422 & -0.380430 \\ -0.380430 & 1.313245 \end{bmatrix} \begin{bmatrix} 0.761768 \\ 0.406171 \end{bmatrix} = 0.864103,$$

which is to be evaluated by writing

$$F = \frac{(1139 - 2 - 2 - 1)(0.864103)}{2(0.00355680)(1139 - 2 - 2)} = 121.36.$$

This is to be referred to the F-table with 2 and 1134 degrees of freedom. It is the same value of F and the same numbers of degrees of freedom that we obtained in the preceding section from an application of the T^2-test.

When there are more than two test variables, $\mathbf{d}_{y.x}$ will be a column vector of three or more differences between adjusted group means and $\mathbf{W}_{y.x}$ will be a 3×3 or larger matrix. When there are more than two covariance variables, $\mathbf{d}_x$ will be a column vector of three or more differences between group means on the covariance variables, and $\mathbf{W}_{xx}$ will be a 3×3 or larger matrix.

3. The Λ-test. To apply Wilks's Λ-test in the case of two or more test variables and two or more covariance variables, we need a matrix of adjusted total sums of squares and cross products, analogous to the "within" matrix $\mathbf{W}_{y.x}$ in the preceding sections.

In Table 14 we present the total sums of squares and cross products of both test variables and both covariance variables. In the preceding section we computed the

Table 14 Total sums of squares and cross products for Case IHD

$$\mathbf{T} = \begin{array}{c} \\ y_1 \\ y_2 \\ \\ x_1 \\ x_2 \end{array} \begin{bmatrix} \overset{y_1}{989.6120} & \overset{y_2}{339.4924} & \overset{x_1}{232.5673} & \overset{x_2}{225.0448} \\ 339.4924 & 996.6845 & 198.0130 & 240.4203 \\ \hline 232.5673 & 198.0130 & 2468.0581 & 2157.4504 \\ 225.0448 & 240.4203 & 2157.4504 & 3596.1826 \end{bmatrix}$$

$\mathbf{W}_{y.x}$-matrix from the partitioned $\mathbf{W}$-matrix of all four variables. In an exactly analogous way, using the information in Table 14, we compute

$$\mathbf{T}_{y.x} = \mathbf{T}_{yy} - \mathbf{T}_{yx}\mathbf{T}_{xx}^{-1}\mathbf{T}_{xy},$$

where the terms on the right refer to the submatrices of the T-matrix in Table 14:

$$\mathbf{T} = \begin{bmatrix} \mathbf{T}_{yy} & \mathbf{T}_{yx} \\ \hline \mathbf{T}_{xy} & \mathbf{T}_{xx} \end{bmatrix}.$$

This yields

$$\mathbf{T}_{y.x} = \begin{bmatrix} 967.420471 & 319.977486 \\ 319.977486 & 978.147394 \end{bmatrix}.$$

Then

$$\Lambda = \frac{|\mathbf{W}_{y.x}|}{|\mathbf{T}_{y.x}|} = \frac{10^5(6.951081)}{10^5(8.438942)} = 0.823691.$$

From this we compute

$$F = \frac{1 - \Lambda}{\Lambda} \frac{N - t - c - 1}{t},$$

where $t = 2$ and $c = 2$.

$$F = \frac{1 - 0.823691}{0.823691} \frac{1139 - 2 - 2 - 1}{2} = 121.36.$$

This is to be referred to the F-table with 2 and 1134 degrees of freedom.

These calculations for this two-group case are algebraically equivalent to applying Hotelling's T^2-test or the appropriate adaptation of Mahalanobis' D^2-statistic to the same data.*

For the still more general case where the number k of groups is greater than two, or the number t of test variables is greater than two, or the number c of co-

---

* M. M. Tatsuoka has derived Hotelling's T^2 corrected by covariance for any number c of covariance variables. This derivation is on file with the Educational Research Corporation in Cambridge, Mass. The notation we have employed in the present discussion was suggested by Dr. Tatsuoka.

variance variables is greater than two, or any combination of these extensions, we will still write

$$\mathbf{W}_{y.x} = \mathbf{W}_{yy} - \mathbf{W}_{yx}\mathbf{W}_{xx}^{-1}\mathbf{W}_{xy}$$

and

$$\mathbf{T}_{y.x} = \mathbf{T}_{yy} - \mathbf{T}_{yx}\mathbf{T}_{xx}^{-1}\mathbf{T}_{xy},$$

and use these in the calculation of Λ.

When we had $t = 2$, $\mathbf{W}_{yy}$ was a 2×2 matrix. In the general case it will be a $t \times t$ matrix. Similarly, $\mathbf{T}_{yy}$ will be a $t \times t$ matrix in the upper left-hand corner of the **T**-matrix. Also, $\mathbf{W}_{xx}$ and $\mathbf{T}_{xx}$ will be $c \times c$ matrices in the lower right-hand corners of the **W**- and **T**-matrices, respectively. $\mathbf{W}_{yx}$ and $\mathbf{T}_{yx}$ will be $t \times c$ matrices in the upper right-hand corners of the **W**- and **T**-matrices. Then, finally, $\mathbf{W}_{xy}$ and $\mathbf{T}_{xy}$ will be $c \times t$ matrices in the lower left-hand corners of the **W**- and **T**-matrices, respectively. Thus if $t = 3$ and $c = 4$, the **W**-matrix will be a 7×7 as follows:

$$\mathbf{W} = \begin{bmatrix} \mathbf{W}_{yy} & \mathbf{W}_{yx} \\ \hline \mathbf{W}_{xy} & \mathbf{W}_{xx} \end{bmatrix},$$

in which $\mathbf{W}_{yy}$ is a 3×3, $\mathbf{W}_{yx}$ is a 3×4, $\mathbf{W}_{xy}$ is a 4×3, and $\mathbf{W}_{xx}$ is a 4×4 matrix, regardless of the number of groups. The **T**-matrix will be similarly constructed and similarly partitioned.

Case IIE: Any Number of Groups, Any Number of Test Variables, Any Number of Covariance Variables

For this most general case, only the Λ-test is applicable. When the number k of groups is greater than two, the dimensions of the matrices are still determined by t and c, but with $k > 2$, the within-groups sums of squares and cross products will come from pooling the sums of squares and cross products from more than two groups. And, of course, the **T**-matrix will be computed from all the data from the k groups.

From $\mathbf{W}_{y.x}$ and $\mathbf{T}_{y.x}$ we compute

$$\Lambda = \frac{|\mathbf{W}_{y.x}|}{|\mathbf{T}_{y.x}|}$$

and the Rao approximate F:

$$F = \frac{1 - \Lambda^{1/s}}{\Lambda^{1/s}} \frac{ms - v}{t(k-1)},$$

where

$$m = N - c - 1 - \frac{t+k}{2}, \qquad s = \sqrt{\frac{t^2(k-1)^2 - 4}{t^2 + (k-1)^2 - 5}},$$

$$v = \frac{t(k-1) - 2}{2}.$$

The obtained value of F is to be referred to the F-table with $t(k - 1)$ and $ms - v$ degrees of freedom.

Substituting appropriate values of t, c, and k in the above general treatment will reduce it to one of the particular cases we have discussed. If, for example, k groups are tested on one test variable without covariance adjustment, then $t = 1$, $c = 0$, and $k = k$. Substitution gives

$$m = N - 0 - 1 - \frac{1 + k}{2} = N - 1 - \frac{1 + k}{2},$$

$$s = \sqrt{\frac{(k - 1)^2 - 4}{(k - 1)^2 - 4}} = 1,^* \qquad v = \frac{(k - 1) - 2}{2} = \frac{k - 3}{2}.$$

Then

$$ms - v = N - 1 - \frac{1 + k}{2} - \frac{k - 3}{2} = N - k.$$

Hence

$$F = \frac{1 - \Lambda^{1/s}}{\Lambda^{1/s}} \frac{ms - v}{t(k - 1)} = \frac{1 - \Lambda}{\Lambda} \frac{N - k}{k - 1};$$

this was the Λ for the conventional F-test with k groups, one test variable, without covariance, Case IB, 1.

Or consider the case of two groups, one test variable, one covariance variable. In this case

$$\Lambda = \frac{|\mathbf{W}_{y.x}|}{|\mathbf{T}_{y.x}|},$$

wherein the numerator and denominator are computed as in Case IIA, 5, from data in a table like Table 7. In such a case

$$m = N - c - 1 - \frac{t + k}{2}$$

becomes, with $k = 2$, $t = 1$, $c = 1$,

$$m = N - 1 - 1 - \frac{1 + 2}{2} = N - 2 - \frac{3}{2},$$

and

$$s = \sqrt{\frac{1^2 \cdot 1^2 - 4}{1^2 + 1^2 - 5}} = 1, \qquad v = \frac{1(1) - 2}{2} - \left(-\frac{1}{2}\right).$$

Then

$$ms - v = N - 2 - \tfrac{3}{2} - (-\tfrac{1}{2}) = N - 3,$$

$$t(k - 1) = 1,$$

---

* When $k = 3$ we adduce L'Hôpital's rule. See footnote, p. 74.

and, by substitution,

$$F = \frac{1 - \Lambda^{1/s}}{\Lambda^{1/s}} \frac{ms - v}{t(k - 1)}$$

becomes

$$F = \frac{1 - \Lambda}{\Lambda} \frac{N - 3}{1},$$

which is just the form we arrived at in Case IIA, 5, dealing with this situation.

Substituting $k = 2$ groups, $t = 1$ test variable, and $c = 0$ for no covariance variable reduces this most general test to Fisher's t-test,* discussed in our opening section, Case IA, 1. Each of the other particular tests is similarly contained in the most general Λ-procedure.

ACKNOWLEDGMENTS

A number of people have contributed to the exposition herein presented, and their assistance is greatfully acknowledged. Dr. John E. Murray of the U. S. Naval Training Device Center made numerous and thoughtful suggestions for improving the presentation. Professor M. M. Tatsuoka of the University of Illinois showed how Hotelling's T^2 with covariance adjustment could be treated as a particular case of Wilks's Λ with covariance adjustment. He also suggested the notation used in the latter parts of the treatment. Professor C. R. Rao of the Indian Statistical Institute in Calcutta was helpful in clarifying certain questions about his F-approximation to Wilks's Λ; Professor M. S. Bartlett of the University of Manchester clarified the relation between his approximation and that of C. R. Rao; Professor W. G. Cochran of Harvard University assisted in the exposition of the material on t adjusted by covariance; and Mr. Richard Willard of Massachusetts Institute of Technology suggested sources for some of the material on Wilks's Λ.

While all the above workers contributed to the substance of this exposition, none of them is to be taxed with any responsibility for its deficiencies.

REFERENCES

BARTLETT, M. S., "Multivariate analysis." *J. Roy. Stat. Soc. Supp.* **9,** 76 (1947)

COCHRAN, W. C., and GERTRUDE M. COX, *Experimental Designs (2nd ed.).* New York: John Wiley & Sons, Inc., 1957

FISHER, R. A., "On a distribution yielding the error functions of several well-known statistics." *Proc. Int. Math. Congress,* Toronto, 1924, pp. 805–813

FISHER, R. A., *Statistical Methods for Research Workers.* Edinburgh: Oliver and Boyd

FRAZER, R. A., W. J. DUNCAN, and A. R. COLLAR, *Elementary Matrices.* Cambridge: Cambridge University Press, 1955

HOTELLING, H., "The generalization of Student's ratio." *Ann. Math. Stat.* **2,** 360–378 (1931)

---

* Since $t(\alpha ; n) = \sqrt{F(\alpha ; 1, n)}$.

LINDQUIST, E. F., *Statistical Analysis in Educational Research*. Boston: Houghton Mifflin, 1940

MAHALANOBIS, P. C., "On the generalized distance in statistics." *Proc. Nat. Inst. Sci. (India)* **12,** 49 (1936)

RAO, C. R., *Advanced Statistical Methods in Biometric Research*. New York: John Wiley & Sons, Inc., 1952

RULON, P. J., "Fisher's t-test as a special case of his z-test." *J. Exp. Educ.* **11,** 245–249 (1943)

SNEDECOR, G. W., *Calculation and Interpretation of Analysis of Variance and Covariance*. Ames, Iowa: Collegiate Press, 1934

WERT, J. E., C. O. NEIDT, and J. D. AHMANN, *Statistical Methods in Educational and Psychological Research*. New York: Appleton-Century-Crofts, 1954

WILKS, S. S., "Certain generalizations in the analysis of variance." *Biometrika* **24,** 471–494 (1932)

CHAPTER 3

THE USE OF MULTIVARIATE ANALYSIS OF VARIANCE IN BEHAVIORAL RESEARCH*

R. DARRELL BOCK, *University of Chicago*
ERNEST A. HAGGARD, *University of Illinois*

1. PURPOSE AND SCOPE OF MULTIVARIATE ANALYSIS OF VARIANCE

In recent years there have been remarkable advances in the application of formal methods of statistical inference to multivariate problems. Of foremost importance for behavioral research is the formulation, most recently expounded by Roy and Gnanadesikan (1959), of a complete generalization of analysis of variance to the multivariate case. (See Wilks, 1932, Bartlett, 1947, Tukey, 1949, and Anderson, 1958, for earlier work in this area, and Morrison, 1967, for a recent review.) The practical effect of this development is to make available, to fields of research where many dependent variables must be studied simultaneously, the principles and techniques of experimental design, linear estimation, and tests of hypothesis which have proven so successful in univariate applications.

Typical multivariate problems in behavioral research involve both multiple independent and multiple dependent variables. Some of the independent variables may represent classes or cross classifications of an experimental design. Others may be continuous measurements carrying information about the experimental units (usually subjects). The purpose in applying multivariate statistical analysis to these problems is to determine how and to what extent the independent variables explain or predict the responses of the subjects represented in the dependent variables.

If the dependent variables can be assumed distributed in multivariate normal form, statistical procedures of sufficient scope for this purpose are available in the multivariate generalizations of analysis of variance, and the associated techniques of multiple regression analysis and analysis of covariance. In this chapter we present an expository account of these methods in Sections 2 through 5. In a final

* The final version of this chapter was prepared while the first author was Visiting Professor of Human Development at the University of Chicago. Earlier work was supported in part by Grant M–912 of the National Institute of Mental Health, U.S. Public Health Service, by Grants G–5824 and GB–939 of the National Science Foundation, and by a Public Health Service Career Program Award (NIH–K6-9415) to the second author. We are indebted to Jeremy Finn for programming the calculations of Section 3. Computer time for this purpose was donated by the Computation Center, University of Chicago.

section we refer the reader to some of the literature of more specialized applications of multivariate analysis of variance.

To acquaint the reader with the practical use of multivariate methods, we begin our discussion with an example of their application to a behavioral experiment. The following is based on an unpublished study recently conducted by Daniel and Hall (see Bock, 1965b).

Daniel and Hall compared experimentally the effectiveness of a programmed text in elementary psychology (J. G. Holland and B. F. Skinner, *Analysis of Behavior,* New York: McGraw-Hill, 1961) with a conventional text covering the same content (B. F. Skinner, *Science and Human Behavior,* New York: Macmillan, 1953). Approximately 25 students in general psychology were assigned randomly to each of 24 laboratory and discussion sections. Each of 12 graduate teaching assistants served as instructors for two of these sections. The programmed text was assigned at random to one of each instructor's sections, and the conventional text assigned to the other. All students completed one semester of instructions and study based on the text used in their respective sections. They were then administered a six-part final examination evaluating knowledge of specific content (Parts 1 and 2), knowledge of concepts and principles (Parts 3 and 4), applications (Part 5), and problem solving (Part 6).

A six-variate multivariate analysis of variance was performed using as variables the mean scores of each laboratory section for these six parts of the examination. The analysis took the form appropriate to a 2×12 randomized block design in which the textbooks were the "treatments" and the instructors, the "blocks." The instructors were also classified by sex. A multivariate test of the textbook effect, using the interaction of textbook with instructor within sex as the error term, gave a probability less than 0.005 on the null hypothesis. The hypothesis that the textbooks were equally effective was therefore rejected. An estimate of the difference between the effects of the two textbooks showed the programmed text superior on all six measures of performance in the course. However, when the measures of "knowledge of specific content" were taken as covariates and their effect eliminated statistically from the remaining four measures, no significant difference in test scores measuring knowledge of concepts and principles, applications, and problem solving was demonstrated. This result was interpreted to mean that the students using the programmed text showed better performance in knowledge of concepts and principles, applications, and problem solving because they had better command of the content which these generalizations and applications contained.

This study illustrates the essential features of the design and analysis of an experiment with multiple response variables: The investigators find it necessary to include more than one dependent variable in order to evaluate what they consider the salient objectives of the course. In particular, they wish to cover the possibility that the programmed text better facilitates learning of specific content, while the conventional text is more effective for more general skills such as problem solving.

The design of the experiment (in the technical sense of how the comparisons are arranged in the experimental material and exclusive of the choice of dependent variables) is the same as would have applied in a similar univariate experiment. Indeed, all the principles and techniques of experimental design which have been worked out for univariate experimentation (Fisher, 1949; Quenouille, 1953) also apply when there are multiple dependent variables.

In the statistical analysis the probability, on the null hypothesis, of the observed mean difference between textbooks for all six variables simultaneously is obtained by an exact multivariate test of significance. Although univariate tests, such as F-tests, could be performed on each variable separately, a single probability statement applicable to all variables jointly cannot in general be obtained from the separate F's. Because all six variables have been obtained from the same subjects, they are correlated in some arbitrary and unknown manner, and the separate F-tests are not statistically independent. No exact probability that at least one of them will exceed some critical level on the null hypothesis can be calculated. The multivariate tests, on the other hand, are based on sample statistics which take into account the correlations between variables and have known exact sampling distributions from which the required probabilities can be obtained.

After significant departure from null hypothesis has been demonstrated, the differences between the treatment effects (in this case the textbook effects) are estimated and inspected to determine the direction and relative sizes of the effect on each of the dependent variables. Since all the differences are in the same direction in this example, the interpretation of the effect is especially easy.

Finally, a further analysis is performed to characterize in more detail the treatment effect. The approach used in the example is to determine whether the effect can be attributed entirely to a specified subset of variables in the sense that effect-differences in the remaining variables can be predicted completely by a linear combination of the effects of the specified subset. The statistical procedure for this purpose is the multivariate generalization of analysis of covariance.

In Sections 3, 4, and 5 of this chapter we discuss the essential features of the statistical methods which provide a thorough and exact analysis of a multiple response experiment such as illustrated by the Daniel-Hall study. Before taking up these multivariate methods, however, we must comment on how the necessary computations are to be performed. The modern view of analysis of variance represented by Roy and Gnanadesikan (1959) includes, in addition to the multivariate generalization, a method of solution based on matrix operations. This method applies to any design, complete or incomplete, with proportionate or disproportionate subclass numbers, and with or without concomitant variables. Heretofore, treatises on analysis of variance have devoted many pages to desk-calculator solutions for innumerable special cases and designs. The matrix solution, implemented by electronic computers, makes these tedious special solutions unnecessary. With a suitable system of matrix subroutines incorporated in convenient interpretive language, a completely general multivariate analysis of variance solution can easily be programmed. For any crossed and/or nested design, including all those currently catalogued by Cochran and Cox (1957), a form of solution well suited to computer programming is given in Bock (1963a). A program based on this solution is documented by Bock (1965a). A production version of this program is available from the Biometric Laboratory, University of Miami (Clyde, Cramer, and Sherin, 1966).*

The computations for Section 3 of this chapter were performed using the matrix operations subroutines of the Statistical Laboratory, Department of Education, University of Chicago (Bock and Peterson, 1967); see also Smith, Gnanadesikan, and Hughes (1962) for computational methods in multivariate analysis of variance.

2. THE GENERAL MULTIVARIATE LINEAR MODEL

It is convenient and natural to discuss multivariate models in the language of coordinate geometry. A set of measurements obtained from each subject is called a vector response and may be represented by a boldface lowercase letter which is subscripted to identify it with a subclass or group and a subject within the subclass or group. For example, written as a column, the vector

$$\mathbf{y}_{ijk} = \begin{bmatrix} y_{ijk}^{(1)} \\ y_{ijk}^{(2)} \\ \vdots \\ y_{ijk}^{(p)} \end{bmatrix}$$

represents the p-component vector response of the ith subject in the j, k-subclass of a two-way classification. The corresponding row vector is written $\mathbf{y}'_{ijk}$. The usual rules of vector algebra apply, so that the arithmetic mean of the vector observations in the j, k-cell is the component-by-component sum of the n_{jk} vectors in the cell multiplied by the scalar quantity $1/n_{jk}$:

$$\mathbf{y}_{\cdot jk} = \frac{1}{n_{jk}} \sum_{i=1}^{n_{jk}} \mathbf{y}_{ijk}. \tag{1}$$

The multivariate linear model for analysis of variance designs may also be expressed as a vector sum. Consider the simple case of a two-way design with a classes in the A way of classification and b classes in the B way of classification. A model assuming additivity of main-class effects is:

$$\mathbf{y}_{ijk} = \boldsymbol{\mu} + \boldsymbol{\alpha}_j + \boldsymbol{\beta}_k + \boldsymbol{\epsilon}_{ijk}. \tag{2}$$

---

* Some subroutine systems for matrix computation are: (1) Matrix Operations Subroutines for Statistical Computation, Statistical Laboratory, Department of Education, University of Chicago; (2) STORM system, IBM Federal System Branch, Bethesda, Maryland (see Bargmann, 1965); (3) Matrix Macros, Institute of Science and Technology, University of Michigan; (4) P–STAT; A System of Statistical Programs for the 7090–7094, Computer Center, Princeton University; (5) the matrix operators calculus devised by Beaton (1964), and the System/360 Scientific Subroutine Package of IBM.

The components of the $p \times 1$ vector $\boldsymbol{\mu}$ represent the general mean of each response variable. The component of the $p \times 1$ vectors $\boldsymbol{\alpha}_j$ and $\boldsymbol{\beta}_k$ represent the effect of the jth class of A and the kth class of B, respectively. The components of the random $p \times 1$ vector $\boldsymbol{\epsilon}_{ijk}$ represent discrepancies, or errors, between the observed vector response and the vector sum of the general mean and the main-class effects. $\boldsymbol{\epsilon}_{ijk}$ is assumed to have a multivariate normal distribution with zero mean vector and covariance matrix $\boldsymbol{\Sigma}$. Note that $\boldsymbol{\Sigma}$ does not carry a subscript; this implies that a common (homogeneous) error covariance matrix is assumed in all subclasses. The elements of $\boldsymbol{\Sigma}$ measure the variation and covariation of the sampling errors.

Sometimes the investigator will have other measurements on the subjects which he can combine with the general mean and main-class effects and possibly improve prediction of response. These measurements are the "concomitant" variables. Suppose there are q concomitant variables represented by the $q \times 1$ vector $\mathbf{x}_{ijk}$. Then the model is:

$$\mathbf{y}_{ijk} = \boldsymbol{\mu} + \boldsymbol{\alpha}_j + \boldsymbol{\beta}_k + \boldsymbol{\Gamma}\mathbf{x}_{ijk} + \boldsymbol{\epsilon}^*_{ijk}. \tag{3}$$

The columns of the $p \times q$ matrix $\boldsymbol{\Gamma}$ contain the coefficients of the multiple regression equation for the regression of the respective response variables on the concomitant variables. The error vector $\boldsymbol{\epsilon}^*_{ijk}$ represents discrepancies between the observations and this larger model. The conditional distribution of the errors given $\mathbf{x}_{ijk}$, i.e., the distribution of $\boldsymbol{\epsilon}^*_{ijk}$, is assumed to have mean zero and covariance matrix $\boldsymbol{\Sigma}^*$. Note that $\boldsymbol{\Gamma}$ and $\boldsymbol{\Sigma}^*$ do not carry subscripts; i.e., the regression equations are assumed identical (homogeneity of regressions) and the covariance matrix of the errors equal (homogeneous) in all subclasses. Tests of these assumptions are available (see Bock, 1965b, for a discussion of these tests). Because it represents the effects of conditions in the experiment structured by the investigator, the vector sum $\boldsymbol{\mu} + \boldsymbol{\alpha}_j + \boldsymbol{\beta}_k$ is called the *design* part of the model. The term $\boldsymbol{\Gamma}\mathbf{x}_{ijk}$, which represents the effects of variables measured by the investigator but not under his control, is called the *regression* part of the model.

In a narrower sense than used in the title of this chapter, *multivariate analysis of variance* applies to the design part of the model. Multivariate multiple regression analysis applies to the regression part. And multivariate analysis of covariance applies to both parts jointly. In the following three sections we discuss these analyses in turn. Data from a long-term study of children in the University of Chicago Laboratory School (Haggard, 1957) provide realistic examples of their use and interpretation.

3. MULTIVARIATE ANALYSIS OF VARIANCE

Data for the example to be discussed are scores on tests of achievement in reading, arithmetic, spelling, and language skills obtained from the files of the Records Office, University of Chicago Laboratory School.* For the period from May 1950

---

* We are indebted to Dr. William J. Hicklin, at the time of the study Director of the Records Office of the Laboratory School, University of Chicago, for making these data available.

to May 1955, achievement measured by these tests was followed from the fourth to seventh grade level for pupils in three successive year groups. The number of pupils of each sex in each year group is shown in Table 1.

Table 1 Composition of the Laboratory School Sample

	Year-group			
	1	2	3	Total
Sex: M	18	25	20	63
F	20	20	19	59
Total	38	45	39	122

In the analyses which follow, we make use of the mean of each pupil's scores over the four-year period as the response variable in a sex × year-group design. The scores at each grade level were standardized before the mean scores were computed; that is, within each grade level the scores on the four achievement tests were adjusted to zero mean and unit standard deviation. These scores for grades four through seven were then averaged for each pupil. An analysis of trends in the separate scores over the four grade levels has been reported elsewhere (Bock, 1963b).

3.1 Summary Statistics

The initial stage in the calculations for the multivariate analysis of variance consists of forming the $p \times 1$ vector mean for each subclass and the $p \times p$ matrix of within-subclasses sum of squares and cross products (briefly, "sum of products"). In matrix notation, these summary statistics are represented respectively by

$$\mathbf{y} \cdot_{jk} = \frac{1}{n_{jk}} \sum_{i}^{n_{jk}} \mathbf{y}_{ijk}, \tag{4}$$

and

$$\mathbf{S}_w = \sum_{k}^{b} \sum_{j}^{a} \left(\sum_{i}^{n_{jk}} \mathbf{y}_{ijk}\mathbf{y}'_{ijk} - n_{jk}\mathbf{y} \cdot_{jk}\mathbf{y} \cdot'_{jk} \right). \tag{5}$$
$$p \times p$$

Note that the $p \times p$ matrix product of vectors,

$$\mathbf{y}_{ijk} \qquad \mathbf{y}'_{ijk} ,$$
$$p \times 1 \quad 1 \times p$$

is the multivariate analogue of the square of a variable. If it is substituted for the square in any univariate formula for a sum of squares, the corresponding multivariate formula for sum of products results.

For the example, $p = 4$, $a = 2$, $b = 3$, and the values of n_{jk} are given in Table 1. The vector means, listed in the natural order of subscripts, are shown in Table 2. The within-subclasses sum of products is shown in Table 3.

Table 2   The vector subclass means

Subclass	Subscript	Response variables			
		Reading	Arithmetic	Spelling	Language
Boys: Group 1	11	0.3788	0.3558	−0.0524	−0.1005
Group 2	12	−0.1528	0.1449	−0.3988	−0.4674
Group 3	13	0.1597	0.2410	−0.0810	−0.2718
Girls: Group 1	21	0.0926	−0.0655	0.5566	0.7030
Group 2	22	−0.3183	−0.4191	0.0219	0.0777
Group 3	23	−0.0884	−0.2714	0.0507	0.1745

Table 3   Within-subclasses sum of products (d.f. = 116)

	Reading	Arithmetic	Spelling	Language
Reading	96.0248			
Arithmetic	43.6740	73.0800		
Spelling	43.9524	41.2728	85.1324	
Language	50.8660	50.0888	60.7376	71.3748

3.2 Tests of Multivariate Hypotheses

Before explicitly estimating parameters or, more accurately, functions of parameters in a multivariate linear model, we usually wish to test the statistical significance of discrepancies between the fitted model and the data. When the simple additive model in (2) is assumed, a test of its goodness-of-fit is equivalent to testing for interaction of main-class effects. If the main-effect additive model can be accepted, we usually test also one or more of the main-class effects. If some of the ways of classification have no effect in the data, then the model will be more parsimonious, and subsequent analysis and interpretation simpler if they are ignored. These statistical tests are in most cases a necessary preliminary to estimation. On the assumptions discussed in Section 2, the multivariate analyses of variance provide exact tests of significance for this purpose.

In the same way that tests of hypotheses in the univariate analysis of variance are based on a partition of the total sum of squares, the multivariate tests depend on a partition of the total sum of products. The within-groups sum of products is obtained by subtracting the between-groups sum of products from the total. The between-groups sum of products is partitioned further according to the various effects in the model. The method of calculating the latter partition depends on whether the subclass numbers are equal, proportional to the number of observations in the main classes, or disproportionate.

If the subclass numbers are equal, the partition may be calculated in a simple manner from the vector general mean and the vector means of the A and B main

Table 4 Partition of the between-subclasses sum of products for p-variate observations in a two-way design with $n_{jk} = r$ observations per subclass

Source of variation	Degrees of freedom	Sum of products $(p \times p)$	Expected sum of products
General mean	1	$S_M = abr \mathbf{y}... \mathbf{y}'...$	
A-classification	$a - 1$	$S_A = br \sum_j^a \mathbf{y}_{\cdot j \cdot} \mathbf{y}'_{\cdot j \cdot} - S_M$	$br \sum_j^a (\alpha_j - \alpha_\cdot)(\alpha_j - \alpha_\cdot)' + (a - 1)\Sigma$
B-classification	$b - 1$	$S_B = ar \sum_k^b \mathbf{y}_{\cdot\cdot k} \mathbf{y}'_{\cdot\cdot k} - S_M$	$ar \sum_k^b (\beta_k - \beta_\cdot)(\beta_k - \beta_\cdot)' + (b - 1)\Sigma$
$A \times B$ interaction	$(a - 1)$ $(b - 1)$	$S_E = S_G - S_A - S_B - S_M$	$(a - 1)(b - 1)\Sigma$
Between subclasses	ab	$S_G = r \sum_k^b \sum_j^a \mathbf{y}_{\cdot jk} \mathbf{y}'_{\cdot jk}$	

classes. For the two-way design these means are, respectively,

$$\mathbf{y}... = \frac{1}{ab} \sum_k^b \sum_j^a \mathbf{y}_{\cdot jk}, \qquad \mathbf{y}_{\cdot j \cdot} = \frac{1}{b} \sum_k^b \mathbf{y}_{\cdot jk}, \qquad \text{and } \mathbf{y}_{\cdot\cdot k} = \frac{1}{a} \sum_j^a \mathbf{y}_{\cdot jk}.$$

In terms of these means the partition of the sum of products takes the form shown in Table 4. Note again that formulas in Table 4 differ from those of the univariate case only in that sums of matrix products of vector observations and vector means take the place of sums of squares.

In the case of proportionate subclass numbers, Table 4 can be modified in a manner strictly analogous to the univariate solution for this case (see Winer, 1962, p. 375).

If the subclass numbers are disproportionate, a general regression solution is necessary to obtain the partition (Kempthorne, 1952, p. 79; Graybill, 1961, p. 245). This type of solution is called a nonorthogonal analysis of variance. A method of performing the calculation of a nonorthogonal analysis has recently been described by one of the authors (Bock, 1963a) and will not be repeated here. The calculations for the example discussed in this paper were performed by this method. In practical work, one of the computer programs described in the footnote, Section 1, would be used.

Designs with disproportionate subclass numbers are all too common in behavioral research, and their treatment in nonorthogonal analyses deserves special attention. Because the disproportionality of subclass numbers confounds the main effects, problems arise in the logic of the analysis which are peculiar to the nonorthogonal case. In this type of analysis we must choose the order in which

Table 5 Partition of the between-subclasses sum of products: first order of elimination

Source of variation	Degrees of freedom		Sum of products			
			R	A	S	L
General mean	1	R				
		A		[Identically zero]*		
		S				
		L				
Year-groups, eliminating the general mean	2	R	4.3428		(Symmetric)	
		A	2.2267	1.1893		
		S	4.4569	2.3798	4.7620	
		L	5.0061	2.7322	5.4665	6.3458
Sex, eliminating the general mean and year-group effects	1	R	1.6008		(Symmetric)	
		A	3.5037	7.6687		
		S	−2.6942	−5.8970	4.5346	
		L	−4.1393	−9.0600	6.9668	10.7036
Interaction, eliminating the general mean and main-class effects	2	R	0.0793		(Symmetric)	
		A	−0.0855	0.1054		
		S	−0.0490	0.1724	1.1146	
		L	−0.1205	0.2088	0.7897	0.6549
Between subclasses	6	R	6.0229		(Symmetric)	
		A	5.6449	8.9634		
		S	1.7137	−3.3448	10.4112	
		L	0.7463	−6.1190	13.2230	17.7043

* The sums of products for the general mean are identically zero because the scores at each grade level have been standardized sample.

confounded effects are to be eliminated. For a two-way design there are two possibilities—either the effects of the *A* way of classification can be eliminated from those of the *B* way, thus providing a test of *B* effects unconfounded by *A*— or, conversely, the *B* effects may be eliminated from *A* to obtain an unconfounded test of *A* effects. Both orders of elimination may be carried out on the same data, of course, but the resulting tests of significance will not be independent. A decision *a priori* to consider only one of them is preferable, and in most analyses there is a logical basis for the choice. For example, one of the ways of classification may represent extraneous variation which is known to exist but is of no substantial interest. The effects of such a classification should always be eliminated from those of real interest.

In the sample problem it is the classification by sex which is of interest. The solution for the exact partition, eliminating year-group from sex effects, gives the values shown in Table 5. The within-subclasses sum of products is the same as that shown in Table 3. To demonstrate that this partition is not the same when sex is

Table 6 Partition of the between-subclasses sum of products: second order of elimination

Source of variation	Degrees of freedom		Sum of products			
			R	A	S	L
General mean	1	R				
		A		[Identically zero]*		
		S				
		L				
Sex, eliminating the general mean	1	R	1.2588		(Symmetric)	
		A	3.0181	7.2359		
		S	−2.5476	−6.1079	5.1558	
		L	−3.8478	−9.2252	7.7871	11.7613
Year-group, eliminating the general mean and sex effects	2	R	4.6847		(Symmetric)	
		A	2.7122	1.6221		
		S	4.3103	2.5907	4.1408	
		L	4.7147	2.8974	4.6462	5.2881
Interaction, eliminating the general mean and main-class effects	2	R	0.0793		(Symmetric)	
		A	−0.0855	0.1054		
		S	−0.0490	0.1724	1.1146	
		L	−0.1205	0.2088	0.7897	0.6549
Between subclasses	6	R	6.0228		(Symmetric)	
		A	5.6448	8.9634		
		S	1.7137	−3.3448	10.4112	
		L	0.7464	−6.1190	13.2230	17.7043

* See Table 5.

eliminated from year-group effects, we show the converse partition in Table 6. The interaction sum of products is, of course, the same in both these partitions and its significance may be tested in either. In the absence of interactive effects, the significance of main effects in the linear model may be tested. The sex effect is tested using the sum of products due to sex in the first partition. If the year-group effect were of interest, it would be tested using the corresponding sum of products in the second partition.

3.2.1 Criteria for Statistical Tests

Having obtained a partition of the sum of products appropriate to the hypotheses of interest, we move to the next stage of the calculations and compute criteria for the multivariate tests of hypothesis. Four distinct criteria have been proposed for testing whether two independent p-variate samples have been drawn from the same multivariate normal distribution. In the context of multivariate analysis of variance, one of these "samples" is associated with the degrees of freedom for hypotheses and the other with the degrees of freedom for error. The number of degrees of freedom for each are the respective "sample sizes." For sake of generality, let us suppose there are n_h degrees of freedom for some hypothesis and n_e degrees of freedom for error. Let the corresponding sums of products from the partition of the total sum of products be the $p \times p$ matrices $\mathbf{S}_h$ and $\mathbf{S}_e$. For a test of the effects of the B way of classification in Table 4, for example, $\mathbf{S}_B$ would play the role of $\mathbf{S}_h$, and $\mathbf{S}_E$ that of $\mathbf{S}_e$. The matrices $\mathbf{S}_h$ and $\mathbf{S}_e$ are all that are needed in the computation of the following test criteria.

1. Roy's largest root criterion. Let λ_i be a characteristic value of the matrix $\mathbf{S}_h$ in the metric $\mathbf{S}_e$, and let $\mathbf{a}_i$ be the corresponding characteristic vector. That is, λ_i is a root of the determinantal equation

$$|\mathbf{S}_h - \lambda_i \mathbf{S}_e| = 0, \tag{6}$$

and $\mathbf{a}_i$, a solution of the system of homogeneous equations

$$(\mathbf{S}_h - \lambda_i \mathbf{S}_e)\mathbf{a}_i = 0. \tag{7}$$

Equation (6) will have all real-valued solutions only if $\mathbf{S}_e$ is positive-definite, which will generally be the case if $p \leq n_e$. In other words, the number of variables must not exceed the number of degrees of freedom for error. Let the roots of (6) be put in decreasing order of size. Then the first min (n_h, p) roots will in general be nonzero and any remaining roots will be exactly zero. Roy (1957) suggests the largest root of (6) as a statistic for testing departure from the null hypothesis and gives the null distribution of

$$\theta = \frac{\lambda_1}{1 + \lambda_1}.$$

Percentage points for θ are given by Heck (1960) and by Pillai (1960, 1964, 1966) for the arguments

$$s = \min(n_h, p), \qquad m = \frac{|p - n_h| - 1}{2}, \qquad \text{and} \qquad n = \frac{n_e - p - 1}{2}.$$

Heck and Pillai use the symbol θ_s for θ.

2. Hotelling's trace criterion. Hotelling (1951) suggests the sum of the roots of (6), which equals the trace of $\mathbf{S}_h \mathbf{S}_e^{-1}$, as a multivariate test statistic:

$$\tau = \sum_{i=1}^{s} \lambda_i = \text{trace}\,(\mathbf{S}_h \mathbf{S}_e^{-1}).$$

Pillai (1960) has derived and tabled the null distribution of τ, also for the arguments s, m, and n. Pillai uses the symbol $U^{(s)}$ for τ.

3. Wilks's likelihood ratio criterion. Wilks (1932) gave the likelihood ratio criterion for testing departure from a multivariate hypothesis:

$$\Lambda = \prod_{i=1}^{s} \frac{1}{1 + \lambda_i} = \frac{|\mathbf{S}_e|}{|\mathbf{S}_h + \mathbf{S}_e|}.$$

Excellent approximations to the percentage points of the null distribution of Λ may be obtained from the Chi-square distribution using Bartlett's approximation,

$$\chi_B^2 = -[n_h + n_e - \tfrac{1}{2}(n_h + p + 1)]\log_e \Lambda,$$

as Chi-square on pn_h degrees of freedom (see Anderson, 1958, p. 208). If n_e is small relative to n_h and p, the more accurate F-approximation described by Rao (1952, p. 262) or Jones (1960) should be used.

When $n_h = 1$, all three of these criteria may be referred to the F-distribution for exact percentage points. In particular, Hotelling's T^2 is proportional to τ:

$$T^2 = n_e\tau.$$

Percentage points for T^2 are obtained from the F-distribution using

$$F = (n_e - p + 1)T^2/n_e p,$$

on p and $n_e - p + 1$ degrees of freedom (see Anderson, 1958, p. 109).

When either p or $n_h = 2$, exact percentage points for the null distribution of Λ can be obtained from the F-distribution using relationships given by Rao (1952, p. 260).

Before considering the last of the multivariate test criteria, let us apply the first three to the analysis in Table 5. We test first the hypothesis of no interaction. A standard computer subroutine (see Bock and Peterson, 1967) for characteristic values of a real symmetric matrix in the metric of a positive-definite symmetric matrix gives us the solution of the determinantal equation (6). In this equation, the residual sum of products in Table 3 is $\mathbf{S}_e$, and the sum of products for interaction in Table 5 is $\mathbf{S}_h$. The two nonzero roots obtained are

$$\lambda_1 = 0.0219 \quad \text{and} \quad \lambda_2 = 0.0068.$$

Then

$$\theta = 0.0219/1.0219 = 0.0214,$$
$$\tau = 0.0219 + 0.0068 = 0.0287,$$
$$\Lambda = 1/1.0219 \times 1.006 = 0.97196,$$

and

$$\chi_B^2 = -\left(112 + 2 - \frac{2 + 4 + 1}{2}\right)\log_e 0.97196$$
$$= 3.25.$$

Interpolating in Pillai's tables for the 0.05 critical values of θ and τ with the arguments

$$s = 2, \quad m = \frac{|4 - 2| - 1}{2} = \frac{1}{2}, \quad \text{and} \quad n = \frac{111}{2} = 55\tfrac{1}{2},$$

we obtain approximately $\theta_{0.05} = 0.115$ and $\tau_{0.05} = 0.161$. For χ^2 on $4 \times 2 = 8$ degrees of freedom, Hald's (1952) table gives the 0.05 critical value of 15.5. Thus the data clearly do not contradict the additive main-effect model. We can proceed with a test of the sex effect.

The one nonzero root of the determinantal equation (6) with S_h set equal to the sum of products due to sex in Table 5 and S_e again taken from Table 3 is $\lambda_1 = 0.9556$. Hotelling's T^2 is therefore

$$T^2 = 116 \times 0.9556 = 110.85,$$

and the corresponding F-statistic is

$$F = (116 - 4 + 1) \times 110.58/116 \times 4$$
$$= 27.0$$

on 4 and $(116 - 4 + 1) = 113$ degrees of freedom. The sex effect is highly significant. We will discuss its interpretation in Section 3.3.

4. The step-down test.   In computing Λ as the ratio of the determinants $|S_e|$ and, say, $|S_t| = |S_h + S_e|$, the usual method is to perform the Gauss-Doolittle reduction on S_e and S_t, and obtain the determinants from the product of the pivotal elements (row divisors, pivots) (see Rao, 1952, p. 30; Fox, 1964, p. 62). Call these elements $d_e^{(1)}, d_e^{(2)}, \ldots, d_e^{(p)}$, and $d_t^{(1)}, d_t^{(2)}, \ldots, d_t^{(p)}$, respectively. It has been shown by Roy and Bargmann (1958) that the so-called step-down F-statistics with n_h and $n_e - i + 1$ degrees of freedom,

$$F_i = \frac{n_e(d_t^{(i)} - d_e^{(i)})}{n_h d_e^{(i)}} \qquad (i = 1, 2, \ldots p),$$

are independent under the null hypothesis. (Roy and Bargmann use beta statistics; J. Roy, 1958, uses F.)   Thus, if we adopt the rule that we will reject the null hypothesis if at least one of the step-down F-statistics is significant at an assigned level, we can easily calculate the error of the first kind for the rule. Suppose we so choose the critical value for a particular F_i that the probability of exceeding this value under the null hypothesis is α_i. Then the probability that at least one of these F-statistics will exceed its critical value when the hypothesis is in fact true is

$$\alpha = 1 - (1 - \alpha_1)(1 - \alpha_2) \cdots (1 - \alpha_p).$$

Choosing $\alpha_1, \alpha_2, \ldots,$ and α_p appropriately, we can therefore set α (the error of the first kind of the over-all test) to any conventional value, say 0.05.

The multivariate test of hypothesis obtained in this way gives a unique result only when the order in which the variables are taken in the Gauss-Doolittle reduction, and the critical values, are specified. To make use of the step-down test the investigator must choose this order and assign the critical values to the step-down F-statistics. He should do this according to his priority of interest in the dependent variables. He should place first in the ordering the variables which are crucial to his thesis and assign less extreme critical values to the corresponding step-down F-statistics. He should place last in the ordering the variables of only marginal interest and assign more critical values to the step-down F-statistics. This strategy enables the investigator to include a greater number of variables in his study without

Table 7 Step-down test of the year-group effect

Variables	Univariate F	Degrees of freedom	Step-down F	Degrees of freedom	Critical values	α_i
1. Reading	2.83	2/116	2.83	2/116	4.07	0.02
2. Arithmetic	1.29	2/116	0.13	2/115	4.07	0.02
3. Spelling	2.82	2/116	0.87	2/114	5.56	0.005
4. Language	4.29	2/116	1.32	2/113	5.56	0.005

weakening the power of the multivariate test to detect effects which, *a priori,* he expects to observe in the more crucial variables.

Let us use the step-down test in this way to test the hypothesis of no year-group effects in the example. To the error sum of products from Table 3, we add the sum of products of year-groups from the partition in the second order of elimination (Table 6) to obtain S_t; we perform the Gauss-Doolittle reductions of S_e and S_t, and from the corresponding pivotal elements, obtain the step-down F-statistic in Table 7. (The conventional univariate F-statistics for each variable are also shown in this table.)

The variables enter the step-down analysis of Table 7 in the same order that they appear in previous tables. We might justify this order on the grounds that the teaching of reading and arithmetic are likely to vary more in quality from one teacher to another than would the teaching of spelling and language. (The language test covers only rather mechanical skills of punctuation, capitalization, etc., and has none of the verbal content of the reading test.) Thus the different year-groups, not having had the same teacher in all cases, might be expected to differ in reading and arithmetic skills if they differ at all. On the same reasoning we assign the greater part of the rejection region to the first two variables as shown in Table 7. The Type I error for this choice of critical values is 0.0492. None of the step-down F-statistics are significant according to these values.

Note, however, that if we had fixed on the language test as the variable of primary interest and put it first in the step-down ordering, we would have rejected the null hypothesis. The first step-down F-statistic, which always equals the univariate F-statistic, would then have been significant at 4.29. But since in fact there was no reason to single out the language test for the most sensitive position in the analysis, we can only regard the observed univariate F of 4.29 as the fortuitous result of picking the largest among four F-statistics. (See Dempster, 1963, for an application of step-down analysis to principle components in the sample.)

3.3. Estimation

If the statistical tests of Section 3.2 leave us satisfied that a nontrivial model is tenable for the data, we may proceed to the next stage of the solution—that of estimation. In this stage we calculate the estimates of the parameters, or rather functions of parameters, which fit the model to the data. For most experimental designs the model of interest is the sum of the general mean and main effects as in Eq. (2). We exclude from consideration models in which all interactive effects appear, since they are merely tautologies stating that the subclass mean can be predicted only by the observed mean of that subclass. (An exception is a factorial investigation of a response surface. In this context the interactions represent cross-product terms in the equation for the surface and may have a physical interpretation. See Bose and Carter, 1962.) At the other extreme, a model which consists only of the general mean plus error is excluded because it states that the ways of classification in the design give no information about the subclass means.

For the model of interest, the additive main-effect model, we obtain estimates by the method of least squares. This method yields linear estimators which are unbiased and have the smallest sampling variance of all possible linear unbiased estimates (Graybill, 1961, p. 110). In deriving the least-squares estimators we find that individual effects in the model cannot be estimated without bias, but that certain useful linear functions of the effects can be so estimated (Graybill, 1961, p. 227). The estimable functions of primary interest are so-called "contrasts" of main-class effects. A contrast is defined as any linear combination of effects in which the combining coefficients sum to zero. Thus a difference of two effects with coefficients 1 and -1 is a contrast, as is a deviation between the effect of one class and the mean of the effects of all classes (e.g., $\frac{2}{3}, -\frac{1}{3}, -\frac{1}{3}$). Since in behavioral studies we usually attempt to detect and describe differences between classes, estimation of contrasts is quite satisfactory.

As in the partition of the sum of products, the method of calculating the least-squares estimates depends on whether an orthogonal or nonorthogonal solution is required. In the orthogonal solution the least-squares estimate of, say, the difference between the effects of two main classes is simply the difference of the corresponding main-class vector means. Thus $\alpha_j - \alpha_l$, the difference between the effects of the j and l classes of the A way of classification, is estimated by

$$\mathbf{y}_{\cdot j \cdot} - \mathbf{y}_{\cdot l \cdot}.$$

The sampling covariance matrix of this vector difference is $(2/rb)\, \Sigma$. The matrix Σ may be estimated from the error sum of products in the multivariate analysis of variance divided by the error degrees of freedom, i.e., by $(1/n_e)\, S_e$. The standard error of each component in the vector estimate is therefore the square root of the corresponding diagonal element of this matrix times $\sqrt{2/rb}$. These standard errors may be used to put confidence bounds on individual components in the estimates (Graybill, 1961, p. 241) and certain types of joint confidence bounds for several components (Roy and Gnanadesikan, 1957).

If subclass numbers are disproportionate, a general nonorthogonal least-squares solution is required to obtain the estimates. The version of this solution used to obtain the estimates of the general mean and main-class contrasts shown in Table 9 is given in Bock, 1963a. It entails heavy calculations but they are easily disposed of by machine computation. A complete computer program for multivariate analysis of variance should produce the estimates, and their standard errors, for contrasts which are specified by the user.

The properties of estimates obtained in a nonorthogonal solution differ somewhat from those in the orthogonal solution. In particular:

1) The number of linear functions in the main-effect model which can be estimated is equal to the number of degrees of freedom in the model. This includes one degree of freedom for the general mean plus one less than the number of classes in each way of classification.

2) The number of linear functions to be estimated must be decided beforehand. If additional effects are included in the model and the least-squares estimates recalculated, all the estimates will in general change. For this reason, statistical tests of possible models must precede estimation in the nonorthogonal case.

3) Unlike the analysis of variance, estimation depends only on the number of effects in the model and not on the order in which they appear in the model.

4) In general, the estimates differ from one another in precision, and are correlated. A matrix of variance and covariance factors associated with the estimates is obtained in the course of the nonorthogonal solution. The elements of this matrix times the error variance for a particular variable give the variances or covariances of corresponding contrasts.

Table 8 Linear parametric functions of the main-effect model

Degree of freedom	Estimate	Linear parametric function (expectation of the estimate)	Interpretation
1	$\hat{\theta}_1$	$\mu + \frac{1}{2}(\alpha_1 + \alpha_2) + \frac{1}{3}(\beta_1 + \beta_2 + \beta_3)$	"General mean"
2	$\hat{\theta}_2$	$\alpha_1 - \alpha_2$	Male $-$ female
3	$\hat{\theta}_3$	$\beta_1 - \beta_3$	Year-group 1 $-$ year-group 3
4	$\hat{\theta}_4$	$\beta_2 - \beta_3$	Year-group 2 $-$ year-group 3

The foregoing properties are illustrated by the estimates obtained in the sample problem. Since there is no significant interaction of sex and year-groups, we assume the additive main-effect model and proceed with the least-squares fitting. Four degrees of freedom for estimation are at our disposal; typically we would assign them as shown in Table 8.

Note that the function called "general mean" is a combination of the general effect, μ, and the main-class effects α_j and β_k. It is not interpretable in the presence of main-class effects, but must be included in the model so that the least-squares estimate for each cell in the design can be obtained from the estimated linear parametric functions. For example, the mean of the male, year-group 1 subclass is estimated by

$$\hat{\theta}_1 + \frac{1}{2}\hat{\theta}_2 + \frac{2}{3}\hat{\theta}_3 - \frac{1}{3}\hat{\theta}_4.$$

The expected value of this estimate is $\mu + \alpha_1 + \beta_1$ as required by Eq. (2).

Table 9 Least-squares estimates and standard errors

Linear function	Estimates (standard errors in parentheses)			
	Reading	Arithmetic	Spelling	Language
1. General mean	0.0103 (0.0826)	0.0005 (0.0721)	0.0186 (0.0778)	0.0226 (0.0712)
2. Male − female	0.2297 (0.1652)	0.5028 (0.1441)	−0.3867 (0.1556)	−0.5941 (0.1424)
3. Year-group 1 − year-group 3	0.1983 (0.2075)	0.1624 (0.1810)	0.2698 (0.1954)	0.3535 (0.1789)
4. Year-group 2 − year-group 3	−0.2750 (0.1992)	−0.1186 (0.1737)	−0.1785 (0.1875)	−0.1454 (0.1717)

Table 10 Variance-covariance factors of the estimates

		Estimate			
		1	2	3	4
Estimate	1	0.00825	(Symmetric)		
	2	−0.00046	0.03297		
	3	0.00021	0.00129	0.05200	
	4	−0.00112	−0.00141	0.02559	0.04792

The values of the estimates for the sample problem are shown in Table 9. The standard errors are calculated from the error standard deviations, derived from Table 2, and the variance-covariance factors of the estimates in Table 10. (See Bock, 1963a, for the method of calculating these variance-covariance factors.) For example, the standard error for the sex contrast in reading is

$$\sqrt{96.0248/116} \times \sqrt{0.03297} = 0.1652.$$

The standard error of any linear combination of contrasts can also be obtained from Table 10. The difference between year-group 1 and year-group 2 for language, for example, is estimated by the difference of estimates in Table 9:

$$0.3535 - (-0.1454) = 0.4989.$$

The standard error of this difference is

$$\sqrt{71.3748/116} \times \sqrt{0.05200 + 0.04792 - 2 \times 0.02559} = 0.7844 \times 0.2208 = 0.1732.$$

Relative to its standard error, this difference is the largest simple contrast anywhere in the data and in isolation would be clearly significant. Nevertheless, the comprehensive multivariate tests (e.g., the step-down test in Table 7) show that the year-group effects are not significant, illustrating that conventional univariate tests cannot safely be applied to a difference picked out of multivariate data *because it is observed to be large.*

The significant sex contrast has some interesting substantive interpretations. As an aid to interpretation, it is helpful to remove arbitrary units of measurement from the contrast by standardizing its components. This is done by dividing each component by the error standard deviation of the corresponding variable. The standardized sex contrast is

$$0.2297/\sqrt{96.0248/116} = 0.2525,$$

$$0.5028/\sqrt{73.0800/116} = 0.6335,$$

$$-0.3867/\sqrt{85.1324/116} = -0.4514,$$

$$-0.5941/\sqrt{71.7348/116} = -0.7574.$$

The sex effect is evidently a difference in the achievement "profiles" of the two groups. The boys are superior in reading and arithmetic, the girls, in spelling and language. The difference is most pronounced in arithmetic and language. As indicated in the description of the data, these results apply to the average performance of the subjects in fourth through seventh grade. As a matter of interest, we performed the same analysis at each grade level. A similar significant sex effect was found at each level, but the contrast was not as great in the fourth grade. Although these effects are undoubtedly due in part to the special population represented by children who attended the University of Chicago Laboratory school, when the data were collected, there is other evidence of sex difference in achievement, especially where arithmetic or other mathematical skills are involved (Aiken, 1960).

3.3.1 Discriminant Functions

Two-group and multiple-group methods of linear discriminant analysis are now familiar in many fields of behavioral science (Rao, 1952, p. 370; Cooley and Lohnes, 1962; Jones and Bock, 1960; Tatsuoka and Tiedeman, 1954). These procedures determine the coefficients of the linear combination of variables which best discriminates between groups of subjects, in the sense that the between-groups sum of squares is a maximum with respect to the within-groups sum of squares. The combination of variables obtained in this way is called a discriminant function and may be used to select or classify subjects for educational, industrial, military, or other purposes.

The formal equivalent of discriminant analysis can also be incorporated in multivariate analysis of variance. In this context it is used primarily as an aid in characterizing differences between groups, rather than as a device for classifying subjects. The analysis determines the linear combination of variables most sensitive to departure from the null hypothesis, in the sense that the sum of squares for hypothesis for the combination is a maximum with respect to the sum of squares for error. The calculation involves the same equation (7) which appears in the multivariate tests of hypotheses. The coefficients of the required linear combination are the elements of the characteristic vector a_1 corresponding to the largest characteristic value, λ_1. Note that when the sum of squares for hypothesis refers to between-groups variation in a one-way classification, this characteristic vector contains the coefficients of a conventional "discriminant function." We will use the same term to describe the function derived from any sum of products for hypothesis. For example, the discriminant function for the sex effect in the sample problem is

$$\nu_{\text{sex}} = -0.4758R - 1.3806A - 0.2619S + 2.0358L.$$

It is apparent that this function acts primarily as a contrast between arithmetic scores and language scores. The numerical value of the function tends to be negative for boys and positive for girls. The sense is arbitrary, of course; all the signs could be changed. In calculating the coefficients, it is conventional to set a scale constant so that the error variance of the discriminant score is unity. Thus, if the function is applied to the sex contrast in Table 9, its value represents the number of within-groups standard deviations separating the mean discriminant scores of the two sexes. This value is -1.9117. The function is evidently a powerful detector of the sex effect—much more so than any one of the variables taken separately.

The interpretation of discriminant function coefficients raises problems similar to those encountered in the interpretation of multiple regression coefficients. Comparison of their magnitudes requires that the variables be in standard form analogous to beta weights in regression equations. This form is obtained by multiplying each coefficient by the error standard deviation of the respective variable. For example, the standardized coefficients for the discriminator of the sex effect are calculated using the standard deviations in Table 13 (Section 4.1):

$$R: \quad -0.4758 \times 0.9098 = -0.4329,$$
$$A: \quad -1.3806 \times 0.7937 = -1.0958,$$
$$S: \quad -0.2619 \times 0.8567 = -0.2244,$$
$$L: \quad 2.0358 \times 0.7844 = 1.5970.$$

These coefficients are in the form which applies to the standardized contrasts of Section 3.3.

Even when standardized, the coefficients of the discriminant functions do not always reflect closely the direction or magnitude of effects in corresponding variables. For example, if two variables are highly correlated and show similar values in the standardized contrast, the function will treat the variables effectively as one, and divide the weight between them. On the other hand, if a single variable with a contrast of the same magnitude is unrelated to other variables, it will take all the weight and show a larger coefficient. In other instances a variable may act as an "error-suppressor"; that is, it will contribute to discrimination primarily by removing error from another variable. Hence, a suppressor variable may have an algebraic sign in the discriminant function contrary to that of the component for the same variable in the standardized contrast. Finally, like regression coefficients, all the discriminant function coefficients change in value if a variable is added or deleted from the analysis. It therefore cannot be assumed that a discriminant function may be abbreviated merely by dropping variables with small coefficients. Instead, the function must be recomputed with the fewer number of variables. A statistical test of whether an additional variable should be added to or dropped from the discriminant function is provided by the step-down analysis.

In the step-down ordering the variable in question is placed after the variables already in the function. If the step-down F-statistic for this variable is significant, the variable is worth adding to or retraining in the function in the sense that it significantly decreases the likelihood ratio criterion associated with the function (see Rao, 1952, p. 252).

3.3.2 Canonical Representation

When the number of degrees of freedom for an effect is greater than one, but fewer than the number of variables, departure from the null hypothesis can occur in as many dimensions as there are degrees of freedom. It is sometimes useful to have a representation of the effects in this space, since its dimension is often much smaller than the number of variables. Coordinates of the estimated effects in such a representation can be calculated from the multiple discriminant functions defined by the characteristic vectors corresponding to all nonzero roots in Eq. (6) (Rao, 1952, p. 364). This amounts to setting the first reference axis of the space in the direction where variation due to departure from the null hypothesis is maximal. The second axis is then set in a direction orthogonal to the first, relative to the error metric, in which departure from the null hypothesis is again maximal. The third is set in a direction orthogonal to the first two in which variation is maximal, and so on, for as many axes as there are degrees of freedom for hypothesis.

The linear combinations of the variables calculated with the discriminant functions and represented on these axes are called "canonical variates." By construction, they are uncorrelated and have unit error variance in the sample. When the discriminant functions are applied to the contrasts associated with each degree of freedom for hypothesis, a canonical representation of the contrasts is obtained which may be depicted graphically.

For example, the discriminant functions for the year-group effects in the sample problem are

$$\nu_{\text{year-groups, 1}} = \quad 0.3374R - 0.4092A + 0.0636S + 1.2044L,$$

$$\nu_{\text{year-groups, 2}} = -1.1628R - 0.3738A - 0.7681S + 1.9424L.$$

Applied to the contrasts of Table 9, these functions give the following values of the canonical variates.

	First canonical variate	Second canonical variate
Year-group 1 − year-group 3	0.4434	0.1881
Year-group 2 − year-group 3	−0.2307	0.2188

The third possible contrast with group 3, viz., group 3 minus group 3, is identically zero and is implicit in the origin of the coordinate system. Thus the canonical representation of the three groups in Fig. 1 consists of the origin and the two points specified by the above coordinates.

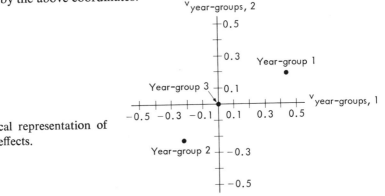

Fig. 1. Canonical representation of the year-group effects.

Conceivably, departure from the null hypothesis could be confined to fewer dimensions than are possible according to the number of degrees of freedom for hypothesis. For example, two or more points representing contrasts might fall in a straight line through the origin, in which case we would say that the departure is "collinear." Three or more points might occupy a plane including the origin and we would say the departure is "coplanar." And so on. Variation in the remaining dimensions will almost always be present, of course, but may be small enough to be attributed to error variation. An approximate test of the hypothesis that deviation from collinearity, coplanarity, etc., is due to error is obtained by applying one of the criteria of Section 3.2.1 to variation remaining after eliminating variation due to one or more of the canonical variates (Bartlett, 1951; Rao, p. 370). For example, the χ^2-approximation for the distribution of Wilk's criterion can be partitioned into a part due to the first $r < s$ canonical variates, say, and a remainder (see Table 11).

Table 11   Test of residual canonical variation

Source of variation	Degrees of freedom	χ^2
Due to the first r canonical variates	$r(p + n_h - r)$	$-\left(n_e + n_h - \dfrac{n_h + p + 1}{2}\right) \displaystyle\sum_{i=1}^{r} \log_e \dfrac{1}{1 + \lambda_i}$
Residual	$(p - r)(n_h - r)$	$-\left(n_e + n_h - \dfrac{n_h + p + 1}{2}\right) \displaystyle\sum_{i=r+1}^{s} \log_e \dfrac{1}{1 + \lambda_i}$
Total	pn_h	$-\left(n_e + n_h - \dfrac{n_h + p + 1}{2}\right) \displaystyle\sum_{i=1}^{s} \log_e \dfrac{1}{1 + \lambda_i}$

For the year-group effects in the sample problem, the total χ^2, calculated by the method of Section 3.2.1, was 10.11 on 8 degrees of freedom. The residual χ^2 is 1.11 on 3 degrees of freedom. Since there is no clear evidence of year-group effect in the data, the variation associated with the second characteristic value could not be expected to be significant, and it is not. Had the total χ^2 been significant, and the residual not significant, we would consider the effect significant but unidimensional. In this case, a plot of the positions of the group on axis 1 of Fig. 1 would have sufficed to represent the group differences. The purpose of the canonical analysis is to produce such a simplified representation whenever possible.

4. MULTIVARIATE MULTIPLE REGRESSION ANALYSIS

Many multivariate studies include independent variables other than those represented in the experimental design. These "concomitant" variables carry information about the subjects in the form of measurements, but, unlike the experimental variables, they cannot be set at prearranged values. If only a few concomitant variables are involved, there are advantages to grouping the scores in a number of evenly spaced levels and incorporating the levels in ways of classification in the design. By this device (1) a separate analysis of regression is avoided; (2) the interactions between levels of the concomitant variables and the experimental classes can be tested as a check on the homogeneity of regression (see Section 4.4 for a discussion of the importance of these tests); and (3) orthogonal polynomials can be employed to facilitate the regression analysis of possible curvilinear relationships between the dependent and concomitant variables (Graybill, 1961, Chapter 8; Fisher, 1958, p. 147). Provided four or five levels are used for each variable, the loss of efficiency due to grouping the scores is usually not appreciable (Feldt, 1958).

4.1 The Multivariate Regression Model

In the event the concomitant variables cannot be incorporated in ways of classification, the multivariate multiple regression analysis may be used to study their relationship to the dependent variables. In matrix notation this analysis takes a form which is an obvious generalization of the usual univariate multiple regression analysis (see Anderson, 1958, p. 179). Let the scores of N subjects for p dependent variables be represented by the $N \times p$ matrix $\mathbf{Y}$, and for q independent variables by the $N \times q$ matrix $\mathbf{X}$. Then the linear relationship between the two sets of variables may be represented by the matrix equation

$$\mathbf{Y} = \mathbf{X}\mathbf{\Gamma}' + \mathbf{E}.$$

The columns of the $q \times p$ matrix $\mathbf{\Gamma}'$ are the multiple regression coefficients of the regression of the dependent variables in the corresponding column of $\mathbf{Y}$ on the independent variables represented in $\mathbf{X}$. The matrix $\mathbf{E}$ contains the deviations from regression. Rows of $\mathbf{E}$ are assumed independent, but elements within rows of $\mathbf{E}$ are assumed distributed in multivariate normal form with mean vector $\mathbf{0}$ and covariance matrix $\mathbf{\Sigma}$.

Table 12 Partition of the total sum of squares for the regression analysis

Source of variation	Degrees of freedom	Sum of products	Expected sum of products
Regression	$n_h = q$	$\mathbf{S}_h = \mathbf{R}_{yx}\mathbf{R}_x^{-1}\mathbf{R}_{xy}$	$\mathbf{\Gamma'R}_x\mathbf{\Gamma} + q\mathbf{\Sigma}$
Residual	$n = N - q - 1$	$\mathbf{S}_e = \mathbf{R}_y - \mathbf{R}_{yx}\mathbf{R}_x^{-1}\mathbf{R}_{xy}$	$(N - q - 1)\mathbf{\Sigma}$
Total	$N - 1$	$\mathbf{R}_y$	

In the field of psychometrics there is a long-standing precedent for expressing regression models in terms of variables standardized in the sample. The computations for the regression analysis may then be performed with correlations, rather than sums of products. Because they are all in the same scale, the correlations are better conditioned for hand calculation when the same number of decimal places must be retained throughout. The same advantage holds for fixed-point calculation in computers, but not for floating-point calculation in which each number is scaled separately. In this section we follow psychometric precedent and formulate the regression analysis in terms of the $p \times p$ correlation matrix for the dependent variables, the $q \times q$ correlation matrix for the independent variables, and the $q \times p$ matrix of intercorrelations between the two sets of variables. Call these matrices $\mathbf{R}_y$, $\mathbf{R}_x$, and $\mathbf{R}_{xy}$; call the $p \times q$ transpose of the latter, $\mathbf{R}_{yx}$. In terms of these matrices the estimate of the matrix of standardized regression coefficients, say, $\mathbf{\Gamma}^0$, is

$$\hat{\mathbf{\Gamma}}^0 = \mathbf{R}_{yx}\mathbf{R}_x^{-1}.$$

Like the estimated effects in the design model, this is the unbiased, minimum variance estimate of $\mathbf{\Gamma}^0$.

As a preliminary to any interpretation or use of the fitted regression model, we may wish to test the hypothesis that no linear relationships actually exist between the two sets of variables, that is, the hypothesis $\mathbf{\Gamma}^0 = \mathbf{0}$. Multivariate tests of this hypothesis may be formulated in terms of sums of products partitioned from the total sum of products of the dependent variables. The formulas for this partition, expressed in terms of correlation matrices, are shown in Table 12. The statistical criteria of Section 3.2.1 applied to the sum of products $\mathbf{S}_h$ and $\mathbf{S}_e$ in Table 12 provide the required tests of the hypothesis $\mathbf{\Gamma}^0 = \mathbf{0}$.

Table 13 Error correlation matrix and standard deviations for the sample problem ($N - 1 = 116$)

	Reading	Arithmetic	Spelling	Language
Reading	1.0000			(Symmetric)
Arithmetic	0.5214	1.0000		
Spelling	0.4861	0.5233	1.0000	
Language	0.6144	0.6935	0.7792	1.0000
S.D.	0.9098	0.7937	0.8567	0.7844

Table 14 Analysis of regression of standardized variables for the sample data

1. Variance-covariance factors of the estimated regression coefficients (inverse of the independent variable correlation matrix)

	R	A
R	1.3773	(Symmetric)
A	−0.7160	1.3733

2. Standardized regression coefficients

		Dependent variables	
		S	L
Independent	R	0.2929	0.3472
variables	A	0.3705	0.5125

3. Sum of products for regression (d.f. = 2)

	S	L
S	0.3363	(Symmetric)
L	0.4370	0.5688

4. Residual sum of products (d.f. = 114)

	S	L
S	0.6637	(Symmetric)
L	0.3422	0.4312

To illustrate this part of the analysis let us regard the reading and arithmetic tests in the sample data as the independent variables, and the spelling and language tests as the dependent variables. We may then examine linear relationships between these sets of variables by applying the regression analysis to the within-subclasses sum of products in Table 3. In this case the degrees of freedom for the total sum of products in Table 12 equals the within-subclasses degrees of freedom, n_e. A general multivariate regression program performs the necessary calculations.* The program first converts the error sum of products to the correlations in Table 13. It then computes the inverse of independent variable correlation matrix, the regression coefficients, the sum of products for regression, and the sum of products for residual shown in Table 14. Since the calculations are performed on correlation matrices, the regression coefficients are in standard form and the diagonal elements of the regression sum of products are the multiple correlation coefficients for the respective dependent variables. Table 14 shows that the prediction of scores on the language skills test by reading and arithmetic scores is substantially better than prediction of spelling scores. The respective multiple correlation coefficients are $\sqrt{0.5688} = 0.7542$ and $\sqrt{0.3363} = 0.5799$. Note that the standardized coefficients for the regression equations are all positive, but that the arithmetic test contributes the greater part of the weight, especially in the prediction of language scores.

---

* Calculations in this section were performed by a General Precision LGP-30 using a program by Spiegel and Bock (1962).

Apparently the tasks of punctuation, capitalization, grammar, etc., in the language skills test require abilities more similar to those required by arithmetic than to the verbal tasks in the reading test.

The sampling variances and covariances of the standardized regression coefficients depend on factors which are given in the inverse of the correlation matrix of independent variables. When multiplied by the estimated error variance of one of the dependent variables, the inverse matrix becomes the sampling covariance matrix of the coefficients for that particular dependent variable. Obtaining the standard error of a coefficient, or of a linear combination of coefficients, is thus a simple matter. For example, the standard error of the coefficient 0.2929 in the equation for spelling is

$$\sqrt{1.3733 \times 0.4312/114} = \sqrt{0.005195} = 0.02279.$$

Similarly, the standard error of the difference of the coefficients in this equation predicting language scores is

$$\sqrt{[1.3733 + 1.3733 + 2(-0.7160)] \times 0.4312/114]} = \sqrt{0.004973} = 0.07052.$$

Thus the hypothesis that the coefficients are equal may be tested by the t-statistic with 114 degrees of freedom:

$$\frac{0.5125 - 0.3472}{0.0705187} = 2.344.$$

Since this value of t exceeds the 0.05 level, the hypothesis is rejected. Other examples of tests of regression coefficients are described by Rao (1952, p. 104).

4.2. Canonical Correlation

To obtain criteria for the multivariate tests of association between the dependent and independent variables, the program solves the equations

$$(\mathbf{R}_{yx}\mathbf{R}_x^{-1}\mathbf{R}_{xy} - r_i^2\mathbf{R}_y)\, \mathbf{a}_i = 0, \tag{8}$$

where the r_i^2 are the roots of the determinantal equation

$$|\mathbf{R}_{yx}\mathbf{R}_x^{-1}\mathbf{R}_{xy} - r_i^2\mathbf{R}_y| = 0. \tag{9}$$

The characteristic values r_i^2 are the squares of the so-called "canonical correlation" coefficients of Hotelling (1936). The test criteria can be expressed in terms of these squared correlation coefficients as follows.

1) *Roy's* (*largest root*) *criterion:*

$$\theta_1 = r_1^2$$

2) *Hotelling's criterion.* Pillai (1960) tables this criterion as the sum of the squared canonical correlations, for which he uses the symbol $V^{(s)}$:

$$V^{(s)} = r_1^2 + r_2^2 + \cdots + r_s^2.$$

The tabular arguments for these criteria in Heck's (1960) nomographs and Pillai's (1960) tables are

$$s = \min(p, q), \qquad m = \frac{|p - q| - 1}{2}, \qquad n = \frac{N - p - q - 2}{2}.$$

3) *Wilks's criterion* is

$$\Lambda = \prod_{i=1}^{s} (1 - r_i^2),$$

and Bartlett's χ^2-approximation takes the form:

$$\chi^2 = -[(N - 1) - \tfrac{1}{2}(p + q + 1)] \log_e \Lambda,$$

with pq degrees of freedom (Bartlett, 1947).

4) Finally, for the step-down test, the Gauss-Doolittle reduction is carried out on the matrices $S_e = R_y - R_{yx} R_x^{-1} R_{xy}$ and $S_t = R_y$. The degrees of freedom of the ith step-down F-statistic are q and $N - i - q$ (see Section 3.2.1).

For the sample problem the canonical correlation program gives, as roots of (9),

$$r_1^2 = 0.56895, \qquad r_1^2 = 0.00150.$$

The multivariate test criteria are

$$\theta_1 = 0.56895 \qquad V^{(s)} = 0.56895 + 0.00150 = 0.57045,$$

with

$$s = 2, \qquad m = \frac{|2 - 2| - 1}{2} = -\frac{1}{2}, \qquad \text{and} \qquad n = \frac{116 - 2 - 2 - 2}{2} = 55;$$

and

$$\chi^2 = \left(116 - \frac{2 + 2 + 1}{2}\right) \log_e (0.43105 \times 0.99850) = 95.69$$

with $2 \times 2 = 4$ degrees of freedom.

The 0.05 points of these statistics are 0.075, 0.089, and 9.48, respectively. The step-down F-statistics are

S	L
28.9	30.6

with $2/114$ and $2/113$ degrees of freedom.

The evidence against the hypothesis $\Gamma^0 = 0$ is clear; the spelling and language scores are substantially associated with the reading and arithmetic scores. The relationship between the two sets appears to be unidimensional, however, for the second canonical correlation is near zero. This also is evident when the step-down F-statistics are computed in the other order:

L	S
74.5	0.11.

The fact that the step-down F for spelling is now well below expectation shows that the relationship between the spelling scores and the reading and arithmetic scores is eliminated when the language scores are held fixed. The relationship between the two sets of variates can be attributed entirely to variation represented in the language scores. In mental test terminology, the two sets of tests have only one factor in common.

The step-down F-statistics have an interpretation in terms of partial correlation coefficients. The first F-statistic tests the hypothesis that the coefficient of correlation of the observed spelling scores and the scores predicted by the regression equation for spelling is drawn from a population in which the correlation is zero. The second F-statistic tests a similar null hypothesis for the partial correlation of the observed and predicted language scores, given the spelling scores. Both of these correlations are obviously significant.

The canonical correlation coefficients are the product-moment correlation coefficients of maximally correlated linear combinations of the two sets of variables (see Anderson, 1958, p. 288). The coefficients of the linear combination of dependent variables are given by the characteristic vector, $\mathbf{a}_i$, obtained in the solution of (8). The coefficients for the independent variables are derived from them by the transformation

$$\mathbf{b}_i = \lambda_i^{1/2} \mathbf{R}_x^{-1} \mathbf{R}_{xy} \mathbf{a}_i.$$

For the sample data, the standard score combinations of the two sets of variables with the squared correlation of 0.5690 are

$$0.4594R + 0.6804A \quad \text{and} \quad -0.0278S + 1.0216L.$$

The combinations with squared correlation of 0.0015 are

$$-1.0780R + 0.9541A \quad \text{and} \quad -1.5950S + 1.2259L.$$

The first of these functions represents the relationship of variation in the language scores to variation in the reading and arithmetic scores, especially the latter. The second function relates contrasts between reading and arithmetic in one set and spelling and language in the other. (See Meredith, 1964, for further discussion of the interpretation of canonical correlation functions.)

4.3. Multivariate Stepwise Regression Analysis

Although canonical correlation analysis is useful for testing association between the two sets of variables and assessing the dimensionality of linear relationships, it seldom indicates clearly the contribution of individual variables to these relationships. A better technique for this purpose is a multivariate generalization of stepwise regression analysis. Stepwise procedures are widely used in univariate multiple regression analysis (i.e., regression problems with one dependent variable) to determine whether the addition of a given independent variable to the regression equation significantly improves prediction (Wherry, 1940; Efroymson, 1960). A similar procedure applied to multiple dependent variables and employing step-down F-tests as the multivariate test criterion provides a revealing method of examining linear relationships between two sets of variables (Spiegel and Bock, 1963; Spiegel, 1964). Other multivariate test criteria are also suitable. Kabe (1963) suggests the use of Wilks's criterion.

The calculations required for multivariate stepwise regression are simple to describe.* Suppose that i independent variables have already been included in the regression. The sum of products for the residual is then, say,

$$\mathbf{S}_e^{(i)} = \mathbf{R}_y - \mathbf{R}_{yx}^{(i)} [\mathbf{R}_x^{(i)}]^{-1} \mathbf{R}_{xy}^{(i)} .$$
$$p \times p \quad p \times p \quad p \times i \quad i \times i \quad i \times p$$

The independent variable $i + 1$ is then added to the regression and the residual sum of squares is recomputed:

$$\mathbf{S}_e^{(i+1)} = \mathbf{R}_y - \mathbf{R}_{yx}^{(i+1)} [\mathbf{R}_x^{(i+1)}]^{-1} \mathbf{R}_{xy}^{(i+1)} .$$
$$p \times p \quad p \times p \quad p \times (i+1) \quad (i+1) \times (i+1) \quad (i+1) \times p$$

For the test of any significant contribution which the $i + 1$ independent variable has made to prediction of the dependent variables, the step-down F-statistics are computed as in Section 3.2.1, with $\mathbf{S}_e^{(i+1)}$ in place of $\mathbf{S}_e$, and $\mathbf{S}_e^{(i)}$ in place of $\mathbf{S}_t$. The jth step-down F-statistic in this case has 1 and $N - i - j$ degrees of freedom. If at least one of the p step-down F-statistics is significant at a preassigned level, the $i + 1$ independent variable is accepted in the regression. Furthermore, if the investigator has arranged dependent variables in order of their importance, he can determine from the step-down F-statistics whether the contribution of the $i + 1$ variable to regression is confined to the more important variables, or whether it also extends to the remaining variables after the regression accounted for by the more important variables has been eliminated. In other words, the multivariate stepwise regression analysis serves the same purpose as a partial correlation analysis.

We can illustrate the technique in a small way with the sample data. The step-down F-statistics corresponding to the first independent variable and the partial contribution of the second are:

	S	L	
R	35.6	25.9	d.f. 1/116; 1/115,
A	17.2	29.0	d.f. 1/115; 1/114.

These large F-statistics show that the contribution of the arithmetic tests to prediction of the dependent variables jointly is definitely significant. Since we know that the relationship between the two sets of variables most strongly involves arithmetic and language, however, it is of interest to examine the contributions to prediction in the other order. The step-down F-statistics for the order A, R in the independent variables and L, S in the dependent are:

	L	S	
A	106.6	0.2	d.f. 1/116; 1/115,
R	23.2	0.1	d.f. 1/115; 1/114.

---

* The program of Spiegel and Bock, 1963, actually uses a more efficient computation method which does not require recalculating the inverse matrix at each stage.

Reading clearly improves prediction of the dependent variables jointly. However, the contribution to prediction of the spelling scores is not significant when variation predicted in the language scores is eliminated. In terms of partial correlations, this means that the partial correlation of reading and spelling scores given the arithmetic and language scores is not significantly different from zero. Similarly, the small value for the step-down F for spelling, as predicted by arithmetic alone, indicates that the partial correlation of spelling and arithmetic given the language scores is not significant.

It is important to understand that a significant improvement in prediction contributed by an independent variable does not necessarily imply that the variable is measuring a new factor of individual differences. If the measures of the independent variables are unreliable, the addition of another variable may improve prediction merely by producing a composite measure of greater reliability. This phenomenon is identical with the well-known improvement in validity which results from increasing the length of a mental test (Gulliksen, 1950). Other effects on regression of measurement error in the independent variables are discussed in Lord (1963) and Madansky (1959).

When there are a number of independent and dependent variables, the multivariate stepwise regression analysis can be used less formally to find a sort of "kernel" of variables which carry most of the relationship between the two sets. This is done by rearranging the order of variables in both sets until the large step-down F-statistics are concentrated in the upper left-hand corner of the table of step-down F-statistics. If there are variables which show no significant step-down F's in rows at the bottom or columns at the right, they may be excluded. The variables remaining constitute the kernel. Indeed, this process can be mechanized in a computer program to provide a multivariate generalization of the Wherry-Doolittle technique.

4.4. Testing Homogeneity of Regression

In applying regression analysis to the within-subclasses sum of products, we have assumed that the same regression equation was appropriate for deviation about the mean to each subclass of the design. If this is true, the analysis based on the within-subclasses sum of products gives the best estimate of the common regression equation. It is possible, however, that the various combinations of experimental conditions represented by the subclasses affect the slopes of the regression planes as well as their elevations, so that a common equation cannot be assumed. If there is any question, the homogeneity of regression within the subclasses can be tested statistically. The test consists of (1) computing the pooled sum of products of deviations from regressions computed separately for each of the n subclasses in the design, and (2) using one of the multivariate criteria of Section 3.2.1 to test the hypothesis that this sum of products and the within-subclasses sum of products are drawn from the same population. The former sum of products, with $n_e - n$ degrees of freedom, is the matrix $\mathbf{S}_e$ of Section 3.1.2, and the latter, with n_e degrees of freedom, is $\mathbf{S}_t$. The univariate version of this test is discussed by Williams (1959, Chapter 8).

The multivariate version has recently been illustrated by Bock (1965b), and need not be repeated here.

The assumption of homogeneous regression of the dependent on the concomitant variables in each subclass of the experimental design is an essential part of the analysis of covariance technique presented in the next section. With biological data, this assumption is usually accepted without question when analysis of covariance is discussed (e.g., Anderson and Bancroft, 1952, Chapter 21). With behavioral data the assumption is more questionable and a preliminary verification of it is usually recommended (Walker and Lev, 1953, Chapter 14). In the following section we consider the case where the assumption is warranted and the multivariate generalization of analysis of covariance can proceed.

5. MULTIVARIATE ANALYSIS OF COVARIANCE

We now assume the complete multivariate linear model including both the regression and design parts. In the first stage of the analysis under this model (Section 5.1) we test whether some or all of the effects in the design part significantly improve the prediction of the subclass means provided by the regression part. If so, we estimate linear functions of these effects in the second stage (Section 5.2) and thus complete the fitting of the full model.

The results of an analysis of covariance depend on the extent to which correlation of the concomitant and the dependent variables is concentrated in the errors or in the effects of the experimental conditions. If the concomitant variable is correlated appreciably with the errors, but little or not at all with the effects, the analysis of covariance increases the power of the statistical tests to detect effect differences. In other words, the concomitant variable acts as a so-called "suppressor" variable. In a behavioral experiment in which, for example, experimental and control groups of subjects are compared, the major source of error in the comparison of the group means is usually the individual differences among subjects. Introducing a "pretest" as a concomitant variable is a common method of eliminating some of this error.

If the concomitant variable is correlated with the experimental effects as much or more than with the errors, the analysis of covariance will show that the effect observed in the dependent variable can be largely accounted for by the concomitant variable. This is the result looked for when we introduce the concomitant variable in the experiment as a possible explanatory variable. The study by Daniel and Hall described in Section 1 is an example of analysis of covariance applied for this purpose. The difference in the effects of the two text books on the subjects' achievement in knowledge of principles, applications, and problem-solving in general psychology was eliminated when knowledge of specific content was used as the concomitant variable.

It is frequently assumed that when pretest scores are available, individual differences can be eliminated and the usual requirement of random assignment of the subjects to the experimental and control groups relaxed. Actually, this is true only if all individual differences in the "posttest," i.e., the dependent variable, are represented in the concomitant variable. In mental test terminology, the pre- and posttests must have the same factorial composition. If not, the groups may be biased with respect to factors of performance which affect the posttest but are not present in the pretest scores and cannot be eliminated by analysis of covariance. A fair test of the experimental effect would not then be possible. The safer strategy is to randomize the assignment of subjects and to rely on analysis of covariance to reduce, but not necessarily to nullify, individual differences among subjects. For other problems in the use of analysis of covariance see Walker and Lev (1953) and Cochran (1957).

5.1. Tests of Hypotheses

Analysis of covariance is essentially an analysis of variance of residuals from the common within-subclasses regression. The tests of hypotheses are not actually carried out in this manner, however, because to do so would not take into account the sampling errors in the estimated regression coefficients (see Fisher, 1958, p. 279). In the exact tests the sum of squares for hypothesis, adjusted for the concomitant variables, is obtained by subtraction. The procedure is as follows.

First, the concomitant variables are included with the dependent variables in the multivariate analysis of variance. That is, the observations in the analysis are vectors of q concomitant variables and p dependent variables such as:

$$[x_{ijk}^{(1)}, x_{ijk}^{(2)}, \ldots, x_{ijk}^{(q)}, y_{ijk}^{(1)}, y_{ijk}^{(2)}, \ldots, y_{ijk}^{(p)}].$$

For each effect to be tested eliminating variation due to the concomitant variables, there will be a $(p + q) \times (p + q)$ hypothesis sum-of-products matrix in the multivariate analysis of variance. As before, call this matrix $\mathbf{S}_h$. There will, of course, also be the $(p + q) \times (p + q)$ sum-of-products matrix for error, $\mathbf{S}_e$.

Next, the matrices $\mathbf{S}_e$ and the sum of $\mathbf{S}_e$ and $\mathbf{S}_h$, say $\mathbf{S}_{t_h}$, are partitioned into sections corresponding to the concomitant and dependent variables:

$$\mathbf{S}_e = \begin{bmatrix} \mathbf{S}_e^{(x)} & \mathbf{S}_e^{(xy)} \\ \mathbf{S}_e^{(yx)} & \mathbf{S}_e^{(y)} \end{bmatrix} \begin{matrix} q \\ p \end{matrix}, \qquad \mathbf{S}_{t_h} = \mathbf{S}_e + \mathbf{S}_h = \begin{bmatrix} \mathbf{S}_{t_h}^{(x)} & \mathbf{S}_{t_h}^{(xy)} \\ \mathbf{S}_{t_h}^{(yx)} & \mathbf{S}_{t_h}^{(y)} \end{bmatrix} \begin{matrix} q \\ p \end{matrix}.$$
$$\qquad\qquad q \qquad p \qquad\qquad\qquad\qquad\qquad q \qquad p$$

From these are computed the reduced error matrix, say,

$$\mathbf{S}_e^* = \mathbf{S}_e^{(y)} - \mathbf{S}_e^{(yx)}(\mathbf{S}_e^{(x)})^{-1}\mathbf{S}_e^{(xy)}, \tag{10}$$

and the reduced "total matrix," say,

$$\mathbf{S}_{t_h}^* = \mathbf{S}_{t_h}^{(y)} - \mathbf{S}_{t_h}^{(yx)}(\mathbf{S}_{t_h}^{(x)})^{-1}\mathbf{S}_{t_h}^{(xy)}. \tag{11}$$

Both of these matrices are $p \times p$. The adjusted sum of products for hypothesis is then obtained by subtraction:

$$\mathbf{S}_h^* = \mathbf{S}_{t_h}^* - \mathbf{S}_e^*.$$

Table 15 The sum of products for error plus the sum of products for the sex effect (d.f. = 117)

	R	A	S	L
R	97.6256			(Symmetric)
A	47.1777	80.7487		
S	41.2582	35.3758	89.6670	
L	46.7267	41.0288	67.7044	82.0784

Any or all of the multivariate tests of Section 3.2.1 may be applied to S_h* with degrees of freedom n_h and to S_e* with degrees of freedom $n_e - q$ to test the null hypothesis—viz., that the effect in question is zero when the subjects' responses are adjusted linearly to the values they would have if all subjects were at the same levels on the concomitant variables.

We can apply this analysis to the sample data to test whether there is any effect of sex on the spelling and language scores when individual differences in reading and arithmetic scores have been eliminated. The reduced error matrix for this purpose has already been calculated in standardized form in the regression analysis and appears in Table 14. The form for raw scores appears in Table 16 (Section 5.2). The total matrix obtained by adding the sum of products for error and the sum of products for the sex effect is shown in Table 15. This matrix is partitioned and the reduced sum of products computed by formula (11). The result is shown in Table 16. The difference between the reduced total and the reduced error matrix gives the adjusted sum of products for hypothesis also shown in Table 16.

The solution of Eq. (6) using the reduced error matrix as S_e and the adjusted hypothesis matrix as S_h gives the one nonzero root 0.7664. Since there is one

Table 16 The reduced error and "total" sum of products and the adjusted sum of products for hypothesis

1. Reduced error sum of products (d.f. = 114)

	S	L
S	56.5032	(Symmetric)
L	26.6758	30.7781

2. Reduced "total" sum of products (d.f. = 115)

	S	L
S	68.1181	(Symmetric)
L	43.0424	53.8407

3. Adjusted hypothesis sum of products (d.f. = 1)

	S	L
S	11.6148	(Symmetric)
L	16.3666	23.0626

degree of freedom for hypothesis and $n_e - q = 114$ degrees of freedom for error, we may convert the root to an F-statistic by the formula in Section 3.2.1:

$$F = \frac{(114 - 2 + 1)0.7664}{2} = 43.3.$$

On 1 and $114 - 2 + 1 = 113$ degrees of freedom, this value is highly significant. Similarly, the step-down F-statistics on 1 and 114 and on 1 and 113 degrees of freedom are also highly significant:

S	L
23.4	52.6.

There is evidently a sex difference in performance on the spelling and language skills test which persists when the scores of the boys and girls are adjusted to the same level of reading and arithmetic performance. We might consider this difference to represent a single ability, however, for the step-down F-statistics in the other order show the difference in the spelling, eliminating the language differences, to be insignificant:

L	S	
33.7	1.1	d.f. = 1/114 and 1/113.

This is precisely the result that would have been obtained if reading, arithmetic, and language had been used as concomitant variables in the analysis of covariance. In other words, when applied in tests of effects in the design part of the model, the step-down test is equivalent to a succession of analyses of covariance taking each variable in turn as the dependent variable and all previous variables as the concomitant variables.

5.2. Estimation

The estimate of $\mathbf{\Gamma}^0$, the matrix of coefficients in the regression part of the model, has already been obtained in the regression analysis of Section 4. In Table 14 these coefficients appear in standardized form, but may be "unstandardized" by multiplying each element by the corresponding standard deviation of the dependent variable and dividing by the standard deviation of the independent variable. Alternatively, the coefficients may be computed from sums of squares and products instead of correlations to obtain the raw-score coefficients directly. The sampling variance-covariance factors from which the standard errors of the raw-score coefficients are calculated are the elements of the inverse of the sum of products matrix for the independent variables. A complete computer program for regression should produce regression coefficients and their variance-covariance factors in both standard and raw-score form. For the sample data the raw-score versions of the quantities are given in Table 17.

Estimates of linear function of effects in the design part of the full model are conveniently obtained by adjusting the estimates for the design part alone. Those

Table 17 Estimated raw score regression coefficients and their variance-covariance factors

1. Raw score regression coefficients

		Dependent variables	
		S	L
Independent	R 0.2758	0.2993
variables	A 0.3999	0.5065

2. Variance-covariance factors (inverse of the independent-variable sum of products)

	R	A
R	0.01430	(Symmetric)
A	−0.00847	0.01879

adjustments consist simply of subtracting from the original estimates of effects in the dependent variables, estimates of the same effects in the independent variables multiplied by the respective raw-score regression coefficients. The results are called estimates of "adjusted" effects. If the matrix of raw-score regression coefficients is $\hat{\Gamma}$, and the vector effect, partitioned into dependent and independent variables is $[\hat{\theta}^x, \hat{\theta}^y]$, then the adjusted effects are, say,

$$\begin{array}{cccc} \hat{\theta}^* & = & \hat{\theta}^{(y)} & - & \hat{\Gamma} & \hat{\theta}^{(x)} \\ p \times 1 & & p \times 1 & & p \times q & q \times 1 \end{array}.$$

The sampling variance of the adjusted estimate for a particular variable is obtained by adding the quantity

$$\hat{\theta}^{(x)\prime}(S_e^{(x)})^{-1}\hat{\theta}^{(x)}$$

to the variance-covariance factor for the unadjusted estimate (Section 3.3) and multiplying by the estimated residual error variance for that variable (Section 4.1). The matrix $(S_e^{(x)})^{-1}$ is the inverse of the error sum-of-products matrix for the independent variables. For example, in the sample problem the sex effect (male − female) in spelling and language, adjusted for reading and arithmetic, respectively, is

$$-0.3867 - 0.2758 \times 0.2297 - 0.3999 \times 0.5028 = -0.6511,$$
$$-0.5941 - 0.2993 \times 0.2297 - 0.5056 \times 0.5028 = -0.9175.$$

Taking the variance-covariance factor for the estimated sex effect from Table 10, we calculate the variance-covariance factor for the adjusted estimate as follows:

$$0.03297 + [0.2297, 0.5028]\begin{bmatrix} 0.01430 & -0.00847 \\ -0.00847 & 0.01879 \end{bmatrix}\begin{bmatrix} 0.2297 \\ 0.5028 \end{bmatrix} = 0.03297 + 0.04130$$

$$\times (0.2297)^2 + 0.01879 \times (0.5028)^2 - 2 \times 0.08847 \times 0.2297 \times 0.5028 = 0.0365.$$

Multiplying this factor by the residual variances for spelling and language, respectively, as calculated from Table 1, gives the sample variances of the adjusted sex effects; taking the square root gives the standard errors:

$$\sqrt{0.0365 \times 56.5032/114} = 0.1345,$$

$$\sqrt{0.0365 \times 30.7781/114} = 0.0993.$$

Since the adjusted effects are greater in magnitude than the unadjusted, the superiority of the girls' performance in spelling and language is more evident when girls are compared with boys of the same level of performance in reading and arithmetic.

6. SPECIAL USES OF MULTIVARIATE ANALYSIS OF VARIANCE

6.1. Trend Analysis

Problems of comparing trends in time-dependent measures under different experimental conditions occur widely in behavioral research. Longitudinal studies of growth and development, and repeated-measurement studies of learning, work output, progress in therapy, etc., invariably raise questions about the statistical significance of observed differences between average time curves (see Harris, 1963, for other examples). To answer these questions many workers recommend the use of a mixed-model univariate analysis of variance with subjects as the random dimension (Grant, 1956; Gaito and Wiley, 1963; Winer, 1962, Ch. 7).

Formal justification of a mixed-model analysis for this purpose is based on the assumption that the correlation of residuals from the fitted time curves is constant between all trials (time points). That some form of correlation of the residuals must be expected is a consequence of repetition of measurements on the same subjects. If the correlation is in fact constant, it will be eliminated when the subject effect is removed and the residuals will be left independent as required in the univariate analysis. The mean square for trials × subjects within groups then provides a valid denominator for an F-test of the trials × group interaction which measures trend differences.

Unfortunately, the assumption of constant correlation between trials is not very plausible for time-dependent data. More commonly, such data show the so-called "simplex" pattern of correlation (Humphreys, 1960). This pattern is the result of autoregressive effects which cause measurements proximate in time to be more highly correlated than those remote in time (Anderson, 1960). To obtain a valid test of trend differences in data of this type, multivariate methods have been widely proposed (Box, 1950; Rao, 1959; Greenhouse and Geisser, 1959; Bock, 1963b).

In essence, the multivariate approach is simply to consider the measurements obtained from each subject at a number of time points to be a vector observation with as many variables. Then overall differences of trends in the mean vectors of the experimental groups may be tested statistically and estimated by multivariate analysis of variance. In those cases where the trends depend on the initial level of subjects in the groups, a multivariate analysis of covariance with the first measurement as the concomitant variable may be recommended (Box, 1950).

A considerable refinement of the multivariate approach results upon introducing orthogonal polynomials (Fisher, 1958, p. 147) to decompose the trend differences into constant, linear, quadratic, cubic, etc. components. The only alteration required in the multivariate analysis of variance is pre- and postmultiplying the $p \times p$ sums of product matrices by the pth-order orthogonal polynomial matrices before performing the tests of significance.* Since the orthogonal polynomials have a natural order according to their degree, the step-down F-statistics may be conveniently used in the multivariate test of significance. In many cases, there is strong reason to expect the differences in trend to be constant or linear; if so, the critical values for testing these effects may be set more liberally than those for the higher effects (see Section 3.2.1).

A fairly detailed discussion of multivariate analysis of variance procedures in trend analysis is given by Bock (1963b) and need not be repeated here. We might emphasize, however, the importance of providing for the linear transformation of variables by a given transformation matrix when programming multivariate analysis of variance. This greatly facilitates trend analysis by orthogonal polynomials or any redefinition of variables by sums, differences, or other linear combination.

6.2. Multivariate Analysis of Qualitative Data

In the preceding sections of this chapter we have assumed that the dependent variables are in sufficiently close approximation to continuous joint normal variates to justify analyses based on the multivariate normal distribution. This is not always the case in behavioral research and is indeed the exception in fields such as sociology and social psychology. More typical data in these fields record choices of the subjects among predetermined alternatives, as in opinion questionnaires, or the occurrence of defined categories of behavior, as in the study of interpersonal relationships in small groups. When the alternatives or categories are nominal and not intended to represent points or intervals of a continuum, this type of data is usually called "qualitative." It should be distinguished from ratings made on a presumed continuum, as in Thurstone's method of successive categories, which are better analyzed by methods other than those discussed here (see Bock and Jones, 1957).

If the classes in which the subject's responses or behavior are recorded are mutually exclusive and exhaustive, data obtained by simple random sampling of subjects from a given population will follow the multinomial probability distribution. In the large samples which are the rule in sociological research, statistical methods based on the χ^2-distribution are sufficiently accurate for the analysis of such multinomial data. The versatility of these methods has been extended in

---

* Matrices of orthogonal polynomials to order 26 are available in DeLury (1950).

recent years by procedures for partitioning Chi-square in complex data (Irwin, 1949; Lancaster, 1951; Maxwell, 1961; Williams, 1952). These methods give the investigator a more powerful and detailed analysis of specific sources of association in qualitative data than do the conventional χ^2-tests of overall association.

Although it is not widely known, methods for partitioning of χ^2 due to association in qualitative data can be formulated in terms of a weighted analysis of variance. The weights are determined by the expected or observed marginal frequencies (Claringbold, 1961). If the data have been obtained in a complex crossed design, components of χ^2 attributable to various main effects and interactions can be partitioned. This is in effect a special application of the "use of scores for the analysis of association in contingency tables" (Williams, 1952). The contrasts among classes which are implicit in analysis of variance provide the necessary scores.

A productive application of this form of analysis in behavioral research is in "scaling" qualitative data. In psychometric terminology a "scale" is a set of numbers to be assigned to classes of qualitative data so that they may be analyzed by statistical methods for continuous variables. For example, the simplest method of scaling data for purposes of multivariate normal analyses is to assign weights, not necessarily all positive, to the classes and categories, then use the weighted sum of the response proportions as a variable. The central limit theorem guarantees that such a sum will be more nearly normally distributed than any single proportion. Moreover, the weights can be chosen in a way which largely suppresses the expected negative correlation of multinomial proportions.

All information in a number of multinomial samples, as measured by χ^2, can be extracted by applying as many such (linearly independent) scales as there are categories (Williams, 1952, p. 278). The single scale which extracts the maximum possible information can be calculated by methods formally equivalent to those for obtaining discriminant functions (Bartlett, 1951). This is the "additive" (Fisher, 1958, p. 289) or "optimal" scale (Bock, 1960; Bradley, Katti, and Coons, 1962). The significance of association accounted for by this scale, and the significance of association remaining after that due to the scale is removed, can also be tested using the χ^2-distribution. If the latter is not significant, the scores obtained by use of the optimal scale extract all the useful (i.e., nonerror) information in the data and no further scales are needed. Such a scale is often of substantive interest because it indicates the order and distance between the classes or categories. Convenient numerical procedures for constructing optimal scales are given by Bock (1960).

In many cases the optimal scale does not exhaust all significant association in the data, however, and the investigator is faced with the problem of devising one or more additional scales which are capable of accounting for more of the association. Whether such a scale is accounting for a significant portion of the total χ^2, and whether or not the χ^2 left unaccounted for is insignificant, can be tested statistically by likelihood ratio tests described by Bartlett (1951).

In the scaling of multinomial data for multivariate normal statistical analysis, a strong argument can be made for the use of scale values which are linear combinations of the *logarithms* of the observed frequencies. This approach has been suggested by Plackett (1962), Goodman (1964), and others, as a means of obtaining simple tests of significance for interactions in contingency tables. These tests make use of the fact that the log frequencies have a particularly simple large-sample covariance matrix under the null hypothesis. As a consequence, the covariance matrix of any linear contrasts of the log frequencies can be readily computed. A test of the hypothesis that the expectations of the contrasts are simultaneously zero can be obtained by employing the covariance matrix of the contrasts in the computation of a statistic similar to Hotelling's T^2. Since this covariance matrix is assumed *known,* this statistic can be referred to as the χ^2-distribution for percentage points.

Contrasts of the log frequencies are especially suitable as scale values for use in subsequent multivariate analyses because, unlike contrasts of the original frequencies, they are unrestricted in range. Thus a linear model for predicting the contrasts of log frequencies will always predict values which are actually possible, whereas linear models fitted directly to contrasts of frequencies or proportions may predict values beyond the possible range of such contrasts.

The device of transforming a multiplicative model for response probabilities into an additive logarithmic model provides an analysis of qualitative data which parallels exactly the multivariate analysis of variance for quantitative data. It applies to data obtained in behavioral experiments of the following sort. The investigator arranges a number of experimental conditions and assigns subjects randomly to groups which will be exposed to these conditions either singly or in a factorial or other design. He then observes the response of each subject in each group and accordingly classifies the subject in one of a number of preconceived response categories. Like the experimental conditions, the response categories may have a design corresponding to a cross classification or nesting of broader behavioral categories. The investigator's problem is to predict the effect of the experimental conditions on the probability of a subject's being classified in categories at various levels of the response design.

The merit of the logarithmic models is that the parameters take the familiar form of contrasts of effects of experimental conditions, effects of response categories, and interactions of these effects. These parameters may be estimated straightforwardly by the method of maximum likelihood and subsequently transformed into ratios of parameters of the original multiplicative model. A general matric form of the maximum likelihood solution, including large sample tests of hypothesis and standard errors for the parameter estimates, has been presented by Bock (1966). Like the multivariate analysis of variance, this solution is easy to program for computers if a suitable set of matrix operations subroutines is available.

Unfortunately, this solution does not generalize to the qualitative analogue of a repeated-measures experiment—i.e., to an experiment in which each subject makes a number of responses and each response is assigned to a defined category. An example of an experiment in this type is the comparison of two groups of subjects on the basis of their statements about what they see in the inkblots of the Rorschach test. Each subject responds as many times as he wishes, and his responses are classified according to the aspect of the blot which determines the response, according to the objective content of the response, etc. Each subject is then represented in the data by the number of responses he produces and the distribution of these responses over the categories.

This type of data presents difficulties in any attempt to compare statistically the responses of the two groups of subjects. Perhaps the best that can be done at the present time is to perform a multivariate analysis of variance using contrasts of the log frequencies as variables.* If the response productivity of the subject is thought to influence the distribution of his responses, the total number of responses—or some polynomial function of it—can be used as a covariate in the analysis. This method of analysis appears to give reasonable results when applied to monte carlo data where the response probabilities for the two populations is known, but a more vigorous justification is lacking. In view of the importance of this type of data in behavioral research, further development of multivariate statistical methods for an appropriate analysis is needed.

REFERENCES

AIKEN, L. R., JR., "Mathemaphobia and mathemaphilia: an analysis of personal and social factors affecting performance in mathematics." Unpublished doctoral dissertation, University of North Carolina, 1960

ANDERSON, R. L., and T. A. BANCROFT, *Statistical Theory in Research.* New York: McGraw-Hill, 1952

ANDERSON, T. W., *An Introduction to Multivariate Analysis.* New York: John Wiley & Sons, 1958

ANDERSON, T. W., "Some stochastic process models for intelligence test scores," in K. J. Arrow, S. Karlin, and R. Suppes (eds.), *Mathematical Methods in the Social Sciences.* Stanford: Stanford University Press, 1960

BARGMANN, R. E., "A statistician's instructions to the computer: A report on a statistical computer language," in *Proceedings of the IBM Scientific Computing Symposium on Statistics, October 21–23, 1963.* White Plains, N.Y.: IBM Data Processing Division, 1965

BARTLETT, M. S., "Multivariate analysis." *J. Roy. Stat. Soc. Series B,* **9,** 176–197 (1947)

BARTLETT, M. S., "The goodness of fit of a single hypothetical discriminant function in the case of several groups." *Ann. Eugenics* **16,** 199–214 (1951)

BEATON, A. E., "The use of special matrix operators in statistical calculus." *ETS Research Bulletin 65–61.* Princeton: Educational Testing Service, 1964

BOCK, R. D., "Methods and applications of optimal scaling." University of North Carolina at Chapel Hill, Psychometric Laboratory Research Memorandum No. 25, 1960

---

* The problem of zero frequencies can be handled by adding one-half to each observed frequency.

BOCK, R. D., "Programming univariate and multivariate analysis of variance." *Technometrics*, **5,** 95–117 (1963a)

BOCK, R. D., "Multivariate analysis of variance of repeated measurements," in C. W. Harris (ed.), *Problems in Measuring Change*. Madison: University of Wisconsin Press, 1963b

BOCK, R. D., "A computer program for univariate and multivariate analysis of variance," in *Proceedings of the IBM Scientific Computing Symposium on Statistics, October 21–23, 1963*. White Plains, N. Y.: IBM Data Processing Division, 1965a

BOCK, R. D., "Contributions of multivariate statistical methods to educational research," in R. B. Cattell (ed.), *Handbook of Multivariate Experimental Psychology*. Chicago: Rand McNally, 1965b

BOCK, R. D., "Estimating multinomial response relations," in R. C. Bose (ed.), *Contributions to statistics and probability: Essays in memory of Sumarendra Nath Roy*. Chapel Hill, North Carolina: University of North Carolina Press, 1967, in press

BOCK, R. D., and L. V. JONES, *The Measurement and Prediction of Judgment and Choice*. San Francisco: Holden-Day, 1967

BOCK, R. D., and A. PETERSON, "Matrix operations subroutines for statistical computation." University of Chicago: Department of Education Statistical Laboratory, Research Memorandum No. 7, 1967

BOSE, R. C., and R. L. CARTER, "Response model coefficients and the individual degrees of freedom of a factorial design." *Biometrics* **18,** 160–171 (1962)

BOX, G. E. P., "Problems in the analysis of growth and wear curves. *Biometrics* **6,** 362–389 (1950)

BRADLEY, R. A., S. K. KATTI, and IRMA J. COONS, "Optimal scaling of ordered categories." *Psychometrika* **27,** 355–374 (1962)

CLARINGBOLD, P. J., "The use of orthogonal polynomials in the partition of χ^2." *Australian Journal of Statistics* **3,** 48–63 (1961)

CLYDE, D. J., E. M. CRAMER, and R. J. SHERIN, *Multivariate Statistical Programs*. Coral Gables, Fla.: Biometric Laboratory of the University of Miami, 1966

COCHRAN, W. G., "Analysis of covariance: Its nature and uses." *Biometrics* **13,** 261–281 (1957)

COCHRAN, W. G., and GERTRUDE M. COX, *Experimental Designs* (2nd ed.). New York: John Wiley & Sons, 1957

COOLEY, W. W., and P. R. LOHNES, *Multivariate Procedures for the Behaviorial Sciences*. New York: John Wiley & Sons, 1962

DELURY, D. B., *Values and Integrals of the Orthogonal Polynomials up to n = 26*. Toronto: University of Toronto Press, 1950

DEMPSTER, A. P., "Stepwise multivariate analysis of variance based on principle variables." *Biometrics* **19,** 478–491 (1963)

EFROYMSON, M. A., "Multiple regression analysis," in A. Ralston and H. S. Wilf (eds.), *Mathematical Methods for Digital Computers*. New York: John Wiley & Sons, 1960

FELDT, L. S., "A comparison of the precision of three experimental designs employing a concomitant variable." *Psychometrika* **23**, 235–353 (1958)

FISHER, R. A., *The Design of Experiments* (*5th ed.*). Edinburgh: Oliver and Boyd, 1949

FISHER, R. A., *Statistical Methods for Research Workers* (*13th ed.*) New York: Hafner, 1958

FOX, L., *An Introduction to Numerical Linear Algebra.* Oxford: Clarendon Press, 1964.

GAITO, J., and D. E. WILEY, "Univariate analysis of variance procedures in the measurement of change," in C. W. Harris (ed.), *Problems in Measuring Change.* Madison: University of Wisconsin Press, 1963

GOODMAN, L. A., "Simple methods for analyzing three-factor interaction in contingency tables." *J. Amer. Stat. Assn.* **59**, 319–352 (1964)

GRANT, D. A., "Analysis-of-variance tests in the analysis and comparison of curves." *Psychol. Bull.* **53**, 144–154 (1956)

GRAYBILL, F. A., *An Introduction to Linear Statistical Models.* New York: McGraw-Hill, 1961

GREENHOUSE, S. W., and S. GEISSER, "On methods in the analysis of profile data." *Psychometrika* **24**, 95–112 (1959)

GULLIKSEN, H., *Theory of Mental Tests.* New York: John Wiley & Sons, 1950

HAGGARD, E. A., "Socialization, personality and academic achievement in gifted children." *School Review* **65**, 388–414 (1957)

HALD, A., *Statistical Tables and Formulas.* New York: John Wiley & Sons, 1952

HARRIS, C. W. (ed.), *Problems in Measuring Change.* Madison: University of Wisconsin Press, 1963

HECK, D. L., "Charts of some upper percentage points of the distribution of the largest characteristic root." *Ann. Math. Stat.* **31**, 625–642 (1960)

HOTELLING, H., "Relations between two sets of variates." *Biometrika* **28**, 321–377 (1936)

HOTELLING, H., "A generalized *T*-test and measure of multivariate dispersion." *Proceedings of the Second Berkeley Symposium on Mathematical Statistics and Probability* **2**, 23–41 (1951)

HUMPHREYS, L. G., "Investigations of the simplex." *Psychometrika* **25**, 313–323 (1960)

IRWIN, J. O., "A note on the subdivision of χ^2 in certain discrete distributions." *Biometrika* **36**, 130–134 (1949)

JONES, L. V., and R. D. BOCK, "Multiple discriminant analysis applied to 'Ways to Live' ratings from six cultural groups." *Sociometry* **23**, 162–176 (1960)

KABE, D. G., "Stepwise multivariate linear regression." *J. Amer. Stat. Assn.* **58**, 770–773 (1963)

KEMPTHORNE, O., *The Design and Analysis of Experiments.* New York: John Wiley & Sons, 1952

LANCASTER, H. O., "Complex contingency tables treated by the partition of χ^2." *J. Roy. Stat. Soc., Series B* **13**, 242–249 (1951)

LORD, F. M., "Elementary models for measuring change," in C. W. Harris (ed.), *Problems in Measuring Change*. Madison: University of Wisconsin Press, 1963

MADANSKY, A., "The fitting of straight lines when both variables are subject to error." *J. Amer. Stat. Assn.* **54**, 173–205 (1959)

MAXWELL, A., *Analysing Qualitative Data*. New York: John Wiley & Sons, 1961

MEREDITH, W., "Canonical correlations with fallible data." *Psychometrika* **29**, 55–65 (1964)

MORRISON, D. F., *Multivariate Statistical Methods*. New York: McGraw-Hill, 1967

PILLAI, K. C. SREEDHARAN, *Statistical Tables for Tests of Multivariative Hypotheses*. Manila: The Statistical Center, University of the Philippines, 1960

PILLAI, K. C. SREEDHARAN, "On the distribution of the largest of seven roots of a matrix in multivariate analysis." *Biometrika* **51**, 270–275 (1964)

PILLAI, K. C. SREEDHARAN, "On the distribution of the largest characteristic root of a matrix in multivariate analysis." *Biometrika* **52**, 405–414 (1966)

PLACKETT, R. L. A., "A note on interactions in contingency tables." *J. Roy. Stat. Soc. Series B* **24**, 162–166 (1962)

QUENOUILLE, M. H., *The Design and Analysis of Experiments*. New York: Hafner, 1963

RAO, C. R., *Advanced Statistical Methods in Biometric Research*. New York: John Wiley & Sons, 1952

RAO, C. R., "Some problems involving linear hypotheses in multivariate analysis." *Biometrika* **46**, 49–58 (1959)

ROY, J., "Step-down procedure in multivariate analysis." *Ann. Math. Stat.* **29**, 1177–1187 (1958)

ROY, S. N., *Some Aspects of Multivariate Analysis*. New York: John Wiley & Sons, 1957

ROY, S. N., and R. E. BARGMANN, "Tests of multiple independence and the associated confidence bounds." *Ann. Math. Stat.* **29**, 491–503 (1958)

ROY, S. N. and R. GNANADESIKAN, "Further contributions to multivariate confidence bounds." *Biometrika* **44**, 399–410 (1957)

ROY, S. N., and R. GNANADESIKAN, "Some contributions to anova in one or more dimensions: I and II." *Ann. Math. Stat.* **30**, 304–317; 318–340 (1959)

SMITH, H., R. GNANADESIKAN, and J. B. HUGHES, "Multivariate analysis of variance (MANOVA)." *Biometrics* **18**, 22–41 (1962)

SPEIGEL, D. K., "Relations between two test batteries." Unpublished doctoral dissertation, University of North Carolina, 1964

SPEIGEL, D. K., and R. D. BOCK, "Canonical correlation program for the Royal McBee LGP-30." Chapel Hill, N.C.: University of North Carolina Psychometric Laboratory Research Memorandum No. 8a, 1962

SPEIGEL, D. K., and R. D. BOCK, "Multivariate step-wise regression analysis: A program for General Precision LGP-30." Chapel Hill, N.C.: University of North Carolina Psychometric Laboratory Research Memorandum No. 13, 1963

TATSUOKA, M. M., and D. V. TIEDEMAN, "Discriminant analysis." *Rev. Ed. Res.* **24**, 402–420 (1954)

TUKEY, J. W., "Dyadic anova, and analysis of variance for vectors." *Human Biology* **21,** 65–110 (1949)

WALKER, HELEN, and J. LEV, *Statistical Inference.* New York: Holt, Rinehart, and Winston, 1953

WHERRY, R. J., "Appendix V," in Stead, Shortle and Associates, *Occupational Counseling Techniques.* New York: American Book Company, 1940

WILKS, S. S., "Certain generalizations in the analysis of variance." *Biometrika* **24,** 109–116 (1932)

WILLIAMS, E. J., "Use of scores for the analysis of association in contingency tables." *Biometrika* **39,** 274–289 (1952)

WILLIAMS, E. J., *Regression Analysis.* New York: John Wiley & Sons, 1959

WINER, B. J., *Statistical Principles in Experimental Design.* New York: McGraw-Hill, 1962

CHAPTER 4

FACTOR ANALYSIS*

HARRY H. HARMAN, *Educational Testing Service*

Factor analysis is a multivariate statistical technique, and as such is especially useful in the social sciences, where numerous interacting measurements frequently are obtained. Because of its early development and extensive use by psychologists the method itself is often mistakenly viewed as psychological in nature. However, a statistical technique which assists in the understanding of the interrelationships among many variables is not restricted to any particular discipline. Recent applications of factor analysis have been made in such diverse fields as sociology and meteorology, political science and medicine, geography and business, as well as in psychology.

BRIEF HISTORY

Factor analysis came into being at the turn of this century and made relatively slow progress for several decades; then came a period of heated controversy involving proponents of particular psychological theories based upon factor analysis, and finally the subject reached full maturity in recent years as high-speed electronic computers made it feasible to put factor analysis on sound, objective scientific grounds.

The origin of factor analysis is generally ascribed to Charles Spearman. His monumental work in developing a psychological theory involving a single general factor and a number of specific factors goes back to his paper, "General Intelligence, Objectively Determined and Measured" (Spearman, 1904). Of course, this investigation was only the beginning of his work in developing the two-factor theory, and his early work is not explicitly in terms of "factors." Perhaps a more crucial article, certainly insofar as the statistical aspects are concerned, is the paper by Karl Pearson (1901) in which he sets forth "the method of principal axes." Nevertheless, Spearman, who devoted the remaining forty years of his life to the development of factor analysis, is regarded as the father of the subject.

A considerable amount of work on the psychological theories and mathematical foundations of factor analysis followed in the next twenty years. The principal contributors during this period included Charles Spearman, Cyril Burt, Karl Pearson, Godfrey H. Thomson, J. C. Maxwell Garnett, and Karl J. Holzinger; the topics

---

* The ideas and methods discussed in this chapter are founded on the more extended analysis in H. H. Harman, *Modern Factor Analysis* (*Rev. Ed.*) Chicago: University of Chicago Press, 1967.

receiving the greatest attention were attempts to prove or disprove the existence of general ability, the study of sampling errors of tetrad differences, and computational methods for a single general factor which included the fundamental formula of the centroid solution.

The early modern period, including the bulk of the active and published controversy on factor analysis, came after 1925, with a real spurt of activity in the 1930's. By this time it had become quite apparent that Spearman's two-factor theory was not always adequate to describe a battery of psychological tests. So group factors found their way into factor analysis—although the experimenters, at first, were very reluctant to admit such deviation from the basic theory and restricted the group factors to as small a number as possible. What actually happened was that the theory of a general and specific factors in Spearman's original form was superseded by theories of many group factors, but the early method continued to be employed to determine these many factors. Then it naturally followed that some workers explored the possibility of extracting several factors directly from a matrix of correlations among tests, and thus arose the concept of multiple-factor analysis in the work of Garnett (1919).

Although the term, "multiple-factor analysis" may be attributed to L. L. Thurstone, and although he undoubtedly has done most to popularize the method, he certainly was not the first to take exception to Spearman's two-factor theory, nor was he the first to develop a theory of many factors. It is not even the centroid method of analysis for which Thurstone deserves a place of prominence in factor analysis. The centroid method is clearly admitted by Thurstone to be a computational compromise for the principal-factor solution. The truly remarkable contribution of Thurstone was the generalization of Spearman's tetrad-difference criterion to the rank of the correlation matrix as the basis for determining the number of common factors. He saw that a zero tetrad-difference corresponded to the vanishing of a second-order determinant, and extended this notion to the vanishing of higher-order determinants as the condition for more than a single factor. The matrix formulation of the problem has greatly facilitated further advances in factor analysis.

A generation ago, the arduous computational task required to do a factor analysis tended to frighten away the otherwise serious researcher, and it was by sheer perseverance that a student completed a master's or doctoral dissertation in the field. However, the computations in factor analysis no longer loom so ominously as they did for more than twenty years. Although some very effective methods of analysis were developed in the 1930's and 1940's, a good deal of the effort during that period was devoted to short-cut or approximate techniques in order to reduce the burdensome labor of computation. Then, with the availability of high-speed electronic computers in the 1950's, creative effort could be directed toward solving many of the existing problems in factor analysis that previously had to be laid aside for sheer lack of time. The objective solutions to Thurstone's intuitive notion of "simple structure" constitute a good case in point. Now, in the 1960's, with many of these problems well along the road to solution, factor analysis is recognized for its feasibility and is being applied extensively in many and diverse fields.

Moreover, the creative worker in factor analysis now is free to generate problems which his predecessor would not even permit himself to dream about. It is no longer a question of whether problems involving hundreds (perhaps thousands) of variables are amenable to factor analysis, but rather of just how soon we can have computer programs to cope with such problems, or can make comparative studies of several alternative computing schemes. But this is just an extension (albeit a tremendous extension) of presently known techniques. Even more startling are such new explorations as the factor analysis of triple-dimension matrices by Tucker (1963), work on nonlinear factor analysis by K. R. Wood, for which a computer program was recently made available (1964), and the reexamination of the problem of oblique transformations by Jennrich (1966). Without going into an explanation of these advanced and novel techniques, suffice it to say they involve tremendous amounts of computation and would hardly have been the kinds of problems conceived by these investigators were it not for the modern electronic computer.

FACTOR ANALYSIS IN STATISTICS

The place of factor analysis in the statistical family of multivariate analysis is described in an excellent manner by Kendall (1950, pp. 60–61). He classifies the study of statistical relationships into two broad categories: "analysis of *dependence*" and "analysis of *interdependence*." The former class includes analysis of variance and regression analysis, while the latter includes various types of correlation analysis and contingency analysis. Factor analysis is then considered in the category "analysis of interdependence" but far on the scale towards "analysis of dependence." The important distinction is that the several techniques under analysis of dependence (e.g., regression analysis) all require the designation of one or more of the variables as dependent, while the techniques under analysis of interdependence focus attention upon relationships among the total set of variables without singling out any of them for special consideration.

Factor analysis addresses itself to the study of interrelationships among a total set of variables, no one of which is selected for a different role than any of the others. In some sense all variables in such a study are construed to be dependent, with the independent variables being the new hypothetical constructs called factors. As one of its results, factor analysis actually leads to linear regression of each of the observed variables on the factors. This is not strictly in the sense of Kendall's analysis of dependence, but should indicate why he places factor analysis close to this category.

As a statistical method, factor analysis has several functions or uses. Since it is concerned primarily with the resolution of a set of variables linearly in terms of new categories or factors (usually a small number), a principal aim is to attain scientific parsimony or economy of description. Additional uses of factor analysis include the investigation of hypotheses and the suggestion of new hypotheses. A discussion of these aims of statistics in general is presented by Kelley (1947, pp. 12–24) and for factor analysis in particular by Eysenck (1953).

BASIC CONCEPTS

Factor analysis is applicable whenever measurements are available for a sample of N individuals or entities (e.g., persons, census tracts, documents, etc.) from a given population on each of n quantitative variables.

Analysis begins with the calculation of the correlation coefficients among all the variables. From these correlations it is possible to get linear expressions for each of the variables in terms of some new factors in such a way that the linear model provides an adequate fit to the observed data. Within this degree of fit it is usually desirable to change the basis of reference from the first set of mathematically arbitrary factors to some more meaningful factors in the substantive field. The final set of factors may then be expressed linearly in terms of the observed variables and thereby factor measurements can be obtained for the individuals of the sample, or forecast for new individuals.

Although the techniques of factor analysis are mathematical in nature, the present chapter is written primarily with the nonmathematician in mind, and with few exceptions, is largely expository.

Mathematical Model

Since an objective of factor analysis is to describe a body of observed data in some simpler terms, it is appropriate to inquire into the nature of the simplification. In order to make the mathematical model as simple as possible the linear form is selected. Specifically, the model may be exhibited as follows:

$$
\begin{aligned}
z_1 &= a_{11}F_1 + a_{12}F_2 + \cdots + a_{1m}F_m + d_1 U_1 \\
z_2 &= a_{21}F_1 + a_{22}F_2 + \cdots + a_{2m}F_m \qquad\quad + d_2 U_2 \\
&\vdots \\
z_n &= a_{n1}F_1 + a_{n2}F_2 + \cdots + a_{nm}F_m \qquad\quad + d_n U_n,
\end{aligned}
\tag{1}
$$

from which it can be seen that each variable is described linearly in terms of a number of common factors and a factor unique to the particular variable. This is the classical model for factor analysis. While psychologists have in the past distinguished general and group factors among the common factors, and have also broken down the unique factors into specific and error factors, none of these refinements will be considered in the present chapter.

What is more important is to distinguish the model as exhibited in (1) from the alternative model*

$$
z_j = a_{j1}F_1 + a_{j2}F_2 + \cdots + a_{jn}F_n,
\tag{2}
$$

in which any variable j is described in terms of common factors only.

---

* Sometimes referred to as "component analysis" to distinguish it from the classical factor analysis model.

Whether model (1) or (2) is employed, the investigator usually is concerned with only a few common factors, especially if they account for a very large portion of the total communality† in the case of model (1), or the total variance in the case of model (2). This distinction can best be appreciated from the basic factor analysis problem—namely, the fitting of a set of data (the observed correlations) with a model. Under the assumption of model (1) the correlations are reproduced by means of the common-factor coefficients alone. If the reproduced correlations are to provide an appropriate fit to the observed correlations, the diagonal elements must also be reproduced from the common factor portion of (1). If numbers approximating the communalities are put in the diagonal of the matrix of observed correlations, the factor solution will involve both common and unique factors; if unities are placed in the diagonal, then the factor solution must necessarily involve *only* common factors (since only common-factor coefficients are involved in reproducing the correlations, and unities must be reproduced). Thus it should be clear that *"the values put in the diagonal of the observed correlation matrix determine what portions of the unit variances are factored into common factors"* (Harman, 1967, p. 28).

Reference Basis

Various procedures are available (see section on Direct Solutions) which yield mathematical solutions of either model (1) or (2). From such solutions a determination can be made on both statistical and practical grounds as to the number of factors that are significant to a study. Once an appropriate number of factors has been selected there remains the choice of reference basis for best interpretation of the factors in the particular field of application. This is frequently referred to as the "rotation problem" in factor analysis. In this chapter we use the term *direct solution* for the mathematical fit to the observed data, and *derived solution* for the rotation to a new basis.

A set of criteria for the determination of "more desirable" or "more meaningful" derived factors has been formulated by Thurstone in what is known as his principle of "simple structure." The psychological basis for the principle is summarized by him as follows: "Just as we take it for granted that the individual differences in visual acuity are not involved in pitch discrimination, so we assume that in intellectual tasks some mental or cortical functions are not involved in every task. This is the principle of 'simple structure' or 'simple configuration' in the underlying order for any given set of attributes" (1947, p. 58). In his 1935 work he cited three conditions for simple structure but he subsequently proposed two additional conditions as insurance for the reference hyperplane to be distinct and

---

† By definition, "communality" of a variable is its common factor variance, i.e., the sum of the squares of the common factor coefficients in model (1). By total communality we mean the sum of the communalities of all the variables or, in mathematical terms, the trace of the correlation matrix with communalities in the diagonal.

overdetermined by the data (1947, p. 335). His criteria may be put in the following form (Harman, 1967, p. 98):

1) Each row of the factor matrix should have at least one zero.

2) If there are m common factors, each column of the factor matrix should have at least m zeros.

3) For every pair of columns of the factor matrix there should be several variables whose entries vanish in one column but not in the other.

4) For every pair of columns of the factor matrix, a large proportion of the variables should have vanishing entries in both columns when there are four or more factors.

5) For every pair of columns of the factor matrix there should be only a small number of variables with nonvanishing entries in both columns.

In the foregoing it was tacitly assumed that the factors are uncorrelated, otherwise the term "factor matrix" would be completely ambiguous. In a factor solution like (1) the coefficients of the common factors are usually exhibited as a matrix or in a table that is defined as the "factor pattern." Another concept important in factor analysis is the correlation between each variable and each factor. A table of such correlations is called a "factor structure." Only in the case of *uncorrelated* factors are the elements of a structure identical with the corresponding coefficients of a pattern (Harman, 1967, pp. 19–21). Thus when the factors are oblique (i.e., correlated) the pattern is distinct from the structure and any reference to the "factor matrix" is vague and can be misleading. It should be noted that Thurstone's criteria for simple structure may lead to either an orthogonal or an oblique factor solution, which is frequently called a "multiple-factor" solution.

In the attempt to get simplified descriptions of a set of variables by rotation of an arbitrary factor solution to one that exhibits simple structure, researchers have for many years resorted to graphical methods. It was realized that this subjective approach would have to yield to some objective definition of simple structure if an associated analytical procedure for simple structure solution were to be attained. The first truly objective method for determining psychologically meaningful factors was developed by Carroll (1953). While he considered Thurstone's criteria for simple structure, he quickly ruled out the likelihood of a single mathematical expression embodying all these characteristics. This conscious departure was aptly stated by Kaiser (1958, p. 188) as "the first attempt to break away from an inflexible devotion to Thurstone's ambiguous, arbitrary, and mathematically unmanageable qualitative rules for his intuitively compelling notion of simple structure." Some of the currently popular analytical rotation methods are indicated in the section on Derived Solutions.

Measurement of Factors

Another major concept in factor analysis is the measurement of factors or "factor scores." All too often in the past the researcher was content with the linear descriptions of the variables in terms of the factors, especially after rotation to a basis which approximated simple structure. However, the analysis at this stage is still incomplete for many purposes. It would seem to be useful and desirable to have profiles for the individuals in terms of the new hypothetical constructs, the factors. But these, not being directly measurable, have to be obtained through the observed variables. If we can get linear expressions for the factors in terms of the observed variables, then upon substituting the values of such variables for an individual, we can get his corresponding "factor score."

The task of getting factor measurements is rather simple and direct in the case of model (2) but becomes much more involved in the case of factor model (1). However they are calculated, the expression for any factor p in terms of the observed variables may be put in the form

$$\hat{F}_p = \beta_{p1}z_1 + \beta_{p2}z_2 + \cdots + \beta_{pn}z_n, \tag{3}$$

where the caret is placed over the F to call attention to the fact that it is an estimate of the actual factor.

NUMERICAL EXAMPLE

In order to illustrate the main features of a factor analysis—direct solution, derived solution, and factor measurements—the same very simple numerical example is employed throughout the chapter. Only $N = 12$ individuals and $n = 5$ variables are considered in order to bring out all aspects of factor analysis, while at the same

Table 1   Raw data

| Individual (Tract No.) | | Variable | | | | |
		Total popula- tion 1	Median school years 2	Total employ- ment 3	Misc. profess. services 4	Median value house 5
1	(1439)	5,700	12.8	2,500	270	25,000
2	(2078)	1,000	10.9	600	10	10,000
3	(2408)	3,400	8.8	1,000	10	9,000
4	(2621)	3,800	13.6	1,700	140	25,000
5	(7007)	4,000	12.8	1,600	140	25,000
6	(5312)	8,200	8.3	2,600	60	12,000
7	(6032)	1,200	11.4	400	10	16,000
8	(6206)	9,100	11.5	3,300	60	14,000
9	(4037)	9,900	12.5	3,400	180	18,000
10	(4605)	9,600	13.7	3,600	390	25,000
11	(5323)	9,600	9.6	3,300	80	12,000
12	(5416)	9,400	11.4	4,000	100	13,000
Mean		6,242	11.4	2,333	121	17,000
Standard deviation		3,440	1.8	1,241	115	6,368

time keeping the computation at a minimum. Although artificial data might have been contrived to yield exact mathematical solutions, it was deemed more advisable to use objective, fallible data, even though most of the standards regarding experimental design, sampling, and reliability are obviously ignored. So, while the data are "real" the results are not intended to have any real substantive value but merely to illustrate the methods, and perhaps to provide a convenient numerical problem for checking of computer programs.

With this understanding, the data in Table 1 were taken (not entirely arbitrarily) from a study (Burns and Harman, 1966) involving 67 socioeconomic variables for 1169 census tracts of the Los Angeles region. The study was designed to include groups of variables involving population, employment, income, and housing characteristics. The resulting factor analysis employing model (2) yielded seven factors. For demonstration purposes we will carry out all the steps involved in the several phases of factor analysis, in subsequent sections. However, working with the small set of data, we should not expect to replicate the results of the original study.

We begin the analysis with the computation of the correlation coefficients among all the variables. Conventionally, the correlations are displayed in tabular form along with the names of the variables, but in the present case of only five variables they are shown in the following matrix:*

$$\mathbf{R} = \begin{bmatrix} 1.00000 & 0.00975 & 0.97245 & 0.43887 & 0.02241 \\ 0.00975 & 1.00000 & 0.15428 & 0.69141 & 0.86307 \\ 0.97245 & 0.15428 & 1.00000 & 0.51472 & 0.12193 \\ 0.43887 & 0.69141 & 0.51472 & 1.00000 & 0.77765 \\ 0.02241 & 0.86307 & 0.12193 & 0.77765 & 1.00000 \end{bmatrix} . \tag{4}$$

While the calculation of the correlations is singled out as a separate step, it is done so only for ease of presentation. Nowadays, when large electronic computers are quite readily available for factor analysis work, the determination of the correlations is a trivial step in the computer process going from the raw data to the final solution. As this example is used again and again in the following sections the thread will be picked up from the correlations to the next phase and subsequent ones.

DIRECT SOLUTIONS

Computing methods for factor solutions have engaged the interest of many workers for many decades. There are several specialized techniques—Spearman's two-factor, Holzinger's bi-factor, Thurstone's centroid, and the multiple-group solu-

---

* There is no intent, of course, to impute any real statistical significance to the correlation coefficients. The only reason for showing five decimal places (as output from an IBM 7094) is to provide a means for checking numerical calculations. Most of the subsequent calculations with this example also are shown to five decimal places.

tions—which, for lack of space, cannot be developed here [see Harman, 1967, Chapters 7 and 11; and Thurstone, 1947, Chapter 8]. Before setting these aside, however, it is important to note that the centroid method provides an efficient computational compromise for the principal-factor solution when electronic computing facilities are not available.

In this section we shall consider two techniques—principal-factor and maximum-likelihood—for obtaining mathematical solutions directly from the correlation matrix of a set of variables. An alternative method, involving the minimization of off-diagonal residuals of the correlation matrix, and hence called "minres," has recently been developed [Harman, 1967, Chapter 9]. Such a procedure that would "best" reproduce the observed correlations has been sought for a long time in factor analysis. Now that it is available, it might become the preferred procedure for initial factorization of a correlation matrix in place of the very popular principal-factor and the more complex maximum-likelihood methods. In any event, the adequacy of fit of the model to the empirical data is judged on the basis of any such direct solution. After the determination of an appropriate number of factors has been made there may follow a rotation to a new reference basis, which is the subject of the following section.

Principal-Factor Solution

The most prevalent procedure for getting a factor solution from a matrix of correlations, now that high-speed computers are generally available, is the principal-factor method. The foundation was laid by Karl Pearson (1901) when he set forth "the method of principal axes," but it was not until the 1930's that the principal-factor method as we now know it was developed by Hotelling (1933).

The nature of the method can be appreciated from some geometric considerations. Just as a set of N values of two variables may be represented by a scatter diagram of N points in the plane of the two variables (as axes), so more generally the *point representation* of n variables may be conceived as one point for each of the N individuals, referred to a system of n reference axes. The loci of the swarm of points of uniform frequency density are more or less concentric, similar, and similarly situated n-dimensional ellipsoids.* The axes of these ellipsoids correspond to the factors in the principal-factor solution.

From an algebraic point of view the selection of these axes is equivalent to choosing a set of factors F_p in decreasing order of their contributions to the total variance (or communality) of a set of variables. The analysis is begun with a factor F_1, whose contribution to the variance of the variables has as great a total as possible. Then the first factor residual correlations are obtained. A second factor F_2, independent of F_1, with a maximum contribution to the residual variance is found next. This process is continued until the total variance, or a suitably large portion, is analyzed.

---

* Strictly speaking, these ellipsoids would be n-dimensional in the case of model (2) but m-dimensional for the case of m common factors of model (1).

The first step in the principal-factor method then involves the determination of the first factor coefficients a_{j1} so as to make the sum of the contributions of F_1 to the variance a maximum. In other words, the sum

$$V_1 = a_{11}^2 + a_{21}^2 + \cdots + a_{n1}^2 \tag{5}$$

is to be maximized under the conditions

$$r_{jk} = \sum_{p=1}^{m} a_{jp} a_{kp} \qquad (j, k = 1, 2, \ldots, n), \tag{6}$$

where $r_{jk} = r_{kj}$ and r_{jj} is either unity in the case of model (2) or an estimate of the communality for variable j in the case of model (1). The conditions (6) say that the observed correlations are to be replaced by the reproduced correlations from the factor analysis model, implying the assumption of zero residuals. The process of maximizing (5) under the condition (6) leads to a system of n linear homogeneous equations for the solution of the n unknown a_{j1}'s. A necessary and sufficient condition for such a system of equations to have a nontrivial solution leads to another expression known as a *characteristic equation* (Harman, 1967, Sec. 8.3). In the mathematical literature the roots of a characteristic equation are sometimes referred to as "eigenvalues" and corresponding to each eigenvalue a solution, called an "eigenvector," is obtained to the system of n linear homogeneous equations. The first or largest eigenvalue is actually equal to the sum of the contributions of the first principal factor, namely V_1, and the first eigenvector, when properly scaled, is the set of first factor coefficients.

While the method indicated above is appropriate for desk calculators* (as is an associated iterative computing procedure suggested by Hotelling), it is not the most expeditious method for programming an electronic digital computer. When it is recognized that the principal-factor method is closely related to a classical problem in mathematics—the determination of the eigenvalues and associated eigenvectors of the correlation matrix—the computation procedures of the more general mathematical field become available. The most expedient modern-day techniques actually exploit the original work in such numerical methods done by Jacobi (1846) more than a century ago.

Programs for the principal-factor solution based on a modified Jacobi method are now available for almost any electronic computer. Perhaps the most widely distributed program is BMD 03M, "Factor Analysis" (1964). While this program is specifically for the IBM 7094, it is written in FORTRAN and can easily be adapted to other computers. More generally, up-to-date reports on program developments in this area appear in the "Computers in Behavioral Science" section of *Behavioral Science.*

---

* The calculation of a principal-factor solution on a desk calculator is very laborious for problems beyond a small number of variables (say 10).

Numerical example. A principal-factor solution will now be shown for the data of the numerical example of the preceding section. Since the original study employed model (2), in which all the variance of the n variables is explained in terms of common factors, this was also done for the selected set of five variables. The results are referred to, more precisely, as a principal-component solution. A variant of the BMD 03M program was employed to do the entire analysis. First, the five eigenvalues of the matrix **R** were produced, namely,

$$2.87331, \quad 1.79666, \quad 0.21484, \quad 0.09993, \quad 0.01526.$$

Only two of these eigenvalues are greater than unity, a standard frequently employed for the determination of the number of factors to be retained for subsequent interpretation. It will be noted that these two eigenvalues (and hence the contributions of the first two components) account for 93.4% of the total variance. Of course, such a remarkable result cannot ordinarily be expected. While there is no real basis on either statistical or practical grounds for the determination of the number of factors that are significant to the "study" (consisting of the arbitrary 12 tracts and 5 variables), two factors certainly should suffice for illustrative purposes. The resulting principal-component solution is shown in Table 2.

Table 2 Principal-component solution

Variable	F_1	F_2	Variance
1	0.58096	0.80642	0.98783
2	0.76705	−0.54478	0.88515
3	0.67243	0.72604	0.97930
4	0.93239	−0.10429	0.88023
5	0.79115	−0.55816	0.93746
Contribution of factor	2.87331	1.79666	4.66997
Percent of total variance	57.5	35.9	93.4

Maximum-Likelihood Solution

In the preceding section it was stated that the principal-factor method could be employed for either of the factor analysis models (1) or (2). The maximum-likelihood method is specifically for the classical factor analysis model (1), that is, in terms of a set of common factors and a factor unique to each variable. Now, whenever the factor analysis model (1) is employed, there arises a circular problem —namely, that to distinguish common factor variance (communality) from unique variance requires an estimate of communality. In other words, the self-correlations in the diagonal of the correlation matrix must be communality values for the variables. These are difficult to come by. A vast literature exists on the "problem of communality" (Harman, 1967, Chapter 5) but no ready solution is available. The usual procedure in employing model (1) is to start with some estimates of communalities (and perhaps modify them in the course of the analysis), and with these values in the correlation matrix to get a factor solution which in some sense fits the observed data reasonably well. While the maximum-likelihood method does not require estimates of communalities in advance, it is dependent on an assumption of the number of common factors.

There is still another distinction between the maximum-likelihood solution and other methods of determining factor solutions. Although observed sample correlations must be employed in applied statistics, the treatment of the sample values is fundamentally different in the present section from that in the preceding one. Previously the sample correlation matrix was tacitly assumed to yield results interpretable in terms of the population from which the sample was drawn. There is no explicit consideration of the *statistical* problems of the uncertainty of conclusions that might be derived from the empirical data. In contradistinction, the method of the present section considers the differences between the correlations among the observed variables and the hypothetical values in the universe from which they were sampled. The method yields estimates of the universe factor weights under the assumption of the factor model (1).

In the early 1940's the first concerted efforts to provide a sound statistical basis for factor analysis were made by Lawley (1940, 1942) when he suggested the use of Fisher's "method of maximum likelihood" to estimate the universe values of the factor loadings from given empirical data. The maximum-likelihood method requires a hypothesis regarding the number of common factors and then, according to such hypothesis, there is derived a factor solution with the accompanying communalities. A test of significance to determine the adequacy of the hypothesis regarding the number of factors is associated with the method.

Although the maximum-likelihood principle for the estimation of factor weights is relatively simple, the algebraic manipulations certainly are not. Apart from the intricate mathematical development there remains the laborious computing task in handling the rather complex equations resulting from the maximum-likelihood method. Even with modern high-speed electronic computers it frequently takes considerable time to obtain a maximum-likelihood factor solution. One of the troublesome things about the maximum-likelihood method is that convergence cannot always be assured. While there has been no mathematical proof of the convergence of the method there is strong indication that it will do so for most practical cases.

In recent years a number of workers have attempted to develop more efficient algorithms for the computation of maximum-likelihood factor solutions. No such solution is unique (in the same sense as the principal-factor solution is unique for a given body of data), but any one solution uniquely determines the common-factor space to a given degree of significance. In other words, one maximum-likelihood factor solution differs from another only by a rotation. To remove this inherent indeterminacy each algorithm provides some side condition which fixes the particular solution.

Table 3 Maximum-likelihood solution

Variable	L_1	L_2	Communality
1	0.99916	−0.00826	0.99838
2	0.01862	0.89923	0.80897
3	0.97415	0.10949	0.96096
4	0.44552	0.78542	0.81538
5	0.02990	0.96045	0.92335
Contribution of factor	2.14702	2.36002	4.50704

All maximum-likelihood computing methods go back to some of the original work of Lawley. A variant of the method, developed by Rao (1955), was programmed for the Illiac at the University of Illinois by Golub as early as 1954. Just in the last year or two, maximum-likelihood programs have become available for most of the well-known computers.

Numerical example. A maximum-likelihood solution for the numerical data can be obtained under the hypothesis of two common factors. While a hypothesis of one factor or perhaps three factors might have been considered, from the knowledge we already have about this problem two factors obviously was a reasonable number. The maximum-likelihood solution is exhibited in Table 3. This solution was determined with a requirement of computing accuracy for agreement within one-half unit in the third decimal place between successive iterations for any factor weight. For this degree of accuracy an initial set of factor weights* converged to the maximum-likelihood factors of Table 3 in less than one minute on a relatively slow Philco 2000 computer.

Again it should be noted that the mathematical model (1) is employed in the maximum-likelihood method and the communalities for the variables are obtained as well as the factor weights. The total communality of 4.5 represents 90% of the total variance of the five variables. This is a very exceptional situation that should not ordinarily be expected. In spite of the very high proportion of the variance accounted for by the two maximum-likelihood factors, it still is less than the amount accounted for by the first two principal components—as it should be. Of course, one of the important properties of the principal-factor solution is that each factor in turn accounts for a maximum possible portion of the variance.

The question now arises as to the adequacy of the hypothesis of two factors. From the factor weights in Table 3 we obtained the reproduced correlations in the upper triangle of Table 4, and by subtracting these, respectively, from their corresponding observed values in the correlation matrix (4) the residuals in the lower triangle of Table 4 are obtained. To determine whether these residuals are small

---

* The principal-component solution of Table 2 was employed as the starting point for the maximum-likelihood solution.

Table 4 Reproduced correlations and residuals*

Variable	1	2	3	4	5
1	0.99838	0.01118	0.97243	0.43866	0.02195
2	−0.00143	0.80897	0.11660	0.71458	0.86422
3	0.00002	0.03768	0.96096	0.52000	0.13429
4	0.00021	−0.02317	−0.00528	0.81538	0.76768
5	0.00046	−0.00115	−0.01236	0.00997	0.92335

* Reproduced correlations in the upper triangle, with communalities in the diagonal and residuals in the lower triangle.

enough, i.e., whether there is sufficient agreement between theory and fact, we resort to a statistical test. The maximum-likelihood method leads to a statistic (likelihood ratio) which is asymptotically distributed as χ^2. Hence, for large samples this χ^2-statistic may be employed to test the hypothesis regarding the number of common factors (Harman, 1967, Sec. 10.4). While our numerical example involving but twelve cases certainly is not a large sample, we did employ this statistical test just as an exercise and, again, to provide a means for checking numerical calculations. The result is $\chi^2 = 2.21306$, and since this falls well below the 5% value for one degree of freedom (namely, $\chi^2 = 3.841$), it is reasonable to regard the data as consistent with the hypothesis of two factors. Corresponding to the obtained χ^2 is the probability $P = 0.15$, which indicates that in about 15 out of 100 cases we could expect a deviation from the expected result (of zero residuals based upon two factors) at least as great as that actually observed.

DERIVED SOLUTIONS

For interpretation of factors in his particular field of application, the factor analyst usually would want to select a reference basis other than the arbitrary one produced by one of the direct solutions. Thus one is led to the "rotation problem" after getting a principal-factor or maximum-likelihood solution. In this section, objective computer procedures—analytical rotation methods—for approximating simple structure are briefly described for both orthogonal and oblique factors.

Orthogonal Multiple-Factor Solution

Basically, the rotation problem requires the determination of a matrix $\mathbf{B} = (b_{jp})$ of final factor weights from an initial factor matrix $\mathbf{A} = (a_{jp})$ employing an orthogonal transformation matrix $\mathbf{T} = (t_{qp})$, that is,

$$\mathbf{B} = \mathbf{AT}. \tag{7}$$

The problem is more easily stated than accomplished. In trying to select a preferred solution out of an infinitude of possible solutions, parsimony is a prime consideration, and it is also the basis of the simple structure principles listed on page 148. Several workers have attempted to ascribe precise mathematical meaning to a measure of parsimony with consequent variations in their solution of the rotation problem (Harman, 1967, Chapter 14). Underlying all these methods is the maximization (or an equivalent minimization) of the sum of fourth powers of the elements of the final factor matrix **B**. It should be clear that the very concept of engaging in this type of computation could hardly have been conceived before the days of large electronic computers. In the early 1950's independent approaches to the problem were made by Carroll (1953), Neuhaus and Wrigley (1954), and Saunders (1953). Each viewed the rotation problem as an attempt to reduce the complexity in **A** of the factorial descriptions of the variables so that in **B** each variable would have one or a few large weights and many values near zero. Since the several criteria which they developed all lead to identical results for an orthogonal solution **B**, these methods are generally encompassed under the term "quartimax method," due to Neuhaus and Wrigley. The object of the quartimax method is to determine the orthogonal transformation **T** which will carry the original factor matrix **A** into a new factor matrix **B** for which the variance of squared factor loadings (i.e., fourth powers) is a maximum.

While the emphasis in the quartimax method is on simplification of the description of each *row,* or variable, of the factor matrix **B**, Kaiser (1958) places more emphasis on simplifying the *columns,* or factors, in an attempt to meet the requirements for simple structure. In getting simplification of each variable it is quite possible that a large loading might appear on the same factor for most of the variables, i.e., a general factor. In Kaiser's approach a general factor is precluded by the simplicity constraint on each factor. Kaiser's solution, known as the "varimax method," is perhaps the most popular method for obtaining orthogonal multiple-factor solutions.

The essence of the varimax method involves the variance of the squared loadings of a factor p, namely,

$$\sigma_p^2 = \frac{1}{n}\sum_{j=1}^{n}(b_{jp}^2)^2 - \frac{1}{n^2}\left(\sum_{j=1}^{n}b_{jp}^2\right)^2 \qquad (p = 1, 2, \ldots, m). \tag{8}$$

When this variance is at a maximum the factor has the greatest interpretability or simplicity in the sense that its components (the b's) tend toward unity and zero. The varimax criterion of maximum simplicity of a complete factor matrix is defined as the maximization of the sum of the simplicities of the individual factors as follows:

$$V = n\sum_{p=1}^{m}\sum_{j=1}^{n}(b_{jp}/h_j)^4 - \sum_{p=1}^{m}\left(\sum_{j=1}^{n}b_{jp}^2/h_j^2\right)^2, \tag{9}$$

in which adjustments are made in the correlations of variables with factors by introducing the h_j (the square roots of the communalities of the variables). The varimax method yields an orthogonal multiple-factor solution in which the final factor loadings maximize the function V.

Many computer programs are available for the varimax method, usually as part of a "factor analysis package" which has the principal-factor method for the direct solution.

Numerical example. To carry out the factor analysis for the illustrative problem we next consider a change in the reference system which yields more meaningful derived factors for the interpretation of the five socio-economic variables. So far the analysis is in terms of either the principal-axis or the maximum-likelihood factors. Either one of these can serve as a starting point for rotation to the varimax solution. The initial factor matrix actually employed in our computer program was the principal-component solution of Table 2. The derived orthogonal multiple-factor solution is shown in Table 5, where the factors are designated by M's to distinguish them from the initial factors (F's). Of course, the individual factor coefficients are altered as the result of the rotation, as is also the contribution of each of the two factors. However, the variance of each variable and the total contribution of the two factors remain the same. Put another way, the proportion of the total variance accounted for by either set of factors is unaltered. This probably can best be appreciated from geometric considerations—once the space is determined by the choice of the number of principal factors, a rotation to a new basis in the same space has no effect on the lengths of the vectors representing the variables. The square of the length of each vector is its variance (Harman, 1967, pp. 64–66) which is given in the last column of Table 5. Since these are common-factor variances they represent the communality of each of the variables.

Table 5   Final orthogonal solution: varimax rotation from two principal components

Variable	M_1	M_2	Variance
1	0.01602	0.99377	0.98783
2	0.94079	−0.00883	0.88515
3	0.13702	0.98006	0.97930
4	0.82479	0.44714	0.88022
5	0.96821	−0.00604	0.93747
Contribution of factor	2.52182	2.14815	4.66997
Percent of total variance	50.4	43.0	93.4

If one were to compare the values in Table 5 with those in Table 3 he would find a remarkable correspondence between the varimax solution and maximum-likelihood solution (M_1 being most like L_2, and M_2 like L_1). This agreement is quite striking but probably spurious. Although other workers also have found some tendency of the maximum-likelihood solution to resemble the varimax solution, the contrary also is true—there are examples of maximum-likelihood solutions which no more resemble simple structure than the principal-factor solution.

The varimax solution of Table 5 is indeed a multiple-factor solution satisfying the simple structure criteria (see p. 148). Of course, for so few variables the conditions cannot be taken too literally. The factor weights of 0 or 1 in the first decimal place certainly may be viewed as essentially zero. In this sense the factor matrix exhibits one zero in each row, with the exception of variable 4; two zeros in each column; and several variables whose entries vanish in one column but not in the other. Even the exception of variable 4 is not contradictory to the set of simple-structure criteria (see number 5). Again it should be emphasized that the simple-structure criteria have compelling intuitive value but lack the precision necessary for mathematical computation. The varimax solution, on the other hand, is a precisely defined method which indeed approximates simple structure.

At this point in the analysis the researcher usually is concerned with naming and interpreting the final factors. In the study (Burns and Harman, 1966) from which this little example was taken, the results included seven factors. There is actually little relationship between the experimental design of the original study and our trivial example. However, the five variables were selected with the prior knowledge of their factorial composition in the larger study, and hence the resulting analysis might be expected to be interpretable in the setting of the former. Specifically, M_1 is most like the "education-economic factor" while M_2 bears resemblance to the "population-employment factor." These rough conclusions were drawn from a comparison of the factor weights as obtained in the present example with the factor weights for the same five variables embedded in the larger study.

Oblique Multiple-Factor Solution

During the 1930's the strong preference among factor analysts was for orthogonal multiple-factor solutions. Sometime in the middle 40's there was a resurgence of interest, following Thurstone, in oblique multiple-factor solutions. Of course, the approach was subjective, employing graphical methods, just as in the orthogonal case. Then, in the early 1950's, analytical methods for oblique solutions followed on the heels of the new developments for the orthogonal multiple-factor solutions. However, while the problem of analytical rotation in the orthogonal case is essentially resolved, analytical methods for the oblique case are fundamentally different and still in a developmental state, with several distinct methods available for getting oblique factor solutions (Harman, 1960, Chapter 15).

As noted in the last section, the problem of getting a derived multiple-factor solution from some initial solution involves a rotation or transformation, namely (7) for the orthogonal case. In order to distinguish the oblique case, the general form of the transformation may be noted as follows:

$$\mathbf{V} = \mathbf{A}\mathbf{\Lambda}, \tag{10}$$

where the matrix $\mathbf{A} = (a_{jp})$ of an initial orthogonal factor solution is carried into a final oblique factor structure matrix $\mathbf{V} = (v_{jp})$ by means of the transformation matrix $\mathbf{\Lambda} = (\lambda_{qp})$, whose columns contain the direction cosines of the oblique axes with respect to the orthogonal frame of reference. It should be clear that oblique solutions involve some additional concepts and therefore may be somewhat more complicated than orthogonal solutions.

In an orthogonal solution the basic concept is that of resolution of a set of variables linearly in terms of factors, as indicated in (1), where the problem is that of determining the coefficients (a's). Even after rotation to a derived orthogonal solution it is just a set of coefficients (b's) that is sought. In the oblique case, however, two sets of numbers are required for the complete factor analysis as well as the correlations among the factors. These two sets are referred to as the *factor pattern,* consisting of the coefficients of the factors in the linear description of the variables, and the *factor structure,* consisting of the correlations between the variables and the factors. Only in the case of orthogonal (uncorrelated) factors are the elements of a structure identical with the corresponding coefficients of a pattern.

The resolution of a set of variables into oblique factors becomes even more complicated. Not only do we have the distinct concepts of pattern and structure, but because of the way that the oblique solution was developed by Thurstone (1947, Chapter 15) we actually have two sets of these. In his attempt to satisfy the simple structure criteria (p. 148) by graphical means, Thurstone introduced an ingenious concept of a reference axis orthogonal to a hyperplane,* thereby assuring that all variables in that hyperplane would have a zero projection on that axis. While each such reference axis is orthogonal to a corresponding hyperplane, the reference axes in general are not at right angles to one another. The matrix of projections of the vectors representing the variables on the set of oblique reference axes (Λ_p) is classically referred to as the "oblique factor matrix **V**." Such a matrix, of course, is a factor structure showing the correlations between the variables and factors, in this case the reference axes. There is actually little interest in these reference axes *per se,* but there is an exact mathematical relationship between such reference axes and the desired primary factors [Harman, 1967, Eq. (13.43)]. The primary factors (also oblique) lie in the respective hyperplanes to which the reference factors are orthogonal. Hence, for each set of factors (reference and primary) there is associated a structure and a pattern.† There is essentially a proportionality relationship between the structure of one system and the pattern of the other. For this reason, emphasis has been placed on the "oblique factor matrix **V**" because any deductions therefrom apply to the primary factor pattern as well. A fuller discussion of these concepts is beyond the scope of this chapter (Harman, 1967, Secs. 2.5, 13.5, 15.5).

Carroll's original work (1953) sets forth a criterion for solving (10) which involves a minimization of the sum of cross products of squared factor loadings. By lifting the constraint that the factors be orthogonal in the rotated solution and taking the term "loadings" to stand for the reference structure values (the v_{jp}'s) this criterion can also serve to get an oblique simple structure solution. Kaiser (1958) also proposes an oblique version of the varimax criterion. Carroll's method

---

* For a given space, a hyperplane in a linear subspace of dimension one fewer than the total space.
† Jennrich and Sampson (1966) dispense with this bi-orthogonal system in their development of a direct analytical procedure for obtaining an oblique primary-factor solution.

has come to be called "quartimin" and Kaiser's oblique version, "covarimin." From a consideration of these two methods, Carroll first proposed the simple sum of the two criteria to combine their advantages. Subsequently he generalized the sum of the two separate criteria to permit varying weights of the "quartimin" and "covarimin" components. This final "biquartimin" criterion (in terms of normalized loadings) is given by:

$$B = \sum_{p<q=1}^{m} \left[n \sum_{j=1}^{n} (v_{jp}^2/h_j^2)(v_{jq}^2/h_j^2) - \gamma \sum_{j=1}^{n} v_{jp}^2/h_j^2 \sum_{j=1}^{n} v_{jq}^2/h_j^2 \right] = \min, \qquad (11)$$

where the parameter γ determines the relative weights of the two criteria in the particular oblique solution.

A computer program using this criterion was developed by Carroll as early as 1958 for use on the IBM 704 (Carroll, 1960). Again, because the program is written in FORTRAN, it can readily be adapted to other computers. In the illustration that follows, this program was used on a Philco 2000.

Numerical example.   To get an oblique factor solution for the five socioeconomic variables any suitable orthogonal factorization of these variables can serve as the starting point. In what follows there are actually several distinct oblique solutions, all derived from the initial principal-component solution of Table 2. Specifically, values of 0, 1, and 0.5 were employed for the parameter γ in the criterion (11) to obtain the three oblique reference structures shown in Table 6. Although any value of γ between 0 and 1 can be employed, the three particular values give the special types of oblique solutions that have been of interest to factor analysts. It has been found from experience that the quartimin solution ($\gamma = 0$) tends to be "too oblique" while the covarimin ($\gamma = 1$) tends to be "too orthogonal," hence, the biquartimin solution ($\gamma = 0.5$) is offered as a compromise to correct for these biases. These properties are borne out even with the trivial example of five variables.

To clarify the distinction between the two coordinate systems inherent in an oblique solution, we present the primary factors (T_p) as well as the reference factors (Λ_p) for the quartimin solution.* One of the outputs of the computer program is the transformation matrix

$$\Lambda = \begin{pmatrix} 0.7515 & 0.4758 \\ -0.6597 & 0.8795 \end{pmatrix}.$$

It can readily be verified that if the initial matrix **A** (from Table 2) is postmultiplied by this matrix Λ, then according to (10) the quartimin reference structure **V** is obtained (first section of Table 6). In place of (10), the transformation which carries the initial orthogonal solution **A** into the oblique primary-factor structure **S** can be denoted by

$$S = AT, \qquad (12)$$

---

* This solution was selected for illustration only because it was the most oblique and would, therefore, best point out the special features of an oblique solution.

Table 6   Three oblique factor matrices **V**

Variable	Quartimin ($\gamma = 0$) reference structure		Covarimin ($\gamma = 1$) reference structure		Biquartimin ($\gamma = 0.5$) reference structure	
	Λ_1	Λ_2	Λ_1	Λ_2	Λ_1	Λ_2
1	−0.0954	0.9857	0.0160	0.9938	−0.0366	0.9909
2	0.9359	−0.1142	0.9408	−0.0088	0.9399	−0.0669
3	0.0264	0.9585	0.1370	0.9801	0.0850	0.9697
4	0.7695	0.3519	0.8248	0.4471	0.8000	0.3954
5	0.9628	−0.1145	0.9682	−0.0061	0.9672	−0.0658
Correlation between primary factors	0.2226		−0.0000		0.1144	
Angle between axes	77°		90°		83°	

where now the matrix **T** contains in its columns the direction cosines of the oblique primary axes with respect to the orthogonal frame of reference [not to be confused with the transformation matrix **T** employed in (7) for an orthogonal rotation]. It is not necessary to obtain this transformation from **A** to **S** independently. As noted earlier, there is a fixed relationship between the reference structure **V** and the primary pattern **P**, and within each system a structure can be obtained from a pattern or *vice versa*.

The matrix **T** can be obtained from the matrix **A** by normalizing (i.e., dividing by the square root of the sum of squares) the rows of $\mathbf{A}^{-1}$. The diagonal matrix that accomplishes this is

$$\mathbf{D} = \begin{bmatrix} 0.97488 & 0 \\ 0 & 0.97488 \end{bmatrix},$$

and the transpose of the primary-factor transformation matrix is

$$\mathbf{T}' = \mathbf{D}\mathbf{A}^{-1} = \begin{bmatrix} 0.8795 & -0.4758 \\ 0.6597 & 0.7515 \end{bmatrix}. \quad (13)$$

The matrix of correlations among the primary factors is given by

$$\mathbf{\Phi} = \mathbf{T}'\mathbf{T} = \begin{bmatrix} 1.0000 & 0.2226 \\ 0.2226 & 1.0000 \end{bmatrix}. \quad (14)$$

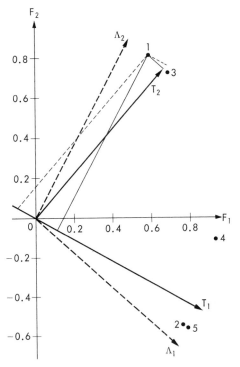

Fig. 1. Distinction between primary [*T*] and reference (Λ) factors (quartimin solution).

Table 7 Final oblique primary-factor solution: quartimin rotation from two principal components

Variable	Structure: **S**		Pattern: **P**	
j	r_{jT_1}	r_{jT_2}	T_1	T_2
1	0.1272	0.9893	−0.0979	1.0111
2	0.9339	0.0966	0.9600	−0.1171
3	0.2460	0.9892	0.0271	0.9832
4	0.8697	0.5367	0.7893	0.3610
5	0.9614	0.1023	0.9876	−0.1175

Actually, it is not necessary to carry out the transformation (12) which involves the initial factor matrix because the primary-factor pattern is given by [Harman, 1967, Eq. (13.43)]:

$$\mathbf{P} = \mathbf{VD}^{-1} \tag{15}$$

and the primary-factor structure is given by [Harman, 1967, Eq. 13.24]:

$$\mathbf{S} = \mathbf{P\Phi}. \tag{16}$$

From the foregoing relationships the final solution, shown in Table 7, is obtained by simple matrix multiplications. Here the structure and pattern are for the same (primary) factors and together with the correlations among the factors (only the one correlation $r_{T_1T_2} = 0.2226$ in the case of our simple example) constitute the complete solution. The structure consists of the correlations between the variables and the respective factors and usually is displayed in tabular or matrix form. The pattern consists of the linear descriptions of the variables in terms of the factors and may be displayed in equation form as in (1), or, more compactly, the coefficients of the factors may be exhibited in a table. Both the structure and pattern for the quartimin primary factors are shown in Table 7, while only the structure for the quartimin reference factors is shown in Table 6. The distinction between these factors is exhibited in Fig. 1. The property of reference factors being orthogonal to hyperplanes is immediately evident—in the case of a two-space (a plane), a hyperplane is merely a one-space (a line). Thus Λ_1 is perpendicular to T_2 and Λ_2 is perpendicular to T_1. Of course, each set of factors (the T's or the Λ's) is oblique. The primary factors are separated by an angle of less than 90° and have a positive correlation while the reference factors are separated by more than 90° and have a negative correlation.

The distinction between structure values and pattern values in an oblique solution can be demonstrated geometrically also by use of Fig. 1. The four numbers on the first line of Table 7 may be interpreted in the following manner. The correlations of variable 1 with the two primary factors are simply the orthogonal projections of point 1 on T_1 and T_2, respectively. The coefficients in a factor pattern may be considered as the coordinates of a point representing the variable. Such interpretation may be made whether the coordinates are with respect to orthogonal or oblique axes representing the factors. Thus the last two numbers for variable 1 in Table 7 are the coordinates for T_1 and T_2, respectively. The first value (-0.0979) is obtained by drawing a line through point 1 parallel to the T_2-axis and reading the intercept on the T_1-axis. Similarly, the second coordinate (1.0111) is the intercept on T_2 of a line through point 1 parallel to the T_1-axis. It should be noted that the coordinates (factor coefficients) may be positive or negative and may be greater than one. A correlation coefficient (structure value) also may be positive or negative but can never exceed unity. It may also be observed that the coordinates and correlations approach coincidence as the factors approach orthogonality.

The structure and pattern have unique meanings and complement each other in providing complete understanding of an oblique solution. In general, for a set of positively correlated primary factors, the structure contains all positive entries while the pattern has many high positive values and many values near zero. The primary-factor structure is useful in obtaining factor measurements for which correlations of the variables with the factors are necessary (see following section). However, the structure does not provide a very good indication of "saturation" of the variables with the factors. The primary-factor pattern gives this precisely and thereby is most useful for identification of the factors.

By way of illustration, variable 1 correlates 0.1272 with the first primary factor and 0.9893 with the second factor. However, its saturation with these factors can best be obtained from the linear equation

$$z_1 = -0.0979T_1 + 1.0111T_2,$$

which comes from the first line of the factor pattern. The direct contributions of factors T_1 and T_2 to the variance of variable 1 and 0.0096 and 1.0223, respectively, while $2(-0.0979)(1.0111)(0.2226) = -0.0441$ is attributable to the joint influence of the two factors. The sum (0.9878) of these three portions is the common-factor variance of variable 1 as employed in the initial solution (see Table 2). By truncating the solution to two common factors, only 0.0122 of the variance of this variable is lost. In other words, as far as this variable is concerned, the combined contributions of the three additional factors stemming from a complete component analysis would be only this small amount. It is for such practical reasons that a relatively small number of components are retained when model (2) is employed.

FACTOR MEASUREMENTS

After an initial factorization of the correlation matrix and the subsequent rotation to approximate simple structure, there remains the problem of the measurement of these final factors. When a set of n variables is analyzed in terms of common factors only, employing unities in the diagonal of the correlation matrix $\mathbf{R}$, the component solution of model (2) may be put in matrix form as follows:

$$\mathbf{Z} = \mathbf{AF}. \tag{17}$$

The solution is in terms of n common factors so that $\mathbf{A}$ is a square nonsingular matrix which then has an inverse. The required factor measurements are given simply by

$$\mathbf{F} = \mathbf{A}^{-1}\mathbf{Z}. \tag{18}$$

In this case the factor measurements are calculated immediately from the factor matrix $\mathbf{A}$.

On the other hand, for the factor model (1), involving both common and unique factors, the solution is not so simple. The matrix $\mathbf{A}$ would then be singular and it would be meaningless to speak of its inverse. In this case the accepted practice is to resort to the "best fit" in the least squares sense. The linear regression of any factor F_p on the n variables is formally expressed by (3). The determination of the coefficients in such a regression equation involves the correlation matrix $\mathbf{R}$ and the correlations between the variables and the factors. In matrix form the factor measurements are given [Harman, 1967, Eq. (16.19)] by:

$$\hat{\mathbf{F}} = \mathbf{S}'\mathbf{R}^{-1}\mathbf{Z}. \tag{19}$$

While this formula employs the factor structure explicitly, by taking into account the relationship (16) it can be rewritten in the form

$$\hat{\mathbf{F}} = \mathbf{\Phi}\mathbf{P}'\mathbf{R}^{-1}\mathbf{Z} \tag{20}$$

which is in terms of the factor pattern and the correlations among the oblique factors. Of course, if the factors are orthogonal, formulas (19) and (20) collapse to the same expression not involving any factor correlations.

The estimation of factors by means of formulas (19) or (20) may be too time-consuming even with large electronic computers. The inverse of an $n \times n$ matrix of correlations is involved, and this task is very laborious as n becomes large. A substitute method may be employed which involves the calculation of the inverse of an $m \times m$ matrix where m is the number of factors and usually is considerably smaller than the number of variables. This method (Harman, 1967, Sec. 16.7) is based on the assumption that the correlations reproduced by the factor solution are equal to the observed correlations (i.e., the residuals vanish). This condition will not be met with empirical data, but if the factor solution provides a reasonable explanation of the correlations, then the short method for estimating factors will approach the complete estimation method.

Numerical example. While several factor solutions have been obtained—the direct principal-factor and maximum-likelihood solutions (Tables 2 and 3), and the derived orthogonal multiple-factor solution (Table 5) and oblique multiple-factor solution (Table 7)—the procedure for getting individual factor measurements is demonstrated only for the varimax factors (Table 5). As noted earlier, such measurements can be obtained only indirectly through the observed variables. If expressions like (3) can be found for the factors in terms of the variables, then the factor measurements for any individual can be obtained by putting his values in these expressions.

The process of getting expressions for the factors in terms of the variables involves the inversion of the correlation matrix. For the present example, this was produced by the computer as follows:

$$\mathbf{R}^{-1} = \begin{bmatrix} 31.83863 & 7.29003 & -31.20393 & -1.17161 & -2.28968 \\ 7.29003 & 5.62699 & -7.34701 & -0.25599 & -3.92501 \\ -31.20393 & -7.34701 & 32.44735 & -0.82318 & 3.72429 \\ -1.17161 & -0.25599 & -0.82318 & 4.66689 & -3.28166 \\ -2.28968 & -3.92501 & 3.72429 & -3.28166 & 6.53678 \end{bmatrix},$$

and is presented here for possible use in checking numerical calculations. Another incidental value of $\mathbf{R}^{-1}$ is that it provides a simple means of getting the multiple correlation of each of the observed variables on all remaining ones. The squared multiple correlations are obtained immediately from $\mathbf{R}^{-1}$ by use of the formula

$$SMC_j = R^2_{j.12\cdots)j(\cdots n} = 1 - \frac{1}{r^{jj}}, \tag{21}$$

where r^{jj} is the diagonal element in $\mathbf{R}^{-1}$ corresponding to variable z_j. For the five variables of the example these SMC's are as follows:

$$R^2_{1.2345} = 0.96859, \qquad R^2_{2.1345} = 0.82229, \qquad R^2_{3.1245} = 0.96918,$$

$$R^2_{4.1235} = 0.78572, \qquad R^2_{5.1234} = 0.84702.$$

The computer program for factor measurements first calculates equations for the factors in terms of standardized variables and then makes the simple transformation to the raw scores. To save space, only the latter are presented.

$$\hat{M}_1 = -0.00003X_1 + 0.21970X_2 - 0.00003X_3 + 0.00261X_4 + 0.00006X_5 - 3.66818,$$

$$\hat{M}_2 = 0.00014X_1 - 0.05396X_2 + 0.00037X_3 + 0.00120X_4 - 0.00002X_5 - 1.01984.$$

The 12 pairs of individual measurements are then obtained by substituting the raw data from Table 1 into these equations; the results are shown in Table 8. These serve as index numbers, giving factor profiles for each individual (census tract) so that those with high, average, or low values on the varimax factors can be noted.

Table 8 Factor measurements for individuals (varimax factors derived from principal components)

Individual	$\hat{M}_1$	$\hat{M}_2$	Individual	$\hat{M}_1$	$\hat{M}_2$
1	1.20288	-0.03075	7	-0.16815	-1.54934
2	-0.65906	-1.38356	8	-0.44118	0.73439
3	-1.25941	-0.76738	9	0.32042	0.91301
4	1.11491	-0.79697	10	1.57629	1.02554
5	0.93703	-0.76317	11	-0.94632	0.96186
6	-1.22530	0.54864	12	-0.45209	1.10773

The multiple correlation for each of the factors is precisely unity because the component analysis model (2) was employed. For the same reason the factor measurements are actually standard scores. If model (1) had been employed it would be expected that the multiple correlation in the prediction of any factor from the variables would have a value less than 1, and the associated factor measurements would have a standard deviation equal to that multiple correlation (< 1) and hence not be precise standard scores.

USES AND ABUSES

This chapter contains a concise treatment of factor analysis—its key aspects, underlying assumptions and areas of choice, and operational procedures. It also touches lightly on some of the historical developments. Before leaving the subject, a few more comments and cautions may be in order.

Factor analysis has had a turbulent history including many able students and ardent admirers as well as a considerable number of critics. It was early recognized by many as a powerful means for coping with large bodies of interrelated data. This, in spite of the fact that the statistical problems and computational demands appeared to be insurmountable at times. The critics pointed out the inadequate statistical treatment on the one hand, and the seeming deification of factors by psychologists on the other. Nonetheless, in retrospect the development of factor analysis has not been too unlike the history of any other new discipline.

The pro and con of factor analysis has been the subject of the retiring presidential address of the Psychometric Society in at least a half-dozen instances. While these usually contained a liberal sprinkling of facetiousness and good humor, they also carried with them the not-so-hidden admonition to mend or improve our ways. In his satirical and critical appraisal of the behavior of factor analysts, McNemar noted "the apparent fact that after twenty years of factoring there is altogether too little acceptance of the method and the results obtained thereby" (1951, p. 353). While he presumed that the methods of factor analysis had reached scientific maturity, he could not say as much for its users. In reality vast advances have been made to enhance the scientific merit of factor analysis since 1951, but along with many proper applications of the technique there also have been instances of misuse.

Strangely enough, certain practices which were perfectly acceptable with more conventional statistical tools were questioned or frowned upon when similarly applied with factor analysis. For example, one required no justification for the use of multiple-regression techniques in an exploration for a "best" set of predictor variables, but his exploratory work with factor analysis was taboo. Frequently a factor analysis study was condemned as invalid because of lack of statistical rigor when such rigor was not even implied. In this regard it is important to distinguish between statistical and practical significance in applied work. Statistical significance implies a formal test with an associated probability level. Inferences about certain numerical values obtained from an empirical study cannot be made in an absolute sense, but must be made in terms of some kind of degree of belief, i.e., in a probabilistic sense. Then, if the difference between the theoretical value of a statistic and its value derived from the observed data were significant, say, at the one percent level, one would conclude that the difference was "real," and reject the null hypothesis of no difference. However, there may be practical considerations which vitiate such a conclusion. There may be real statistical additional information but it may have no practical importance. Thus in testing a hypothesis for the number of common factors required to explain the relationships in an observed correlation matrix (based upon a very large sample), the last one or two factors may prove to be highly significant in a statistical sense and still have no practical significance.

Through long and extensive experience factor analysts have developed crude guides for "when to stop factoring," which come remarkably close to the more exact statistical tests. One such guide is to consider the incremental value of any additional factor after a large portion of the total variance is accounted for. Thus after 75% of the variance is explained by several factors, any additional factor accounting for less than 5% would not be retained. Such arbitrary consideration is quite apart from the statistical significance of such an additional factor—the factor is dropped because the decision was made beforehand that any factor having such small impact on the total variance could hardly have any practical value. Another standard stemming from experience is to retain a number of common factors which is equal to the number of eigenvalues greater than unity in the principal-component solution based upon model (2). This number generally runs from one sixth to about one third of the total number of variables (despite the apparent exception of two out of five variables for our little example). The foregoing guides provide a practical basis for finding the number of common factors that are necessary, reliable, and meaningful for explanation of the correlations among the variables.

Many of the troublesome problems of factor analysis have been resolved, and the method and the wherewithal for its use is available to any serious researcher. Now, the pendulum has swung in the other direction—it is almost too easy to use factor analysis and, unfortunately, it is sometimes employed indiscriminately. The fact that it is easy to turn over to the computer any amount of data is no excuse to use the computer as a dumping ground and expect any meaningful results. The facility with which data can be handled by the computer should not lead to the use of masses of data without purpose. Instead, even more attention should be paid by the researcher to the problems of appropriate experimental design, collection of data, correction and refinement of data, as well as the analysis and interpretation of results.

In designing his experiment the researcher should plan to have groups of variables measure some common attributes. At the same time he should avoid inadvertent mathematical dependence, where one variable is an exact linear combination of several others. This can easily happen if one merely collects all the variables at hand. The simplest example is to take a given variable for males and females separately, and then also to include the total. Instances of linear dependence can creep in without being so obvious. When a factor analysis study is well planned, the full correlation matrix **R** (with ones in the diagonal) will ordinarily be of rank n for n variables. In employing the classical factor analysis model, the problem is to select new values for the diagonal (the communalities) so that the rank of the "reduced" correlation matrix is less than n. Of course, this is not intended in the exact mathematical sense, but rather statistically as in the maximum-likelihood method.

In the computer age, there is inherent a potential for fundamentally new methods and techniques of research and the discovery of new knowledge in the behavioral sciences. However, to attain such goals we must guard against blind commitment to the machine. There is real danger in becoming so dependent upon the machine that problems which could properly be treated by simpler and more penetrating means might actually—without due consideration—be directed to the computer for solution. As in all scientific discoveries, we must examine most carefully where the new methods may lead us.

With proper use of the technique and of the computer, factor analysis provides a most effective means for studying and synthesizing the multidimensional characteristics of a wide variety of data in the social sciences.

REFERENCES

BMD: Biomedical computer programs. Los Angeles: U. of California, Health Sciences Computing Facility, School of Medicine, 1964

BURNS, L. S., and A. J. HARMAN, "The complex metropolis," Part V of *Profile of the Los Angeles Metropolis: Its People and its Homes.* Los Angeles: University of California Press, 1966

CARROLL, J. B., "An analytical solution for approximating simple structure in factor analysis." *Psychometrika* **18,** 23–38 (1953)

CARROLL, J. B., "IBM 704 program for generalized analytic rotation solution in factor analysis." Unpublished, Harvard University, 1960

EYSENK, H. J., "The logical basis of factor analysis." *Amer. Psychologist* **8,** 105–114 (1953)

GARNETT, J. C. M., "On certain independent factors in mental measurement." *Proc. Roy. Soc. London* **46,** 91–111 (1919)

GOLUB, G. H., "On the number of significant factors as determined by the method of maximum likelihood." Unpublished, University of Illinois, 1954

HARMAN, H. H., *Modern Factor Analysis (Rev. Ed.)* Chicago: University of Chicago Press, 1967

HOTELLING, H., "Analysis of a complex of statistical variables into principal components." *J. Educ. Psychol.* **24,** 417–441; 498–520 (1933)

JACOBI, C. G. J., "Über ein leichtes Verfahren die in der Theorie der Säcularstörungen vorkommeden Gleichungen numerisch aufzulösen." *J. Reine Angewandte Mathematik* **30,** 51–94 (1846)

JENNRICH, R. I., and P. F. SAMPSON, "Rotation for simple loadings." *Psychometrika* **31,** 313–323 (1966)

KAISER, H. F., "The varimax criterion for analytical rotation in factor analysis." *Psychometrika* **23**, 187–200 (1958)

KELLEY, T. L., *Fundamentals of Statistics*. Cambridge: Harvard University Press, 1947

KENDALL, M. G., "Factor analysis as a statistical technique." *J. Roy. Stat. Soc.* **12**, 60–73 (1950)

LAWLEY, D. N., "The estimation of factor loadings by the method of maximum likelihood." *Proc. Roy. Soc. Edinburgh Series A* **60**, 64–82 (1940)

LAWLEY, D. N., "Further investigations in factor estimation." *Proc. Roy. Soc. Edinburgh Series A* **61**, 176–185 (1942)

MCNEMAR, Q., "The factors in factoring behavior." *Psychometrika* **16**, 353–359 (1951)

NEUHAUS, J. O., and C. WRIGLEY, "The quartimax method: An analytical approach to orthogonal simple structure." *Brit. J. Stat. Psychol.* **7**, 81–91 (1954)

PEARSON, K., "On lines and planes of closest fit to systems of points in space." *Phil. Mag.* **6**, 559–572 (1901)

RAO, C. R., "Estimation and tests of significance in factor analysis." *Psychometrika* **20**, 93–111 (1955)

SAUNDERS, D. R., "An analytic method for rotation to orthogonal simple structure." *Research Bulletin* 53–10. Princeton: Educational Testing Service, 1953

SPEARMAN, C., "General intelligence, objectively determined and measured." *Amer. J. Psychol.* **15**, 201–293 (1904)

THURSTONE, L. L., *Multiple Factor Analysis*. Chicago: University of Chicago Press, 1947

TUCKER, L. R., "Implications of factor analysis of three-way matrices for measurement of change," in Chester W. Harris (ed.), *Problems in Measuring Change*. Madison, Wisc.: University of Wisconsin Press, 1963

WOOD, K. R., R. L. MCCORNACK, and L. T. VILLONE, *Non-Linear Factor Analysis Program A–78*. Santa Monica, Calif.: System Development Corporation, TM–1764, 1964

CHAPTER 5

RATIO SCALES OF OPINION*

S. S. STEVENS, *Harvard University*

Although the newer methods of psychological scaling were developed to measure how attributes like brightness or loudness increase with stimulus intensity, these same methods have proved provocative and useful when applied to the measurement of a social consensus. The procedure called magnitude estimation, for example, has been used to scale such variables as strength of expressed attitude, pleasantness of musical selections, seriousness of crimes, and other variables for which the stimulus can be measured only on a nonmetric or nominal scale. These applications presage an advance beyond the indirect methods developed by Thurstone (1927, 1959), who undertook to extend the Fechnerian procedures of sensory psychophysics to the domain of attitudes and opinions. The aim of Thurstone's procedures was to adjust the scale in such a way that the dispersion or variability of judgment would be equal in all parts of the continuum. By that means he hoped to achieve a scale of equal intervals, but with an arbitrary zero point.

Evidence that the new procedures of direct scaling can produce scales of a higher order than those produced by the Fechner-Thurstone approach stems mainly from a direct comparison of the results of the two kinds of methods. If, as many have believed, the way toward progress in the behavioral sciences lies in the creation of tools to quantify such elusive variables as opinions, attitudes, preferences, esthetic values, utility, and so forth, the outcome of more than a dozen different experiments lays a foundation for optimism. On many attitudinal continua, the Thurstonian scale generated by the unitizing of variability or confusion shows an invariant relation to the scale of magnitude, as determined by the new and more direct procedures. The relation bears a remarkable resemblance to that found when the same two kinds of procedures are applied to judgments of continua whose stimuli are measurable on ratio scales, as, for example, when judgment is made of the apparent brightness of lights of different intensity, or the apparent length of lines of different physical length.

---

* The preparation of this article was supported in part by the National Science Foundation and the National Institutes of Health (Laboratory of Psychophysics Report PPR–313–107). Much of this chapter is similar to an article by the author, entitled "A metric for the social consensus," *Science* **151**, 530–541 (1966).

171

Direct estimation shows that perceived or apparent length is approximately proportional to physical length (Stevens and Galanter, 1957). Obvious as this result may appear, the assurance that a line of 20 cm is judged to look about twice as long as one of 10 cm constitutes an important check on the method of direct magnitude estimation. Moreover, the scale of apparent length provides one more instance of the psychophysical law, which states that equal stimulus ratios produce equal perceptual ratios (Stevens, 1957). The Fechnerian scale of length, which is obtained by counting off units of variability, often called just noticeable differences (jnd), has quite a different form. The Fechnerian jnd scale is approximately a logarithmic function of physical length, and hence of apparent length. The reason the Fechnerian scale is logarithmic is that, since error tends to be relative, the variability of judgment, the jnd, is roughly proportional to the magnitude of the stimulus. A simple test of these relations is to plot the Fechnerian scale against the logarithm of the magnitude-estimation scale. The result approximates a straight line. A similar straight line is obtained when the "pair-comparison" scale of Thurstone is plotted against the logarithm of the magnitude scale produced by direct estimations of nonmetric stimuli such as, for example, the seriousness of criminal offenses. The constancy of these relations, regardless of whether the stimuli are measurable on physical scales or have no known metric, suggests a degree of invariance in the field of psychological measurement that may prove useful.

THEORY OF MEASUREMENT

In its broad sense, measurement can be defined as the assignment of numbers to aspects of objects or events according to a rule of some kind. The rules vary, because they rest upon operations contrived by human ingenuity. But the vast multitude of measurement scales known to science falls mostly into four classes: nominal, ordinal, interval, and ratio. Each scale is defined by its mathematical group. Thus the question of the class of scale achieved by a given procedure can be answered by specifying what transformations can be made on the scale numbers without the loss of empirical information. The group of permissible transformations defines the scale form (Stevens, 1946).

Although the theory of scales has been elaborated elsewhere (Stevens, 1959a), it may be helpful to refer to Table 1, which attempts to present the salient facts in a compact form. As Table 1 suggests, there are two principal aspects to measurement, the empirical operations and the number system. The process of measuring is the process of mapping the one into the other. The mapping is possible because one or another degree of isomorphism usually obtains between the empirical properties of objects or events, on the one hand, and some of the formal properties of the number system, on the other. Both aspects, the empirical and the formal, are essential to measurement.

Sometimes the formalists, perhaps out of an urge for tidiness, have seemed to deny the relevance to measurement theory of the empirical operations by which the relations among objects or events are determined. The logical and mathematical

Table 1 A classification of scales of measurement

Measurement is the assignment of numbers to objects or events according to rule. The rules and the resulting kinds of scales are tabulated below. The basic operations needed to create a given scale are all those listed in the second column, down to and including the operation listed opposite the scale. The third column gives the mathematical transformations that leave the scale form invariant. Any number x on a scale can be replaced by another number x' where x' is the function of x listed in column 3. The fourth column lists, cumulatively downward, examples of statistics that show invariance under the transformations of column 3 (the mode, however, is invariant only for discrete variables).

Scale	Basic empirical operations	Mathematical group-structure	Permissible statistics (invariantive)	Typical examples
Nominal	Determination of equality	Permutation group $x' = f(x)$ where $f(x)$ means any one-to-one substitution	Number of cases Mode "Information" measures Contingency correlation	"Numbering" of football players Assignment of type or model numbers to classes
Ordinal	Determination of greater or less	Isotonic group $x' = f(x)$ where $f(x)$ means any increasing monotonic function	Median Percentiles Order correlation	Hardness of minerals Grades of leather, lumber, wool Intelligence-test raw scores
Interval	Determination of the equality of intervals or of differences	Linear or affine group $x' = ax + b$ $a > 0$	Mean Standard deviation Product moment correlation (r)	Temperature (Fahrenheit and Celsius) Position on a line Calendar time Potential energy Intelligence-test "standard scores" (?)
Ratio	Determination of the equality of ratios	Similarity group $x' = cx$ $c > 0$	Geometric mean Harmonic mean Per cent variation	Length, density, numerosity, time intervals, work Temperature (Kelvin) Loudness (sones) Brightness (brils)

side of measurement has received much-needed attention from those interested in formal analysis, but the enthusiasm for formalism exhibited by such writers as Suppes and Zinnes (1963) must not be allowed to obscure the importance of the stubborn empirical problem. The admissible transformations by which a scale type is defined are those that accord with or at least do not offend the scientist's judgment about a matter that is thoroughly empirical. At some point the scientist must manipulate and observe. Although it would be convenient if the untidy empirical problem could somehow be banished, the formal model of measurement remains an empty shell until it is furnished with empirical observations.

Since tastes about semantic questions often differ, some writers have preferred not to call the nominal scale an instance of measurement. The naming problem aside, it is important to note that the use of numbers to designate classes of objects, such as items in a catalogue, is an example of assignment according to rule. The rule is: Do not assign the same number to different classes or different numbers to the same class.

The forming of classes of equivalent objects or events is not a trivial matter. It is the basis of all our categorizing and conceptualizing, of all our coding and recoding of information. By it we identify, recognize, label, and sort.

A development that has created new scientific interest in nominal scaling is information theory, which provides tools for the treatment of data at the nominal level of measurement. Thus it deals with categories (alternatives) without regard for any ordinal relations that might obtain among the categories, and it makes possible a measurement of association at the level of nominal scales.

Ordinal scales are too familiar in the behavioral sciences to need comment here. Suffice it to say that the types of statistics that are strictly appropriate to interval and ratio scales are often employed with ordinal data—and the results appear to be useful. This pragmatic sanction presumably rests on the fact that many of the scales built on such operations as psychological tests may approximate equal-interval scales, even though no very satisfactory operations may exist for assuring the equality of the intervals. The size of the departure from equal intervals that can be tolerated in a given circumstance will depend, of course, on the nature of the statistical treatment and the purpose to which the answer is to be put. Whether the risk is large or small, a caveat nevertheless remains in order whenever the statistics, such as means and standard deviations, that are appropriate to interval scales are used with data about which only the rank order is known.

As a general rule, the less restrictive scales, nominal and ordinal, are relatively easy to achieve. The invention of operations adequate to erect interval and ratio scales usually presents greater difficulty. It is a curious and interesting fact that in psychophysics it has proved relatively easy to create ratio scales, whereas direct attempts to set up satisfactory interval scales have often failed for one reason or another. Many scales built on "equal-appearing intervals" contain biases that distort the equality of the intervals. Distortions inherent in the interval scale need not hinder progress, however, because the interval scale is itself contained within the ratio scale. If a ratio scale has been established, an interval scale can be marked off whenever one is needed.

PROGRESS IN PSYCHOPHYSICS

Beginning in the 1930's, when a commercial need arose to measure subjective loudness (because the decibel scale did not sound like a good loudness scale), methods of several varieties have been developed to assess subjective magnitude (Stevens, 1958). It has been found that observers can match numbers to stimuli and stimuli to numbers—they can estimate the apparent ratios between stimuli, and they can adjust stimuli to produce prescribed apparent ratios. All these methods give results that are related to the stimulus values by a power function. The power function is a necessary consequence of the ratio invariance of the psychophysical law. If equal stimulus ratios produce equal perceptual ratios, the perceived magnitude ψ grows with the physical value φ raised to a power β:

$$\psi = k\varphi^{\beta}.$$

The measure of φ begins at threshold; k is a constant that depends on the units used. Each modality or continuum appears to have its characteristic exponent, ranging in value from 0.33 for the brightness of luminous fields to about 3.5 for the apparent intensity of electric current passed through the fingers. A convenient feature of the power function is that in log-log coordinates it takes the form of a straight line.

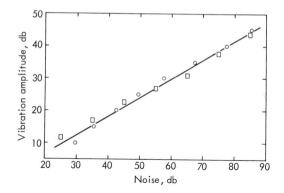

Fig. 1. Equal-sensation function for cross-modality matching between loudness and vibration. The squares indicate that the observers adjusted the intensity of vibration on the fingertip to match the loudness of a noise delivered by earphones. The circles indicate that the observers adjusted the loudness to match the vibration. Each point is the decibel average of 20 matches, two by each of ten observers.

Perhaps the most reassuring development in psychophysics is the validation of the various exponents by the procedure of direct cross-modality matching. Just as lights of different hue may be matched for brightness (as in heterochromatic photometry), so may sensations in one modality be matched to those in another. Thus a person may adjust the loudness of a sound in his ear to equal the apparent strength of a 60-cps vibration on the finger. When the vibration is changed, the observer changes the loudness to match the new apparent strength. The example in the log-log coordinates of Fig. 1 shows how the matching function turns out to be a straight-line power function whose slope (exponent) is given by the ratio between the exponent for loudness (0.6) and the exponent for vibration (0.95).

The basis for this result is as follows. If, given an appropriate choice of units, two modalities are governed by the equations

$$\psi_1 = \varphi_1^{\alpha} \quad \text{and} \quad \psi_2 = \varphi_2^{\beta},$$

and if the subjective values ψ_1 and ψ_2 are equated by cross-modality matches at various levels, then the resulting equal-sensation function will determine a relation between the two kinds of stimuli of the form

$$\varphi_1^{\alpha} = \varphi_2^{\beta}.$$

In terms of logarithms,

$$\log \varphi_1 = (\beta/\alpha)(\log \varphi_2).$$

In other words, in log-log coordinates the equal-sensation function becomes a straight line whose slope is given by the ratio of the two exponents. An interconnected net of exponent values has been validated by this direct matching procedure (Stevens, 1962). On more than a dozen different continua the power-function relation has been confirmed and the value of the exponent checked by cross-modality comparisons.

This rather happy, if unexpected, development has demonstrated an important possibility. The stimulus-response relations for all the sense modalities can be mapped out without resort to numerical estimation on the part of the observers. The power functions obtainable by cross-modality matching make methods like magnitude estimation entirely dispensable.

On the other hand, magnitude estimation has the great advantage of convenience. Its prescription is simple. It calls for the presentation of a series of stimuli in irregular order, if possible a different order to each observer. The instructions may be modeled on the following example.

You will be presented a series of stimuli in irregular order. Your task is to tell how intense they seem by assigning numbers to them. Call the first stimulus any number that seems to you appropriate. The task is to assign successive numbers in such a way that they will reflect your subjective impression. For example, if a stimulus seems 20 times as intense, assign a number 20 times as large as the first. If it seems one-fifth as intense, assign a number one-fifth as large, and so forth. Use fractions, whole numbers, or decimals, but make each assignment proportional to the intensity as you perceive it.

A decade of experience with magnitude estimation suggests that the experimenter should studiously avoid any constraining of the observers in any way other than to direct attention to the property of the stimulus that is of interest. It is not necessary to present a standard; in fact, it is probably better not to. The experimenter should not try to "help" by limiting the range of numbers to be used. He should keep hands off and let the observers make their own judgments. The first stimulus presented may be any one of the set, but preferably it will be a stimulus from near the middle of the range.

Because the concept of proportionality is not familiar to all people, it has sometimes proved helpful first to run an experiment on apparent length of lines. The lines, six to ten in number, should cover a wide range of lengths, say, 50 or 100 to 1. After judging such lines in irregular order, most observers seem to achieve a reasonably firm grasp on the concept of assigning numbers proportional to magnitude.

The variability of magnitude estimations has been found to grow approximately in proportion to the magnitude and to produce distributions that are roughly log normal. Consequently, averaging is best done by taking geometric means of the estimations. This method of averaging also has the advantage that, despite the different ranges of numbers used by different observers, no normalizing is needed prior to averaging.

THREE KINDS OF MEASUREMENTS

In the course of the development of these new facets of psychophysics, it has been possible to clarify the relations among the three principal types of measures commonly encountered.

Magnitude measures. As already noted, the magnitude of a sensation is a power function of the stimulus. This is true on all prothetic (intensive) continua thus far explored—a total of about three dozen. The power function may or may not obtain on metathetic (qualitative) continua such as the pitch of a sound or the position of a point.

Partition measures. All scales produced by asking observers to judge or produce what seem to be equal-appearing intervals belong to the general class called partition scales. Perhaps the most common form of this measure is the rating scale consisting of a prescribed set of categories to which stimuli are to be assigned, such as very large, large, medium, small, and very small. The result is commonly called a category scale.

When observers try to partition a continuum into equal intervals, the result, if successful, ought logically to represent a linear segment of the magnitude scale. Curiously enough, it seldom if ever does. On prothetic continua the partition scale is practically always nonlinear relative to the magnitude scale. A typical result, one of dozens, is shown in Fig. 2. Relative to the magnitude scale, the curvature of the category scale is usually intermediate between linear and logarithmic.

On metathetic continua the partition scale tends to be linearly related to the magnitude scale. Thus the mel scale of pitch was constructed by combining the results of a partitioning experiment (equisection) with the results of a ratio production experiment. Both procedures gave results in sufficient agreement to justify their combination (Stevens and Volkmann, 1940).

Confusion measures. The measurement of a jnd typically requires a person to categorize stimuli as greater or less than a standard. The stimuli are chosen to cover such a small range that the judgments are necessarily inconsistent. The

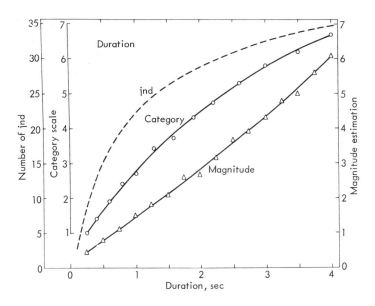

Fig. 2. Jnd scale, category scale, and magnitude scale for apparent duration. Triangles: represent Mean judgments of 12 observers who estimated the apparent duration of a white noise. Stimuli were presented in a different irregular order to each observer. Circles: represent Mean category judgments made by 16 observers on a scale from 1 to 7. The end stimuli were presented at the outset to indicate the range, and each observer judged each duration twice in an irregular order. The dashed curve is the function obtained by summating just noticeable differences.

problem is to find the stimulus difference that will evoke the judgment "greater" on 75% of the presentations. That is the difference usually employed to define the jnd. As an aid in the process the percentage of judgments "greater" is often plotted against the stimulus values to form a poikilitic or scatter function, usually an S-shaped curve. These functions were called "psychometric" by Urban in 1908 in order to reflect the belief that the jnd provided a unit, and hence a metric, for the measurement of psychological magnitudes. With the passing of that belief, it seems appropriate to call the functions by a more descriptive name. The term "poikilitic" suggests that the function displays the scatter, variability, or confusion that obtains among the observer's responses. In another context the term "poikilitic function" is also appropriate as a substitute for the misleading term "generalization gradient" (Stevens, 1965).

The summation of jnd—the counting off of equivariability steps along the stimulus continuum—produces a Fechnerian scale, an example of which is shown in Fig. 2. A jnd scale is a confusion scale in the sense that the basic operation for determining the steps along the scale is the assessment of equal degrees of confusion in the observer's responses.

Thurstone perceived the further possibility that if confusion or dispersion can be used to create a scale in psychophysics, it can also be used to create scales in other contexts, for variability characterizes all human judgment. Thurstone's famous "equation of comparative judgment," together with its various elaborations, provides a means for transforming measures of variability, dispersion, or confusion into units of a scale. The confusions themselves may derive from any of a variety of procedures, among them pair comparisons and category scaling. With pair comparisons the observer says which stimulus in each pair of stimuli has more of some attribute. The inconsistencies among the choices provide the data for scaling. With category scaling, it is the confusions among the categories that are processed. The resulting scale goes by many names, but ought probably to be called the category confusion scale.

As noted above, when scales on prothetic continua are erected by direct magnitude estimation and are compared with scales derived by the procedures of Fechner and Thurstone, the relation is found to be approximately logarithmic (see Galanter and Messick, 1961). This relation provides a test that can be applied to nonmetric continua, such as seriousness of crimes, in order to determine the nature of the continuum. If the same relations that have been shown to obtain in sensory psychophysics among the three general kinds of measures can also be shown to characterize the comparable scales created with nonmetric stimuli, added confidence attaches to the outcome.

ATTITUDE SCALES

In 1929 Thurstone and Chave used a version of the category scaling procedure in order to scale the strength of the attitude expressed by each of 130 statements concerning one or another aspect of religion. The resulting scale, based on the responses of 300 subjects, achieved a well-deserved fame, for it represented a serious and effective effort to introduce a metric where none had existed before.

In 1959 Finnie and Luce undertook to apply a larger battery of scaling devices to some of the same attitude statements and to gauge thereby the apparent strength of the expressed attitudes. When they used Thurstone's method of sorting the statements into 11 categories, the resulting partition scale correlated highly with the original partition scale of Thurstone and Chave. The passage of 30 years and the use of a new sample of subjects apparently made little difference.

A large difference resulted, however, when the subjects made magnitude estimations of the strength of the attitudes expressed by the various statements and the results were compared with the category confusion scale for the same items. The relation then became highly nonlinear, as shown in Fig. 3. The curved relation in Fig. 3 between the category confusion scale and the scale obtained by direct estimation is roughly logarithmic. This is the approximate relation to be expected if the perception of apparent strength of attitude constitutes a prothetic continuum.

Finnie and Luce comment on the direct scaling procedure by saying, "In addition to the theoretical interest in extending those methods and relations to areas other than psychophysics, knowledge of such a relation [as in Fig. 3] can have considerable practical benefit. A magnitude scale on 10 or 100 items can be obtained from a group of people in, literally, a matter of minutes. The corresponding

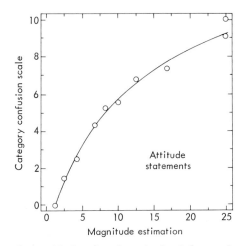

Fig. 3. Comparison of two kinds of scales obtained from observers who judged the strength of the attitude expressed by various statements concerning the church.

data for a Thurstonian analysis . . . requires more time to collect and is considerably more expensive to analyze, even with modern computation aids."

The ease with which a magnitude scale can be obtained from subjects instructed to match numbers to assorted items in a manner that preserves a proportional relation is indeed impressive, but a serious scaling venture will usually demand additional studies and may profitably undergo validation by other procedures including cross-modality matching. As in any empirical inquiry, much depends on the level of accuracy required.

Finnie (1965) has pursued the problem much further in a Ph.D. thesis devoted to a comparison of magnitude and confusion scales for several kinds of nonmetric stimuli: attitude statements about the church, adjectives, adverbs, occupational prestige, and statements expressing various degrees of cynicism. He also scaled the inverse continuum, e.g., degree of unfavorableness expressed by a statement. This work provides impressive new evidence to support the generality of the relation depicted in Fig. 3.

Thurstone and Chave went on to apply their attitude scale to measure the attitudes of individuals drawn from various classes of people: freshmen, graduate students, divinity students, etc. An individual's position on the attitude scale is determined by which statements he is willing to endorse. As expected, the divinity students endorsed only the statements that were favorable to the church. Graduate students, on the other hand, showed a wide spread among their attitudes.

EKMAN'S LAW

At about the same time that Finnie and Luce were scaling attitude statements at Harvard University, experiments were under way at the University of Stockholm designed to show the relation between the Thurstonian indirect methods of scaling and the direct procedures of ratio and magnitude estimation. On seven different nonmetric continua thus far studied in Stockholm, the Thurstonian confusion scale has been shown to be a logarithmic function of the magnitude scale. Since this effort, led by Gösta Ekman, is perhaps the most extensive yet undertaken, the case for the use of the direct scaling methods in all areas involving human judgment receives much of its support from the Stockholm studies. Some of the studies are reviewed below.

Ekman (1956, 1959) has also been at pains to establish the generality of a principle that was conjectured in 1874 by Brentano and that has been demonstrated by others (Harper and Stevens, 1948). The principle states that variability measured in psychological units is linearly related to psychological magnitude measured in the same units. This relation is the analogue of Weber's law, which concerns the linear growth of variability among human judgments as a function of the stimulus measure. Both Fechner (in deriving his law) and Thurstone (in his Case V) proposed a different assumption, namely, that variability in psychological units is constant along the psychological continuum. That assumption has been found to be adequate for metathetic continua, but not for prothetic continua. As Ekman and his collaborators (Ekman and Künnapas, 1957; Björkman, 1958, 1960; Eisler, 1962) have repeatedly demonstrated, on prothetic continua the variability, in subjective units, tends to grow as a linear function of the subjective magnitude.

Since it seems more important to have established the empirical generality of a principle than merely to have conjectured it as Brentano did, it would appear that the principle of the linear growth of subjective variability deserves to be called Ekman's law, the subjective counterpart of Weber's law.

The importance of Ekman's law in the present context is clear. Although the principle was developed and tested with metric stimuli in the area of psychophysics, there is every reason to believe that the same principle applies when the stimuli are describable only in terms of a nominal scale. Indeed, the repeated finding that the Thurstonian scale for nonmetric stimuli is related to the scale of magnitude in a logarithmic manner constitutes direct evidence for Ekman's law.

Thurstonian scales are usually erected on the assumption (Case V) that subjective variability is constant all up and down the continuum. If Thurstone had gone on to what has been called Case VI (Stevens, 1959b), he would, in effect, have been adopting Ekman's principle. Under Case VI, the Thurstonian scale would tend to be a power function of the magnitude scale, but the exponent would be arbitrary.

STUDIES BY EKMAN AND OTHERS

Preferences for wristwatches. Before turning to the Stockholm studies, we may note how busily the Zeitgeist has been at work producing similar experiments in different places. In that same year, 1959, Indow (1961) was presenting pictures and descriptions of wristwatches to 127 university students in Japan and asking for pair comparisons and ratio judgments. The student was asked to say which of each pair of watches he preferred, and also to indicate by marking a position on an 8-cm line what the relative strength of his preference was. The subjects, in effect, matched

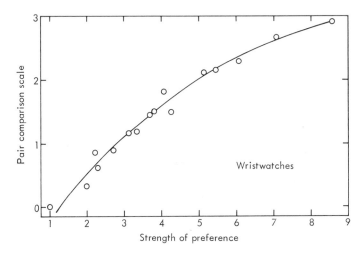

Fig. 4. The curved relation between the pair-comparison scale (Case V) and the scale of preference for wristwatches derived from ratio judgments made by adjusting line segments.

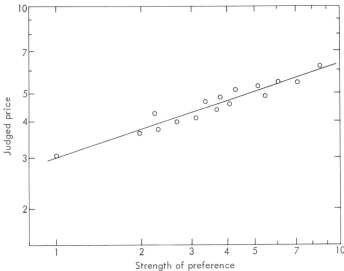

Fig. 5. The judged fair price (in yen $\times 10^3$) for various wristwatches is plotted against judged strength of preference. The coordinates are logarithmic. The line through the data determines a power function with an exponent of 0.32.

length of line to subjective value, a kind of cross-modality procedure. By comparing the ratio scale determined with the aid of the 8-cm line to the Thurstonian scale (Case V) derived from the "noise" or confusions in the pair comparisons, Indow was able to demonstrate an approximately logarithmic relation between the two kinds of scales. This nonlinear relation is shown in Fig. 4.

In another part of Indow's experiment the students were asked to state what they would regard as a fair price for each of the wristwatches, given that the price of a particular watch was a stated number of yen. For each of three different groups of students a different standard watch and price were designated. The interesting aspect of the outcome concerns the relation of the averages of the price estimates to the ratio scale of desirability previously established. This relation is shown in log-log coordinates in Fig. 5. The fact that the data approximate a straight line suggests that fair price is judged to be a power function of degree of desirability. The low value of the exponent, 0.32, indicates that the relation between judged price and judged desirability is rather far from linear. It would be interesting to know whether a power function with a similarly low exponent would be obtained in other circumstances.

Esthetic value of handwriting, drawings, and music. Two separate studies of the esthetic value of handwriting were carried out by Ekman and Künnapas (1960, 1962a). In both studies, samples of handwriting were scaled by Thurstone's method of pair comparisons and by a variant of the method of ratio estimation (Ekman, 1958). The first study, which used seven samples of handwriting, is especially instructive because it failed to show a logarithmic relation between the scale by pair comparisons and the scale by ratio estimation. The second study used 18 samples of handwriting covering a wider range of quality. This second experiment demonstrated that the approximately linear relation of the first experiment became an obviously logarithmic relation when the wider stimulus range made the form of the function easier to determine.

A related study by similar methods was carried out on 17 drawings of a tree. The samples were selected from some 200 drawings produced by sixth-grade students (Ekman and Künnapas, 1962b). Again it was found that the confusion scale derived from pair comparisons was quite accurately proportional to the logarithm of the magnitude scale derived from ratio estimations.

Esthetic judgment in the musical sphere was investigated by Koh (1965), who played 51 vocal selections and 60 piano pieces to various populations of subjects, including college students and patients in the alcoholic ward of a hospital in North Dakota. Each musical excerpt lasted from about 15 seconds for the piano pieces to about 60 seconds for the vocal pieces. The total population of subjects, numbering 330, was divided into six groups, two groups each of college males, college females, and alcoholics. Half of the groups, one of each kind, heard vocal selections; the other half heard piano selections. The subjects in each group made magnitude estimations of the affective value of each selection and also judged each selection on a category scale expressed in terms of nine adjectives ranging from "most pleasant" through "indifferent" to "most unpleasant." The category values were treated as a 9-point numerical scale, and the ratings of each piece of music were averaged.

For all six groups, the average rating scale value was approximately proportional to the logarithm of the geometric means of the magnitude estimations. The product-moment correlations between the category values and the logarithms of the magnitude values ranged from 0.90 to 0.96. For some groups there was a slight upward concavity, which is usually the case when category scales are plotted against the logarithm of the magnitude scale.

As Koh remarked, the relation between the category and the magnitude scales was strikingly invariant under differences in the age, sex, education, occupation, and pathology of the subjects. "These empirical invariances," he concluded, "strongly suggest the usefulness of magnitude estimation for complex judgmental processes."

Importance of Swedish monarchs. The direct method of ratio estimation and the indirect method of pair comparisons were used by Ekman and Künnapas (1963a) to construct scales of the political importance of eleven Swedish monarchs who lived between 1550 and 1850. Eighty-three students of psychology made the judgments. The scale, derived from pair comparisons based on the assumption of Thurstone's Case V, was a logarithmic function of the magnitude scale derived from direct ratio estimation. The scale of magnitude shows that on the average these students considered the leading monarch to be about four times more important than the one who was least well regarded. Whether it is useful to determine ratios among items of this kind remains to be seen. The point here is to note that ratio determinations are possible.

Occupational preferences. The degree of prestige that attaches to each of 100 different occupations was judged by means of two procedures, magnitude estimation and a 7-point category rating scale (Perloe, 1963). The subjects were 40 undergraduates at Haverford College. Despite a certain mix-up about the instructions, the data suffice to show that the relation between the category scale and the magnitude scale is essentially the same for judgments of occupations as it was in Koh's experiments for judgments of musical selections. As with loudness, brightness, or other attributes for which there exists a stimulus metric, the mean category judgments define a scale that is almost but not quite a logarithmic function of the median magnitude estimations. This is the expected outcome when the "noise" or variability in the experiment is large. When the variability is low, the category scale departs farther from the logarithmic form (Stevens and Guirao, 1963). Under more favorable circumstances where, for example, the subject may be permitted to adjust a stimulus to bisect the apparent distance between two other stimuli, the partition scale may approach fairly close to the magnitude scale (Stevens, 1955).

For those of Perloe's observers who appeared to have grasped the instructions correctly, the judged range from the most to the least prestigious occupation was about thirtyfold.

It is interesting that a roughly comparable range characterized the judgments of 74 students at the University of Stockholm who expressed their preference for 17 different occupations (Künnapas and Wikström, 1963). The Stockholm study used two different procedures to scale occupational preference, ratio estimation and magnitude estimation, and a third procedure to produce a Thurstonian scale, pair comparisons processed according to Case V. The two magnitude scales were found to be linearly related, as expected. The confusion scale derived from pair comparisons approximated a logarithmic function of both magnitude scales.

The occupations appear in Fig. 6 in the position assigned them by the geometric means of the magnitude estimations. Among university students in Sweden the physician appears to be far out in front.

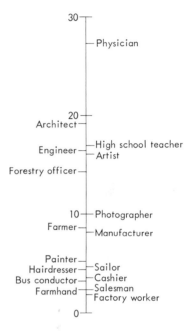

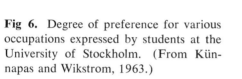

Fig 6. Degree of preference for various occupations expressed by students at the University of Stockholm. (From Künnapas and Wikstrom, 1963.)

Pleasantness of odors. The scaling of odors presents an especially instructive example of the potentialities of the ratio scaling methods. The apparent intensity of each of a variety of odors has been scaled by magnitude estimation, always with approximately the same results. The apparent intensity of the odor grows according to a power function of the concentration and the exponent is of the order of 0.5 or 0.6. Furthermore, the range from the faintest to the strongest perceptible odor is rather small—nothing like the wide dynamic range of loudness or brightness.

The subjective range increases to more than a hundredfold when, instead of the intensity of a single odor, the pleasantness of 18 different odors becomes the attribute that is estimated (Engen and McBurney, 1964). The hedonic aspect of odor exhibits a wider dynamic range than the intensity aspect.

When the pleasantness of the odors was judged on a 9-point category scale the result was typical of category judgments on other prothetic continua. Plotted against the scale produced by magnitude estimation, the category scale of pleasantness is concave downward. Plotted against the logarithm of the magnitude scale, the category scale is concave upward. This latter relation demonstrates the principle that the curvature of the category scale is generally intermediate between a linear and a logarithmic function of the magnitude scale.

Liberal-conservative. Thus far there appears to be one possible exception to the finding that a scale based on the unitizing of variability approximates a logarithmic function of the magnitude scale generated by the direct estimation of some attribute of a series of nonmetric stimuli. Ekman and Künnapas (1963b) assembled a set of 17 statements designed to sample the liberal-conservative continuum and asked 82 subjects to assess the degree of conservatism expressed by each statement. As it turned out, the scale defined by ratio estimations was related in roughly linear form to the scale defined by the procedure of pair comparisons (Case V). This unusual result was further examined in a series of experiments by Künnapas and Sillén (1964), who used as stimuli the same 17 statements used in the first study. In this second study judgments were also made of the degree of liberalism expressed by the statements. Except in one part of the second study there was no clear evidence for a logarithmic relation between the Thurstonian and the magnitude scales.

The authors entertain the hypothesis that this continuum is qualitative or metathetic, which, if true, would account for the general nature of the results. An alternative hypothesis is that the heterogeneity of content among the statements made the assessment of the degree or intensity of one particular attribute rather difficult. The statements concerned such diverse matters as world government, church and state, sex education, movie censors, school prayers, abortions, capital punishment, etc. The problem is analogous to the task of judging loudness when every tone presented has a different pitch. Such loudness judgments have indeed

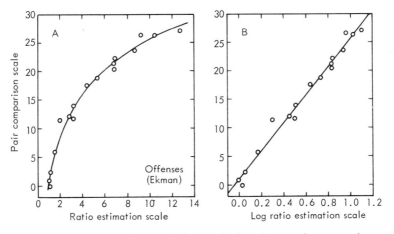

Fig. 7. The relation between the confusion scale based on pair comparisons and the magnitude scale based on ratio estimations of the seriousness of offenses. Plot A shows the relation in linear coordinates. Plot B shows the relation in semilogarithmic coordinates. The variability or confusion among the pair comparisons grows as a linear function of the judged magnitude, which entails a logarithmic relation when units of variability are plotted against magnitude. (From G. Ekman, "Measurement of moral judgment: a comparison of scaling methods." *Percept. Motor Skills* **15**, 3–9, 1962. Used by permission of the author and publisher.)

proved possible, but they have also proved to be more variable than those obtained when only the intensity of the tones is varied (Stevens, Guirao, and Slawson, 1965). It is possible that the 17 statements used in the foregoing experiments did not elicit judgments related to the same subjective continuum for all the subjects. By contrast, all the statements scaled by Finnie and Luce contained explicit reference to the church. Perhaps the chief problem in these areas is to refine the statements until a sufficient homogeneity is achieved to make it easy for the subjects to judge degree or intensity. Thurstone and Chave gave many helpful rules for the elimination of ambiguous and irrelevant statements and for the refinement of scale items.

With simpler materials, such as single adjectives describing personality traits, it is apparently quite possible for people to abstract an attribute and judge its intensity. Ekman and Künnapas (1963c) asked 95 subjects to judge the degree of masculinity expressed by each of eleven personality adjectives. The subjects also judged the degree of femininity expressed. In both instances the scale derived from pair comparisons (Case V) approximated a logarithmic function of the scale derived from direct ratio estimation.

Seriousness of offenses. On the basis of a preliminary study of a larger number of offenses, descriptions of 17 more-or-less immoral actions were selected for study by Ekman (1962). They ranged from hit and run by a drunken driver down to stopping in a no-parking zone to mail a letter. Eighty subjects made pair comparisons and ratio estimations. As shown in Fig. 7, the pair-comparison scale based on a processing of the noise or confusion (Case V) is very close to a logarithmic function of the scale based on direct ratio estimations.

THE SELLIN-WOLFGANG DELINQUENCY STUDY

Ekman's study on seriousness of offenses, like most of the studies described thus far, was methodological in intent; the object of interest was method, not the achievement of a practical, substantive outcome. A full-length study in which method is the means rather than the end has been reported by Sellin and Wolfgang (1964). Their 423-page book is directed at the improvement of the methods used to compile police and court statistics for the purpose of measuring criminality in general and delinquency in particular. The research design placed major emphasis on delinquent *events,* not on delinquent persons, for the purpose was to measure the amount and type of harm to the community committed by juveniles.

The general strategy of this three-year study was as follows. First a representative 10% sample of delinquency events was selected by random sampling from the universe of all such recorded events in Philadelphia, Pennsylvania, in the year 1960. Scaling procedures were then applied to events selected from the sample in order to convert the judged seriousness of the events into numerical scores. A final combination of all the information produced a delinquency index, a device that can be used to gauge the total incidence of delinquency and the effectiveness of whatever preventive measures may be brought to bear on the grave problem of antisocial behavior.

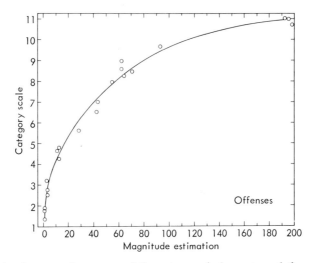

Fig. 8. Relation between the means of the category judgments and the geometric means of the magnitude judgments for seriousness of offenses as rated by juvenile court judges. The coordinates are linear. (Adapted from Sellin and Wolfgang, 1964.)

It is the second stage of the study that most concerns us here, the quantification of the gravity of delinquent acts, a quantification that must rest ultimately on the judgment of members of society. In brief outline, the authors proceeded as follows. A list of 141 offenses was first compiled and a carefully phrased statement made of each offense. These statements, typed on cards, were submitted for trial testing to 17 raters, mostly college students, who rated the seriousness of each offense on a 7-point category scale. Three representative offenses were then selected from each of the seven categories for use in further testing. These 21 offenses, presented in carefully randomized orders, were judged by 569 people comprising 38 juvenile-court judges, 286 police officers, and 245 students from two universities. About half of each class of rater made magnitude estimations of the seriousness of the offenses. The other half rated the offenses on an 11-point category scale.

The next question concerns the relation between the two kinds of judgments, category and magnitude. Figure 8 shows a direct comparison between the results for the 38 juvenile-court judges, 20 of whom used the category scale and 18 of whom made direct magnitude estimations. As is characteristic of prothetic continua, the category scale of degree of delinquency is concave downward when plotted against the magnitude scale. When the same category ratings are plotted against the logarithm of the magnitude scale, the result is more nearly linear, but actually slightly concave upward, as shown in Fig. 9. Finally, when instead of using the averages of the category assignments, the scaling procedure makes use only of the variability or confusion among the category assignments in order to generate a category confusion scale, the result is more nearly a linear function of the logarithm of the magnitude estimations, as shown in Fig. 10.

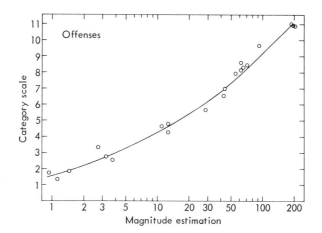

Fig. 9. Relation between the category scale and the magnitude scale in semilogarithmic coordinates. Data are the same as in Fig. 8. (Adapted from Sellin and Wolfgang, 1964.)

For different groups of raters, the age of the offender was specified as 13, 17, 27 years, or it was left unspecified. As a result, ten different plots like that in Fig. 10 could be made from the judgments of the ten subgroups of raters. The impressive feature of the ten plottings is their invariant form. Provided that the total ordinate scale is taken as one unit, the slopes of the ten functions ranged from 0.22 to 0.31. The slope in Fig. 10 is 0.29. There were no significant differences attributable to the age of the offender. It was the offense itself that seemed to determine the judgment of seriousness.

More important, perhaps, there was also impressive invariance across raters. Juvenile-court judges produced scales comparable to those produced by police

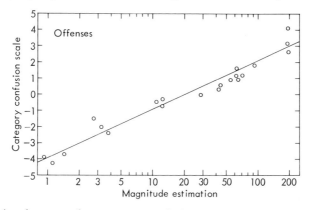

Fig. 10. Relation between the category confusion scale and the magnitude scale in semilogarithmic coordinates. Data are from Fig. 8. The ordinate represents the Thurstonian scale derived from the confusions or variability among the judgments made on the category scale of seriousness of offenses. (Adapted from Sellin and Wolfgang, 1964.)

officers and college students. It may be surprising that all three classes of raters concluded, for example, that stealing and abandoning a car is only about one-tenth as serious as robbing a man of $5 and wounding him in the process. According to the consensus, this latter crime becomes about two-and-a-half times as serious if the victim dies. Out of these magnitude estimations, say the authors, "a pervasive social agreement about what is serious and what is not appears to emerge, and this agreement transcends simple qualitative concordance; it extends to the estimated degree of seriousness of these offenses" (p. 268).

The next major step was an item analysis designed to refine further the statements used to define the offenses. The revised items were used to conduct a retest on a new population, a group of 195 students from still another university. This final testing gave results that correlated highly with the earlier data and thereby provided added justification for the construction of an index of delinquency based on a representative ratio scale of seriousness.

An important feature of the final index is its provision for the additivity of offenses, a feature justified to a large extent by the outcome of the magnitude estimations of seriousness. Thus the stealing of $5 is given a rounded score value of 1. Breaking into a building also has the value 1. Breaking in *and* stealing $5 has the value 2, because the magnitude estimation score for the seriousness of the combined act was approximately double the estimate for each act separately. As another example, forcible rape has the value 11, which comprises 8 for the forced sex act, 2 for the intimidation of the victim, and 1 for the inflicting of minor injury. The extraction of the additive components of the complex delinquent acts was achieved, of course, through the process of analyzing the results of the magnitude estimations. It is perhaps doubtful that any of the raters would have been conscious of the underlying additivity in any explicit way, and some of them would probably be offended by the thought that one forcible rape can be equated to some number of money thefts. Nevertheless, both the quantitative estimates of large numbers of raters and the gradations in the punishments prescribed by law make a strong argument for equatability and additivity among delinquent events.

Value of money. Among the offenses rated by magnitude estimation there were a few items that dealt with the stealing of money. Statements naming stolen amounts of $5, $20, $50, $1000, and $5000 had been scattered at random among the other statements describing offenses. The geometric means of the judged magnitude of the seriousness of the offenses involving money grew as a very precise power function of the amount of money stolen (Fig. 11). The value of the exponent, 0.17, suggests that in order for a crime to be twice as serious the amount stolen must be about 60 times as large. Although it is worse to steal $2 than to steal $1, it is certainly not twice as bad.

The argument that the subjective value of money, the economists' "utility," may be a power function of the number of dollars goes back to the mathematician, Gabriel Cramer, who made the conjecture in 1728 (see Bernoulli, 1738). Ten years later, and quite independently, Daniel Bernoulli hypothesized a different law, a logarithmic function. Bernoulli's proposal became very well known while Cramer's was long forgotten. But the power function, with an exponent less than 1.0, has empirical backing to recommend it (Stevens, 1959a; Galanter, 1962). This power function also accords with the universally agreed-upon fact that to the average man each added dollar has less utility (value) than the one preceding it—the economic principle of "decreasing marginal utility." It is interesting that, in the context of loss due to delinquent acts, the appraisal of money also takes the form of a power function.

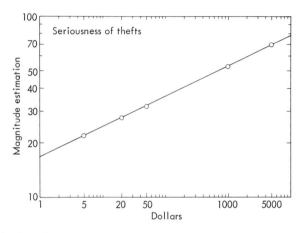

Fig. 11. Magnitude estimations of the seriousness of stealing various amounts of money. The ordinate values are the geometric means of the estimates of 105 university students. The line in the log-log coordinates defines a power function with an exponent of 0.17.

Punishment. How well does society's accumulated wisdom, or lack thereof, in meting out punishments for offenses compare with the judged gravity of the offense? In particular, what does the Pennsylvania Penal Code say about maximum penalties for the 21 offenses scaled in the main study? The answer is both interesting and encouraging. The product-moment correlation between seriousness of offense as judged by university students and maximum penalty stated in terms of time in jail was 0.88, provided a death sentence is interpreted as a jail term equal to the life expectancy of the median perpetrator of homicide. The correlation was even slightly higher, 0.94, for the magnitude judgments by police officers. Both sets of results are shown in logarithmic coordinates in Fig. 12. As Sellin and Wolfgang express it, "These correlations are surprisingly high considering the fact that the Penal Code provides no variation in the maximum [penalty] for amounts of money stolen and relatively few intervals between thirty days' imprisonment and death" (p. 327). Note also that the punishment scale is truncated at its lower end, for the smallest maximum penalty is 30 days in jail.

Another point of interest is the general form of the relation in Fig. 12. The straight line through the data represents a power function, because the coordinates are logarithmic. The slope of the line in these coordinates gives a measure of the

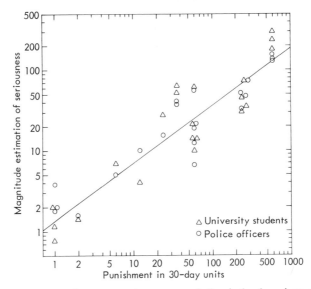

Fig. 12. Relation between the geometric means of the judged seriousness of 21 offenses and the maximum penalty prescribed by the Pennsylvania Penal Code. The raters were police officers (circles) and university students (triangles). For plotting purposes the police ratings were multiplied by 0.5. The line through the data has a slope of 0.7. (From data of Sellin and Wolfgang, 1964.)

value of the exponent. The slope (exponent) is clearly less than 1.0. Its value, 0.7, means that the penalty, time in jail, fails to be proportional to the seriousness of the offense. This fact would be seen clearly in linear coordinates, for then the line in Fig. 12 would appear as a curve concave downward.

In order to have the full story on the justice of the maximum penalty specified by the Code, we would need to know another function, namely, the judged seriousness or severity of various periods in jail, i.e., the subjective value function for terms of imprisonment. Since this function was not directly scaled by Sellin and Wolfgang, we can approach the question only indirectly by way of an assumption. The assumption we shall make is that in this, the best of all possible worlds known thus far to *Homo sapiens,* the punishment fits the crime, provided both are assessed by direct subjective judgment. If that assumption holds, it follows that the subjective value function for time in jail has an exponent that is the same as the exponent in Fig. 12, namely, 0.7. That exponent, with a value less than 1.0, raises the interesting question whether people regard the severity of punishment that goes with various periods in jail as a decelerating function of calendar time. Is a sentence of two months less than twice as punishing as a sentence of one month? This author would think so. If others agree, then perhaps the Pennsylvania Penal Code does indeed mete out roughly proportional justice.

In the preceding argument, the absolute value of the intercept of the hypothetical punishment function has been neglected. It will need, of course, to be considered before the complete story is told, because the *absolute* amount of punishment for a given offense merits as much concern as does the *relative* amount of punishment for different offenses.

However that may be, Sellin and Wolfgang have shown how to attack an urgent social problem with the methods that were developed in psychophysics for the study of human sensory systems. The methods they borrowed have produced impressive and useful results. It is a large and onerous task to develop and refine by repeated revisions a scale with useful properties in an area as complex as delinquent behavior. The one-shot experiment, so typical of the academic investigator, will not suffice when the goal is serious and substantial. The ratio-scaling methods used by Sellin and Wolfgang have a long history, but it is instructive that their development got its biggest push from a practical problem in acoustics (see Stevens, 1936). In the three-year study of delinquency, the extension of the ratio-scaling methods to social variables has been dramatically achieved, largely because the challenge of the problem has justified the investment needed to track down and eliminate needless sources of noise and variability. Science seems to do its best when it faces a problem worth solving.

INDIVIDUAL FUNCTIONS

Assessments of subjective value like those shown in Fig. 12 represent averaged results, and someone may object that the scale of seriousness of delinquent acts does not represent the opinion of some particular person. Indeed it may not, for the first task must be to discover the consensus, if there is one. After a representative value function has been spelled out, it may or may not become profitable to ask about the exceptions. Whether, in a given domain, the consensus is sufficiently homogeneous to justify averaging is an empirical question, and one that has begun to receive attention in psychophysics.

It was for groups of observers that loudness and brightness were found, on the average, to grow in proportion to the stimulus intensity raised to a power (Stevens, 1953). As might be expected, little attention was paid at first to the question whether the power law would describe the reactions of each individual. Understandably, therefore, the question arises whether the ubiquitous power function may not be the result of group averaging. Upon finding that some of their six observers did not produce power functions when judging apparent weight, Pradhan and Hoffman (1963) concluded that individual functions "were found not to follow Stevens' law although averaging over observers does yield a power function. Stevens' power function thus seems to be an artifact of grouping." The answer to that conjecture can be made in two ways, one by an appeal to probability, the other by empirical test.

The first answer invites consideration of what a reasonable likelihood may be. How many times would the average judgments of different groups of ten observers produce a power function if each observer produced some other function? The improbability of the averaging "explanation" grows greater as power functions continue to accumulate. Ekman and Sjöberg (1965) have described it thus:

After a hundred years of almost general acceptance . . . , Fechner's logarithmic law was replaced by the power law. The amount of experimental work performed in the 1950's on this problem . . . was enormous. . . . The power law was verified again and again, in literally hundreds of experiments. As an experimental fact, the power law is established beyond any reasonable doubt, possibly more firmly established than anything else in psychology.*

The empirical answer to the problem of the individual function calls for the straightforward procedure of measuring and exhibiting the functions for individual observers. An early attempt to exhibit a collection of individual power functions was vetoed by a journal editor who pointed out, quite rightly, that nothing was shown by 39 straight lines in log-log coordinates that could not be summarized in a sentence or two. The power functions in question were later published elsewhere (Stevens, 1961). Since then, the problem of the individual function has led members of this laboratory to develop new procedures. Lee McMahon made the first experiments on loudness with a technique that leaves the observer free to set the level of the sound intensity and also to estimate the loudness. It is a combined production-estimation technique which produces data that cannot be averaged, because each observer sets different stimulus levels and makes different estimates, at his pleasure. He may be asked simply to set as many levels as he likes and to assign numbers proportional to the loudness, as he hears it. Results obtained with this technique by J. C. Stevens and Guirao (1964) are shown in Fig. 13.

After the power law has been verified in a sufficient number of experiments, perhaps the burden of proof shifts to the opposite side: What characterizes an observer who does *not* give a power function when his results are cross-checked by a variety of procedures? A single experiment or a single technique may not be enough to establish that, for a given person, the perceived magnitude fails to grow as a power function of the stimulus magnitude. Almost anything may happen in a single experiment. A firm decision about an individual case may call for a multiple attack by estimation procedures, production procedures, and cross-modality comparisons. Hopefully, the multiple approach may prove adequate to reveal abnormal sensory functions, such as auditory recruitment, in individual subjects.

Two features of Fig. 13 deserve comment. All eleven observers produced good approximations to power functions, but the slopes (exponents) varied from person to person. The analogue of this second feature showed up also in the study of delinquency by Sellin and Wolfgang, where the range of the magnitude estimations of the seriousness of the offenses varied from person to person.

How should we regard these individual differences in range, or in exponent? Admittedly, it would be something of a miracle if everybody gave exactly the same

---

* G. Ekman and L. Sjöberg, "Scaling." *Ann. Rev. Psychol.* **16,** 451–474 (1965). Quoted by permission of the publisher.

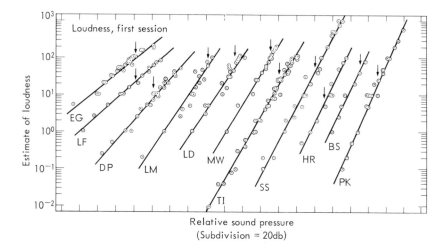

Fig. 13. Individual loudness functions obtained from 11 observers in the first session, in which they both set the level of the stimulus and judged the loudness. The observers varied greatly in the range and number of stimuli they produced and estimated, but all the data approximate power functions. The small arrow above each function indicates a level of 80 dB on the abscissa.

function for delinquency, for loudness, or for anything else. Perhaps the variations in how people use numbers and how they regard ratios are no more than the inevitable noise that characterizes these complex processes. The fact of two different slopes in Fig. 13 may mean that the two observers in question have different mechanisms at work in their auditory systems, but it may also mean that the two observers happen merely to differ about what they consider an apparent ratio. There is growing evidence that the differences in the observed exponents among a reasonable sample of observers have one of the very important properties of noise, namely, the capacity to be averaged out. Note, for example, in Fig. 12 how nearly the average estimations of seriousness by the police officers determine the same function as the average estimations by university students. It is the stability of the function from group to group that makes the result useful.

FRUSTRATION AND AGGRESSION

A review of the potential leverage that may accrue from the use of psychophysical scaling procedures would be incomplete without mention of an attempt to produce measurable amounts of frustration in a group of subjects and to scale the consequent acts of aggression. A series of realistic and imaginative experiments were devised by Hamblin, Bridger, Day, and Yancey (1963) in which genuine feelings of aggression were produced in college R.O.T.C. students by means of a simulated game. The student could advise a "leader" concerning the tactics of the game, but the leader had the final say and he could thereby cause game points to be lost. This interference with the goal of winning points may be taken as a measure of the amount of the frustration. At various stages of the procedure the subjects were asked to estimate numerically the degree of their dislike for the leader, who had been represented to the subjects as a candidate for promotion whose qualities of leadership they were to judge. The subjects were also asked to squeeze a hand dynamometer to express the degree of their dislike for the leader. In expressing their dislike the subjects were in effect aggressing against the leader, because, to the best of their knowledge, their dislike would injure the leader's chance of promotion.

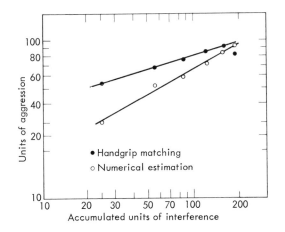

Fig. 14. Aggression, expressed as degree of dislike for a "leader" who interfered with the success of the subjects in a game, is plotted against the amount of the interference (number of points lost by reason of the leader's wrongheadedness). Forty subjects made magnitude estimations of their dislike and also squeezed a hand dynamometer by an amount proportional to the intensity of their feeling. (From R. L. Hamblin *et al.*, "The interference-aggression law?" *Sociometry* **26**, 190–216, 1963. Used by permission of the publisher.)

The results obtained from 40 subjects are plotted in log-log coordinates in Fig. 14. For both magnitude estimation and handgrip, the data approximate straight-line power functions. The authors suggest that the deviant point on the handgrip function probably resulted from the fact that, for both the last value and the one before it, many subjects had squeezed "as hard as they could." However that may be, it is interesting to compare the slopes (exponents) of the two functions, 0.53 for magnitude estimation and 0.30 for handgrip. The ratio, 0.53/0.3 = 1.77, is close to the value found in psychophysical experiments when observers estimate directly the apparent force of their handgrips. In the experiment on frustration we seem to have another example of the utility of the cross-modality matching procedure—a procedure whose power and versatility are coming slowly to be recognized.

CONCLUSIONS

In all these manifold and diverse experiments involving human judgment, a remarkable convergence of evidence from fields as disparate as psychophysics and criminology has pointed to stable and constant relations. One such relation is that subjective magnitude is a power function of stimulus magnitude. The underlying invariance then becomes the simple principle that equal stimulus ratios produce equal subjective ratios.

On many of the continua discussed above, the stimuli can be measured only on a nominal scale, for the stimuli are verbal statements, occupations, crimes, musical selections, and other nonmetric items. On those continua the power law cannot be confirmed directly, but there emerges another notable invariance. For both kinds of continua, those based on metric stimuli and those based on nonmetric stimuli, there is a constant relation between the scale erected by direct judgment and the scale derived from a unitizing of variability or confusion. Whether the stimuli are measurable on ratio scales or only on nominal scales, the judgmental scale based on units of variability is approximately proportional to the logarithm of the scale constructed by one or another of the direct scaling methods. The extensive invariance of this logarithmic relation attests to a principle known throughout all of science, namely, that error or variability tends to be *relative*—it grows with magnitude: the standard deviation increases with the mean; the signal-to-noise ratio stays put. The fact that also in the subjective domain the variability increases in proportion to the apparent magnitude suggests an essential unity among the principles that govern quantitative relations in widely diverse endeavors.

For those who must build their science on one or another consensus of human judgment, a way now seems open for an effective quantification.

REFERENCES

BERNOULLI, D., "Exposition of a new theory on the measurement of risk." Originally published in Latin in 1738. Translation in *Econometrica* **22**, 23–35 (1954)

BJÖRKMAN, M., "Some relationships between psychophysical parameters." *Rep. Psychol. Lab., University of Stockholm, No. 65* (1958)

BJÖRKMAN, M., "Variability data and direct quantitative judgment for scaling subjective magnitude." *Rep. Psychol. Lab., University of Stockholm, No. 78* (1960)

EISLER, H., "Empirical test of a model relating magnitude and category scales." *Scand. J. Psychol.* **3**, 88–96 (1962)

EKMAN, G., "Discriminal sensitivity on the subjective continuum." *Acta Psychologica* **12**, 233–243 (1956)

EKMAN, G., "Two generalized ratio scaling methods." *J. Psychol.* **45**, 287–295 (1958)

EKMAN, G., "Weber's law and related functions." *J. Psychol.* **47**, 343–352 (1959)

EKMAN, G., "Measurement of moral judgment." *Percept. Motor Skills* **15**, 3–9 (1962)

EKMAN, G., and T. KÜNNAPAS, "Subjective dispersion and the Weber fraction." *Rep. Psychol. Lab., University of Stockholm, No. 41* (1957)

EKMAN, G., and T. KÜNNAPAS, "Note on direct and indirect scaling methods." *Psychol. Rep.* **6**, 174 (1960)

EKMAN, G., and T. KÜNNAPAS, "Measurement of aesthetic value by direct and indirect methods." *Scand. J. Psychol.* **3**, 33–39 (1962a)

EKMAN, G., and T. KÜNNAPAS, "Scales of aesthetic value." *Percept. Motor Skills* **14**, 19–26 (1962b)

EKMAN, G., and T. KÜNNAPAS, "A further study of direct and indirect scaling methods." *Scand. J. Psychol.* **4**, 77–80 (1963a)

EKMAN, G., and T. KÜNNAPAS, "Scales of conservatism." *Percept. Motor Skills* **16**, 329–334 (1963b)

EKMAN, G., and T. KÜNNAPAS, "Scales of masculinity and femininity. A further study of direct and indirect scaling methods." *Rep Psychol. Lab., University of Stockholm, No. 162* (1963c)

EKMAN, G., and L. SJÖBERG, "Scaling." *Ann. Rev. Psychol.* **16**, 451–474 (1965)

ENGEN, T., and D. H. McBURNEY, "Magnitude and category scales of the pleasantness of odors." *J. Exp. Psychol.* **68**, 435–440 (1964)

FINNIE, B., "An empirical comparison of magnitude and category scaling procedures applied to nonphysical stimuli." Unpublished doctoral dissertation, Harvard University, 1965

FINNIE, B., and R. D. LUCE, "Magnitude-estimation, pair-comparison, and successive-interval scales of attitude items." Department of Psychology, University of Pennsylvania, *Memorandum MP–9* (1960)

GALANTER, E., "The direct measurement of utility and subjective probability." *Amer. J. Psychol.* **75**, 208–220 (1962)

GALANTER, E., and S. MESSICK, "The relation between category and magnitude scales of loudness." *Psychol. Rev.* **38**, 363–372 (1961)

HAMBLIN, R. L., D. A. BRIDGER, R. C. DAY, and W. L. YANCEY, "The interference-aggression law?" *Sociometry* **26**, 190–216 (1963)

HARPER, R. S., and S. S. STEVENS, "A psychological scale of weight and a formula for its derivation." *Amer. J. Psychol.* **61**, 343–351 (1948)

INDOW, T., ["An example of motivation research applied to product design."] Published in Japanese in *Chosa to gijutsu* **102**, 45–60 (1961)

KOH, S. D., "Scaling musical preferences." *J. Exp. Psychol.* **70**, 79–82 (1965)

KÜNNAPAS, T., and M. SILLÉN, "Measurement of political preferences. A comparison of scaling methods." *Rep. Psychol. Lab., University of Stockholm, No. 172* (1964)

KÜNNAPAS, T., and I. WIKSTRÖM, "Measurement of occupational preferences. A comparison of scaling methods." *Rep. Psychol. Lab., University of Stockholm, No. 156* (1963)

PERLOE, S. I., "The relation between category-rating and magnitude-estimation judgments of occupational prestige." *Amer. J. Psychol.* **76**, 395–403 (1963)

PRADHAN, P. L., and P. J. HOFFMAN, "Effect of spacing and range of stimuli on magnitude estimation judgments." *J. Exp. Psychol.* **66**, 533–541 (1963)

SELLIN, T., and M. E. WOLFGANG, *The Measurement of Delinquency.* New York: John Wiley & Sons, 1964

STEVENS, J. C., and M. GUIRAO, "Individual loudness functions." *J. Acoust. Soc. Amer.* **36,** 2210–2213 (1964)

STEVENS, S. S., "A scale for the measurement of a psychological magnitude: loudness." *Psychol. Rev.* **43,** 405–416 (1936)

STEVENS, S. S., "On the theory of scales of measurement." *Science* **103,** 677–680 (1946)

STEVENS, S. S., "On the brightness of lights and the loudness of sounds." *Science* **118,** 576 (1953) (Abstract)

STEVENS, S. S., "The measurement of loudness." *J. Acoust. Soc. Amer.* **27,** 815–829 (1955)

STEVENS, S. S., "On the psychophysical law." *Psychol. Rev.* **64,** 153–181 (1957)

STEVENS, S. S., "Problems and methods of psychophysics." *Psychol. Bull.* **55,** 177–196 (1958)

STEVENS, S. S., "Measurement, psychophysics, and utility," in C. W. Churchman and P. Ratoosh (eds.), *Measurement: Definitions and Theories.* New York: John Wiley & Sons, 1959a, pp. 18–63

STEVENS, S. S., "Review of L. L. Thurstone, The Measurement of Values." *Contemp. Psychol.* **4,** 388–389 (1959b)

STEVENS, S. S., "The psychophysics of sensory function," in W. A. Rosenblith (ed.), *Sensory Communication.* New York: M.I.T. Press and John Wiley & Sons, 1961, pp. 1–33

STEVENS, S. S., "The surprising simplicity of sensory metrics." *Amer. Psychologist* **17,** 29–39 (1962)

STEVENS, S. S., "On the uses of poikilitic functions," in D. J. Mostofsky (ed.), *Stimulus Generalization.* Stanford: Stanford University Press, 1965, pp. 24–29

STEVENS, S. S., and E. H. GALANTER, "Ratio scales and category scales for a dozen perceptual continua." *J. Exp. Psychol.* **54,** 377–411 (1957)

STEVENS, S. S., and M. GUIRAO, "Subjeetive scaling of length and area and the matching of length to loudness and brightness." *J. Exp. Psychol.* **66,** 177–186 (1963)

STEVENS, S. S., M. GUIRAO, and A. W. SLAWSON, "Loudness, a product of volume times density." *J. Exp. Psychol.* **69,** 503–510 (1965)

STEVENS, S. S., and J. VOLKMANN, "The relation of pitch to frequency: A revised scale." *Amer. J. Psychol.* **53,** 329–353 (1940)

SUPPES, P., and J. L. ZINNES, "Basic measurement theory," in R. D. Luce, R. R. Bush, and E. Galanter (eds.), *Handbook of Mathematical Psychology* (*Vol. 1*). New York: John Wiley & Sons, 1963, pp. 1–76

THURSTONE, L. L., "Psychophysical analysis." *Amer. J. Psychol.* **38,** 368–389 (1927)

THURSTONE, L. L., *The Measurement of Values.* Chicago: University of Chicago Press, 1959

THURSTONE, L. L., and E. J. CHAVE, *The Measurement of Attitude.* Chicago: University of Chicago Press, 1929

URBAN, F. M., *The Application of Statistical Methods to the Problems of Psychophysics.* Philadelphia: Psychological Clinic Press, 1908

CHAPTER 6

SAMPLING

GILBERT F. PEAKER, *C.B.E.*

THE POPULATION AND THE SAMPLE

Workers in the fields with which this book is concerned are interested in whole populations, but in practice, their work is almost always done on samples drawn from those populations. It is therefore of prime interest to them to know how closely a given sample represents the population from which it is drawn. This fact is generally recognized, and the recognition accounts for the frequent occurrence of the word "significance" in the literature.

In this context, "significance" is a term of art, and like other terms of art is easily misunderstood. The layman is apt to think it is synonymous with "important," which is by no means the case. The researcher, if he is primarily interested in his subject and has no more than a nodding acquaintance with probability and statistics, usually distinguishes between a significant and a chance result, but is often vague about the nature of the chance that is involved. Because of this the calculations of chances are rather frequently wrong, as a scrutiny of the literature shows. By far the most common mistake is to treat what is actually a complex sample as though it were simple, and thereby to underestimate, often seriously, the standard errors of the estimates, which in turn leads to regarding results as significant when they may very well be mere chance fluctuations. This produces rather frequent apparent contradictions between the conclusions of A and those of B, when the fact is that the standard errors calculated by A, or B, or both, have been underestimated, so that the conclusions rest upon what are mere sampling fluctuations.

Sampling Error

The researcher uses his sample to calculate means, medians, proportions, percentiles, correlations, regressions, factors, and other statistics. These sample statistics are estimates of the corresponding population parameters, and as such, they are subject to sampling error. In this context the word "error" does not mean "mistake." It means "wandering," as in knight errantry. The estimates will vary from sample to sample, but if the sampling procedure is properly designed they will not vary very much, and the chance of a variation of given size can itself be estimated. "Properly designed" here means that the sample is drawn by a suitable random procedure, and that the estimates are made in accordance with this procedure. Now, although "randomness" means chaos in excelsis, a "random" procedure is by no means a "haphazard" one. A good deal of careful organization is often needed to produce a random sample—i.e., a sample in which every member of a specified population has a specifiable probability, not zero, of appearing. The probabilities need not all be the same, but none of them must be zero. If practical difficulties make it impossible or too expensive to sample some classes of the population, these classes should be set aside, and the target population divided into the sampled population and the excluded population. Thus every member of the sampled population will have a nonzero probability of appearing in the sample, and the zero probabilities will be confined to the excluded population. It follows that the sample gives information about the sampled population, but not about the excluded population. In fact, if it is regarded as applying to the whole population the sample will be more or less biased, the seriousness of the bias depending on the relative size of the excluded population and on how far it differs from the sampled population. On the latter point the sample itself can of course throw no light, although other information may make it possible for a rough estimate to be made.

The technical sense, in which a random sample means a probability sample, may be illustrated by the stock example in which we have a barrel filled with red and white beans. If we take a scoopful from the top of the barrel, is this a random sample? Clearly not, if by a random sample we mean a probability sample. It is plainly not the case that every bean in the barrel has a specifiable nonzero probability of appearing in the scoop. Furthermore, if the white beans are predominantly at the top of the barrel and the red beans at the bottom, the proportion of red and white beans in the scoop will be quite different from the proportion in the barrel as a whole. To give every bean in the barrel a chance of appearing in the scoop, a very vigorous and prolonged stirring process must be associated with the scooping. The amount of stirring needed is considerable. Actual trial will show how inferior stirring the beans is to the corresponding process of diffusion in nonviscous liquids. This accounts for the prolonged churning that is given to the balls in a large sweepstake or lottery. And in fact, random or probability sampling means sampling conducted on the principles of a well-run lottery. But to avoid the labor of continuous churning, the draw in random sampling is made by the use of random numbers, which are, as it were, prechurned in the process of making the table of random numbers. A serial number is given to each member of the population, and he is drawn if this number appears in the chosen part of the table of random numbers. What part is chosen does not matter; the onus of good mixing or churning has been transferred to the maker of the table, which will have been tested for randomness.

SIMPLE AND COMPLEX SAMPLING

In simple random sampling every member of the population is in effect given one ticket in the lottery, and every ticket independently has the same chance of being drawn. These are the conditions under which the simple random sampling formulae for standard errors and significance, as given in all elementary textbooks on statistics, apply. But such conditions do not often obtain in the sampling of human populations. In practice, the sampling is often not random at all, but is based on judgment or convenience. Therefore, the probabilities of selection are unknown, and the formulae do not apply. But even when the sampling is random it is rarely simple. On the contrary, the sampling structure is usually complex, either because it is stratified or because it is carried out in several stages—or more commonly, for both reasons. In these circumstances the proper formulae for standard errors and significance may be extremely complex. Indeed, they may be so complex that in practice they can hardly be applied to cases in which the subject matter is also complicated, i.e., when there are a great many estimates, including estimates of correlations, regressions, or factors, to be obtained from the sample. Nonetheless, good approximations can usually be obtained by replicating the sampling procedure and comparing the results of the replications—that is, of the independent interpenetrating subsamples. *Stratification, stages,* and *replication* are therefore key words that need more attention.

Stratification. The idea of stratification is to divide the population into layers or strata such that the variation within the strata is less than the variation in the whole population. If we replaced our barrel of red and white beans by two barrels, one containing only white and the other only red beans, we should have an extreme case of stratification. The variation would now be entirely between the barrels; there would be no variation within each barrel. Provided that we knew the number of beans in each barrel, a sample of two beans, one from each barrel, would tell us how the whole population was made up.

A less extreme case would be that of eleven barrels containing 100%, 90%, 80%, . . . , 10%, and 0% of red beans, and complementary proportions of white. Here the variation is partly between and partly within barrels. Samples obtained by taking 100 beans from each barrel will be less variable than samples of 1100 beans from the original unstratified barrel with the same total content. If each barrel contains the same number of beans, the variation in the estimates is in fact given by the products of the proportions, that is, by 0.00, 0.09, 0.16, 0.21, 0.24, 0.25, 0.24, 0.21, 0.16, 0.09, and 0.00, which average to 0.15, against 0.25 for the unstratified single barrel. The variance of the estimate of the proportion is reduced to 60% of the unstratified estimate, and the standard error to the square root of this, or 78%. To get the same accuracy without stratification the sample would have to be increased from 1100 to 1100/(0.6), or 1833.

Thus stratification, *if it is successful,* enables a smaller sample to do the work of a larger one. The proviso is needed because the gains from stratification depend on the extent to which the variation can be transferred from within strata to between strata, and this in turn depends both on the subject matter and on our prior knowledge. In sampling students in schools or universities, for example, there is usually a good deal of prior knowledge about organization and standards of ability and work, and this knowledge can be effectively used for stratification. In public opinion polling and market research, stratification on socioeconomic variables is usually very effective. It is true that in these fields the sampling is often not probability sampling at all, the final selection being left to the interviewer who has to fill his stratified quota as quickly as he can from those he encounters, so that the probabilities of selection are unknown. But although this may bias the results, by excluding those who are rarely encountered unless sought out, and although probability calculations do not apply, the advantages of stratification remain. Even in cases where there is little prior knowledge it is usually worth while to build in one or two hopeful stratifications. They may prove effective, and if not, at least they can do no harm.

In the illustration above, a variable with only two values (red and white, or 1, 0) has been used, but stratification is equally appropriate for a variable that can take many values, such as the score in a test. The only difference is that σ^2, the variance per unit, replaces the product of the proportions, which is of course the variance per unit in the case of two values.

It is plain that if the main object is to obtain the least standard error in the general mean, the heaviest sampling should be concentrated on the strata where the variance is largest, and it is easy to show that for this purpose the most economical arrangement is to make the sampling fraction, n_i/N_i, proportional to σ_i, where N_i is the number of units in the ith stratum, σ_i the standard deviation in that stratum, and n_i the number of units drawn into the sample. This rule, often named after Neyman, who first drew attention to it in 1934, is less useful than might appear at first sight, however, because usually many variables, each giving different proportions in the rule, are of interest. Furthermore, the smaller strata may be of interest in themselves.

Stages. A multistage sample is one which is drawn in two, three, or more stages. Thus in England since 1950 the first stage in drawing a national sample of pupils in schools has often consisted of drawing a sample of areas, the second stage of drawing a sample of schools within selected areas, and the third of drawing a sample of pupils within selected schools, with stratification at each stage. One reason for this procedure is that if a sample of 3000 pupils were drawn in one stage from 35,000 schools, there could be nearly 3000 schools represented in the sample, and the burden of correspondence and visiting would be far too great. Another reason for multistage sampling, which is sometimes of crucial importance, is that it greatly reduces the amount of prior information needed. Thus if the stages are areas, schools, and pupils, the only requirement in the first stage is that the sampling units (areas) together cover the whole country. The second-stage units (schools) then need only be enumerated for the selected areas before the sample of schools is drawn. Similarly, the third-stage units (pupils) need only be enumerated for the selected schools. Thus for the sampling at each stage the sampling frame need only be constructed for the units selected at the previous stage. This may be a very great economy in a country where there are not already extensive national statistics relating to the subject matter of the inquiry, which is the case for all subjects in some countries and for some subjects in all. The choice of stages will of course depend on the subject and the amount of prior information.

Naturally, there is a price to be paid for the economies of a multistage procedure. The price consists in a greater complication in making the estimates of error. So far as the estimates of first-order parameters such as means and proportions are concerned, a multistage sample can be treated just like a single-stage sample. But for the estimates of error the position is quite otherwise. The simple random sampling formulae no longer apply, because these formulae depend on the assumption that the independently selected sampling units are also the units of analysis. In a single-stage sampling of students the student, who is the unit of analysis, is also the independently selected unit of sampling. But if the sampling is in two stages, with classes as the first stage and students within selected classes as the second, students are no longer independently selected. Either no students from a class are selected, or several. This is important for the same reason that stratification is important, namely, that birds of a feather tend to flock together. The students in any given class tend to resemble one another rather more closely than they resemble students in general. For any variable this additional resemblance can be measured by ρ, the intraclass correlation. If the component of variance between classes is C, and the component for students within classes S, then

$$\rho = C/(C + S),$$

and the variance of the mean for a sample of n classes and k students per class is given by

$$\frac{C}{n} + \frac{S}{nk} = \frac{kC + S}{nk} = \frac{(k - 1)C + C + S}{nk} = \frac{(k - 1)\rho + 1}{nk}(C + S).$$

If ρ is zero, the results will be as accurate as the results for simple sampling. But if, for example, ρ is 0.3 and k is 11, the numerator above becomes 4; this means that four times as many students will be needed in the sample to give the same accuracy for two-stage as for single-stage sampling.

It is plain that unless ρ is zero it is not possible to make up for too small a value of n by increasing the size of k. This is generally true for multistage sampling; it is always important to have enough first-stage units. This may easily be seen directly from the case of the barrels of beans. Suppose that we now have 101 barrels, containing 0%, 1%, 2%, etc., of red beans. We apply two-stage sampling by first drawing barrels, and then beans within selected barrels. If the sample is to consist of nk beans, of which k are from each of n barrels, it would be useless to set n equal to 1 and take all the nk from a single barrel. This would give us a very good estimate of the constitution of that barrel, but would tell us nothing about the other barrels in the population. Other things being equal, it would pay to spread the sampling over *all* the barrels, with a corresponding reduction in the number of beans per barrel sampled. Two-stage sampling pays only in the cases where other things are not equal—which happen, of course, to be the great majority of cases. Thus in industrial sampling the cost of opening bales, barrels, and other containers must be taken into account. In sampling educational institutions a large part of the cost is proportional to the number of institutions, as distinct from the number of students. Because of this a desired degree of accuracy may often be obtained more economically by taking fewer institutions, at the expense of having to take more students.

How many more students must be taken to compensate for the loss of accuracy through two-stage sampling depends on the size of the clusters and the value of the intraclass correlation—that is, the extent to which birds of a feather do, indeed, flock together. For estimating a mean the factor is, as shown above, $(k - 1)\rho + 1$. Some values of this factor are shown in Table 1. The estimate given by the simple random sampling formula must be multiplied by the square root of this factor to give the true standard error; alternatively, the number of persons in the sample should be divided by the factor itself to give the size of the simple equivalent random sample. Thus with $k = 50$ and $\rho = 0.2$ a sample of 10,800 persons would be equivalent to a simple sample of 1000. This illustrates the point made above, that confidence limits are often greatly understated when the fact that the sampling structure is not simple but complex is ignored.

Table 1

	ρ			
k	0.1	0.2	0.3	0.4
5	1.4	1.8	2.2	2.6
10	1.9	2.8	3.7	4.6
20	2.9	4.8	6.7	8.6
50	5.9	10.8	15.7	20.6
100	10.9	20.8	30.7	40.6

Replication. Although, as has been shown, it is of the highest importance that a complex sample should not be treated as though it were simple, the labor of complicated calculations of standard errors can be largely avoided by the simple device of replication. If the sample is drawn as, say, four independent subsamples, each of these subsamples will provide an independent estimate for any parameter whose value is sought. By comparing these independent estimates an estimate of the error in the mean value of the four can be obtained. Note carefully that the subsamples must be independent—that is, each must be drawn in accordance with the full complexity of the design.

With only four subsamples each estimate of error will rest on only three degrees of freedom. Other things being equal, more subsamples would be desirable. But unless the total sample is rather large it may be difficult to preserve the advantages of stratification if there are more subsamples. Furthermore, where correlations, regressions, and factors are involved, having more subsamples will involve a large increase in the amount of computation. An advantage of keeping the number of subsamples small, and consequently the size of the subsamples large, is that we may then be confident that the subsample estimates will be normally distributed, whatever the shape of the parent distributions. Consequently the *t*-table can be applied. Alternatively, using the *G*-test, we may say that there is a 90% probability that the true mean lies within half the range each way from the sample mean, or that there is an 88% probability that the true median lies between the highest and the lowest of the four subsample estimates. These all come to very much the same thing.

A scrutiny of the obtained ranges between subsample estimates may show that it is reasonable to adopt a single value, covering the whole field of the survey, of a factor by which the standard errors given by the simple random sampling formulae should be multiplied to obtain the standard errors proper. Or different factors may cover estimates of different kinds (e.g., means and correlations). Only moderate accuracy is needed here; it is important to distinguish between a factor of 1 and a factor of 4, but not between 3.5 and 4.5. What is to be avoided is a wholesale acceptance of mere sampling fluctuations as significant because of failure to take account of the complexity of the sampling structure. Replication with only four subsamples is quite effective for this purpose. There are many other ways in which replication may be applied. For instance, where there are many strata, replication with only two subsamples per stratum may be quite effective. What is always wrong is to use simple random sampling formulae when the sampling is complex.

Survey and Experimental Data

It is often said that survey data are to be distinguished from experimental data, but the distinction is less clear than is sometimes thought. In both cases the nature of the sampling structure needs to be taken into account if calculations of standard error and tests of significance are to be made. This was recognized by Laplace, and important discoveries in astronomy have rested on the detection of internal correlation between observations. But failure to allow for internal correlation is still an important source of mistakes in the social sciences—chiefly because enough attention is not given to the question of whether the members of the sample can properly be described as a simple random sample of some specifiable population, and if so of what population.

The meaning to be attached to any standard errors or significance levels calculated depends on the answer to this question. It is usually easy to see when the answer given by implication is wrong, but harder to find the appropriate answer. For example, it is plainly wrong to regard the population of Cambridge, Massachusetts, as a random sample of the same number of people from the whole of the United States. Regarded as a sample of the United States the population of Cambridge is a sample of one unit, namely, Cambridge. No estimate of error can be obtained from a sample of one unit only. If, on the other hand, it is regarded as a sample of Cambridge at the time of the inquiry there *is* no sampling error, because the sample is now identical with the population. To neither of these two ways of looking at the matter do the simple random sampling formulae apply. This is true also in the common case when an educational experiment is carried out with the cooperation of the entire tenth-grade population of some high school, or of all the patients with a particular complaint in some hospital.

This is not to say that in such cases it is useless to calculate the standard errors by the simple random sampling formulae. But the *meaning* of these standard errors, and the derived significance levels, is not what is often supposed. If we find that on this calculation an effect is significant, we are entitled to suppose that it would generally be found in other closely similar institutions or towns, or in the same town or institution during a run of years in which circumstances did not change much. The inquiry itself provides no evidence that such other institutions or towns exist, but it does encourage us to look for them, whereas if the effect is not significant we are not so encouraged. Furthermore, when the effect is strikingly significant on this calculation we may be encouraged to look for it again not in closely similar but in rather widely different circumstances, on the general scientific principle of testing a hypothesis by extrapolating it far beyond its original range of reference. If the effect is still found in the new circumstances, even more remote circumstances may be tried. If, on the other hand, the effect is no longer found, a halfway house might be tried, where the circumstances were less different from the original instead of more. Each new trial may be regarded as a replication of the original trial, and it is reasonable that confidence in the hypothesis should rapidly increase with the number of successful replications.

What is unreasonable is to base a high degree of confidence on a single limited experiment or to attach great importance to a particular boundary between "significant" and "not significant" results. The ratio of an estimate to its standard error is important, but it is a continuous variable and there is no reason for attaching special importance to whether it is, for example, 1.9 or 2.1. From the standpoint of a successor who wishes to combine the evidence of several experiments it is better that an experimenter should give his estimate with its standard error and the number of observations, rather than merely say that the result was significant or not significant.

SIGNIFICANCE AND ESTIMATION

It would also be an advantage if the use of "significant" were restricted to cases where the question is really one of significance, and not of estimation. A question of significance arises when the evidence throws serious doubt upon some previously accepted value of a parameter, or suggests the need for an additional parameter. An obvious example is that of bias in dice. We begin with the assumption that ordinary dice are fair dice, so that the chance of throwing a five or six is one-third. In 315,672 throws W. F. R. Weldon obtained 106,602 cases of a five or six. The ratio is 0.337699, suggesting an excess chance of 0.004366. The odds are about 1600 to 1 in favor of a small bias. The explanation appears to be that in the manufacture of the dice small pits are made in the faces to accommodate the marking material; this lightens the faces that have five or six spots and increases the chance that these faces will settle upwards. This is a genuine question of significance. So also are questions about Mendelian ratios. So also was the choice between Newtonian dynamics and general relativity that arose on the 1919 eclipse observations. On the other hand, most of the questions that arise in medicine, agriculture, or the social sciences are not really questions of significance at all. It is well recognized that different treatments may be expected to give different effects, and the question is not whether this is so but whether the obtained differences are large enough to be worth notice. Such questions are questions of estimation, and not questions of significance.

Simulation

Weldon's data are valuable not only in showing the true nature of a test of significance but also for establishing that for moderate numbers of throws ordinary dice can be regarded as fair. This makes them useful for simulation. The variance of a single throw is 35/12. The distribution of the sum of three or more throws is practically normal, because of the central limit property. Consequently if $u, v, w, x,$ and y are the scores of five dice, and $z = 5(u + v + w) + x + y + 40$, then z has mean 99.5 and standard deviation 15 [because the variance is $(5^2 \cdot 3 + 2)35/12$], and simulates the distribution of IQ on the usual scale. Any given normal distribution can be simulated in this way.

An alternative is to use a nomographic scale, on the slide-rule principle that the voice is Jacob's voice, but the hands are the hands of Esau. In the case of the slide rule the names are numbers and the distances their logarithms. For the normal scale the names are the names of percentile ranks and the deviations are as shown in Table 2. Such a scale used in conjunction with a table of random numbers very rapidly gives samples of any desired size from the standardized normal distribution. Similar scales can be made from the tables of the other standard distributions.

Table 2

% Rank	1	5	10	20	30	40	50	60	70	80	90	95	99
Deviation	−2.33	−1.64	−1.28	−0.84	−0.52	−0.25	0.00	0.25	0.52	0.84	1.28	1.64	2.33

The use of simulation is to be recommended for two reasons. In the first place it quickly gives familiarity with the idea of sampling fluctuation. Second, the thought needed to set up a simulation of any given experimental situation necessarily directs attention to the nature of that situation. Is the simulation proposed justified? If so, why, and if not, why not? Broadly speaking it may be said that if one can set up, and justify, such a model of an experimental situation one understands it, and if not, one doesn't. The great part played in the history of the subject by games of chance provides a most valuable hint for both the teacher and the learner of probability and statistics. The student who proceeds steadily by simulation will find it a powerful and entertaining method of gaining insight into such ideas as stratification, sampling by stages, and replication. He will see what is involved in the analysis of variance and covariance. He will grasp the effect of restriction of range upon correlations, and hence upon regression and factor analysis. He will understand why unduly small values of chi-square demand as much notice as unduly large ones.

MEMORANDA

In working with statistical data it is useful to commit to memory a few simple facts. One of these is that the range factors for samples of 3, 4, and 5 from the normal distribution are 1.69, 2.06, and 2.33 (roughly $\frac{5}{3}$, $\frac{6}{3}$, and $\frac{7}{3}$), while for samples of 10, 25, 100, and 500 the factors are roughly 3, 4, 5, and 6. Now, the range divided by the range factor gives an estimate of the standard deviation, which is rough for the large sample sizes, but almost as accurate as the mean-square estimate for samples of 3, 4, and 5. Thus for a large sample a rough estimate can be obtained at once by finding the highest and lowest values in the whole sample; a very accurate estimate can then be made by dividing the sample, in the order in which it appears, into batches of 4 (or 3, or 5) and averaging the ranges. Such range estimates can be very rapidly made. They are robust—that is, they are not sensitive to the exact shape of the distribution—and for small samples they correlate very highly with the mean-square estimates. (The reason for this is easy to see; for a sample of 4 the range estimate ignores the positions of the two inner members, but these positions cannot vary much, for if they did one of the inner members would become an outer member.) Thus the use of ranges provides a quick and effective substitute for the analysis of variance. Great use has been made of range properties in quality control work, and a large literature exists on them; much more use might be made of them in other fields.

Chi-square, which for k degrees of freedom is the sum of k squares of the standard normal variate, occurs over and over again, in various easily penetrable disguises, in statistical work. Therefore, it is useful to remember that the mean value is k (as is plain from the definition) and the standard deviation is $\sqrt{2k}$. For the upper 5% limit this gives astonishingly good results even when k is small (e.g. 3.82,* 6.00, and 7.89 for $k = 1$, 2, and 3, against tabular values of 3.84, 5.99, and 7.81). For larger values of k the central limit theorem makes the closeness of the approximation less surprising. Variances are disguised chi-squares, and so are many other functions.

It is also useful to remember that the variance, and hence the standard error, of a function of one or several variables can be obtained, with usually adequate accuracy, by differentiation and the Pythagorean theorem. The same fact, that independent errors add by the Pythagorean theorem, has a bearing on the useful size of samples. The final error in an estimate will be the root mean square of the sampling error and the bias. The bias is the error that would still be present however much the sampling size was increased. Some sort of estimate of the length of this leg can usually be made from knowledge of the subject matter of the inquiry, and there is little point in making the length of the sampling leg much shorter, since this will not appreciably reduce the length of the hypotenuse. This is, for example, an argument for more frequent small samples rather than less frequent large ones in changing circumstances.

---

* $3.82 = k + 2\sqrt{2k}$, where $k = 1$.

Diagrams and colors. The use of diagrams can be recommended both at the planning stage and for scrutinizing observations actually obtained. Colors make it easy to distinguish different classes. Thus in a regression problem one class can be represented by red spots, another by blue, a third by green, and so on. The general regression line can be drawn by eye through all the spots without regard to colors, and the class lines for red, blue, green, yellow, etc., can then be added to the diagram. Comparing the positions obtained by eye with those given by calculation will draw attention to any unusual features in the diagram, such as serious departures from the implied conditions that make the model appropriate.

At the planning stage it is helpful to make diagrams with simulated data, along the lines suggested in an earlier section. The process of simulation forces the inquirer to specify what is already known or conjectured about the situation, which may be a great deal or very little, according to circumstances. This knowledge, or lack of it, can be built into the simulation. Both the design of the simulation and the resulting picture may well suggest improvements in the original plan before it is too late. It is usually recommended that the inquirer construct dummy tables as part of his planning, and this is excellent advice as far as it goes. But dummy tables are not much use if the conclusion from most of them is only that there may be some effects but the sample is too small to show them. Consequently, some prior attempt at estimating the standard errors is needed, and for this, simulation and diagram-drawing will be found helpful. Elaborate drawings are not needed; a rough sketch is usually enough to direct attention to what information already exists, and how much more of what kind is needed to give a reasonable chance of answering the questions proposed. "How much more" includes the important question of sample size. Since the sample will generally be of complex structure, any information about intraclass correlation is particularly useful.

Diagrams are also useful in reports to display information. The popularity of the histogram for this purpose is to be deplored, since its dependence on the choice of class interval is excessive and results in the loss of information. It is preferable to use the distribution, or cumulative frequency, diagram. This is easily obtained by setting out the observations along a graduated horizontal axis, which automatically ranks them, and then raising each one vertically by its percentile rank. The resulting diagram is, as it were, the sampling ghost of the population distribution curve, and indicates the shape of that curve much better than the histogram, because no information is lost. If the diagram is drawn on probability paper on which the normal distribution is a straight line, the ghost will show whether an assumption of normality is justified. Moderate departures from normality are unimportant when the question is one of estimating standard errors, because of the effect of the central limit theorem illustrated above in the recipe for producing artificial IQ by throwing dice.

When the shape of the distribution is directly of interest (e.g., in showing educational progress by the scores obtained in the same test in successive national surveys), the sample distribution curve can be used both for display and to produce a table of scores for decile ranks. In such a case it should be graduated (smoothed) algebraically or even by eye. This is because, while there is no reason to suppose that the population curve follows the normal or any other standard distribution, it is reasonable to suppose that it is not only monotonic, as it must be, since it is cumulative, but also smooth and with only one inflection. Consequently, the smoothed diagram will be rather closer to the population curve than the unsmoothed ghost. Smoothing of this kind, which can be justified, should be sharply distinguished from the illegitimate process of finding a normal curve to which the observations give a reasonably good fit and using this curve to calculate population proportions far out in the tails. Extreme-value statistics are not subject to the central limit theorem.

Engineers' quality control charts can also be useful for the scrutiny of data. The control chart for ranges tests whether the data are homogeneous—that is, whether analysis of variance is appropriate—and where it *is* appropriate, the control chart for means gives a simple method of carrying out the analysis. Essentially, this is a visual representation of the method of analysis of variance by ranges suggested above. Besides these, and the probability paper mentioned above, there are many special papers for various purposes. Most of these are worth exploration with simulated data, in order to gain new insights, but it is dangerous to rely on them without such preliminary trials.

REFERENCES

COCHRAN, WILLIAM G., *Sampling Techniques (2nd ed.)*. New York: John Wiley & Sons, 1963

DEMING, W. E., *Some Theory of Sampling.* New York: John Wiley & Sons, 1957

HANSEN, M. H., W. N. HURWITZ, and W. G. MADOW, *Sample Survey Methods and Theory.* New York: John Wiley & Sons, 1956, 2 volumes

JEFFREYS, H., *Scientific Inference (2nd ed.)*. Cambridge, England: Cambridge University Press, 1957

JEFFREYS, H., *Theory of Probability.* Oxford: Clarendon Press, 1961

PEAKER, G. F., "A sampling design used by the Ministry of Education." *J. Roy. Stat. Soc.* **116,** 140–165 (1953)

Part 2   APPLIED AREAS

CHAPTER 7

THE STRUCTURE OF INTELLIGENCE

J. P. GUILFORD, *University of Southern California*

Whatever else may be said about human intelligence, the belief that it is an un-differentiated, monolithic ability, unstructured, and completely measurable by means of a single score, is dead or dying. It dies reluctantly, in spite of the over-whelming weight of evidence against it. Its many advantages have been too appealing—the simplicity of thinking and of operating that it offers; the achieve-ment of the ultimate in satisfaction of the goal of parsimony; and the admitted measure of success in application to many spheres of life.

SOME TRADITIONAL VIEWS OF INTELLECTUAL STRUCTURE

Binet's View of Intelligence

It is a curious historical fact that the man who was most responsible for saddling us with the idea of a unitary intelligence, measurable by a single score, was a firm believer that intelligence is a multiplex of many different abilities. The reference is, of course, to Alfred Binet, a most astute and penetrating experimental psychol-ogist of his day. From his earliest writing to his latest, he consistently maintained that intelligence is a complex of many components. In connection with his last revision of his intelligence scale, and after his extensive experiences in constructing scales, Binet remarked that the problem of intelligence is much more complex than had previously been imagined (Binet and Simon, 1911). In practice, however, his operation of using a single score belied his convictions. Those who followed Binet accepted the fruits of his scale construction, while overlooking and forgetting his basic theory.

Some British Views

While pragmatic American psychologists were exploiting Binet's tests of intelli-gence and developing new ones, without much concern for the basic nature of intelligence (except for futile attempts to define it), British psychologists, beginning with Charles Spearman, were developing methods whereby the nature of intelli-gence could be investigated. They were also developing a theory of the structure of intelligence, as they discovered new components. Spearman's conception of a universal component g, thought to be measured in common by any and all tests that can conceivably be placed in the intellectual category, plus specifics (every specific a unique component for each test), provided support to the one-intelligence idea. Spearman was taken so seriously in Britain that to this day, with very few exceptions, a *g* is almost universally demanded, even by some expatriates.

The need for structural models of intelligence arose only after common factors in addition to *g* were found. Results of factor analysis over the years have contributed a steadily growing list of common factors in the domain of intelligence. Two types of models have emerged. With the British, who insist on a *g* factor, the models have been hierarchical (Burt, 1949; Vernon, 1950). In the United States, where Thurstone's multiple-factor methods have prevailed, no *g* factor is found, except on rare occasions, and a morphological type of model has been proposed (Guilford, 1959b).

Another intercontinental difference is that the hierarchical models have often been broadened to include personality traits other than abilities, and abilities other than intellectual ones (Vernon, 1950; Eysenck, 1952). The writer, although recognizing the virtues of hierarchical models and their applicability to some aspects of personality, particularly to motivational traits (Guilford, 1959a), finds morphological models much more logically representative or descriptive of aptitude areas, and even of temperamental and psychopathological areas. It is possible that either type of model will be found applicable in some areas of personality. It is not a question of which type of model is right or wrong; it is a question of which is more representative and more illuminating when applied.

Hierarchical models. The hierarchical model is an inverted tree pattern. Burt, who is a staunch Aristotelian, conceives of the ideal tree model as branching in successive dichotomies, two twigs to every branch. From *g*, the first dichotomy is between verbal and nonverbal, or intellectual and practical, at what he calls the "relational" level. Lower levels are called "association," "perception," and "sensation." But as Burt applies his model to the known group factors, he has to depart from the strict dichotomization design (Burt, 1949). He insists on a small *g* factor at each level except that of sensation.

Vernon (1950) makes a beginning similar to that of Burt. From *g* there is branching into a *v:ed* factor and a *k,m* factor. Factor *v:ed* is verbal-educational; factor *k,m* is spatial-motor. Factor *v:ed* subdivides into verbal and numerical abilities, and factor *k,m* into space and psychomotor abilities. From there on, Vernon relates subdivided factors rather directly to formal educational areas of instruction, reflecting his educational interests rather than interest in basic psychology.

Burt supports his preference for the dichotomizing principle on the basis of the way in which successive factors come out in his summation method of factoring a correlation matrix. The summation method is essentially the same as Thurstone's centroid method. In analyses of tests of abilities, the first centroid factor is completely general, having nonzero loadings in every test. In the second factor, the tests separate, about half having positive and half negative loadings. Each successive factor shows a similar bifurcation of tests, with different tests having the strongest positive (negative) loadings. This is, indeed, a tree pattern, with successive dichotomizations.

If one does not rotate axes, however, one has to accept the fact that all except one of the factors is bipolar. Among tests of abilities, and from a correlation matrix that has positive coefficients of correlation throughout, tests with negative loadings on factors present a highly illogical picture, as Thurstone pointed out a number of times. Even many of those who want a *g* factor are inclined to rotate reference axes at least a little in order to achieve a positive manifold. In representing presumed psychological dimensions, therefore, there is departure from the tree pattern provided by the centroid factors.

The case against g. Critics of the hierarchical type of model for abilities sometimes point out that its proponents are using a rather incidental mathematical feature of the centroid method of factoring as a shaky basis for adopting that form of model. In all fairness, however, it must be admitted that the tests that stand out at the extremes of the bipolar centroid factors do play special roles, whether one rotates, maintaining a *g*, or whether one does not. Even in the rotations of the multiple-factor analyst, those same tests will take leading loadings on different factors after rotation. Of course, in the latter case, the original dichotomizations lose much of their earlier clusterings. For example, the same test may be at extremes on more than one rotated factor, and some tests extreme on different centroid factors may come together after rotations.

Whether to rotate, maintaining a *g* factor, or to permit the resulting factor structure to have a *g* or not, as the data indicate, is a matter of arbitrary choice. The writer once demonstrated, by the use of two fictitious sets of data into which a *g* factor was introduced, that the rotational methods of multiple-factor analysis did not miss such a factor (Guilford, 1941). It follows that if *g* exists in the data, we may expect to find it by such rotational methods.

It is probable that the vector for an arbitrary *g* factor, after some rotation, is not so very far from the first centroid vector. Sometimes the first centroid vector is taken to represent *g*. In either case, it must be remembered that the location of the first centroid vector is determined by the particular combination of tests used in the analysis. *Such a location is not invariant with changes in battery composition. It is likely, then, that no obtained g is exactly like any other g, at any level in the hierarchy.*

The most often mentioned empirical support for accepting the idea of a *g* factor in tests of a domain like intelligence is that all tests are positively intercorrelated. The facts simply do not support this assertion, which, nevertheless, is made again and again. The writer can cite hundreds of zero intercorrelations among tests of intellectual qualities (Guilford, 1964c). An examination of over 7000 intercorrelations of intellectual tests from 13 correlation matrices showed that about 17 percent of the coefficients were in the range of ± 0.10. Twenty-four percent failed to reach the 0.05 level of statistical significance, where the sample sizes were typically in the neighborhood of 225.

Earlier correlation matrices tended to have only positive correlations for several reasons. The kinds of tests were limited; they were not varied a great deal in factorial content. What is probably more important, the tests themselves tended to be factorially complex, thus producing mutual overlapping. Where there is an effort to construct tests of simple factorial composition, one will find many zero intercorrelations.

Now, our British friends would say that in aiming toward factor-pure tests we are squeezing out g. The writer's interpretation is that we are squeezing out overlapping with other common factors, not g. The charge that g is thus squeezed out of an intellectual test is virtually an admission that intellectual tests can exist without g. The conclusion is strongly indicated: that g is not universal, hence no g, which, by definition, *is* universal.

Another kind of condition that is favorable for producing what appear to be psychological g factors is heterogeneity of the population of individuals sampled for an analysis. Kelly (1934) emphasized this principle many years ago, when he wisely pointed out that a g might simply represent variations in age, sex, education, and so on. If two tests are both correlated with age, they will correlate with one another because of this fact, and perhaps *only* because of this fact. From the writer's point of view, which reflects his being brought up in experimental psychology, keeping an experimental population uniform with respect to age, sex, and other pertinent variables is only a matter of the time-honored principle of experimental control. If a factor represents any one or any combination of such determiners when we use a heterogeneous population, we should certainly want to know this. We should not like to think that we are erroneously calling it g, with the conviction that it represents something of psychological importance.

If we wanted to make a thoroughly experimental approach, we should want to hold constant every determiner of individual differences in scores except one, a particular hypothesized dimension of ability. We should then be able to demonstrate that certain tests show variances and others do not, over persons. A beauty of factor analysis, and other multivariate experimental methods, is that this much experimental control is not necessary. We can solve research problems without having as much. But we must have *some* experimental control; otherwise, we have too much ambiguity in interpreting the results.

The g psychologists make much of the fact that relatively large proportions of the variance in a set of analyzed tests can be attributed to the g factor, and that the group factors claim only a small minority of the total variance. This is because these psychologists ensure such a distribution of variances in applying their procedures. They often complain that the multiple-factor psychologists distribute the variances away from g, in fact entirely away, in most cases. It should be said in fairness to the distributive factorists that the intention is not necessarily to take variances away from g. Being open-minded, they would probably tolerate a g factor if it remained after the rotation process.

There is a good reason, a purely mathematical one, for distributing much of the variance of the first centroid factor, or the first principal component, thus building up variances in later extracted factors. By the very nature of the extraction methods, each factor extracted, at least in the principal-components procedure, takes out the maximum amount of variance remaining. The first factor takes out an overwhelming plurality of the variance. Should this fact be permitted to "prove" the existence of a *g* factor? No, for we should not allow the incidental mathematical feature of a method to determine our psychological theory.

In passing, we might note that the distribution of the variance of the first centroid factor tends also to lower variances in second and third factors, in other words, in all the earlier factors, as well as to lower variance of the first. The principle is to tend toward an evening up of variances in all the factors, but not to insist on this condition, for some factors are represented by more tests than are others.

Thurstone's g factor. Thurstone's compromise with the *g* factorists was to say that *g* comes out in the second-order domain, as a factor of factors. There are several important objections to this idea. First, more than one second-order factor is commonly found; which one of them is *g*, or is any of them? It may well be that none is in common to all first-order factors, and hence to all tests. Second, such a *g* is no more invariant than is a *g* that is found on the first-order level, hence cannot represent any stable psychological concept. One could go on to third- and higher-order factor levels, until only one factor emerged, but the same objections would still apply, even if a single factor were finally reached.

A more basic difficulty in arriving at a *g* by Thurstone's factoring of factors is that there is considerable uncertainty as to how to estimate the correlations among the first-order primary axes, as this writer repeatedly points out (Guilford and Zimmerman, 1963). The degree of obliqueness in a set of primary axes is dependent on the selection of tests in the analyzed battery as well as on the rotator's methods. Until we find better ways of estimating intercorrelations of first-order factors, we would do well to forget about higher-order domains.

The commonality of factor interpretations. The writer's choice of orthogonal rotations is in part for the same reasons. We do not have sufficient basis for locating oblique axes whose positions will be invariant with changes of test battery in application to the same population of persons. In arriving at the multiple-factor psychological dimensions, however, it makes practically no difference whether one uses oblique or orthogonal rotations, so long as the obliqueness is not extreme, where "extreme" means correlations greater than about 0.70 between primary vectors.

The thing that ensures the possibility of comparable interpretations of factors in an analysis is that both oblique and orthogonal rotations start from the same source, the centroid or the principal-component factor matrix. Tests that stand out in that matrix toward the ends of the original bipolar vectors are likely to stand out for interpretation purposes in both orthogonal and oblique solutions. This is also why the group factors of the *g* factorists are so often interpretable in much the same way as for the multiple-factor psychologists. An important consequence, in developing logical models for interrelating the factors, is that much the same factors, excepting *g*, must be considered.

One difference is that the *g* factorists, finding that later-discovered group factors are generally weaker, have more or less stopped looking for them. Multiple-factor psychologists have continued unabated, for they do not let *g* rob other factors of variances, leaving some rather weak group factors. For the multiple-factor psychologist, also, the development of the structure-of-intellect model (Guilford, 1959b) has opened up whole new vistas of intellectual factors to be expected and investigated. From this development, we can see that an insistence on *g* is an example of how a fixed idea can lead one into a cul-de-sac so far as theory development and research progress are concerned.

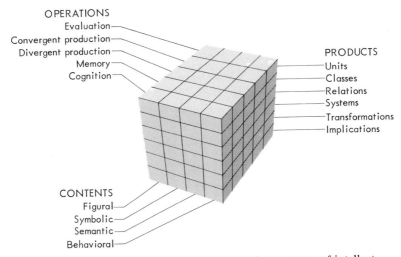

Fig. 1. The geometric model representing the structure of intellect.

THE STRUCTURE-OF-INTELLECT MODEL

The structure-of-intellect model grew out of an attempt to classify logically the intellectual abilities that had been demonstrated by factor analysis (Guilford, 1956a, 1956b, 1957, 1958). After repeated attempts, it was concluded that it requires three independent principles of classification, and therefore a three-dimensional model, to take care of all kinds of intellectual factors. One dimension of the model (see Fig. 1) represents five different kinds of operations—cognition, memory, divergent production, convergent production, and evaluation. Such terms will be given formal definitions a bit later. A second dimension of the model pertains to four different kinds of content—figural, symbolic, semantic, and behavioral. These concepts derive from the general nature of the information given by the examiner and produced by the examinee in special intelligence tests of all kinds. The third basis of classification is in terms of six kinds of psychological products—units, classes, relations, systems, transformations, and implications.

The model in Fig. 1 shows that each category of operation can be combined with any category of content, and any such combination can be further combined with any of the six categories of products. There are 120 such combinations possible ($4 \times 5 \times 6$), each combination being unique and describing the essential nature of an intellectual factor ability. At the beginning of the effort to classify the factors, less than 40 were known; at the time of writing (1964) about 60 were known, many of them found in the literature, but the majority of them found for the first time by the Aptitudes Project at the University of Southern California. Many of the latter were predicted by the model before they were demonstrated, and the model continues to serve as a useful heuristic device for generating hypotheses regarding undiscovered factors and suggesting the kinds of new tests needed to demonstrate those factors.

Formal Definitions of the Model Categories

At this point, formal definitions of the categories will be presented. These definitions are subject to change as new insights arise, but they are stated as accurately as our present knowledge permits. Illustrative information will be provided later to give a clearer idea of the known factors and to make the category concepts more meaningful.

Operations. Major kinds of intellectual activities or processes; kinds of things that the organism does with the raw materials of information. For the purposes of this discussion, "information" is defined as that which the organism discriminates. This meaning of information is consistent with information theory from the field of communications, although it does not carry with it all the connotations from that source.

Cognition: Acquaintance with, knowing, recognizing, discovering immediately, rediscovering, comprehending, or understanding given information.

Memory: Retention or storage of information in any form.

Divergent Production: Generating information (mostly from memory storage) in response to given information, where the emphasis is on multiplicity and variety of output in response to the same given information.

Convergent Production: Generating information (from memory storage) in response to given information, where the emphasis is on achieving fully determined, unique, or conventionally accepted or best outcome.

Evaluation: Making decisions as to the "goodness" (correctness, suitability, adequacy, desirability) of information (cognized or produced from storage) in terms of criteria such as identity, or consistency.

Contents. Broad, general varieties or fields of information.

Figural Content: Information in concrete or tangible form, as perceived or as recalled in the form of images. The term "figural" implies some degree of organization or structuring, but this may be minimal, as a simple color patch on a ground of distinguishably different color.

Symbolic Content: Information in the form of signs, having no significance in and of themselves, sometimes given cultural significance, but could have any newly defined significance, such as letters, numbers, musical notations, or code elements of any kind.

Semantic Content: Information in the form of meanings to which words commonly become attached, hence most notable in verbal thinking, but involved in performing any mental tasks "in thought rather than in deed."

Behavioral Content: Information, essentially nonverbal, involved in human interactions, where awareness of the attitudes, needs, desires, perceptions, intentions, and thoughts of other persons and of ourselves is important. What has been called "social intelligence" belongs here. Empathy, as usually employed, probably refers to behavioral cognition—the cognition of behavioral information.

Products. Results from the organism's processing of information; the basic forms in which information, of any kind of content, may be cast.

Unit: A relatively segregated or circumscribed item of information having "thing" character, such as a perceived object, a word (as a letter combination, a printed word is a visual-symbolic unit), an idea or a concept, or a perceived attitude, to name units of four different kinds of content.

Class: A conception underlying a set of items of information grouped because of their common property or properties.

Relation: A recognized connection between units of information based upon variables that apply to them. Prepositions commonly describe relations, but of course not all relations can be described by prepositions.

System: An organized or structured aggregate of items of information; a complex of interrelated or interacting parts. A verbally comprehended arithmetic problem is an example of a semantic system, as are a sentence, a plan of verbally conceived action, and a verbally stated scientific theory.

Transformation: A change in existing or known information or in its use, as in production. A pun is a semantic transformation (some are also symbolic or have their symbolic aspects). Conceived movement of an object is a figural transformation. Any redefinition, or new way of looking at something, is a transformation.

Implication: An extrapolation of information, in the form of expectancies, predictions, antecedents, concomitants, and consequents. The statement from mathematical logic: "If this, then that" may apply to implications in general.

Role of Factors in Behavior

Many general comments could be made regarding the structure-of-intellect model, its uses, and its implications (Guilford and Merrifield, 1960). One thing that needs to be said here is that the nature of the model, with its compartmentalized cells, should not give the impression that these segregated and uniquely defined abilities represent functions that operate separately in behavior. Far from it. The environment presents problems that demand certain operations to solve them. Problems are presented in contexts of different kinds of content, and different kinds of products are involved. Solution may require the simultaneous involvement of quite a number of the abilities. The strategy applied by the organism also helps to determine which of the abilities shall be involved. Tasks in everyday life, unlike tests designed to measure factors, are factorially relatively complex. If they were not, the problem of isolating the unique components of intellect would have been a much easier one. We have to keep trying to produce factor-pure tests, or tests approaching that condition, before we can demonstrate relative independence of intellectual factors.

It might be thought that only the product of units can enter into classes, relations, systems, transformations, and implications. In fact, this principle was implied earlier. But more recent findings indicate that there may be interactions such as classes of relations and of systems, and transformations of classes and of systems, for example. Such interactions increase even more the many intricate kinds of mutual involvements of abilities in everyday life. The range of ideas offered for psychological theory is also tremendously increased, not only by the model itself, but by these refinements in use of the concepts of the model.

SOME EXAMPLES OF FACTORS AND TESTS

An Introduction to the Factors

In the space of a chapter it is impossible to describe every known factor in detail, to cite its ramifications in mental economy, and to show the light that factors, taken collectively, throw on general psychological theory. More information regarding the factors, as such, is available in previous publications (Berger *et al.,* 1957; Christensen and Guilford, 1963; French, 1951; Frick *et al.,* 1959; Gershon *et al.,* 1963; Guilford, 1967; Guilford *et al.,* 1961; Kettner *et al.,* 1959; Merrifield *et al.,* 1961; Nihira *et al.,* 1964; Peterson *et al.,* 1964). Information on the bearing of the structure-of-intellect (SI) concepts on general psychological theory and research will be touched upon later, as will some implications of the model in testing and in education. Some relations to other conceptions, such as those of Piaget, will also be mentioned. Here we shall simply list factors by location in the model, define them, give examples of representative tests, and offer special comments where it is pertinent to do so.

A coding system for the factors. The location or "address" of a factor in the SI model is indicated by a three-letter code symbol, the first letter of which signifies the *operation,* the second the *content,* and the third the *product* involved in the factor (see Table 1). Initial letters are used except in two cases, where substitute symbols are needed to avoid duplication of symbols within a set. (These exceptions are N, for convergent production—to avoid duplication of C, for cognition—and M, for semantic—to avoid duplication of S, for symbolic.) Duplications across sets should not be bothersome if one keeps in mind the order—operation, content, product. Thus CST stands for the cognition of symbolic transformations; NMR stands for the convergent production of semantic relations; and so on.

Table 1   Code to the structure-of-intellect designation of factors

First letter (Operation)	Second letter (Content)	Third letter (Product)
C — cognition	F — figural	U — unit
M — memory	S — symbolic	C — class
D — divergent production	M — semantic	R — relation
N — convergent production	B — behavioral	S — system
E — evaluation		T — transformation
		I — implication

Cognition Factors

Figure 2 shows which of the 24 potential cognitive abilities have been investigated and are now known, those factors being indicated by inclusion of the code symbols. For the figural, symbolic, and semantic columns, all except factor CST have been found. Six potential factors in the behavioral column were under investigation at the time this was written. Although none of the behavioral factors are considered to have been demonstrated, the behavioral column is shown in all the matrices to follow, with the hope that this will offer challenges to research psychologists. In what immediately follows, the cognitive abilities will be briefly discussed, with some reference to typical tests. The factors will be taken in their order by rows in the matrix. Where a factor was discovered and named before the SI designations were taken seriously, the traditional name of that factor will be given along with the code symbols, in order to provide continuity with previous literature.

	Content			
	F	S	M	B	
U	CFU	CSU	CMU		Units
C	CFC	CSC	CMC		Classes
R	CFR	CSR	CMR		Relations
S	CFS	CSS	CMS		Systems
T	CFT		CMT		Transformations
I	CFI	CSI	CMI		Implications

Fig. 2. Matrix of the cognition factors from the structure of intellect.

CFU(V)—Visual cognition. The ability to cognize visual, figural units. The (V) is added to distinguish this ability from a parallel auditory factor, to be mentioned next. CFU(V) is found to be characteristic of such tests as the following.

Street Gestalt Completion. The examinee (E) writes the name of each object presented in a silhouette figure that has enough parts blotted out to make the task of cognition sufficiently difficult for testing purposes.

Mutilated Words. E recognizes common words in which parts of letters have been erased—a Thurstone test. To the extent that recognition of a word depends on cognition of particular letters, this test measures factor CFU, as results have indicated. To the extent that the total word character is damaged by the omissions, the factor to be described next, CSU, should be involved. CSU would be even more emphasized by omissions of whole letters, as in the Disemvowelled Words test (see below).

Peripheral Span. E names letters flashed in peripheral vision.

Dark Adaptation. E recognizes letters exposed in dim illumination.

In the last two tests, although it is letters that are cognized, and letters are symbolic elements, it is the figural aspect of the letters that makes for individual differences in cognition.

CFU(A)—Auditory cognition. The ability to cognize auditory "figures" from sound stimuli.

Singing. E recognizes words in vocal singing with piano accompaniment.

Haphazard Speech. E recognizes phrases spoken with unusual inflections and pitch changes.

Illogical Groupings. E recognizes phrases spoken with unusual groupings of words.

The mention of phrases in the last two tests, and the possibility that sentences are involved in Singing, might suggest that this factor should be identified as CFS(A), i.e., cognition of auditory figural *systems;* or it might be a confounding of CFU(A) and CFS(A). Further work will be needed to clarify this point.*

A general statement might well be made at this point regarding units and systems. The same collection of elements may be psychologically at one time a unit and at another time a system, depending on the organism's breadth of apprehension. What is a unit for one individual may be a system for another. In learning, there is undoubtedly much conversion of systems into units, both in cognition and in coordinated movements, as tasks become increasingly familiar. As we analyze objects, there is also conversion of units into systems.

CSU—Symbolic cognition. Ability to cognize units of symbolic information, such as printed syllables and words.

Word Combinations. E makes a new word using the last letters of one word and the initial letters of another word, e.g., the combination "beam pledge" gives the word "ample."

Anagrams. E makes shorter words, using only the letters contained in a long word, such as "generations"—a Thurstone test.

Disemvowelled Words. E recognizes a word with vowels missing, e.g., "c rcl s" is recognized as "circles."

Omelet Test. E recognizes a word with letters scrambled, e.g., "ricah" is to be seen as "chair."

---

* Ability CFV(A) has been more recently placed as CFS(A) in the SI model (Guilford, 1967).

CMU—Verbal comprehension. Recognition vocabulary, where recognition is of word meanings. An ordinary multiple-choice vocabulary test is the best representative of this factor. Reading-comprehension tests are strongly loaded on it, but they always have secondary loadings on different factors, depending on the test writer's choice of item form and his emphasis as to item content. Any verbal test has some loading on CMU if the vocabulary level is higher than the lowest-IQ subjects taking the test can cope with perfectly. Thus even some tests that do not look like vocabulary tests gain some CMU variance. This is why the Binet series, above and beyond its repeated use of vocabulary items *per se,* is a strong measure of factor CMU.

The relations of the three cognition-of-units factors to learning to read should be obvious. First comes recognition of letters, then recognition of letter combinations—phonemes, syllables, and words. Progress beyond the earliest stages depends on enlargement of vocabulary. Thus the relative importance shifts from CFU to CSU to CMU. At more mature levels of reading, a large number of different abilities can also become involved. It is rather certain that reading-comprehension tests do not begin to sample all such abilities. The writer has enlarged upon the subject of reading elsewhere (Guilford, 1960c).

Guilford-Zimmerman Verbal Comprehension. A multiple-choice vocabulary test.

Reading Comprehension. E answers multiple-choice items concerning a paragraph or selection that he has just read. There are numerous sources for such a test, each differing somewhat in its secondary common factors, depending on the slants given it by its author.

Information Test. Part of either the Wechsler Adult Intelligence Scale or the Wechsler Intelligence Scale for Children. Inclusion of both this kind of test and a vocabulary test in the Wechsler scales represents a high degree of redundancy of measurement.

CFC—Figural classification. The ability to recognize classes of figural items of information in terms of their common figural properties.

Figure Classification. E places a given visual figure within one of five alternative classes of figures, each represented by the three members E uses to define the class (see Fig. 3).

CSC—Cognition of symbolic classes. The ability to recognize classes of symbolic items of information.

Number-Group Naming. E states what it is that three given numbers have in common, e.g.,

35   110   75

Answer: divisible by 5.

The act of naming in this test introduces a moderate secondary loading in factor NMU, the "naming" factor. Some other approach is needed to eliminate that extra variance.

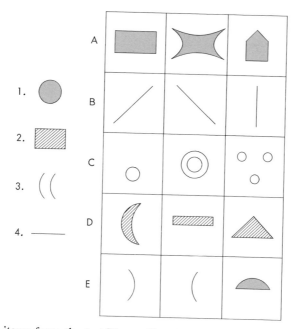

Fig. 3. Sample items from the test Figure Classification. To which of the groups A–E does the first figure at the top belong? The second, and following figures? (From J. P. Gifford, *Personality*. Copyright 1959 by McGraw-Hill Book Company. Used by permission of the publisher.)

Number Relations. In a set of four pairs, E recognizes a pair of related numbers that does not belong for lack of a common relation that determines the class, e.g.,

  (A) 2 – 6   (B) 3 – 9   (C) 4 – 12   (D) 6 – 15
  Answer: (D), since 6 × 3 does not equal 15.

This example shows that a classification factor can pertain to the classification of products other than units; here it is relations that are classified.

CMC—Semantic classification. The ability to recognize classes of verbal meanings or ideas.

Word Classification. E selects the one word in a set of four that does not belong to the class, e.g.,

  ship   engine   canoe   log
  Answer: engine; it does not float on water.

Verbal Classification. E assigns a given word to one of two classes or to neither, each of the two classes being represented by a set of four words, e.g., articles of furniture, animals, or metals.

Sentence Evaluation. E decides whether each given sentence conveys fact, possibility, or a name. Although this test had a relatively low loading in factor CMC, it is mentioned to show that not only word units, but also ideas, can be the subject of classification in the semantic category. It is also interesting that the task of

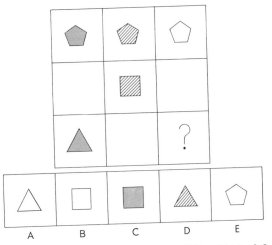

Fig. 4. A sample item from the Figure Matrix test. What kind of figure should appear in the cell with the question mark? (From J. P. Gifford, *Personality*. Copyright 1959 by McGraw-Hill Book Company. Used by permission of the publisher.)

putting idea units into named classes measures factor CMC as well as do tests presenting classes for recognition.

CFR—Figural relations. The ability to recognize or to discover the relation between two given visual, figural objects. Common figure-analogies tests obviously measure this factor, especially when in multiple-choice form. In completion form, another factor, NFR enters into the test, because E then has also the task of generating his own analogous conclusion. In the multiple-choice form the conclusion is given to him. A two-dimensional figure-analogies test is:

Figure Matrix. E chooses a figure among five given alternatives to fill a matrix cell, in a 3 × 3 matrix with a different relation along the rows and along the columns (see Fig. 4).

CSR—Symbolic relations. The ability to recognize or to discover the relation between pairs of items of information in symbolic form.

Seeing Trends II. E sees a repeated relationship between successive pairs of words in a series in terms of letter content, e.g.,

     three   other   either   brother   smooth
     Answer: "th" moves one letter to the right each time.

Word Relations. A kind of analogies test in which the items of information related are words, the relationships being in the form of spelling or alphabetical properties, e.g.,

     calm   call   self   sell   help __?__
     1. helm   2. hell   3. heal   4. held   5. shell
     Answer: 2.

CMR—Semantic relations. Ability to recognize or to discover a relationship between pairs of word meanings or ideas. A verbal-analogies test, with multiple-choice items, is a natural test for this factor, especially if the seeing of the relationship is relatively difficult compared with the act of supplying the item of information needed to fulfill the relationship of the second pair of words. By analogy to the figure-matrix test there is also the following:

Word Matrix Test. E supplies a meaningful word to fill a vacant cell in a 2 × 3 word matrix, e.g.,

stockings	shoes	galoshes
yolk	?	shell

1. wagon   2. set   3. hen   4. white   5. egg
Answer: 4.

CFS—Spatial orientation. The ability to organize the layout of things in visual space with reference to the observer. This is the well-known "space" factor, although in the early results on it, there was frequent confounding of this factor with its neighbor just below it in the SI model, CFT, or spatial visualization.

Cards. A card of a simple shape with a hole in one corner is shown in various positions. E is to say which ones represent the card *not* turned over.

Cubes. E indicates which pairs of pictured cubes can be identical, from the interrelationships of markings on sides that he can see.

Guilford-Zimmerman Aptitude Survey, Part V: Spatial Orientation. E indicates how the position of a boat has changed from one picture to the other, each showing the prow of a boat on a scenic background. Because of the "change" feature, a small amount of CFT variance creeps into the test.

CSS—Symbolic patterns. The ability to recognize or to discover principles, rules, or orders in a collection of symbolic elements.

Circle Reasoning. E discovers the rule for marking one circle in sequences of circles and dashes, such as the rule "the first circle in a set of three circles after the first dash." E need not verbalize the principle; he simply indicates that he has grasped it by marking a circle in an unmarked series.

Letter Triangle. E finds the system by which letters of the alphabet are arranged in a triangular pattern, with some vacant positions, then selects one of five letters to go in a marked position.

CMS—General reasoning. The ability to grasp the structure of a meaningful system. In most tests of CMS, the system has been in the form of an arithmetic-reasoning problem, such as the Guilford-Zimmerman General Reasoning test. Arithmetic-reasoning tests are the best-known measures of the factor, but they are often befouled with secondary variances, such as factor MSI (numerical facility), CFT (visualization), and CMU (verbal comprehension). Tests that show that it is a matter of comprehending the problem that is the crucial aspect for factor CMS are listed below.

Necessary Arithmetical Operations. Given the facts of the problem, E is to say which pair of numerical operations is essential in a complete solution of the problem, selecting the pair from five alternatives.

Necessary Facts. Given all the necessary facts except one, E is to state the one that is missing to make the arithmetical problem structure complete.

Ship Destination. This is a test that requires complete solutions but has minimized secondary variances. E finds the distance of a ship from a port, taking into account the influences of an increasing number of variables, such as current direction, wind direction, and initial heading of the ship. The arithmetical computations are so simple that only small integers are needed, with answers 1–5 in multiple-choice form for every item.

CFT—Spatial visualization. The ability to follow the manipulation or transformation of an object into another spatial position or arrangement.

Paper Form Board. E draws lines in an outline figure to illustrate how a few separated and scrambled black pieces would fit together to form a desired complete figure.

Punched Holes. E indicates the pattern of holes in an unfolded paper that has been shown folded with a hole punched in a certain position.

Surface Development. E indicates which lettered edges in a drawing of a solid figure correspond to numbered edges or dotted "fold" lines in a plane diagram of the unfolded sides of the solid.

Guilford-Zimmerman Aptitude Survey, Part VI: Spatial Visualization. E indicates the position that a clock would have after indicated maneuvers of the clock have taken place, starting from an indicated initial position. E selects an alternative answer.

CMT—Penetration. The ability to go from one interpretation of an idea to another or to see redefinitions.

Similarities. E writes as many as six ways in which two common objects are similar, e.g., "cat" and "mouse." Every time E goes from one similar attribute to another, he is redefining "cat" and "mouse."

Social Institutions. E lists things he sees wrong with institutions such as taxes, divorce, etc. The score for factor CMT is the number of far-reaching or far-sighted improvements he sees are needed. E must "turn over in his mind" the aspects of an institution in order to have insight into its defects. This is the main reason the factor was first called "penetration." Tests of kinds that would more clearly pinpoint the location of the factor in cell CMT would be desirable.

CFI—Perceptual foresight. The ability to explore visually some possible courses of action and to foresee the contingencies involved. Porteus has given this factor "top billing" with his emphasis on paper maze tests. This is not to say, of course, that his tests are confined to this factor.

Competitive Planning. Starting with four incomplete adjacent squares of equal size, E is to add one side at a time, playing for two opponents, in such a way as to maximize the number of squares both players will complete in the most efficient manner.

Route Planning. A maze-tracing test, in which E indicates through which lettered points he *must* pass in order to reach the goal.

Planning a Circuit. E traces visually an electrical circuit diagram with overlapping wires and indicates which pair of terminals should be attached to a battery to make the circuit work.

CSI—Cognition of symbolic implications. The ability to foresee consequences in the manipulation of symbolic information.

Word Patterns. E arranges a given set of words efficiently in a kind of crossword-puzzle pattern, e.g., he is to arrange the words "bats," "easy," "hot," "tea," and "the" in a matrix of empty squares so as to use as few squares as possible, following rules.

Symbol Grouping. E rearranges scrambled symbols of three kinds to achieve a specified systematic order in as few moves as possible, e.g., given the sequence "– O X X X –," he is to achieve the sequence "X X X – – O," by moving a selected number of symbols at a time according to rules.

CMI—Conceptual foresight. Ability to foresee the consequences of acts or events.

Pertinent Questions. E writes as many as four questions, the answers to which would serve as a basis for making a decision in an ambiguous situation.

Alternative Methods. E lists as many as six different ways of accomplishing a certain task.

Memory Factors

Only eight cells of the memory-factor matrix had demonstrated factors in them (see Fig. 5) when this was written. Memory tests typically expose E to some material to be memorized, after which he is given the task of reproducing, completing, or recognizing what he has learned. The recall in such tests is direct, E reporting things exactly as learned, whereas in the productive-thinking tasks the recall is more often indirect, that is, by way of some transfer.

MFU—Visual memory. The ability to reproduce, report, or recognize material presented visually.

Reproduction of Designs. E reproduces geometric designs after having had a brief exposure to them.

Map Memory. E selects among alternatives a section of a map previously examined.

	Content			
	F	S	M	B
U	MFU	MSU	MMU	
C				
R		MSR	MMR	
S	MFS		MMS	
T				
I		MSI		

Fig. 5. Matrix of the memory factors.

MSU—Memory span. Ability to recall immediately a series of symbolic elements. Under these circumstances, a series of letters or digits can be regarded as a symbolic unit, but the memory for the *order* of the elements may involve to some extent the unknown factor MSS.

Memory Span, Digits. E repeats series of digits.

Memory Span, Letters. E repeats series of letters. The common interchangeability of letters and digits in tests suggests that these two tests are but alternative forms of the same test. More varied tests are needed in order to investigate this factor further; for example, there should be a test of memory for a set of nonsense syllables, which need *not* be recalled in the same order.

MMU—Memory for ideas. The ability to reproduce previously learned ideas, not verbatim.

Picture Recall. E reports information, or answers questions, regarding items of semantic information remembered from a picture that he has previously studied.

Memory for Ideas. E reproduces a brief, one-paragraph story in his own words, after hearing it once.

MSR—Rote memory. The ability to remember naturally meaningless connections between pairs of items of information.

Picture-Number. E recalls numbers paired with pictures previously presented, when pictures alone are presented.

Word-Number. E recalls numbers previously observed paired with words, when words alone are presented.

First Names. E recalls the first name of each person whose name had previously been presented in full, when last name alone is given.

Color-Word. E recalls a word previously observed paired with a color, when the color alone is presented.

One important uncertainty clings to the rote-memory factor MSR (and also to MMR, meaningful memory, the next factor to be mentioned); this uncertainty persists for lack of decisive information at the time this was written. It is possible that the factor identified as MSR should be placed in cell MSI and, likewise, the factor identified as MMR should be placed in cell MMI.

The logical defense for placement of these factors in the row for relations is that in the memorizing of pairs the learner is forming relations that tie those pairs together. Yet, with symbolic information, it is difficult to see how the learner can establish many useful symbolic relations that would help him. A relation is a specifiable kind of connection. An implication, by contrast, need not be specified— sheer contiguity may be sufficient to establish an implication such that when the first member of a pair comes the second is expected. Probably this difference is what most clearly distinguishes a relation from an implication.

The main deterring idea against identifying rote-memory ability as MSI is that the factor of numerical facility has been adopted for that cell. There is evidence

(Coombs, 1941) that rote memory and numerical facility are different factors. A verification of this result would be decisive and would necessitate leaving rote memory in cell MSR. There is no known reason for not placing meaningful memory in cell MMI; however, it is not difficult to see how meaningful *units* can be related by the learner, a fact that would be favorable to leaving meaningful memory in cell MMR.

MMR—Meaningful memory. The ability to remember connections between meaningful units of information.

Sentence Completion. E supplies missing words in sentences previously perceived in full.

Related Words. E recalls the second noun of a related pair previously studied.

MFS(V)—Memory for visual, spatial order. Ability to remember how a collection of seen objects were arranged in space.

Space Memory. E identifies the form that was previously exposed in each of five sections within five squares, all having been previously observed.

Position Memory. E recalls the approximate position on a page of a number-word combination, four hours after the initial administration of a test.

MFS(A)—Auditory memory. The ability to recognize auditory systems or patterns heard earlier.

Musical Memory. E recognizes musical compositions heard earlier.

Rhythm. E recognizes rhythmic patterns of taps.

Earlier classifications of auditory memory placed it in the cell symbolized as MFU, as an ability similar to the visual-memory ability. The two tests that represent the factor, however, involve memory for products that seem too complex to be regarded as units, hence the change of this factor to the cell MFS.

MMS—Memory for temporal order. Ability to remember in what order events were experienced.

Position Recall II. E recalls on which of four study pages of a previously administered test each of 48 drawings appeared.

Sequence Memory. For each pair of test titles, E indicates which test was administered earlier in a battery given three days previously.

MSI—Numerical facility. The ability to operate with numbers rapidly and accurately. The well-known number factor was previously identified as factor NSI —convergent production of symbolic implications. There is little doubt about the symbolic implications part of the designation. Numbers are symbols. The information such as $6 + 7 = 13$ is readily interpreted to the effect that $6 + 7$ implies 13. But another factor (to be seen later) makes a strong bid for the spot NSI in the model, hence numerical facility was moved to the spot MSI. In identifying it as a memory ability, it was recalled that number-operation skills are highly practiced symbolic operations. Whether an individual computes rapidly and accurately depends on whether he has retained those practiced implications well.

One somewhat restraining thought in making such an identification is that in most memory tests the memory involved is of short duration; numerical facility depends on long-remembered information. There is evidence from factor analysis, however, to show that a certain test of short-term memory is also related strongly to the numerical-facility factor. The test is the Digit Symbol Test of the Wechsler Adult Intelligence Scale, which was analyzed by P. C. Davis (1956). This finding has been confirmed by de Mille (1962). In the Digit Symbol Test, E learns associations (implications) between pairs, each composed of a number and a geometric form. It has often been questioned whether learning and memory of associations is an important aspect of the test, since the pairing of symbols remains visible. But to gain speed in the test, some memory seems essential. Davis' and de Mille's results furnish the kind of information that is needed both to identify numerical facility as a memory ability and to show that the Digit Symbol Test is primarily a memory test. Not only that, it shows what kind of memory is involved. From the earlier conclusion reached to the effect that rote memory is factor MSR rather than MSI, it can be predicted that the Digit Symbol Test will not correlate substantially with paired-associate tests involving symbolic units. It is probable that relations are harder to form between forms and digits than between names and nonsense syllables.*

Before we leave the memory factors, it is very interesting to note, in passing, that Binet very astutely proposed that there are several kinds of memory, which he said should be investigated separately. He recognized memory for visual objects, sentences, musical notes, colors, and digits. All these proposed abilities except his memory for musical notes have been found as separate factors, and this hypothesized type of memory has a logical place in the SI model, at MFU(A).

Divergent-Production Factors

Divergent-production tests typically provide E with an item or items of information from which to start, and instructions to supply a quantity of different items of information, the nature of the information depending on the task. Some of the tests, e.g., tests of fluency of production, are highly speeded, hence quantity of production is especially emphasized. In other tests, criteria of quality are applied in scoring.

At present, we find parallel sets of factors in three content areas, as shown in Fig. 6. Factors pertaining to divergent production of figural and symbolic information have been investigated only recently (Gershon et al., 1963).

	F	S	M	B
		Content		
	F	S	M	B
U	DFU	DSU	DMU	
C	DFC	DSC	DMC	
R		DSR	DMR	
S	DFS	DSS	DMS	
T	DFT		DMT	
I	DFI	DSI	DMI	

Fig. 6. Matrix of the factors of divergent production.

---

* More recently it has been concluded that the traditional number factor has been a confounding of MSI & NSI plus a strong specific (see Guilford, 1967).

DFU—Figural fluency. The ability to produce figural units rapidly, given a few elements from which to start or to use in composing those units.

Sketches. Given a simple figure, such as a circle or an angle, repeated 12 times, E adds a minimum to make each one into a different object.

Making Figures. Given three lines, e.g., two short, straight lines and a curved line, E makes as many different combinations as he can in limited time.

Making Marks. E makes simple figures of a specified kind, e.g., open figures composed only of curved lines, in limited time.

DSU—Word fluency. The ability to produce rapidly words that conform to some simple literal specification.

Suffixes. E writes words ending with a specified suffix, e.g., "-sion."

Word Fluency. E writes words each containing a specified letter, e.g., the letter "S."

First and Last Letters. E writes words beginning and ending with specified letters, e.g., "r_____l."

Prefixes. E writes words beginning with a specified prefix, e.g., "sub-."

Tests designed for factor CSU frequently have variances of substantial amounts attributable to factor DSU. In cognizing a word under difficult circumstances, being able to run over a list of similar words fitting the incomplete information given is an aid in recognizing the word.

A broader conception of factor DSU is provided by Majewska's (1960) finding that a test requiring a rapid production of number combinations to meet specifications is also loaded strongly on the factor, indicating that the factor needs a broader connotation than its original one of "word fluency."

DMU—Ideational fluency. The ability to produce a quantity of ideas, relevant to given information but not necessarily of high quality, in response to a given idea.

Ideational Fluency. E writes names of things fitting relatively broad classes, e.g., things that are white and edible.

Topics. E writes ideas about a given topic, e.g., working on the railroad.

Brick Uses (fluency). E lists uses for a common brick, the total number of responses being the score.

Plot Titles (nonclever). E lists appropriate titles for a given short short story. (The number of clever responses is used in scoring for another factor, DMT.)

Consequences (obvious). E lists consequences he can see from a proposed unusual event. (The "remote" consequences are scored for another factor, DMT).

DFC—Figural spontaneous flexibility. The ability to shift readily from one class of figural information to another.

Varied Figural Classes. Given a collection of three figural objects that can be conceived as representing different classes, E decides which of five single figures can be classified in different ways with the three.

DSC—Symbolic spontaneous flexibility.   The ability to shift readily from one class of symbolic information to another.

Number Grouping.   Given a set of several numbers, E groups at least three of them to a class, the same numbers being needed in different classes, e.g., the list: 2, 3, 4, 6, 17, 23, 36.

DMC—Semantic spontaneous flexibility.   The ability to shift readily from one class of verbally meaningful information to another.   This was the first of the three similar factors to be demonstrated and it is much more firmly established.

Brick Uses (shifts).   E's list of uses is scored for the number of times he goes from one class of uses to another in two consecutive uses, e.g., the uses "build a house, throw at a cat, make a doorstop, make a tombstone for a bird," given consecutively, represent three shifts.   A string of uses of bricks in building things would have no shifts.

Alternative Uses (a revision of Unusual Uses).   E is to list as many as six uses for an object, such as a newspaper, other than the common use, which is stated with the item.

DSR.   The ability to produce a variety of symbolic relations or a variety of symbolic correlates.

Letter Group Relations.   Given a set of four letters that are related to one another in several ways, E selects other sets of four that have the same relations.   For example, given the set C A E F, which of the following groups exhibit any of the same relations?

> W L C D   P I O S   A D M U   M V B Q.
> *Answer:* All except the last group qualify.

Number Rules.   Given a starting number, E relates one or more numbers to it to achieve a given result, e.g., starting with 2, arrive at 6.   *Answers:* $2 + 4$, 2×3, $2 \times 2 + 2$.

DMR—Associational fluency.   The ability to produce a variety of verbally meaningful correlates.

Associational Fluency.   E writes synonyms for given words, e.g., for the word "hard."   *Possible answers:* difficult, tough, heartless, brittle, solid, etc.

Simile Insertions.   E supplies a variety of appropriate words, each to fill a blank in a given simile, e.g., "The fog is as _____ as a sponge."   *Possible answers:* soft, dense, opaque, full of holes, etc.

DFS.   The ability to organize figural elements, e.g., lines, into larger wholes.

Making Objects.   Given a few figures and lines, E is to construct from them, with nothing added, specified meaningful objects.

Monograms.   Given three initial letters, e.g., A, V, and O, E is to invent a variety of monogram designs.

Designs. Given five figural elements, e.g., a line, a curve, a dot, an angle, and a circle, E is to combine them in various ways to produce designs such as appear on wallpaper, linoleum, or fabrics.

The tests Monograms and Designs also have strong secondary loadings on factor DFU. The Making Figures test, in the DFU list, also has significant secondary loadings on DFS. These results might be interpreted as indicating a substantial correlation between factors DFU and DFS, as oblique rotations of these two axes would suggest. The writer's interpretation, however, is different, in line with a general principle of interpretation in such instances. It is probable that in the overlappings between tests of DFU and DFS there is much uncertainty whether an examinee treats combinations of lines as units or as systems. Complex units may be treated as systems and simple systems may be taken as units. It may be predicted that tests involving more exclusively simplified units on the one hand and tests involving more exclusively complex systems on the other would show a wider separation between tests of the two factors DFU and DFS.

DSS.   The ability to organize patterns of symbolic elements.

Making Codes.   E invents a variety of code systems using numbers and letters.

Number Combinations.   Given a few simple numbers, e.g., 2, 3, 4, 5, 6, E constructs as many correct equations as he can. An equation is one kind of symbolic system.

DSS is one of the most tenuously identified factors. Tests were designed for it with SI specifications in mind, but only the two listed here were used to represent it. Although it emerged in three populations of ninth-grade students, it failed to show up in an analysis based on results from a sample of girls only. Better tests and further verification are needed.

DMS—Expressional fluency.   The ability to construct meaningful patterns of ideas.

Expressional Fluency.   E constructs a variety of four-word sentences, given four initial letters, no word to be used more than once, e.g.,

"W____ f____ r____ d____."
Possible answer: Who found Rover dead?

Simile Interpretation.   E completes a statement involving a simile in a number of ways, with explanatory remarks, e.g.,

"Woman's dress is like the autumn; it _____."
Possible answer: "is highly colorful."

Word Arrangements.   E writes a number of sentences, each containing four specified words.

It should be said that the factor expressional fluency has sometimes appeared heretofore in cell DSS, with the idea that the construction of phrases and sentences, or organized discourse, is a matter of grammar and syntax, hence is symbolic in nature. The finding of a factor better qualified for the cell DSS has forced the relocation of expressional fluency in cell DMS. If this is the correct location for the factor, tests of expressional fluency measure an ability that should be of very great importance. Activities such as programming (except for its symbolic aspects), story telling, and even scientific-theory building should depend on ability DMS.

DFT—Figural adaptive flexibility. The ability to redefine or reinterpret figural properties, e.g., of lines, in a number of ways, so as to permit new approaches to a problem.

Match Problems. Given a set of adjacent squares or triangles of the same size, each line being composed of a match, E takes away a specified number of matches to leave a specified number of squares (triangles) with no matches left over, solving each item in as many as four ways. Other forms of match-problem tests also measure this factor. In one form the number of matches to be removed is specified but the number of squares to be left is not. In another form the number of squares to be left is specified but the number of matches to be removed is not. Still another form emphasizes more drastic insights, such as being left with both large and small squares and having squares left inside other squares. In every form of test, several different solutions to each problem are called for.

Planning Air Maneuvers. E selects the most direct path for an airplane, in "sky-writing" two-letter combinations (capital letters). Considerable trial and error is required to arrive at a solution. Each new trial can be assumed to be a varied approach, with revision of how things appear.

DMT—Originality. The ability to redefine or interpret verbally meaningful information so as to achieve varied results of high quality.

Plot Titles (clever). The score is the number of titles rated as clever. For example, to the fable of the fox and the out-of-reach grapes, the title "The fox and the grapes" would be rated as nonclever, but titles such as "The fox griped about grapes," or "The outfoxed fox" would be rated clever. Note that both the clever titles involve some new twists or transformations in meaning. This is very common with titles rated clever.

Consequences (remote). E gives remote consequences (distant in time or in sequence of events or in space) to proposed events. The score measures originality, probably because the task entails some unusual reinterpretations of the event.

Symbol Production. E is to give simple symbols to stand for the meanings of words, as for the italicized words in the sentence "*Issue* the *order.*" It is likely that E has to run over different connotations of each concept in order to find one that translates readily into figural form.

Riddles (clever). E is to give clever answers to riddles. Example: What city is the favorite of actors? To this he might say "Hollywood," which would not be rated clever, or he might say "Publicity," which would be so rated.

DFI—Figural elaboration. The ability to add reasonable continuations or completions to given figural information.

Decorations. Given articles of furniture and other objects in outline form, E is to add internal markings to decorate them. The same object, repeated, is to be completed in different design.

Production of Figural Effects. Given a very simple line or two, E is to build upon the given to produce a (nonmeaningful) figure of some degree of complexity. Scoring is in terms of the amount of linear information added.

Figure Production. Same as the previous test, except that E is to end with a meaningful object; scored similarly.

DSI—Symbolic elaboration. The ability to extend given symbolic information in several ways.

Limited Words. Given two common words, E is to make a number of new word pairs from the letters included, using all the letters, as given, e.g., "shirt, bean," E might produce: "hairs, bent" or "bears, thin," etc.

Symbol Elaboration. Given two simple equations involving letters, E is to deduce a variety of other equations that follow from them, e.g., $V = R + K$ and $T = K \times C$.

DMI—Semantic elaboration. The ability to produce a variety of ideas implied by a given idea.

Planning Elaboration. E adds detailed operations needed to make a briefly outlined plan succeed. The score is the number of pertinent details suggested.

Possible Jobs. For a symbol that is given, E suggests a number of different occupations or jobs for which it might stand. For example, a glowing electric-light bulb might symbolize an electrical engineer, a missionary, or a night watchman.

Convergent-Production Factors

From the matrix in Fig. 7 it will be noted that all six of the semantic convergent-production factors had been demonstrated, but only four of the symbolic and one of the figural ones. Tests of convergent-production factors call for a single answer to each item rather than multiple answers as with divergent-production factors. The right answer is fully determined by the given information, or it is the conventionally accepted "right" answer.

	Content			
	F	S	M	B
U			NMU	
C			NMC	
R		NSR	NMR	
S		NSS	NMS	
T	NFT	NST	NMT	
I	NFI	NSI	NMI	

Fig. 7. Matrix of the factors of convergent production.

NMU—Concept naming. The ability to produce the name of a cognized concept.

Picture-Group Naming. E provides the class name for a group of five pictured objects.

Word-Group Naming. E provides the class name for a group of five words, e.g., "volcano, sun, fire, Africa, oven."

Seeing Trends I. E names the meaningful trend in a group of words, e.g., "century, year, decade, day, week, second, minute," where the order is not fully correct but there is a trend.

NMC. The ability to produce a set of nonoverlapping classes that take care of all given meaningful items of information.

Word Grouping. Given 12 common words, E is to put them into four, and only four, classes, leaving no extra words.

Figure Concepts (uncommon). Given a collection of pictured objects, E is to combine them in classes. The score is the number of uncommon classes formed. What contributes to measurement of NMC may be the fact that the uncommon classes are likely to be nonoverlapping.

NSR—Symbolic correlates. The ability, given a relation and an item of information, to produce a symbolic item of information that uniquely fits the relationship.

Correlate Completion II. E applies a rule, which he discovers from relations of the letters of two pairs of words, to write the second member of a third pair. This is a kind of analogies test in completion form, with symbolic information. Parallel to the sample item for the Word Relations test given for factor CSR, an item for Correlate Completion II would read:

    calm   call   self   sell   help   _____

Such a test should have a little secondary variance in factor CSR.

Letter Series. E states which letter pair properly continues the sequence of a series of letters, e.g., A R B R C R __ __.

NMR—Semantic correlates. The ability to provide an item of verbally meaningful information in response to a given relation and concept.

Vocabulary Completion. E produces a word that fits a given definition and begins with a certain letter, e.g., "The husband of a queen is a k___." Incidentally, this shows how an intended vocabulary test, which normally is strongest in factor CMU, becomes also a test of a different factor when its format is changed from the usual multiple-choice form. The use of the initial letter for the word to be produced may also introduce some variance in the factor of word fluency (DSU), because E may use the letter information to help reach the answer.

Inventive Opposites. E writes two antonyms for a given word, first letters being given, e.g., "The opposite of 'dry' is w____ or m____." Calling for more than the most direct opposite may introduce some DMR variance into an NMR test. The use of initial letters may bring in some DSU variance.

Associations III. E produces a word that is similar in meaning to two other given words, e.g., "skin _____ conceal." The most natural connecting link, related to both words, is "hide."

NSS. The ability to produce symbolic systems to satisfy restricting requirements.

Operations Sequence. E states the order in which a sequence of numerical operations should be performed in going from one number to another, e.g., starting with 5 to reach 1 by applying the operations: $\times 2$, $\div 7$, -3. An order is a system, here a temporal order of numerical operations.

Word Changes. E tells what sequence must be followed to get from a given starting word to a given goal word. A sample item reads, essentially,

> Starting with the word 'set,' change one letter at a time, to end up with the word 'cry.' The words to be used are: day, sat, dry, and say.
> *Answer:* sat, say, day, dry.

NMS—Semantic ordering. The ability to organize a set of meaningful units into the most acceptable order.

Picture Arrangement. Given the four pictures of a comic strip, E indicates the temporal order needed to make complete sense.

Sentence Order. E indicates the temporal order in which three verbally stated events should be placed to make sense.

Temporal Ordering. E arranges given steps in appropriate order to complete a project, e.g., planting a new lawn.

NFT—Figural redefinition. The ability to redefine figural elements of a given object and reuse them in new ways.

Concealed Figures. E indicates which one of four complex geometrical figures contains a given simpler geometric figure.

Penetration of Camouflage. E locates faces hidden in complex pictorial scenes.

Hidden Figures. E indicates which of five simple figures is concealed in more complex figures of the Gottschaldt type.

NST—Symbolic redefinition. The ability to break up given units composed of symbolic elements and regroup the elements in new ways.

Camouflaged Words. Find the name of a sport or game concealed in a sentence, e.g.,

> I did not know that he was ailing.
> *Answer:* sailing.

Word Transformation. E indicates new divisions between letters in a series of words to form a new phrase, e.g.,

> there do live
> *Answer:* the red olive

NMT. The ability to assign a new function to an object or part of an object, in order to accomplish some given goal.

Gestalt Transformation. E selects one of five alternative objects (or part of it) to be used for a stated purpose. A sample item reads:

To light a fire:
1. cabbage   2. fish   3. pocket watch   4. string   5. pipe stem

Answer: 3. pocket watch (face cover as a condensing lens).

Object Synthesis. E names an object that could be made by combining two given objects, e.g., a stiff coiled wire and a pole. *Answer:* pogo stick.

NSI—Symbol substitution. The ability to draw correct deductions from symbolic information, according to rules.

Form Reasoning. E solves simple equations that are given in terms of combinations of familiar geometric figures. Figure 8 shows a sample of the given information and in addition an item.

Sign Changes. Given the condition that certain numerical-operation symbols are interchanged, E solves simple equations.

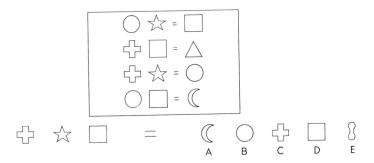

Fig. 8. A sample item from the Form Reasoning test. Given the equations for combinations of forms at the top, what is the figure equalled by the combination of three figures, taking the latter by combinations of two? Answer: A. (From a test by R. I. Blakey).

NMI—Deduction. The ability to draw fully determined, meaningful conclusions from given information.

Sequential Association. E indicates the best order for four words to produce a chain of associations, e.g.,

pen   pig   read   write,
Answer: pig   pen   write   read

Attribute Listing II. E states the essential attributes of an object that is to serve a certain purpose, e.g., to drive a long nail into a hard post, no hammer being available.

Evaluation Factors

The operation category of evaluation had had only two factor-analytic studies, and much of it remained to be explored. As Fig. 9 indicates, only seven factors were thought to be known, the semantic category having had most attention. The first of the two analyses was highly exploratory and was made before the SI model was conceived. The second study (Nihira, *et al.*, 1964), which was concentrated on the semantic category of evaluation abilities, and which designed new tests in the light of structure-of-intellect concepts, has led to some marked changes in the semantic-evaluation abilities as compared with those previously reported.

	Content			
	F	S	M	B
U	EFU	ESU	EMU	
C			EMC	
R		ESR	EMR	
S			EMS	
T				
I			EMI	

Fig. 9. Matrix of the evaluation factors.

EFU—Perceptual speed. The ability to decide whether or not two similar visual objects are identical.

Guilford-Zimmerman Aptitude Survey, Part IV: Perceptual Speed. E identifies the drawing of a common object among five similar ones that is identical with the given object.

Identical Forms. E marks all the forms in a row that are identical with the one given at the left of the row.

This interpretation of the well-known factor that became known as "perceptual speed," after the time of Thurstone's (1938) first discovery of it, represents a drastic change in meaning. The factor cannot be primarily one merely of cognition of visual objects, for there is another factor that has a better claim to that description and has accordingly been located at cell CFU in the structure of intellect. The use of some additional kinds of tests in a new analysis should help to provide the answer to any questions regarding the placement of perceptual speed.

ESU—Symbolic identification. The ability to decide whether or not two symbolic items of information are identical. A type of test commonly found in clerical-aptitude batteries is logically parallel to tests of perceptual speed, hence these tests might well be expected to demonstrate the parallel factor ESU. Such a test calls for deciding whether or not two sets of letters or digits or names are identical, e.g.,

xiejmovrk _____ xiejnovrk
C. M. Peterson _____ C. M. Peterson

A factor has been found in common among letter-cancellation tests. This factor may be a candidate for cell ESU in place of the kind of factor just mentioned, or the two may be the same. Cancellation tests are sometimes found to have loadings on factor EFU, but when enough tests of the two kinds (figural and symbolic) are in the analyzed battery they tend to separate (Dysinger, 1950), suggesting that the two factors EFU and ESU are sometimes confounded in an analysis and that possibly they are correlated. Of course, letters do have figural properties, hence it would not be surprising that tests involving cancellations of single letters would have loadings on EFU. Tests requiring cancellation of letter *combinations* should be better tests of ESU.

EMU—Evaluation of semantic units. The ability to decide whether or not concepts or ideas satisfy certain given specifications.

Double Descriptions. From four alternatives, E selects the one thing that fits two descriptive categories. Example:

> Given descriptions: *round* and *hard*
> (a) Gold   (b) Record   (c) Steel   (d) Coin
> *Answer:* (d)

Incidentally, the test Double Descriptions has much similarity to the test Ideational Fluency, for the parallel factor of DMU. The DMU test asks E to *list* as many objects as he can in limited time to satisfy two or more specifications, such as "round" and "hard." Double Descriptions *presents* alternative responses to such an item and asks E to give evaluative judgments concerning them.

Sentensense. E judges whether a given sentence expresses an internally consistent thought. Example:

> Johnny, who is seven, went with his mother to Europe ten years ago.
> *Answer:* Inconsistent

Sentensense was designed as a test for factor EMS, with the thought that a sentence is a semantic system. Evidently the sentences are sufficiently short that they can be taken as units of thought. An inconsistency in the sentence spoils the unity of the thought. Or, it is more likely that the discordant *components* of the sentence are the units being evaluated. In the illustrative sentence, the unitary thoughts are: "Johnny, who is seven," and "went . . . to Europe ten years ago."

EMC—Evaluation of semantic classes. The ability to decide whether or not a class idea is appropriate for a set of objects, or to decide which of several class ideas is most appropriate.

Class Name Selection. E selects from three alternatives the class name that best fits a group of four given words. Example:

> Given words: cat, cow, mule, mare
> Class names:
> (a) farm animals   (b) four-legged animals   (c) domestic animals
> *Answer:* (c)

Best Word Class. E decides in which of four named classes a given word most appropriately belongs. Example:

> *palm* is in the class of:
> (a) plant   (b) tree   (c) flower   (d) leaf
> *Answer:* (b)

ESR—Symbol manipulation. The ability to decide whether or not symbolically stated relationships are consistent.

Symbol Manipulation. E marks symbolically stated relationships "true" or "false" according as they are consistent or not consistent with other statements. Example:

Given: x S y (where S is defined as "smaller than")
Then: x E y (where E is defined as "equal to")
y G x (where G is defined as "greater than")
y NE x (where NE is defined as "not equal to")

Sign Changes II. E indicates which interchange of algebraic signs will make an equation correct. For example:

Which two of the operation signs should be interchanged to make the following equation correct?

$$(5 \times 4) + 2 = 8 + 2$$

(a) $-$ and $\div$ (b) $+$ and $-$ (c) $+$ and $\times$ (d) $\times$ and $-$ (e) $+$ and $\div$
Answer: (e)

This test would seem to involve operations, in addition to evaluation, but if the typical strategy is for E to try one interchange after another, he must decide in each case whether the interchange works, i.e., whether the two relations are consistent.

A note of reservation must be expressed concerning factor ESR, as just described. Judging from the test Symbol Manipulation alone, the factor it represents may actually turn out to be factor ESI, evaluation of symbolic implications. The statements to be evaluated can be regarded as implications (true or false) from the given premise. It has already been decided that what had been regarded as the parallel factor EMR is better identified as EMI, as the following discussion will bring out.

EMR—Evaluation of semantic relations. The ability to decide which of alternative relationships involving verbalized ideas is most appropriate.

Verbal Analogies III. In a verbal-analogies test, the relation between the first pair of words is fairly obvious, but the choice of alternative to complete the same relationship in another pair of words requires some fine discriminations. Example:

Given pairs: *traffic : signal* as *river :* ___?___
Alternatives: (a) bank   (b) dam   (c) canal   (d) sand bag
Answer: (b); a dam regulates a river as a signal regulates traffic.

Best Trend Name. Select the word that best describes the order of four given words. Example:

Given words: house   push cart   bicycle   car
Given trend names: (a) speed   (b) time   (c) size
Answer: (b)

This factor is represented better by tests tailored to fit the EMR cell than by tests formerly thought to be most representative of the ability. Previously, the leading tests of the factor thought to be EMR were in syllogistic form, with the idea that each premise and each conclusion stated a relationship and that EMR is an ability to decide concerning the consistency between such statements of relationship. But it was also recognized that a conclusion is in the form of an implication from given information, and that a syllogistic test might better represent factor EMI. There was hesitation to accept the latter alternative, however, for the reason that another factor, called "sensitivity to problems" had claim to cell EMI, and there was no other good place for "sensitivity to problems," although there was recognition of some forcing, in the interpretation of that factor as EMI.

The most recent analysis (Nihira *et al.,* 1964) gives some answers to the dilemma. The best marker test for factor EMR had been Logical Reasoning, a syllogism test with four alternative responses to each item. In the latest analysis, with tests like Verbal Analogies III and Best Trend Name in the battery, Logical Reasoning has most of its common-factor variance on the new EMI. A factor which is better than "sensitivity to problems" has been found for cell EMI, as we shall see.

EMS—Evaluation of semantic systems. The ability to detect inconsistencies or incongruities in situations.

Unlikely Things. E selects from four alternatives the two most unlikely or incongruous features in each of the pictorially presented situations. This test was based on an earlier one, Unusual Details, in which there were incongruous elements that E had to find and to name. Unlikely Things is a multiple-choice form of the same test. Each was a leader in its own analysis for identification of factor EMS, hence the identification of this factor has not been changed.

EMI—Evaluation of semantic implications. The ability to decide whether given information follows logically from other given information.

Sentence Selection. E selects the sentence, among alternatives, that is most likely to be true, using only the information in the given statement. Example:

> Given statement:
> In the mid-Pacific on Buna-Buna, the game of ticky-ticky is played outdoors.
> Alternatives:
> (a) People in Buna-Buna like to play games.
> (b) Ticky-ticky is a difficult game to play.
> (c) There is an island called Buna-Buna.
> *Answer:* (c)

Sentence Selection was originally designed to test a hypothesis that there is a common factor that may be called "ability to analyze," and it had the title "Sentence Analysis." No analyzing factor was found. It was recognized later that the test deals with evaluation of inferences, in line with the SI concept of factor EMI, with which it was later found to be substantially related.

Logical Reasoning. Given two verbally stated premises, E selects the correct conclusion from four alternatives. Example:

No birds are insects.
All swallows are birds.
Therefore:

(a) No swallows are insects.   (b) Some birds are not swallows.
(c) All birds are swallows.   (d) No insects are birds.

Answer: (a)

The tests for the factor formerly known as "sensitivity to problems" (the Apparatus test and the Seeing Problems test), did not come out on the same factor as the new EMI tests just listed, in the most recent analysis (Nihira *et al.,* 1964). In fact, Apparatus and Seeing Problems, both involving the citing of defects or deficiencies in familiar objects, correlated so low with one another that they separated, Seeing Problems going on factor CMI and Apparatus having no significant loadings. In some other analyses (Guilford *et al.,* 1961), Seeing Problems has also shown significant loadings on factor DMI. Thus this test, at least, deals with semantic implications, but not with evaluation of them, as was previously supposed.

SOME THEORETICAL AND PRACTICAL IMPLICATIONS

General Psychological Theory

Although general theorists in psychology have not looked to the findings from factor analysis for a source of information to use in theory construction, those findings, when systematized, as in the SI model, have much to offer in the way of stimulation of theoretical thinking. If the intellectual factors are distinguishable, fundamental abilities to perform in certain ways, then they are also distinguishable, fundamental functions of the individuals. They should therefore throw light on the ways in which individuals function intellectually. It should be more generally recognized that factor analysis, properly used, can do much to answer the question of "what," i.e., *what* distinguishable functions exist in mental life. Knowing *what* functions exist and something about their properties also goes part of the way toward suggesting also some answers to the question "how," i.e., *how* the human individual operates.

The relations of the SI model, its factors, and its categories of factors to general behavioral theory have been pointed out in a number of places (Guilford, 1960a, 1960b, 1961, 1962, 1964). There is space here for mentioning only the highlights of those relationships. First, and of potentially most far-reaching importance, is the kind of view of the reacting organism that is suggested. In the SI model, there is overwhelming emphasis on information as a concept. Information was defined earlier as that which the organism discriminates, and discriminations are describable in terms of different kinds of products and differences within any one kind of product, such as units, relations, or systems. The four content categories, combining in all possible ways with the six product categories, give rise to 24 subcategories of information. This systematic classification can serve as a kind of psychological epistemology, with 24 uniquely defined categories of basic kinds of information. There is much need for such a taxonomy of information, a need that goes beyond psychological theory to, for example, the fields of education and computer technology.

The general picture is that the organism, like the electronic computer, is an agent that processes information. The processing is along the lines of the five kinds of operations of the SI model. But the processing action, along any one of the five lines, differs according to the category of information that is being processed. This interaction of kind of operation with kind of information is responsible for the distinguishable abilities in the cells of the SI model. One is reminded of the school of thought known as "act psychology" of a half-century ago. It was a fundamental axiom of that view of behavior that every act implies a content and every content implies an act. Thus so-called "static" and "dynamic" conceptions are but two sides of the same coin.

It is safe to say that the prevailing psychological theory of this century has been based on a stimulus-response model, a neo-associationism that was derived mainly from Pavlov. Such theory has never been adequate in accounting for most of the "mentalistic" concepts such as thinking, imagination, and reasoning. Many of psychology's most important problems have accordingly been seriously neglected. The informational type of theory that is made possible on the basis of SI concepts seems to offer much new hope for an objective psychology that can cope with the important "mentalistic" problems. The "mentalistic" concepts find new definitions in terms of SI concepts, which are empirically based concepts, and new approaches are suggested for attacks on old problems.

The analogy of the living organism to the computer is not an idle one, nor is the reference to the possible use of the SI model in computer technology. Christensen (1963) has recently proposed that the SI categories be shared in consideration of computer functions. He has also pointed out parallels between certain intellectual factors and certain computer programs.

Some Developmental Issues

As matters stand, most of what we know about intellectual factors has come from studies with adult subjects; consequently, the model describes what may be expected of mature intelligence. In addition to much prior evidence, there is accumulating evidence that the same kinds of differentiation of factors also apply in younger subjects, at ninth-grade (Gershon et al., 1963; Guilford et al., 1961), sixth-grade (Merrifield et al., 1963), and even fifth-grade (Lauritzen, 1963) levels. The studies just cited pertain mostly to divergent-production abilities, but also include others. In a more limited way, Meyers et al., (1961) and McCartin (1963) have found some apparent SI differentiations at the six-year-old mental-age level, for both normal and retarded children. There is the very large genetic question of how the structure of intellectual abilities develops and whether it undergoes categorical changes in doing so.

The question of hereditary *versus* environmental determination of the abilities needs new investigations in terms of SI concepts. Hunt (1961) has made a very strong case for the potency of environmental influences in general. His case rests very heavily on the findings of Piaget and his associates, whose views regarding intelligence it is important to consider in connection with SI concepts.

First, let it be said that there appears to be little or nothing that is contradictory or irreconcilable between the conclusions from the Piaget work and the structure of intellect. The genetic approach of Piaget and the factor-analytic approach, having rather different aims, do not bring forth conclusions between which choices must be made. To the extent that both sources of information are sound, there should be supplementation of information from the two directions and the findings should be capable of being logically fitted together.

The task of integration is much too large for the space in a part of one chapter. It can be mentioned, however, that in one respect, especially, there seems to be convergence. Piaget's search for signs that mature intellectual functioning conforms to concepts of modern logic has brought him close to the discovery of the six kinds of products, since for most of those concepts there are parallel logical concepts, most clearly for the products of classes, relations, and implications, which, indeed, employ the same terminology. The product of unit is more or less taken for granted in logic, in the form of a "term" or a "statement." A parallel in logic for the product of "system" is not so clear. Although Piaget had no single, general, explicit term corresponding to "system," he nevertheless felt strongly the need for such a concept and often implied it, in terms of his "schema," for example. As for transformations, Piaget refers to the logical operation of transformation, and such a conception is inherent in his general concept of accommodation, the modification of behavior to meet new needs, and in his basic concept of growth. Thus a full account of the products of information, all of which can be proposed as logical concepts, may provide a "psychologic" for which there have been expressions of need from time to time.

One of the significant differences between Piaget's efforts and those of factor analysis is that he has given more attention to the development of *particular* products than to generic *types* of products. This is not to say that generalizations cannot and have not been made from the study of particulars. But it would seem to the writer that a more systematic and comprehensive program of research could be conducted on the development of intellectual functions by giving attention to the more general classes of functions such as appear in the structure of intellect. If the SI model does describe adult intelligence accurately, we can better orient the study of development by seeking for information along the lines of the model. From this point of view, Piaget's work was selective and correspondingly limited in its scope. For example, he gave considerable attention to the development of the particular conceptions pertaining to space, time, quantity, constancy, and the like. Although these are crucial concepts in human dealings with the world in which we live, there are many other concepts also to be developed.

Implications for Education

Of all the technological fields that may benefit from SI information, probably that of education stands the chance of profiting most. It is an educational institution's prime responsibility to promote the intellectual development of individuals, in terms of both increased skills and increased stored information. In the context of learning, the intellectual factors may be regarded as generalized skills to be cultivated in education. The SI model provides a most extensive and systematic taxonomy of general intellectual skills, for the use of those who are concerned with curriculum development, particularly (Guilford, 1958b). It can also provide specific goals for the teacher who plans the presentation of a particular subject. With the factor concepts in mind, it is possible to find new opportunities for mental exercises that could contribute to development. Balances and places of emphasis could be noted in connection with the philosophy of education, in the context of which values are considered.

Any particular course or subject could be reassessed in terms of the intellectual resources required to master it and in terms of opportunities it offers for promoting development along specified lines. The subject of reading, for example, would be found to emphasize a surprisingly large range of different abilities, at different stages of progress (Guilford, 1960c). Any school subject could be meaningfully specified in terms of the pattern of abilities or skills involved—for example, ninth-grade algebra (Peterson et al., 1964). The factorial description of a subject could be carried so far as to assign to different stages or steps in it certain of the SI factors with certain weights. In diagnoses of student failures, weaknesses could perhaps be meaningfully pinpointed and described in terms of SI factors. Student drop-outs could perhaps be circumvented by finding special, unsuspected talents.

Although nothing has been said thus far about the social and emotional "adjustment" of the student, and perhaps one would not ordinarily look to information regarding intelligence in connection with those problems, SI concepts may have much to offer. Of course there is the problem of academic failure and its implication for adjustment. At this point, information concerning intellectual status has some bearing. But it has not perhaps been sufficiently recognized that many personal and social failures can be traced to deficiency in social skills, which probably means low behavioral intelligence. Certain behavior problems, such as in the case of the delinquent boy who is a manipulator of others to his own advantage, may arise from especially high abilities in the area of behavioral cognition, coupled with low evaluative abilities where behavioral information is concerned. Thus new kinds of information regarding intellectual abilities may yet help a great deal in handling behavioral and personal problems.

Implications for Testing Practices

It is much too early to foresee all the consequences that the new information has for practices in intelligence testing. It would be safe to predict that traditional intelligence tests will be around for some time. We should now recognize, however, the severe limitations imposed by the compositions of those tests, and remember the fact that the "general" in the expression "general intelligence," when applied to tests, does not mean very general at all. Examination of current standard tests or tests of academic aptitude, which amount to essentially the same thing, will show that they sample cognitive abilities most heavily and touch upon divergent-production abilities hardly at all. As to content categories, they emphasize semantic abilities by a wide margin, with figural abilities running second, and with scarcely any attention to symbolic or behavioral abilities. As to products, units and systems are given most attention, with classes least, and with transformations in next-to-last place. Because of the probable prominent roles of divergent production and transformations in potential for creative thinking, something apparently needs to be done in making up for a serious deficiency in the testing of abilities in those two categories.

There are rumors of development of "creativity" batteries, with even suggestions of a "creativity IQ." The writer hopes that such a practice never comes about, for it would probably lead to a new feeling of success in mental measurement, with an attitude of complacency such as that which has followed the use of the present IQ. The result would be continued neglect of many other abilities that may be less glamorized but nontheless very important in certain places. Whatever the outcome in new test practices, the important next steps for those who look toward applications of tests are to contribute to the mountains of needed developmental research aimed at determining where in our intellectual activities of daily life the various factors are of some consequence. Such surveys should turn up some surprises.

It is recommended that studies of predictive validity of intelligence tests be routinely accompanied by the study of construct validity, where the constructs are the factors (Guilford, 1948). Such an approach applied to ninth-grade mathematics, for example, has not only demonstrated that multiple prediction could be materially higher from a combination of factor tests than from standard academic-achievement tests (Peterson *et al.*, 1964), but also has showed which of the factors were more prominently involved in the criteria of mathematics achievement. Such information should be enlightening to teachers of the subject, to counselors, and even to students.

Factor scores, each score representing well its unique ability, have a number of values that are or should be generally recognized. A set of such scores presents a minimum of redundancy, a fact that underlies a number of the virtues of factor scores. Low redundancy means greater potential multiple correlation and predictive validity when tests are used in combinations to predict factorially complex criteria. It means more meaningful profiles of scores, for differences between such scores are more reliable. Where profiles can be used, they convey much more useful information than does a single, composite score, to the eyes of the educated user. Low redundancy or little overlapping of measurement is also needed for differential predictions, as in educational and vocational guidance and in classification of personnel.

SOME FURTHER GENERAL CONSIDERATION OF MODELS

Some Possible Changes in the Structure of Intellect

The SI model is certainly not thought to be fixed for all time. It is obvious that already some factors have been moved from one cell to another, as new information and new interpretations came into the picture. It is not yet certain, by any means, that the structure already seen in three content categories will apply generally to the fourth, or behavioral category.

One of the probable extensions of the model will be to take care of factors for figural information in sense modalities other than vision. We already have three auditory factors, parallel to corresponding visual factors, two in the cognition category and the other in the memory category. There may be as many as six auditory abilities in each of those two operation categories, and possibly in the other three operation categories. The composer undoubtedly deals with divergent production of sound products, particularly systems. It is difficult to think of convergent production of sound effects, but not difficult to think of evaluations of them.

And if there are sets of abilities pertaining to auditory information, how about kinesthetic and tactual information? There is surely enough structuring of such information to lead us to expect that the product concepts may apply. All of these sense-modality categories could be taken care of in terms of a fourth dimension to the model. There will be doubts as to how many intersections the sensory-modality categories will make with categories of other dimensions. The visual category certainly seems to go all the way, but it is generally recognized that we live primarily in a visual world and we expect more elaboration and more uses of visual information than we do of information from other sense modalities.

Possible Applications of Hierarchy

Coming back to the early discussion of hierarchical models, can we find a place for that type of model in connection with the intellectual factors? Classifications of factors are naturally made in terms of their properties, regardless of the kind of model. Their properties would have effects on any hierarchical model that is constructed for the factors, as well as on the morphological model. The two kinds of models would then have certain correspondences.

One difficulty in constructing a hierarchical model is that there is little empirical basis for deciding which factors are of broader psychological scope and which of narrower scope. Those of broader scope would naturally be higher in the hierarchy. How can the degree of generality for a factor be determined? The number of tests in which each factor has loadings is sometimes used as a criterion, but this index is mostly a circumstance of how many such tests one puts in a particular battery for analysis. One could easily "load the data" in favor of greater generality of this kind for a factor. The kind of empirical evidence that is badly needed is in terms of intercorrelations of the basic factors of the model. Until there is a satisfactory way of estimating these correlations, we cannot say much about hierarchical structure.

The "Splitting" of Factors

Burt (1949) cites one kind of factor-analytic result that helps to confirm his belief in hierarchy. This is the so-called "splitting" of factors. By this is meant that one may find what appears to be a unitary trait in one analysis, with two or more tests substantially loaded on it, but that in a later analysis, with these tests and some additional ones in the battery, the group of tests formerly hanging together separate, along with separation of the new tests, to represent two factors.

Thus we face the important methodological and interpretational problem of when an obtained mathematical factor represents a psychological unity of some kind and when it does not. The related theoretical question is whether the splitting can go on and on, arriving at "factors" of narrower and narrower scope. There are some who believe that this description fits factor-analytic reality.

The writer's own impression is that many instances of apparent splitting of factors are due to poor choice of experimental variables for analytical purposes, or to inadequate sampling of those variables. Suppose that two psychological factors, A and B, actually exist as unitary functions and that they are even independent (uncorrelated) in the population. If the factorist puts in his battery tests of factor A, each of which has also a strong loading on factor B, and he puts in the battery tests of factor B, each of which has a strong secondary loading on factor A, the test vectors will lie so close together in space that it may appear decisive that there is only one common factor. Actually, we may say that factors A and B are "confounded." Experimental test construction did not achieve at least two relatively univocal tests for each of the two factors, A and B, either for lack of clear hypothetical conceptions in advance or for lack of skill in test construction. A univocal test for a factor must have good, built-in experimental controls to ensure that variances in its scores overwhelmingly indicate the one factor intended.

Since we have become aware of the kinds of separations between factors and between sets of tests that should be expected on the basis of the structure of intellect, it is much easier to know when confoundings of factors (of the kinds expected) do occur. One such confounding and case of apparent splitting of a factor can be cited. In the first evidence for a factor of elaboration, the two strongest tests were of different content, one semantic and the other figural; other tests loaded significantly on the factor were semantic. The leading semantic test was Planning Elaboration and the figural test was Figure Production. A good hypothesis was that factors DFI and DMI were confounded in that analysis (Berger *et al.,* 1957). It could be that with only one good figural test for a possible DFI, there was no basis for separation of two factors.

In a later analysis (Guilford *et al.,* 1961), one additional semantic test (Possible Jobs) was added and two additional figural tests (Decorations, and Production of Figural Effects) for an expected DFI. The latter test differed from Figure Production mainly in the instruction *not* to produce meaningful objects. In Figure Production, E is told to produce meaningful objects, starting from simple, given lines. In Decorations, E is given outline drawings of common objects (e.g., of dress or furniture) to which he is to add decorative lines.

As expected, the two groups of figural and semantic tests separated very clearly, with Figure Production going with the figural tests, with a loading of less than 0.2 on DMI. This result was not due to any reduction of the correlation between Figure Production and Planning Elaboration, which was 0.30 in the first analysis and 0.31 in the second. The first analysis was based on a population of Naval Air Cadets and the second on ninth-grade students with IQ's of 120 and above, of both sexes. The separation was helped, especially with regard to orthogonal rotation, by the fact that Figure Production correlated only 0.16 with the new test Possible Jobs.

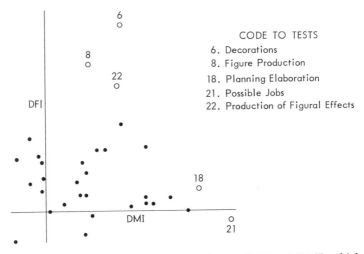

Fig. 10. Plot of axes showing the separation of factors DFI and DMI, which had been confounded, appearing to be one factor, in an earlier analysis.

Figure 10 shows the plot of the rotated orthogonal axes for factors DMI and DFI in the second analysis. Taking into consideration the long test vectors only, one might well argue in favor of an oblique rotation, but there is a strong clustering of short vectors along axis DFI, which can be offered as empirical support for an orthogonal solution such as was adopted. Another cluster of not-so-short test vectors also helped to locate axis DMI. The actual maximum spread for long test vectors is between tests 8 (Figure Production) and 21 (Possible Jobs). If we correct their intercorrelation for uniqueness by using the ratio $r_{8(21)}/h_8 h_{(21)}$, where $h^2_8 = 0.42$ and $h^2_{(21)} = 0.50$, we obtain 0.35 as the estimate of the cosine of their angle of separation, which indicates an angle of approximately $70°$.

It can be maintained, however, that the factors are actually orthogonal and that the three figural tests have some semantic content because enough examinees translate their task into semantic terms. They elaborate semantically in order to obtain ideas to apply to their figural tasks. This would be one example of lack of experimental control. It is interesting that the new test, Production of Figural Effects, seems, on the basis of its projection on axis DMI, not to have any less semantic content than Figure Production. In other words, the instructions to make meaningful objects *versus* not to make them appears to make no difference in the degree of semantic content. The Decorations test calls for the addition of decorative lines to meaningful objects. There is little basis for expecting Possible Jobs to have any figural content, but Planning Elaboration could have some if enough examinees visualize concretely the steps, the materials, and the arrangements that they would use. Incidentally, the remarks in this paragraph are also general, logical support for making orthogonal rotations of axes in connection with intellectual factors.

Most of the confoundings, or threats of confoundings, of factors that we have observed in the Aptitudes Project occur in rather meaningful places, i.e., combining factors that differ in only one respect—content, operation, or product. DFI and DMI differ only in content; the confounding took place across content boundaries. Other near-confoundings have confused products, for example, factors CFU and CFS, an instance that was mentioned earlier. Others have confused operations, such as evaluation and divergent production, for example, EMI and DMI. It is between such pairs of factors that confoundings are most expected. How much of this may be due to actual correlations between factors and how much to inadequately discriminating tests is hard to say on the basis of present evidence. To bring in a point on the techniques of rotations of axes in factor analysis (where conditions favorable for confoundings of factors can be taken into account in graphic-rotational solutions), computer rotations, such as the varimax and quartimax methods, are almost sure to carry out the confounding, even combining more than two factors into one (Guilford and Zimmerman, 1963).

Although there should be little concern when an apparent splitting of factors yields factors in different cells of the SI model, there is a more real problem regarding possible splitting within single cells. In this connection, the writer can cite cases of apparent resistance to splitting and also cases that call for more than one factor per cell in the model.

The case of resistance to splitting is in connection with factor DMT, formerly called "originality." Before this factor was found by the Aptitudes Project, tests for it were constructed on the basis of three principles: (1) some tests were to be scored with responses weighted in proportion to degrees of uncommonness among responses from the population of individuals; (2) some tests were to be scored for degree of remoteness of association; and (3) others were to be scored for degree of cleverness of the responses. Although there is some operational overlapping of these three criteria, there may be enough independence for two or three subfactors to appear. In spite of the fact that a number of each kind of test has been used in the same batteries, no such separations have occurred. Another instance that might be cited is the factor of numerical facility. Quite a variety of tests involving number operations have been introduced from time to time, without resulting in anything that has been recognized as a new, special number-operations factor.

There are several examples, already, of more than one factor to a cell. Three such cases have been mentioned. There are two cognition cells and a memory cell in each of which there is a visual factor and an auditory factor. The general way out, for this kind of case, is to introduce an extension of the SI model to handle auditory-figural factors, parallel with visual-figural factors, which would leave us again with one factor per cell.

But Christal (1958) has reported two factors that qualify for the cell MFU(V). The traditional tests for MFU(V) have been in the form of line drawings in black and white, to be reproduced or recognized. In his analysis, Christal also included two tests involving memory for colors, which brought out a separation of the color tests from the line tests. In connection with the cell for CFS (spatial orientation), in addition to the general visual-space factor, there is evidence for a special right-left space discrimination and perhaps for a compass-space-orientation factor (Guilford, 1959a). How much further such discriminations within cells may go is anybody's guess. If such distinctions are worth knowing about, their discovery is all to the good. Discriminations are the stuff of which information is made. Rejection of a procedure by any scientist because it turns up too much information is incomprehensible. It seems necessary to make this statement, in view of some critics whose rejection of the results of factor analysis appears to rest in part on its finding of "too many factors."

It can be pointed out that the new factors of divergent production, convergent production, and evaluation did not come about by way of "splitting" of old cognitive factors. Nor did they come out in new analyses simply because more tests of the same old types were included in batteries. They came about because many very new and varied types of tests were constructed and analyzed for the first time. Even the new factors of cognition and memory came about because test varieties were extended in new directions. The directions for still other extensions are indicated by the SI model.

Specific and General Factors

A number of people, including some factorists, apparently dismayed by the growing number of intellectual factors, seem to think that because the new factors are late comers, they must be in the nature of *specific* factors, as if the only way we can obtain new factors now is by splitting of old ones to the point of obtaining specifics. There is implication of correspondingly limited significance in the new factors. One should not underrate the importance of many of the new factors, and one should understand that they are by no means "specific" in the factor-theoretical sense.

How can we tell when a factor is genuinely specific and when it is general? It can be offered as a rule, that when the tests that generate a factor in an analysis are clearly not alternative forms of the *same* test, the factor has some generality and is not a specific. Inspection of two tests is ordinarily sufficient to determine whether they are alternative forms of one test, or are indeed two different tests. Anyone who inspects the tests given to represent each factor in the preceding pages should be struck by the fact that rarely, if ever, are two tests merely alternative forms. A statistical test of alternative forms, of course, would consist in correction of their intercorrelation for attenuation. If the corrected correlation is essentially equal to 1.00 (allowing for sampling errors) the tests may be regarded as alternative forms.

SUMMARY

This chapter presented first some traditional views of the nature of the composition of intelligence. Binet perennially emphasized the great complexity of intelligence, a view that he essentially buried by instituting the testing operation of assigning a single score to each individual. Spearman avoided the problem of the structure of intelligence by emphasizing his all-important g factor. British factorists since Spearman, while clinging vigorously to Spearman's g, recognized little g's and factors of lesser scope. The structures envisaged by Burt, Vernon, and Eysenck are quite naturally of hierarchical form, a kind of model that has much logical appeal.

In rejecting a hierarchical model as not being representative, the writer brought out a number of considerations against the supposed empirical basis for that kind of model in the area of intelligence. Most telling is the fact that no g factor, as now derived empirically, big or small, is invariant and stable. The difficulty lies in test-sampling problems in factor analysis and in lack of an acceptable method of estimating correlations among factors.

Attempts to classify the growing numbers of factors in the domain of intelligence have led to the organization of factors, without any g factor or factors, into a morphological model, in which the factors are parallel in three directions. The writer's structure-of-intellect model was briefly described; then there followed a systematic listing of intellectual factors and some of their representative tests. This descriptive material occupies the major portion of the chapter. It should serve to tie the categorical concepts of the model, and the factor concepts, to referents in the form of multiple variations of intellectual tasks.

Implications of the SI model for general psychological theory were brought out, which suggested a new, objective, informational view of human behavior, one that should take into account the whole range of psychological functioning. In discussing problems of development of intelligence, certain linkages with Piaget's findings were pointed out. Implications for educational theory and practice were mentioned, as well as for practices in mental testing.

Refutations are given to the ideas that new factors of intelligence come by way of splitting of old ones and that recently discovered factors verge on specificity and hence are of little consequence. On the contrary, the newly discovered factors reveal aspects of intelligence of considerable potential importance that have been neglected before. The structure-of-intellect theory also points the way to many other possible abilities yet to be demonstrated.

REFERENCES

BERGER, R. M., J. P. GUILFORD, and P. R. CHRISTENSEN, "A factor-analytical study of planning abilities." *Psychol. Monogr.* **71** (Whole No. 435) (1957)

BINET, A., and TH. SIMON, "La mesure de développement de l'intelligence chez les jeune enfants." *Bull. Soc. libre pour l'Etude Psychol. de l'Enfant,* 1911

BURT, C., "The structure of the mind: A review of the results of factor analysis." *Brit J. Educ. Psychol.* **19,** 100–111; 176–199 (1949)

CARROLL, J. B., "A factor analysis of verbal abilities." *Psychometrika* **6**, 279–307 (1941)

CHRISTAL, R. E., "Factor analytic study of visual memory." *Psychol. Monogr.* **72**, (Whole No. 466) (1958)

CHRISTENSEN, P. R., "The function-sharing approach to research on joint man-machine intelligence." Santa Monica, Calif.: System Development Corp., 1963, SP–1368

CHRISTENSEN, P. R., and J. P. GUILFORD, "An experimental study of verbal fluency factors." *Brit. J. Stat. Psychol.* **16**, 1–26 (1963)

COOMBS, C. H., "A factorial study of number ability." *Psychometrika* **6**, 161–189 (1941)

DAVIS, P. C., "A factor analysis of the Wechsler-Bellevue Scale." *Educ. Psychol. Measmt.* **16**, 127–146 (1956)

DE MILLE, R., "Intellect after lobotomy in schizophrenia." *Psychol. Monogr.* **76** (Whole No. 535) (1962)

DYSINGER, DALE W., "Factorial study of speed of responses in simple cancellation tasks." *Iowa Acad. Sci.* **57**, 373–378 (1950)

EYSENCK, H. J., *The Structure of Personality.* New York: John Wiley & Sons, 1953

FRENCH, J. W., "The description of aptitude and achievement tests in terms of rotated factors." *Psychometric Monogr.* **5** (1951)

FRICK, J. W., J. P. GUILFORD, P. R. CHRISTENSEN, and P. R. MERRIFIELD, "A factor-analytic study of flexibility in thinking." *Educ. Psychol. Measmt.* **19**, 469–496 (1959)

GERSHON, A., J. P. GUILFORD, and P. R. MERRIFIELD, "Figural and symbolic divergent-production abilities in adolescent and adult populations." *Rep. Psychol. Lab.*, No. 29. Los Angeles: University of Southern California, 1963

GUILFORD, J. P., "A note on the discovery of a *G* factor by means of Thurstone's centroid method of analysis." *Psychometrika* **6**, 205–208 (1941)

GUILFORD, J. P., "Factor analysis in a test-development program." *Psychol. Rev.* **55**, 79–94 (1948)

GUILFORD, J. P., "Les dimensions de l'intellect," in H. Laugier, *L'analyse factorielle et ses applications.* Paris: Centre national de la Recherche Scientifique, 1956a, pp. 55–74

GUILFORD, J. P., "Structure of intellect." *Psychol. Bull.* **53**, 267–293 (1956b)

GUILFORD, J. P., "A revised structure of intellect." *Rep. Psychol. Lab.*, No. 19. Los Angeles: University of Southern California, 1957

GUILFORD, J. P., "New frontiers of testing in the discovery and development of human talent." *Seventh Annual Western Regional Conference on Testing Problems.* Los Angeles: Educational Testing Service, 1958a

GUILFORD, J. P., "Human abilities in education." *Calif. J. Instructional Improvement* **1**, 3–6 (1958b)

GUILFORD, J. P., *Personality.* New York: McGraw-Hill, 1959a

GUILFORD, J. P., "Three faces of intellect." *Amer. Psychologist* **14**, 469–479 (1959b)

GUILFORD, J. P., "Basic conceptual problems in the psychology of thinking." *Ann. New York Acad. Sci.* **91,** 6–21 (1960a)

GUILFORD, J. P., "An emerging view in learning theory," in *Proceedings of the 1960 Summer Conference.* Bellingham, Wash.: Western Washington College Bulletin, 1960b, 29–46

GUILFORD, J. P., "Frontiers in thinking teachers should know about." *Reading Teacher* 176–182 (1960c)

GUILFORD, J. P., "Factorial angles to psychology." *Psychol. Rev.* **68,** 1–20 (1961)

GUILFORD, J. P., "An informational view of mind." *J. Psychol. Researches,* **6,** 1–10 (1962)

GUILFORD, J. P., "Progress in the discovery of intellectual factors," in C. W. Taylor (ed.), *Widening Horizons in Creativity.* New York: McGraw-Hill, 1964a

GUILFORD, J. P., "Some new views of creativity," in H. Helson and W. Bevan (eds.), *Contemporary Approaches to Psychology.* Princeton: D. Van Nostrand, 1946b

GUILFORD, J. P., "Zero correlations among tests of intellectual abilities." *Psychol. Bull.* **61** (1964c)

GUILFORD, J. P., *The Nature of Human Intelligence.* New York: McGraw-Hill, 1967

GUILFORD, J. P., and R. HOEPFNER, "Current summary of structure-of-intellect factors and suggested tests." *Rep. Psychol. Lab.,* No. 30. Los Angeles: University of Southern California, 1963

GUILFORD, J. P., and P. R. MERRIFIELD, "The structure of intellect model: its uses and implications." *Rep. Psychol. Lab.,* No. 24. Los Angeles: University of Southern California, 1960

GUILFORD, J. P., P. R. MERRIFIELD, and ANNA B. COX, "Creative thinking in children at the junior high school levels." *Rep. Psychol. Lab.,* No. 26. Los Angeles: University of Southern California, 1961

GUILFORD, J. P., and W. S. ZIMMERMAN, "Some variable-sampling problems in the rotation of axes in factor analysis." *Psychol. Bull.* **60,** 289–301 (1963)

HUNT, J. McV., *Intelligence and Experience.* New York: Ronald Press, 1961

KELLEY, T. L., *Crossroads in the Mind of Man.* Stanford: Stanford University Press, 1928

KETTNER, N. W., J. P. GUILFORD, and P. R. CHRISTENSEN, "A factor-analytic study across the domains of reasoning, creativity, and evaluation." *Psychol. Monogr.* **73** (Whole No. 479) (1959)

LAURITZEN, EVELYN S., "Semantic divergent thinking factors among elementary school children." Unpublished doctoral dissertation, University of California at Los Angeles, 1963

MAJEWSKA, M. C., "A study of mathematical ability as related to reasoning and use of symbols." *Publ. Psychomet. Lab.,* No. 12. Chicago: Loyola University, 1960

McCARTIN, R. A., "An exploration at first grade of six hypotheses in the semantic domain." Doctoral dissertation, University of Southern California, 1963

MERRIFIELD, P. R., J. P. GUILFORD, P. R. CHRISTENSEN, and J. W. FRICK, "Some new symbolic factors of cognition and convergent production." *Educ. Psychol. Measmt.* **21,** 515–541 (1961)

MERRIFIELD, P. R., J. P. GUILFORD, and A. GERSHON, "The differentiation of divergent-production abilities at the sixth-grade level." *Rep. Psychol. Lab.,* No. 27. Los Angeles: University of Southern California, 1963

MEYERS, C. E., H. F. DINGMAN, A. A. ATTWELL, and R. E. ORPET, "Comparative abilities of normals and retardates of MA six years on a factor-type test battery." *Amer. J. Ment. Defic.* **66,** 250–258 (1961)

NIHIRA, K., J. P. GUILFORD, R. HOEPFNER, and P. R. MERRIFIELD, "A factor analysis of the semantic-evaluation abilities." *Rep. Psychol. Lab.,* No. 32. Los Angeles: University of Southern California, 1964

PETERSON, H., J. P. GUILFORD, R. HOEPFNER, and P. R. MERRIFIELD, "Determination of structure-of-intellect abilities involved in ninth-grade algebra and general mathematics." *Rep. Psychol. Lab.,* No. 31. Los Angeles: University of Southern California, 1964

PIAGET, P., *The Psychology of Intelligence.* New York: Harcourt, Brace & World, 1950

THURSTONE, L. L., "Primary mental abilities." *Psychometric Monogr.* **1** (1938)

THURSTONE, L. L., "A factorial study of perception." *Psychometric Monogr.* **4** (1944)

VERNON, P. E., *The Structure of Human Abilities.* New York: John Wiley & Sons, 1950

CHAPTER 8

MEASUREMENT OF APTITUDE
AND ACHIEVEMENT

DEAN W. SEIBEL, *Educational Testing Service*

INTRODUCTION

In making educational, psychological, and sociological assessments, we often wish to describe the skills, abilities, and knowledge which an individual possesses. This is particularly true in educational settings, where attempts are made to develop and improve these characteristics in students. The teachers, administrators, counselors, and others who are responsible for the student's education must be constantly aware of and continually assessing the intellectual capacity of the student, if effective teaching is to be accomplished and if the student is to be guided or helped along the sometimes complicated educational path.

Describing an individual's intellectual status is considerably more difficult than describing his physical characteristics. We have no convenient, easily understood measuring tools such as scales, micrometers, tape measures, or balances, and we have no standard units of measurement such as feet, pounds, centimeters, or grams. The science of measuring intellectual factors is young and the tools of measurement are unrefined and easily subject to misunderstanding. Even so, substantial advances have been made in this science. In this chapter we shall discuss some techniques commonly used today in measuring intellectual characteristics.

Psychological Tests as a Means of Observing and Recording Behavior

Since we cannot get inside a person's mind to measure anything, we must be content with measuring that which we can observe—his behavior. Our assumption is that what a person does under certain conditions is an indication of his intellectual characteristics. In fact, since we can only hypothesize about the existence of mental characteristics, it is convenient to define these characteristics in terms of overt behavior. Although there are many ways in which human behavior may be observed and recorded, our concern in this chapter is with only one method, commonly known as "paper-and-pencil" testing; more specifically, we shall discuss only those tests that are usually called "aptitude" and "achievement" tests.

In any attempt to observe human behavior, it is necessary that we exercise some control over the observation. Individuals behave in an infinite variety of ways. We might follow an individual around, day after day, writing down descriptions of everything he does and the circumstances surrounding his behavior. This, of course, is impractical and inefficient, because (1) the individual may or may not exhibit the particular kind of behavior that we wish to observe, and (2) we would rarely observe behaviors which could be directly compared from one individual to another. For example, if we wished to observe "car-driving" behavior and identify differences between the "car-driving ability" of two individuals, it might be many days before we could observe both individuals driving cars. Even then, because of different driving conditions, different makes of cars, etc., our observations might not permit comparison of the two individuals in this area of behavior. It would be a much more efficient and orderly procedure to exercise some control over the situation by specifying the circumstances in which the behavior is to occur and by eliciting, under the specified circumstances, the kind of behavior we wish to observe.

One way of exercising this control is to provide the individual with one or more specific tasks to perform. The nature of the tasks can be varied to elicit the kind of behavior we wish to observe, and the same tasks can be presented to several individuals under the same circumstances in order to elicit behaviors which may be logically compared. We refer to a series of these tasks as a *test* and to each individual task as a *test item*. In the interests of efficiency, our record of behavior usually consists only of a numerical index, or *score,* summarizing the individual's success in performing the series of tasks.

In order to be able to trust our test results, we must have some indication of the accuracy of our observations; that is, we must know how much *error* or inconsistency our measuring system has within it. Error is present primarily because (1) we have selected a small number of specific tasks, (2) we are not able to control all aspects of the circumstances within which the observations are made, and (3) we must make judgments of a person's success in performing the tasks. The extent to which the system is free from inconsistency is a measure of its accuracy, or *reliability.*

Reliability becomes especially important when we consider the use that is to be made of the test results. For some uses, considerable inaccuracy can be tolerated; for others, a high degree of accuracy is necessary. For example, a guidance counselor might administer a scholastic aptitude test to high school students to get a general idea of which students should start thinking about and planning for college. Since he is not trying to make fine discriminations among students and since the test scores are not contributing to any crucial decisions, this could be a relatively short test. (In general, the fewer the number of items in a test the lower the reliability.) On the other hand, an admissions officer at a college might also administer a scholastic aptitude test to students applying for admission to the college, but since he may have to discriminate between students of nearly equal ability, and since the test scores may contribute to a crucial decision to admit or not admit any given student, a longer, more accurate test would probably be used. For example, the Scholastic Aptitude Test of the College Entrance Examination Board requires three hours to administer. In addition, the admissions officer would probably check the accuracy of his measuring system by obtaining other observations of the applicants' behavior through interviews, high school records, and recommendations.

Accuracy of measurement must be paid for in some way. Just as a micrometer costs more and is more difficult to use than a yardstick, a three-hour test, supplemented by other observations of student behavior, requires a larger investment of time and money than a single short test. Therefore, it is usually not worth while to use a costly and quite accurate measuring system when a less accurate one will accomplish the desired results. The system used must be accurate enough, however, to permit us to make the required discriminations.

In addition to having an idea of the reliability of a test, we must have some method of attaching meaning to the scores obtained. As was noted above, in the interests of efficiency, we record only a summary numerical index of success on a series of tasks. In so doing we lose much of the information that might have been recorded had we wished to take the time and effort to do it; e.g., from the test score we cannot tell what success an individual met on each of the specific tasks in the series. In fact, our numerical summary of success has very little direct or usable meaning left in it except that it enables us to compare individuals in terms of their relative amounts of success on a series of tasks. Thus we may, for example, interpret the score obtained by a given individual by comparing it with the scores obtained on the same test by a defined group of similar individuals. The distribution of scores of this defined group of individuals is called a *test norm*. Sometimes the information necessary to make this comparison is incorporated into the test score by converting raw scores into various *standard scores* or *scaled scores*.

Finally, we must have some way of evaluating the utility of the test. At some point the test user must answer the questions, "Did the test provide the kind of information wanted?" or, "How useful was the information in accomplishing the original purpose for using the test?" The *validity* of a test is its quality of providing the desired information or accomplishing the desired purposes.

Later in this article we shall discuss in detail the concepts and definitions just presented. We shall also examine the characteristics of various kinds of tests, and indicate how information on published tests may be obtained. First, however, let us see how tests are classified by content and what is the relationship between teaching objectives and test content.

TEST CONTENT

Currently we tend to classify paper-and-pencil tests into categories on the basis of test content or test title. The categories of interest to us here are *achievement tests, scholastic aptitude tests,* and *intelligence tests.* There are, of course, other categories of tests, such as interest inventories, personality or character tests, manual dexterity tests, mechanical aptitude tests, and clerical aptitude tests, but we shall not concern ourselves here with these types since they are not usually thought of as measures of intellectual skill, ability, or knowledge.

Achievement tests contain test items that are directly related to some specific area of subject matter (e.g., biology, mathematics) or to the educational objectives of a specific course of study (e.g., ninth-grade algebra, English literature). They attempt to assess the skill and knowledge that an individual has acquired in a subject or in a course of study.

Scholastic aptitude tests contain tasks that are directly related to the future performance of some educational activity. They attempt to assess skills and abilities in broad general areas such as "verbal ability" (the ability to deal with words and word relationships) or "quantitative ability" (the ability to deal with numbers or number relationships).

Intelligence tests are often erroneously thought of as measuring some innate capacity which each individual either is born with or mysteriously acquires early in life, and which remains constant throughout life. We know, however, that what we call intelligence is quite complex and is certainly not assessed completely (if at all) by our present intelligence tests. Performance of the tasks in these tests is subject to learning experiences, and therefore does not necessarily remain constant. The tasks included on intelligence tests relate to a wide variety of learned skills and abilities and often encompass the same skills and abilities that are found in achievement tests and scholastic aptitude tests. We can, however, make some general observations about our present group of intelligence tests.

First, each of the many available intelligence tests measures a different concept of intelligence. That is, the tasks in a particular intelligence test represent one concept of what constitutes "intelligent behavior." Usually this is the test author's concept. Another intelligence test will contain different tasks and represents a different person's concept. Although there are usually certain similarities in concepts of intelligent behavior, there are equally often differences. Therefore, two different intelligence tests administered to the same person may provide different and, on the surface, apparently inconsistent results. We cannot say that one is right and one is wrong, but only that the two tests are measuring different skills, abilities, and knowledge.

Second, almost all intelligence tests provide an "IQ" (Intelligence Quotient). Unfortunately, among the general public the IQ has assumed a magical aura concerning its nature and meaning. An IQ, however, is derived from the score on some specific intelligence test. Therefore, it merely represents summary performance on a specific group of tasks and is subject to all the weaknesses and limitations of any test score.

These, then, are some of the factors that tend to distinguish among the three broad categories of tests. The distinctions, though rather superficial and often unclear, have some value. They provide test publishers and others who must categorize tests with convenient classifications, and they help us in narrowing down the field when we are searching for a particular kind of test for a specific use.

It should be pointed out, however, that there are actually more similarities among the categories than there are differences. If we think of achievement tests as measuring what a person has learned, then all three types of tests are achievement tests since they all measure learned skills and abilities. The difference, of course, lies only in the nature of the skills and abilities that are being elicited, observed, and recorded. Similarly, if we think of an aptitude test as a test that is used for predicting some type of learning, then all three types of tests are aptitude tests since all have been found useful in this respect. The difference here is only in the relationship of the tasks in a particular test to the type of behavior we wish to predict. And finally, if we think of intelligence tests as measuring "intelligent behavior," then all three types of tests are intelligence tests, for all require what most persons agree is "intelligent behavior" to successfully accomplish the tasks that are presented. In fact, if we were to look at an item from a test without knowing its source, it would be difficult and perhaps impossible to specify with assurance whether the item came from a test that is labeled as an achievement test, a scholastic aptitude test, or an intelligence test.

Objectives and Test Content

Every person who instructs others has certain goals or teaching objectives that he is trying to attain through the instruction. These objectives, which may or may not be specified or verbalized, relate to the acquisition of knowledge about certain areas of subject matter, to the acquisition of certain skills or abilities, to the establishment of certain attitudes, or to the acquisition or development of other traits. Unless the items in a test require the skills and abilities that the teacher has been trying to develop in the students and unless the subject matter covered by the test is the same as the subject matter used by the teacher in the course, the test is not a completely suitable instrument to use in evaluating the degree to which the teaching objectives are being met. The further the tasks or subject matter of the test deviate from the teacher's objectives, the less suitable the use of the test for this purpose.

As is well known, teaching objectives vary considerably (and rightly so) from teacher to teacher and from school to school. Even two teachers of the same or similarly titled courses (e.g., first-year biology, or American government) can have quite different objectives and cover quite different subject matter. Obviously, tests that purport to measure achievement in similarly specified areas are subject to the same kinds of variations. That is, two achievement tests of the same title or classification can measure quite different skills and cover quite different subject matter. Unless the teacher or test user looks beneath the superficial descriptions of a given test and actually examines the tasks to be performed, there is no assurance that the test results will be meaningful or useful for him. In fact, the results may present a completely false picture of student or class accomplishments.

What has been said above concerning the appropriateness of any achievement test for measuring given teaching objectives is just as applicable when a teacher himself is constructing an achievement test for use with the class—the test, as constructed, must contain tasks that are relevant to the objectives which the teacher wishes to evaluate.

Of course, in order to specify the student behaviors that relate to his own teaching objectives, the teacher must have his objectives clearly in mind. This is likely to present major problems for some teachers or administrators. Often, teachers teach as they do or administrators set policies concerning how certain courses should be taught only because "this is the way it was done before" or "this is the way I was taught the subject." They really have no clear conception of the ends they are trying to achieve. The dangers and weaknesses of this sort of situation are evident. It seems clear that educational objectives must be continually reviewed and evaluated to assure that the ends being achieved are really those that are sought. If, in this process of review and evaluation, the desired objectives can be specified in terms of observable student behavior, then it becomes much easier to evaluate the extent to which the objectives are being achieved.

The process of comparing the items in a test with a set of teaching objectives is not simple or easy. The teaching objectives must be stated in terms of student behavior and the behaviors elicited by the test items must be ascertained. Further, these two sets of behaviors must be expressed in terms that permit meaningful comparisons.

It is certainly not an easy task, first of all, to specify educational objectives in behavioral terms. A teacher or test user faced with this problem as it relates to test selection or test construction may find it helpful to utilize checklists of behaviors or educational objectives that have already been prepared. It is easier to look at a previously stated objective or behavior, and conclude that this particular goal either is or is not important in one's own teaching, than it is to compile an original list. After making this decision about a series of specified goals, a teacher will have a fairly accurate and complete picture of his own major teaching objectives.

There are several possible sources of these ready-made lists. One might, for example, use the lists of skills and abilities (which are behaviors) that are supplied by test publishers with some of their tests. This, of course, has the advantage of allowing immediate and direct comparison between the teacher's goals and the tasks elicited by certain tests. Books such as *Behavioral Goals of General Education in High School* (French *et al.*, 1957), *Elementary School Objectives* (Kearney, 1953), or *Taxonomy of Educational Objectives* (Bloom, 1965 and Krathwohl, Bloom, and Masia, 1964) will also provide lists of objectives. Although the comparison of such lists with the behaviors elicited by test items requires some subjective judgment, it can be done—as, for example, in a folio of over 10,000 test items, *Questions and Problems in Science* (Dressel and Nelson, 1956), which relates each test item to behaviors that are listed in the *Taxonomy of Educational Objectives* (Bloom, 1956). Finally, if no listing of the skills and abilities for a certain test under consideration is available, one might use the test items themselves as a checklist. This, again, will require subjective judgments as to the behaviors being elicited by the items and as to the relevance of these behaviors to the teacher's values and goals.

To aid in identifying and comparing behaviors elicited by test items the test content can be analyzed by classifying the items in one or more ways according to the subject matter covered, the skills required, the type of material, etc. Usually a two-way classification will be sufficient—the content or subject matter of the item, and the skill required for successful completion of the task. The items in a general science test might be classified according to six categories of skill required: (1) define problems, (2) suggest hypotheses, (3) select procedures, (4) draw conclusions, (5) evaluate critically, (6) reason quantitatively. The items might also be classified according to six subject matter areas: (1) biology, (2) chemistry, (3) physics,

Table 1

Skill	Biology	Chemistry	Physics	Astronomy	Meteorology	Geology	Total
						Subject matter	
Define problems	1	4	3	2	1	1	12
Suggest hypotheses	4	2	4	3	4	3	20
Select procedures	1	1	1	0	1	1	5
Draw conclusions	7	8	10	2	3	0	30
Evaluate critically	4	7	6	1	3	2	23
Reason quantitatively	2	2	2	1	2	1	10
Total	19	24	26	9	14	8	100

(4) astronomy, (5) geology, (6) meteorology. A single test item in this two-way scheme could be classified, for example, as requiring the ability to suggest hypotheses in physics, or the ability to evaluate critically in geology. When all the items in a test are placed into such a two-way scheme, it is possible to obtain a "bird's-eye-view" of the entire test in terms of subject matter and skills.

Table 1 shows a hypothetical two-way classification of 100 items for a general science test, using the categories mentioned above. The numbers in each cell of the grid are the numbers of test items classified according to the two intersecting categories. Since there is a total of 100 items in the test, the numbers also reflect the percentage or proportion of each type of item in the total test.

Some tests may require more than two classifications. For example, a social studies test might need three classifications—skills (compare data, distinguish fact from opinion), type of material (map, graph, text, table), and subject matter (geography, American history, economics). Another test in, say, mathematics might require only one classification.

Classifying test items in this manner requires not only subjective judgment, but also insight, ingenuity, and a lot of time. Nevertheless, some scheme like this is necessary in the process of selecting or of planning and constructing appropriate tests. Test publishers have recognized this fact and are endeavoring to supply this kind of information to test users. For example, classifications of test items according to various categories of subject matter and skill are available for the *Sequential Tests of Educational Progress** and for the *Iowa Tests of Basic Skills*.†

---

* *Teacher's Guide, Sequential Tests of Educational Progress.* Princeton: Educational Testing Service (Cooperative Test Division), 1959.
† *Teacher's Manual, Iowa Tests of Basic Skills.* Boston: Houghton Mifflin, 1955.

As we have seen, test content is crucial to our system of observing and recording behavior, and much work needs to be done in this area both on the part of the test user and on the part of those constructing tests. The important thing to remember is that every test, whether by design or by accident, elicits a certain set of behaviors. Anyone using the test must be satisfied that the behaviors elicited are indeed those that will be meaningful and valuable for the intended use of the test results. Therefore, we reiterate, a minimum requirement for anyone who is considering use of a certain test is a *careful examination of each item in the test*. The same careful consideration of each item is required of anyone attempting to construct a test.

TEST RELIABILITY

Sources of Unreliability

We have mentioned that there are three major factors that contribute to inaccuracy, or lack of reliability, in measurement by testing—the selection of specific tasks, the uncontrolled aspects of the observation, and the judgment of success in performing the tasks. Let us look in some detail at each of these.

Selection of specific tasks. When we decide what behaviors we wish to observe, we select for inclusion in the test a limited number of tasks which elicit the desired type of behavior. The number is limited so that the set of tasks can be attempted and completed in a reasonable length of time. There are, however, many other similar tasks that could be included in the test that would also elicit the desired type of behavior. In effect, we select a small representative sample of tasks from a much larger group, any of which would be appropriate.

Consider, for example, all the possible tasks that we might ask a person to perform in order to measure his accomplishments in freshman algebra. The universe of tasks or test items is quite large and, in fact, hypothetical since it is not possible to specify them all. The contents of the universe of tasks, of course, depend on our conception of what constitutes "freshman algebra." Suppose that we decided that "factoring polynomials" is a part of our concept of freshman algebra and is a skill that we want to observe in the test. The variety of tasks that could be presented to elicit this type of behavior is unlimited. One task, for example, might be to factor the expression $16x^2 - 24xy + 9y^2$. Another similar but different task might be to factor the expression $4a^2 - 13ab + 3b^2$, and on and on. We can select only a small sample of these similar tasks for inclusion in the test; therefore, we must use the performance on the sample as an estimate of performance on the universe of tasks.

It is to be expected, however, that a person's performance might be different on one small representative sample of tasks than it would be on another. For example, a person might be able to factor one of the algebraic expressions given above and not the other. And yet it would be only through chance that one of these expressions would appear in the test and the other would not. In other words, the fact that we have selected a specific sample of tasks introduces a degree of inconsistency.

It should be emphasized here that the larger the sample of tasks is, the less chance there is for the occurrence of this type of inconsistency. In the extreme, if the sample contained all the tasks in the universe, the inconsistency would disappear. Therefore, the more tasks there are in the sample, the higher will be the reliability of the system.

Uncontrolled aspects of observation. A second source of inconsistency is the fact that we observe performance on the given tasks at only one point in time. That is, we obtain only one sample of an individual's behavior. Ideally, we should like to obtain a second sample of the *same* behavior at a different point of time. However, even assuming that the undertaking of the tasks on one occasion would not affect performance on a second occasion, and that there would be no change in the person's skills, abilities, or knowledge as required by the tasks from one occasion to the next, there would still be differences in the two samples of behavior because of elements in the situation that change and cannot be controlled.

We can control many aspects of the observation—the nature of the tasks, the physical surroundings, the procedures for attempting the tasks, the time allowed for accomplishing the tasks, etc. But we cannot control factors related to the individual, such as state of health, fatigue, emotional strain, rapport with examiner, temporary lapses of attention, fluctuation in memory for specific information, attitude toward the test, or motivation, all of which can affect performance in an unpredictable way. These uncontrolled factors will introduce inconsistency into the system and, therefore, reflect upon the test's reliability.

Scoring. A third source of inconsistency is present when the system of observing and recording behavior requires that the observer make judgments of the success achieved on the tasks. Within this area there are two kinds of inconsistencies. A single observer might render different judgments when observing the same performance on two different occasions. We can call this "intraobserver" variation. Or, two independent observers might render different judgments of success when observing the same performance at the same time. We call this "interobserver" variation. The inconsistency is present because we have only a sample of *observer* behavior in judging success on the tasks.

On certain kinds of tests, observer-related inconsistency may be effectively eliminated. So-called "objective" tests require, for all practical purposes, no judgment of success on the part of an observer. Instead, the person taking the test is provided with a limited number of responses or solutions to each task, only one of which is considered a successful response. The choice of response, then, determines the success on the task. By contrast, "subjective" or "essay" tests are influenced greatly by observer judgment of success, and this fact reflects heavily on the reliability of the system. Although ways have been devised of reducing scorer inconsistency in essay tests, they are expensive and time-consuming, and hence are infrequently used.

Methods of Assessing Reliability

In judging the accuracy of any system of measurement, we would like to compare the results of the system being considered with the errorless (true) value of the entity being measured. In most instances this is impossible because we never know what the true value is. If we had some way of ascertaining the true value, there would be no need for the system which contains errors. How, then, can one judge the accuracy of a measuring system?

One method is to apply the system several times in measuring the same object. The extent of agreement among the results of the several applications is an indication of accuracy. The logic of this can be seen by considering a physical measurement situation. Suppose that we wish to measure the length of a room. Our measuring system consists of placing a well-constructed and well-marked yardstick end-to-end several times. The first attempt to measure the length of a room might result in a length of 14 feet, 5 inches. A second attempt (using the same system) might result in a length of 14 feet, $5\frac{1}{2}$ inches—rather close agreement with the first measurement. Having made two measurements that agree fairly well, we might conclude that our yardstick system is accurate enough for whatever purpose we had in mind (for example, determining how much asphalt tile to purchase in order to cover the floor). However, if the two measurements differed by 10 inches, we might have serious doubts about the accuracy of the system. A difference of 30 inches would indicate still less accuracy.

In testing, as in physical measurement, the more consistency (agreement) there is in repeated applications of the measuring system, the more accurate the system can be considered. Several methods have been devised for accomplishing repeated applications of the measuring system. Each has certain advantages and certain limitations, and all require that certain statistical assumptions be made. Moreover, the methods employed vary in the degree to which they reveal inconsistency from different sources, and some are more applicable to one measuring system than to another.

We might, for instance, select two samples of items from the universe and have each person in a group attempt both sets of items. Of course, we would want the two samples of items (tests) to be equivalent (elicit the same kinds of behavior) and to be representative of the universe. We would administer the tests to the group with little time intervening in order to reduce the likelihood that the skills, abilities, and knowledge required by the items would change from one testing to the next. We would make the conditions of administration as equivalent (standard) as possible and we would have independent judgments of success (scoring) for each sample of test items. This method of obtaining reliability information is commonly called the *two-form* or *equivalent-form* method. It takes account of all of the major sources of inconsistency, but has the disadvantage that greater expense and time are involved in the preparation of two equivalent forms of the test.

A variation in this method which can be used when only one form of the test is available is to divide the test into two equivalent halves and compare the performance of a group of persons on each half. This method, commonly called the *split-half* method, has the advantage of eliminating time between administrations, since the two halves are administered together (as parts of the same test). The reliability information that we obtain by this method must be adjusted, however, because we are actually dealing with only one-half the number of tasks or test items that are in the initial test. That is, the reliability is higher for the initial test (since it contains more tasks) than it is for either of the halves that we have compared.

Rather than administer two different samples of tasks, we might administer the same sample of items twice to the same group of persons. This method provides what is known as the *test-retest* type of reliability information. It is probably the least satisfactory method of estimating test reliability; it does not take account of the inconsistency resulting from the fact that the second administration of the test is likely to be influenced by practice or memory, since the tasks are exactly the same the second time. Its advantage, of course, is convenience, since only one form of the test is required.

Reporting of Reliability Information

With this general idea of the nature of reliability or consistency as it applies to tests, let us now consider ways that reliability information can be reported. Regardless of which method we use, the basic information that we have is the result of two applications of the measuring system, and we need to report the extent of agreement or disagreement between the outcomes of these two applications. There are essentially two ways that we can compare these sets of data.

The reliability coefficient. The first way of comparing data is through a correlative technique, in which we determine how closely, in general, the individuals maintain their "rank order" from one set of results to the other. In effect, we ask: Do the individuals who attain a high degree of success (relative to the rest of the group) on one application of the tasks also attain a high degree of success on the other application? Similarly, do individuals who attain low scores the first time also attain low scores the second time? The statistic that is used to represent the degree of agreement between any two sets of data is called the *correlation coefficient,* or more specifically, in the case of test data, the *reliability coefficient.* It is reported on a scale extending from 0.00 (indicating no agreement or complete unreliability) to 1.00 (indicating complete agreement or perfect reliability). For example, one might report that the test-retest reliability coefficient for a given test is 0.85 or 85 (sometimes the decimal point is dropped); this would mean that the correlation coefficient for two sets of data obtained by administering the test twice to the same group of persons is 0.85.

Now, how do we attach some practical meaning to the reliability coefficient? We know that in general, the higher the reliability coefficient, the more accurate or consistent the test. But there is no commonly accepted "rule of thumb" that will tell us when the reliability coefficient is "high enough." This type of judgment depends on the *kind* of reliability coefficient we have and on the *use* that we intend to make of the result. Regarding the latter, it is generally accepted that reliabilities in the 90's or high 80's are sufficient for most purposes that involve using test scores as information about individuals, and that reliabilities in the 70's or low 80's are adequate for most purposes that involve using summaries of test scores as information about groups.

The kind of reliability coefficient merits more extensive discussion. One advantage that is often mentioned in connection with the reliability coefficient is that it enables us to compare the accuracy of several different tests, since the coefficient is reported on a common scale (i.e., 0.00 to 1.00). Caution must be exercised here, however. In selecting one test from among several apparently appropriate tests, it is tempting to select the one with the highest reported reliability coefficient. This could result in serious error because at least two factors other than the true reliability have considerable effect on the reported reliability coefficient for a test.

One factor is the method used to obtain the two applications of the measurement system: test-retest, split-half, or two-form. If for one test we computed the reliability coefficient by each of the various methods, we would probably obtain a different reliability coefficient by each method. The extent of the differences among the coefficients would depend on the nature of the test. For some kinds of tests the range of reliability coefficients produced by the different methods would be great; for other kinds of tests it would be less. In any case, we would be likely to get substantial differences resulting from nothing more than the method used. Therefore, in comparing several tests in terms of their reliability coefficients we must at least make sure that all the coefficients were obtained by the same method.

The other factor is the composition of the group of individuals on which the reliability information is based. The nature of the correlation coefficient is such that its size depends partly on the diversity within the sets of data being correlated (in this instance the test scores for the group). The more divergent the group is in the skills and abilities measured by the tasks in the test, the higher the obtained reliability coefficient will be. This means that the size of the reliability coefficient will be affected by the selection of the group of individuals. Again, this is something which has nothing to do with the consistency of the measuring system itself. Thus, assuming that we use a single method of obtaining reliability information for a given test, we might obtain two different reliability coefficients if we used two different groups of individuals. In comparing reliability coefficients for several tests, then, it is important to know that these coefficients were obtained using closely similar groups of individuals. Similarly, in order for the reliability coefficient for a single test to have any meaning for us, we must be sure that the group of individuals on which the information is based is similar to the group with which the test is going to be used.

The standard error of measurement. The reliability coefficient does not help us to estimate the amount of error in an individual's test score. The test score, as we have mentioned, is only a numerical indication of success in performing the tasks in a test. Despite the great variety in the kinds of test scores, the basic element is the number of tasks successfully completed. We would, for practical purposes, like to have reliability information in such a form that it tells us directly how much inaccuracy or inconsistency each individual's test score has. This need gives rise to the second way of reporting reliability information.

Let us return to the two samples of performance. As already explained, the extent of agreement between the two groups of test scores, viewed in correlative terms, results in the reliability coefficient. If, however, we examine the numerical difference between the scores which any given individual receives on the two performance samples, we obtain another index of reliability—the *standard error of measurement*. For example, if an individual receives a score of 30 on the first sample of performance and a score of 33 on the second sample, the difference is +3. This difference is on the same scale (number of tasks successfully completed) as the test score—the individual was successful on three more tasks the second time than the first. Another individual might obtain a score of 48 the first time and 40 the second—a difference of −8. A third individual might obtain scores of 25 both times—a difference of 0. If the differences for all individuals in the group could be summarized in some way, we should have an indication of the inconsistency of the test, given on the same scale that is used for the test score. For the group as a whole, the larger these differences were, the less reliable the test would be considered, and *vice versa*.

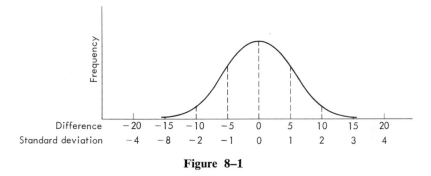

Figure 8–1

In the technical theory of reliability we make the assumption that the kinds of inconsistencies we are concerned with are those that are unpredictable and unsystematic, and that the size of the difference is not in any way related to the magnitude of the test score. If we obtain the two samples of performance for a great number of individuals (theoretically, an infinite number), and compute the difference between the two samples of performance for each of the individuals, these differences will form a "normal" frequency distribution in which the average or mean difference will be zero. We can represent a distribution of hypothetical differences as shown in Fig. 1. The differences are represented along the horizontal line and the frequency of occurrence of each difference along the vertical line. The differences to the right of the zero point represent the performance of individuals who scored higher on the second sample of performance than on the first. Those to the left of the zero point represent performance of individuals who scored higher the first time than the second. The *mean* of the distribution (the sum of all the differences, divided by the number of individuals) is zero, since there is a positive difference (to the right) that matches each negative difference (to the left).

Now, how can we obtain a summary indication of the size of these differences for the whole group? Our natural inclination might be to use the average or mean difference as the summary, but this will not be satisfactory, since the mean will always be zero. Of course, in computing the mean difference, we could ignore the fact that some of the differences are positive and some are negative. This would, in fact, be a workable method, but the statistic so computed would suffer from certain mathematical limitations. Instead, it is most satisfactory to use the *standard deviation* of the distribution as our summary measure of the size of the differences.

The standard deviation, a commonly used statistic, amounts in this case to nothing more than the square root of the mean of the squared differences. Squaring the differences has the effect of making all the negative differences positive, and taking the square root returns the number to its original scale. In testing we have given this type of standard deviation (the standard deviation of the distribution of differences) a special name: the *standard error of measurement* (sometimes abbreviated to the *standard error*). In our example in Fig. 1, the standard deviation of the differences is five score units; therefore, we say that this test has a standard error of measurement of 5.

We are now faced with the question of how to attach some meaning to the standard error, and of how to use the information. It should be pointed out, first, that with this method we are not dealing directly with test scores but rather with differences between test scores. Large differences do not necessarily go with high test scores nor small differences with low test scores. Because of this, the standard error is not affected by the diversity of the group of individuals to any appreciable degree, as is the reliability coefficient. That is, within broad limits we would obtain about the same standard error for a test regardless of the type of group used to provide the reliability information. In this respect the standard error is a much safer measure of reliability to use. It does, however, suffer from the same limitations as the reliability coefficient in that it will vary depending on the methods used to obtain the two samples of behavior.

The standard error of measurement for a test gives us an estimate of the amount of error (in test score units) associated with the score an individual receives on the test. The outstanding advantage of using the standard error is that it permits us to make certain probability statements about an individual's "true score" (the score he would obtain if there were no inconsistencies in the measuring system), given the score he actually received. These probability statements can be made because of the characteristics of a "normal" distribution and of the standard deviation statistic. Although we shall not discuss these characteristics, we can indicate some of the outcomes.

We know, for example, that we shall be right about two out of three times if we conclude that a student's obtained score is within one standard error of his true score. Suppose that the standard error for a given test is five score points, and suppose that an individual receives a score of 135 on the test. The score of 135 is not completely accurate. It is only an estimate of the "true" score. We can nevertheless conclude, with about 68% confidence, that the person's true score lies somewhere within the range of 130–140 (between one standard error above and one standard error below the obtained score of 135). We can make more precise statements if we wish. For instance, there is about 95% confidence that the person's true score lies within two standard errors of this obtained score, i.e., within the band 125–145. Further, there is over 99% confidence that the true score lies within three standard errors of the obtained score, i.e., 120–150.

Obviously, for any given confidence level, the size of the standard error for a test influences the width of the band of scores within which the true score is assumed to fall. The greater the standard error, the wider the band. Conversely, for a given standard error, the width of the band varies depending on the degree of confidence we wish to have in making statements about an individual's true ability. The greater the desired confidence level, the wider the band. As for the degree of confidence desired, this depends, among other things, on the intended use of the test score information. In any case, a test can never tell us with absolute certainty what an individual's true achievement, aptitude, or ability is; it can reveal only the range within which the true score probably lies.

Sometimes we may find that the standard error for a test we are using is not available. However, it may be possible to determine the standard error if certain other information on reliability is available. The standard error can be calculated according to the formula:

$$\text{S.E.} = \text{S.D.} \sqrt{1 - r},$$

where S.E. is the standard error, S.D. is the standard deviation of the obtained test scores in the reliability sample, and r is the reliability coefficient.

Some Examples

To show how the concept of reliability applies in practical situations, we have presented in Table 2 some reliability information for a few commonly used tests of aptitude and achievement. The information was obtained from the test manuals and technical reports that are available from the publishers of the tests.

Column (1) in Table 2 lists the names of the tests and subtests. Most of these tests are batteries (groups of tests constituting a single package) that contain a number of different subtests; we have selected only two or three subtests within each battery for inclusion in the table. Column (2) lists the possible range of scores (total number of items) for each test. These scores, like all the scores in Table 2, are raw scores. That is, they represent directly the number of items answered correctly. Column (3) indicates the grade level for which the reliability data apply. Most of these batteries of tests provide reliability data for all grade levels for which the test is designed; again, we have been selective, choosing only a few grade levels as examples.

Table 2 Some reliability information for several tests*

(1) Test	(2) Range of possible scores	(3) Grade	(4) Reliability coefficient	(5) Standard error	(6) For an obtained score of	(7) Range of scores at 68% confidence level	(8) Range of scores at 95% confidence level
California Achievement Tests†							
Arithmetic Reasoning	0–40	3	0.86	2.7	35	32–38	30–40
Reading Comprehension	0–70	5	0.91	3.9	30	26–34	22–38
Mechanics of English	0–140	10	0.94	5.1	100	95–105	90–110
Differential Aptitude Tests‡							
Abstract Reasoning	0–50	9 (Girls)	0.87	3.7	38	34–42	31–45
Space Relations	0–100	12 (Boys)	0.94	6.4	40	34–46	27–53
School and College Ability Tests§							
Verbal	0–60	11	0.92	3.3	15	12–18	8–22
Quantitative	0–50	9	0.89	2.9	40	37–43	34–46
Sequential Tests of Educational Progress‖							
Social Studies	0–70	5	0.93	3.5	60	57–63	53–67
Mathematics	0–50	8	0.83	3.1	20	17–23	14–26
Reading	0–70	13	0.91	3.4	45	42–48	38–52
SRA Achievement Series#							
Arithmetic Concepts	0–20	4	0.78	2.0	8	6–10	4–12
Vocabulary	0–50	6	0.87	3.3	35	32–38	28–42
Charts	0–49	9	0.85	3.2	23	20–26	17–29
Stanford Achievement Test**							
Word Meaning	0–48	5	0.91	2.9	21	18–24	15–27
Arithmetic Reasoning	0–45	7	0.90	2.7	32	29–35	27–37
Science	0–48	9	0.87	2.6	15	12–18	10–20

* The information in this table is based on *raw* scores.
† Published by California Test Bureau
‡ Published by The Psychological Corporation
§ Published by Educational Testing Service
‖ Published by Educational Testing Service
Published by Science Research Associates, Inc.
** Published by Harcourt, Brace and World, Inc.

Column (4) shows the reliability coefficients. It should be pointed out that these are the *reported* reliability coefficients and they are not all of the same kind. Different methods have been used by different publishers to compute these co-efficients. For example, the coefficients for the Differential Aptitude Tests are computed by the corrected split-half method, whereas the coefficients for the School and College Ability Tests are computed using one of the Kuder-Richardson estimating formulas. Therefore, the data in Table 2 should not be used to draw comparisons between the various listed tests.

Column (5) shows the standard error of measurement for each test in raw score units. The last three columns show the applications of the standard errors to some examples of obtained raw scores: Column (6) lists some sample scores; column (7) shows the ranges of raw scores within which the true scores will lie at the 68% confidence level (two out of three times), and column (8) the ranges at the 95% confidence level. The ranges at the 68% confidence level were computed by adding and subtracting one standard error from the obtained score. (For convenience the standard errors were rounded to the nearest whole number.) The ranges at the 95% confidence level are obtained by adding and subtracting two standard errors (rounded) from the obtained score.

The table shows, for example, that the Reading test of the Sequential Tests of Educational Progress is a 70-item test, since it is possible to obtain raw scores anywhere from 0 to 70. The table further shows that for students in grade 13 the test has a reliability coefficient of 0.91 (high enough for interpretation of individual scores) and a raw-score standard error of 3.4 points. If we are interested in the test results of a grade-13 student who has obtained a raw score of 45 on the test (column 6), we know that we shall be correct about two out of three times in concluding that his true score lies within the interval 42–48, and correct 95 times out of 100 in concluding that his true score lies between 38 and 52. In the following section, we shall see how this reliability information can be used when we begin to interpret the test scores.

Before leaving the subject of reliability, let us emphasize once again that the accuracy of a measuring system can vary depending on the nature of the object being measured. A yardstick may be quite accurate in measuring a flat surface such as a table top, but quite inaccurate in measuring a curved surface such as the circumference of a storage tank (where a tape measure might be more appropriate). Similarly, a test may have one reliability when administered to eighth-grade boys in a rural school and a different reliability when administered to tenth-grade girls from an urban school. Hence, in evaluating and using reliability information for a test, one must be sure that this information is based on individuals who are similar to the ones with whom the test is to be used.

In summary, one point should be perfectly clear. Every test (as we have conceived of tests) contains a certain amount of inconsistency or error, and the test score is merely an estimate of the person's true ability. A person's obtained score is not an exact index of ability, but is, rather, a clue to the range of scores within which the true score lies. Test scores, then, should never be used as the sole basis for making important decisions about people. They should be used with other kinds of information and then only as approximate indicators of ability—not as infallible measures.

INTERPRETATION OF TEST SCORES

As we have indicated before, a test score is a numerical summary of how successfully a person has accomplished the tasks presented in a test. This numerical summary, which we usually call a raw score, has little meaning until it is referred to some standard of accomplishment, or *norm*.

A "norm," according to Webster, is "a set standard of development or achievement." In testing, however, we rarely have a norm as defined by Webster, for reasons outlined at the end of the last section. True, an administrative authority, whether it be a company president, a personnel manager, a school superintendent, or a college admissions officer, might conclude after examining the tasks in a test that unless a person's score is above some minimum score he will not be permitted to graduate, enroll in a college, get a scholarship, have a certain job, advance to the next grade, etc. In these situations the minimum test score *is* a norm in Webster's sense.

In general, however, a norm is any statistic that describes the performance of a group of persons on a test. The group of persons so described is the *reference group*. The norm gives us a means of making a comparison, and the reference group is the object of the comparison. Let us now consider some different kinds of norms and the nature of the comparisons each kind enables us to make.

Kinds of Norms

The *mean* (the average of the scores) is one type of norm, since it serves to describe in a summary way the test scores of all the persons in a reference group. This statistic is valuable because it possesses certain properties that make it amenable to mathematical manipulation. However, by far the most common statistics used in describing the reference group for purposes of comparison are those that reveal the proportion or percentage of the reference group having test scores above or below a given point.

The *median* score for a reference group is the score that divides the reference group in half. That is, 50% of the persons in the reference group had test scores below the median and 50% had test scores above the median. Thus if a person obtained a raw score of 153 on a test and the median raw score for the reference group was 140, that person's score was higher than the scores of at least one-half of the persons in the reference group—he is "in the upper half" of the reference group.

Quartiles permit us to make finer comparisons. They are the scores that divide the reference group into four equal parts. In the reference group one-fourth or 25% of the group have scores below the "lower quartile" and 75% have scores above it. Similarly, 75% of the reference group have scores below the "upper quartile" and

25% have scores above it. The "middle quartile" is the same as the median and represents the exact middle of the reference group. For example, suppose that a reference group has the following quartiles for some test:

Quartile	Raw score	% of reference group scoring below	% of reference group scoring above
Upper	191	75	25
Middle	140	50	50
Lower	98	25	75

If a person's test score is below 98, his score places him in the lowest quarter of the reference group, and at least 75% of the group had scores higher than his. A person with a score greater than 191 ranks within the highest quarter of the reference group, and at least 75% of the group had lower scores. A person whose score is between 98 and 140 ranks in the next-to-lowest quarter of the reference group, which means that at least 50% scored higher and at least 25% scored lower.

Quartile comparison, although more exact than comparison based on only the median, is still fairly gross, for we can compare persons only with given quarters of the reference group. *Deciles* (scores that divide the reference group into ten equal parts) enable us to make finer comparisons than do quartiles; however, the most useful and the most frequently encountered norm is the *percentile*. Percentiles, of course, are those scores that divide the reference group into 100 equal parts. A person whose score is at the 79th percentile, for example, performed better than 79% of the reference group and less well than 21% of the group. Each score on a given test has a *percentile rank* which indicates the proportion of the reference group that received lower scores.

In recent years there has been a trend toward using *percentile bands* rather than percentile ranks for interpreting test scores. Percentile bands represent an attempt to incorporate reliability information about a test into its norms. Recall from our discussion of reliability that an individual's test score should be considered as only an indication of the range of points within which his true score probably lies, and that the probable range may be calculated by adding one or more standard errors (depending on the level of confidence desired) above and below the obtained score. Percentile bands are easily derived from the probable ranges thus calculated. For most tests the bands are based on the range for one standard error (68% confidence level). We can see how this is done by examining again the information from Table 2 for the Reading test of the Sequential Tests of Educational Progress. We noted above that an obtained raw score of 45 has a raw score range of 42–48 at the 68% confidence level. From the data provided by the test publisher, the percentile ranks of the obtained score and of the scores at each end of the range can be determined. A raw score of 45 on this test has a percentile rank of 34 for grade-13 students. The score of our hypothetical student, then, was higher than the scores of about 34% of the grade-13 reference group, and lower than those of about 66% of the reference group. Raw scores of 42 and 48 have percentile ranks of 30 and 40, respectively. The percentile band for a raw score of 45, then, is 30–40. This means that we can be fairly certain (right two out of three times) that the student ranks somewhere between the 30th and 40th percentiles on this test. If we wish to have a higher degree of confidence in our conclusions, we could obtain the percentile band for the 95% confidence level. For this test it is 18–54; thus we will be right 95 times out of 100 if we conclude that the student ranks somewhere between the 18th and 54th percentiles.

This application of reliability information to the interpretation of test scores demonstrates rather forcefully the magnitude of error present in most test scores, and may tend to prevent us from placing too much reliance on test scores and from drawing unwarranted conclusions from them. In this connection it is interesting to note that the standard error of most "intelligence" tests is about 5 IQ points. This means that the true score of a person who obtains an IQ of 100 on a test is likely to lie anywhere between 90 and 110 (95% confidence level).

Norms and Reference Groups

Now let us look at norms in terms of the characteristics of the reference groups, for it is here that we must exercise the greatest caution. The nature of the object of a comparison influences considerably the conclusions that we might draw from the comparison. A gallon of water is a *small* quantity when compared with the quantity needed to fill a swimming pool; it is a *large* quantity when compared with the amount we might drink with our dinner. Similarly, if we compare a student's score on a chemistry achievement test with the scores of a group of students studying first-year chemistry in high school, the student may rank near the top of the group, whereas when we compare his score with the scores obtained on the same test by a group of graduate students majoring in chemistry, he may well rank at the bottom of the group. In other words, if we know nothing of the nature of the group with whom we are comparing the student, it is almost impossible to draw any conclusions about his ability in chemistry. The importance of knowing the characteristics of the reference group is thus evident.

In selecting a reference group for comparison two factors will be important: (1) what norms are available for different kinds of reference groups, and (2) how relevant each of the available reference groups is to the individual whose test performance is being evaluated.

The first factor in selecting a reference group is the availability of data on reference groups for the test in question. Sometimes we know exactly the kind of reference group that is needed for making a comparison but then discover that data on this kind of group have never been compiled for the test being used. It then becomes necessary to settle for a less-than-ideal reference group or to construct norms for the reference group ourselves.

Most test publishers attempt to provide useful norms for the tests that they publish and distribute. It is prohibitively expensive, however, to provide norms for more than a few kinds of reference groups; hence test publishers attempt to provide data on those reference groups that they hope will have widest applicability and greatest value. Especially for tests used extensively in schools and colleges, this has led to the development of so-called "national" norms. These are based on samples of students that purport to be representative of some "general" or "national" population of students. Both the representativeness of the sample and the utility of this kind of norm are open to serious question. Not only is it next to impossible to control a sample on all factors such as geographic region, size of school, type of school, socioeconomic level, sex, age, etc., so that the sample truly represents the population, but the sample, when obtained, will be unavoidably biased because not all schools will cooperate with a test publisher in conducting a norm study. Even if the sample could be made truly representative and were well defined, there would still be doubt as to the value of comparing a student's score on a test with the scores made by such a conglomerate group. We need only to think of the vast differences among schools in the United States, each one controlled by its own independent board of education, among different parts of the country, each with its own cultural values, and among industrial, farming, and suburban communities, each with its own schools reflecting its own needs and values, to be acutely aware of the hodgepodge nature of any "national" or "general" population sample. Comparing a student's score with the scores of this type of reference group usually leads to very limited conclusions.

Although "national" norms are less than adequate they are better than nothing. When a test is being used by a teacher or school for the first time or when a test is infrequently used, so that there is no opportunity for the test user to develop his own more useful local norms, comparisons with this general norms group can be somewhat useful. However, the test user should, in such cases, learn as much as possible about the characteristics of the "national" sample and the methods used to obtain it, for the "national" norms groups identified and used by various test publishers may differ widely in their characteristics.

As was implied above, norms which are custom-made for local situations provide the most useful kinds of comparisons. This is because data on reference groups that include students in the same or similar kinds of schools, students that have taken the same or similar kinds of courses, or students that have similar educational or vocational goals are usually to be obtained only at the local level. Many test publishers do try to provide various kinds of specialized norms; nevertheless, most of them recognize that their ability to provide useful normative information is indeed limited. Therefore, they attempt to provide certain special services to help the test user compile his own local norms. These services may range from helpful instructions on the preparation of local norms to computational services aimed at producing local norms for individual schools. It is suggested that the user of any test ask the publisher what specialized norms have been compiled for the test and what services for computing local norms are available.

The second factor—the relevance of the reference group—is dependent on the extent to which persons in the group resemble the individual whose test performance is being evaluated. For example, if we wish to evaluate the mathematical achievement of a twelfth-grade boy who has taken algebra and plane geometry at a large

Table 3

Description of reference group	Percentile rank of an SAT–M score of 600
1. A representative sample of all girls who are seniors in high school.*	96
2. A representative sample of all seniors in high school who later enter college.†	82
3. All students who enroll as freshmen in a small moderately selective liberal arts college.‡	55
4. All students who enroll as freshmen in a large highly selective private university.‡	19
5. All students who enroll as freshmen in a large technical institute (an extremely select group in terms of mathematical ability).‡	1

* *College Board Score Reports: A Guide for Counselors and Admissions Officers.* New York: College Entrance Examination Board, 1966.
† Dean W. Seibel, *Follow-Up Study of a National Sample of High School Seniors.* College Entrance Examination Board Research and Development Report (Statistical Report SR62–56). Princeton: Education Testing Service, 1962.
‡ *Manual of Freshman Class Profiles.* New York: College Entrance Examination Board, 1963.

urban school, it will not be very meaningful to compare his score with the scores of ninth-grade girls at private preparatory schools who have never taken mathematics courses beyond eighth-grade general mathematics. Characteristics such as sex, age, grade level, type of school attended, educational background, and geographic region should be carefully compared. The more closely the characteristics of the reference group match those of the individual, the more meaningful the comparison will be.

To demonstrate the rather striking difference that can be encountered in using different kinds of reference groups, we have listed in Table 3 the percentile ranks of a single score on the mathematical section of the College Board Scholastic Aptitude Test.

Each of the reference groups listed might be useful for guidance purposes. As we can see, however, the percentile ranks for a single score of 600 range from 1 to 96 with many intermediate points being represented. It seems evident that if we are to use comparisons with reference groups as a method of attaching meaning to a test score, it is vital that we select appropriate reference groups and know their characteristics.

Derived Scores

For some tests an attempt is made to give a score immediate meaning by incorporating a comparison with a reference group directly into the score that is reported for

Table 4

Derived score	Characteristic in terms of a reference group
Z-score	Mean of 0, standard deviation of 1
T-score	Mean of 50, standard deviation of 10
College Entrance Examination Board Score	Mean of 500, standard deviation of 100
Army General Classification Test Score	Mean of 100, standard deviation of 20

or obtained from a test. These scores are sometimes called *derived scores* or *standard scores*. Examples of derived scores, with the characteristics relating them to a reference group, are summarized in Table 4. Derived or standard scores with any given characteristics (mean and standard deviation) can be obtained provided we have the mean and standard deviation of scores obtained by some reference group. (This process is described in most introductory statistical texts.)

The important thing to remember in dealing with any derived or standard score is that again, its normative meaning is entirely dependent on the reference group used to establish the score scale. For example, the score scale of the College Board Scholastic Aptitude Test has a mean of 500. This scale was established for the group of students who took the SAT in April of 1941. For this reference group, the means for both the Verbal and Mathematical scores are 500—but the mean scores of any group *subsequently* taking the test are not necessarily 500. For example, there were means of 457 (Verbal) and 488 (Mathematical) for all students who took the SAT in March of 1957.

Grade equivalents and *age equivalents* are two types of derived scores that are frequently obtained from tests and deserve special mention. These types of scores are popular because, on the surface at least, they seem to be easily understood and used. Such is not the case, however.

Grade equivalents for a test are usually established by simultaneously administering the test to groups of students in consecutive grades. Once the median score for each grade has been obtained, a smooth curve is plotted to show the relationship between the grade levels and the median scores. In plotting the curve, each grade level is usually divided into tenths (corresponding, roughly, to months of the school year) in order to show, between the known medians, the probable medians for earlier and later portions of the school year than that during which the testing occurred. Thus in subsequent applications of the test, any score obtained may be matched against this continuous curve of medians for assignment of a grade equivalent. For example, suppose that a student obtains a score of 45, and that the grade-equivalent curve for the test in question shows 45 as the median score for students at the sixth month of the third grade. The score of 45 is said to have a grade equivalent of 3.6.

Some of the problems associated with establishing and interpreting grade equivalents for a test are as follows:

1) Since each grade level is divided into ten parts, there is the question of whether to consider the ten parts as representing ten school months (with no allowance made for growth over the summer months) or as representing nine school months with the remaining one part representing the three summer months. The assumption is either that there is no growth over the summer, or that the rate of growth is considerably less during the summer than during the school year. Such assumptions are questionable, especially in areas such as vocabulary, reading comprehension, or others that relate more to general mental maturation than to specific in-school instruction.

2) Grade equivalents assume a *smooth* and *continuous* rate of growth during the school months and over a range of school grades. This assumption is likely to be untenable in many instances, depending on the area of learning and the instructional program in particular schools. It seems to be especially questionable at the higher grade levels and in high school, where there is likely to be less continuity of instruction from grade to grade in a subject matter area.

3) The grade equivalents that are established through extrapolation (the upward and downward extensions of the line of relationship between known median test scores and grade levels) are likely to represent at best only educated guesses of what the relationship actually is. For some tests a large portion of the grade equivalent scale is established through extrapolation.

4) Because of their apparent simplicity and directness, grade equivalents are easily misunderstood. It is essential to keep in mind that a grade equivalent represents *median* performance at the given level, and that there is considerable overlap in performance from level to level. For example, if a student entering the sixth grade receives a grade equivalent of 7.0 it does not necessarily mean that he has already mastered the material that will be taught in the sixth grade. It more frequently means that he has done an exceptionally good job of mastering the material taught in the first five grades. To conclude on the basis of a grade-equivalent score that this student should be placed in the seventh grade is indefensible.

5) It is easy to forget that grade equivalents, like any derived scores, are based on comparisons with some reference group(s). Since this type of derived score assumes continuous and smooth growth over a period of years it seems especially necessary to be cognizant of the nature of the educational programs experienced by the pupils in the reference group and to weigh this factor heavily in deciding whether the reference group is relevant to one's own situation.

Age equivalents are similar to grade equivalents except that age level is substituted for grade level when determining the line of relationship between median performance and level. Most of the preceding discussion of grade equivalents also applies to age equivalents.

Intelligence quotients (or *mental age* scores, since IQ's are derived directly from mental age scores) represent another frequently misunderstood type of derived score. Aside from the question of what it is that intelligence tests really measure (which we mentioned earlier), there are problems of interpretation similar to those encountered with grade equivalents. Most intelligence tests provide us with nothing more than a meaningless number which summarizes the success on the tasks. The score is given meaning by comparing it with the *median* score obtained by some reference group of individuals of a specified age. This results in the mental age score. A mental age score of 8 years, 5 months is nothing more than the *median* performance on the test of a reference group of children who are 8 years, 5 months old. The points to remember are that (1) mental age scores represent *median* performance (there were many children in the reference group of this given age who did worse, many who did better), and (2) mental age scores relate to a specific reference group (as with any reference group, we must know something of its characteristics in order to judge the appropriateness of the comparison).

Points to Keep in Mind

The nature of norms and their relationship to reference groups leads to several considerations that are frequently sources of confusion or misuse. We should exercise caution when we work with the findings of group test scores.

1) *Always make certain that the norms table is based on exactly the same kind of score as the score to be interpreted.* On many tests it is possible to obtain more than one kind of score for a given individual's performance. The test user sometimes has a choice of obtaining a raw score, a scaled score, an age score, a grade score, an IQ score, or some other kind of derived score. If he obtains a scaled score of some sort and wishes to interpret it in terms of norms, he must make certain that the norms table he consults is based on exactly the same kind of scaled score— not one of the other kinds of scores that may be available for the test.

2) *Never attempt to compare the percentile ranks of two individuals unless you are sure the percentile ranks are based on the same reference group.* Consider, for example, a situation where two individuals have exactly the same test scores. One individual's score has a percentile rank of 90 when compared with reference group A; the other person's score has a percentile rank of 15 when compared with reference group B. Since they have exactly the same test score, it would obviously be foolhardy to conclude that the first individual has more ability (as measured by the test) than the second.

3) *When recording percentile ranks in any kind of permanent record, always include an identification of the reference group used.* We have seen that the percentile rank assigned to a score depends entirely on the reference group with which that score is compared (in our example a single score could have been assigned percentile ranks ranging from 1 to 96). Anyone looking at a permanent record and finding a percentile rank not identified as to reference group will have no meaningful information concerning the student's performance on the test.

4) *Do not attempt to find the average or mean test performance of a group by averaging the percentile ranks of the individual scores and converting the result to a score.* The average percentile rank for a group is not, in most instances, the same as the percentile rank of the average of the test scores (see below). If you want to know the group mean score, compute it using test scores, not percentile ranks.

5) *In order to determine the percentile rank of a group mean score use norms tables based on group means rather than norms tables based on scores of individuals.* It would be tempting but incorrect to obtain the percentile rank for the class mean score from the same norms table used for obtaining the percentile rank of an individual's score. The mean scores for several groups tend to cluster more closely together (be less divergent) than the individual scores which underlie these mean scores. Consequently, at the high end of the distribution the percentile rank accorded to a mean score will be *higher* than that of an identical individual score, and at the low end of the distribution it will be *lower* than that of an identical individual score. Near the center of the distribution there will be little difference between percentile ranks of individual scores and of mean scores.

TEST VALIDITY

Recall from earlier discussion that the validity of a test is its property of providing information which is useful in terms of the purposes for which the test was administered. This leads us to an important concept—namely, that the validity of a test varies, depending on the kind of information that the test user wants and on the situation in which the information is used. In other words, validity is not some pervasive, invariant characteristic of a test, but rather must be measured by standards specific to the particular set of circumstances in which the test is used. For example, a language test which measures the ability to read and write Spanish may be extremely valid for use in deciding which students should be placed in an advanced course in Spanish—the test measures behavior that is appropriate, and it successfully identifies those students having the necessary ability to do the advanced work. The same test, however, would hardly be valid for identifying students to be placed in an advanced mathematics course.

Any information that bears on the appropriateness of the behaviors measured (test content) or on the utility of the test results provides an indication of the test's validity. There are, however, several aspects from which to view its validity. Three of these are discussed below.

Content validity. Content validity (sometimes called "face validity") is, quite simply, the appropriateness or relevance of the kinds of behavior observed in the test as judged by a person familiar with the subject matter involved. A test is said to have a high content validity when, in someone's opinion, it contains items that seem to measure those abilities that the test publisher claims are being measured or that the test user desires to have measured. Thus a test of arithmetic skills containing items requiring the student to perform addition, subtraction, multiplication, and division would probably have a high degree of content validity. It should be emphasized here, however, that determination of content validity is based on subjective judgments or opinions. In attempting to obtain content validity, test publishers usually rely on the judgments of recognized subject matter experts in the particular area covered by the test. Perhaps, however, judgments which are equally appropriate can be made by the test user, since he knows more precisely what he wants to measure and is actually in the best position to make the judgment. As we emphasized in the earlier discussion of test content, this requires that he give close examination to each item in a test.

Concurrent validity. Concurrent validity is the relationship, expressed in terms of a correlation coefficient, between the results of the test in question and those yielded by another observation, already accepted as valid, of the same behavior. The other observation could consist of grades, an essay, or an interview, but is usually another test whose validity has been demonstrated through extensive use or research studies. The idea, of course, is that if one observation can be accepted as valid, then another observation is valid to the extent that it produces the same results. The term "concurrent" is used because both observations can be made at about the same time, whereas with predictive ability (see below) this is not the case.

Predictive validity. This is probably the most common type of validity information, since tests are so frequently used for predicting some future behavior. Predictive validity is the relationship, expressed as a correlation coefficient, between the test scores and a measure of subsequent behavior. This type of information is particularly important whenever a test is used as a selection device, e.g., to help decide which students should take an advanced course, which students should be permitted to enroll in a college, or which applicant should be hired for a particular job. Unlike concurrent validity, it takes considerable time to determine, since it requires administering the test, waiting until the behavior that was being predicted takes place, and finally, obtaining a criterion measure of this future performance—the student's degree of success in the advanced course, his grades in college, his supervisor's ratings of job success, etc.

A commonsense approach to test validity dictates that the following steps be observed in the selection and use of tests:

1) Make sure that you know *why* you are using the test and *how* the results are going to be used.

2) Examine the items and draw your own conclusions as to the appropriateness of the behaviors being observed for your own purpose in testing. Consider the opinions expressed by others as to the nature of the test content.

3) Examine any reported evidence of validity (concurrent, predictive, etc.) obtained in situations similar to the one in which you will be using the test.

4) If, in your opinion, it appears that a test is likely to accomplish what you want it to, try the test experimentally and assemble your own validity information. That is, try to determine how well the test accomplishes its purpose in your particular situation.

5) As long as you are using the test keep a constant check on its usefulness.

The reader might reasonably ask for some "rule of thumb" which could be easily applied in his own situation to determine whether a test has sufficient validity to warrant its initial or continued use. However, because test validity or usefulness depends on so many factors that are specific to the given circumstances, it is very difficult to make meaningful generalizations.

Thousands upon thousands of studies of test validity have been conducted and reported. Frequently, predictive or concurrent validity is established for tests in school or college settings by comparing test results with the criterion of grades which students earn. The validity coefficients obtained in this type of study (correlations between test scores and school grades) are usually in the range 0.30 to 0.60 although, of course, some studies report coefficients above and below this range. In a few instances validity coefficients have been reported which are nearly as high as the test reliability (upper limit of test validity). Studies of validity which utilize another test as the criterion measure tend to result in higher validity coefficients than studies using grades.

In order to provide the reader with some concrete examples we have presented in Table 5 some of the validity information reported by the publishers of several commonly used tests of scholastic aptitude and achievement. The tests used as examples are, in general, the same ones for which reliability information was given in Table 2.

Several things should be pointed out concerning the data in Table 5. First, the information on test validity is only a small part of the information provided by the publishers. For most tests a great deal of evidence on utility is available either from the publisher or from studies reported in the literature. Second, the reader should not attempt any comparison between the tests listed, merely on the basis of data in the table. Since the data for different tests are based on different studies and since different criteria and groups are involved, the coefficients are not comparable. That is, the fact that a validity coefficient for one test in the table is larger than the coefficient for another test is *not* evidence that the first test is better than the second. Third, the reader may have noticed that no validity information is presented for the Stanford Achievement Test (reliability data were presented in Table 2). This is because the writer was not able to locate validity data in the form of coefficients of concurrent or predictive validity. As the test manual states, "The validity of the Stanford Achievement Test is best thought of as the extent to which the content of the test constitutes a representative sample of the skills and knowledges which are goals of instruction. This *content*, or *curricular*, validity must be assessed through a careful analysis of the actual content of each subtest in relation to the objectives of instruction in the various fields."* The writer shares this view of test validity, with its emphasis on careful examination of the test content to determine whether the test will be useful. Predictive or concurrent validity coefficients are of limited

---

* *Stanford Achievement Test, Directions for Administering.* New York: Harcourt, Brace & World, 1964.

Table 5 Some validity information on several tests

Test	Number of cases	Sample description	Criterion	Validity coefficient
California Achievement Tests				
Arithmetic Reasoning	?—Three complete classes	3rd grade students	Non-Language Score on California Test of Mental Maturity	0.44
Reading Comprehension	?—Three complete classes	5th grade students	Language Score on California Test of Mental Maturity	0.71
Mechanics of English	?—Three complete classes	11th grade students	Language Score on California Test of Mental Maturity	0.63
Differential Aptitude Tests				
Abstract Reasoning	225	9th grade boys in four schools	Grades in mathematics	0.40
Space Relations	44	10th grade boys in one school	Grades in mechanical drawing	0.57
School and College Ability Tests				
Verbal	87	9th grade students in college preparatory curriculum in one school	Grades in English	0.78
Quantitative	155	9th grade students in general curriculum in one school	Grades in mathematics	0.59
Total	506	Entering freshmen in a state university	Grades at end of first quarter	0.55
Sequential Tests of Educational Progress				
Social Studies	271	7th grade students in one school	Grades in social studies	0.55
Mathematics	271	7th grade students in one school	Grades in arithmetic	0.65
Reading	271	7th grade students in one school	Average grades in all subjects	0.71
SRA Achievement Series				
Arithmetic	510	9th grade students	Score on Iowa Tests of Educational Development—Quantitative Thinking	0.73
Science	510	9th grade students	Score on Iowa Tests of Educational Development—Science Background	0.80

value to a test user unless they are based on the test user's own particular circumstances. The writer would, however, encourage test users to undertake their own studies of test utility, and then to rely heavily on the results in deciding whether to use or continue to use a given test.

Although, as we have said, it is not possible to provide rules of thumb for knowing when a test is "valid enough" for a given purpose, we might draw a very broad generalization. In using tests for predictive purposes, any information about a student that enables us to do a better job of predicting than merely "chance guessing" is useful. Depending on how precisely we are trying to predict, tests with validity coefficients as low as 0.30 may be useful.* The more precise we need to be in the prediction, the higher the coefficient we will need. For example, we could use a test of relatively low validity if we wished to predict merely whether a student would pass or fail a course, but not if we wished to predict the specific grade a student would earn in a course.

Most test publishers make considerable effort to ensure that their tests have content validity and most studies seem to show that tests used in educational settings have predictive or concurrent validity coefficients in the range 0.30 to 0.60. It seems justifiable to conclude from this that if "reasonable" judgment is exercised in the selection and use of a test, most standardized tests will have sufficient validity to make them useful, if imperfect, tools.

CHARACTERISTICS OF TESTS

We have noted that a test is nothing more than a system of observing and recording human behavior. Many different kinds of systems can be and have been devised. These systems differ in the kinds of tasks that are presented, the procedures which the individual follows in attempting the tasks, the structure of the situation in which tasks are done, the methods of observing the behavior, the methods of recording the behavior, the methods of summarizing success on the tasks, and the methods of devising the systems and the tasks. In this section we shall look at some of the characteristics of different kinds of aptitude and achievement tests.

Standardized Tests

While there is no uniform definition of a "standardized" test, the term is usually used when certain statistical data concerning the nature and use of the test have been obtained, and when the procedures for administering the test are set and are the same for each individual who takes it.

The statistical data which are obtained vary but usually include norms based on some defined population, data on the difficulty of the test items (to help judge the appropriate range of grade levels or ages of individuals with whom the test can be used), data on the amount of time required to complete the test (to help set appropriate time limits), and information on the test reliability.

---

* "Better Than Chance," Test Service Bulletin No. 45. New York: The Psychological Corporation.

The establishment of standard procedures for administering the test is quite important, for only on this basis can legitimate comparisons be made between scores. Therefore, an attempt is made to control everything concerning the test except the way in which the individual responds to the tasks. This one factor that is left free to vary, then, is the degree to which each individual taking the test is successful in accomplishing the tasks.

In order to exercise control over the testing situation so that comparisons of scores are possible, the procedures for administering and scoring standardized tests are usually written down in some detail and accompany the test in the form of a manual. Test manuals vary in the extent of detail they provide or control they exercise. Some leave nothing to the discretion of the examiner and provide not only step-by-step procedures but also word-for-word directions that are to be read to the examinee. Others provide only generalized directions and leave a considerable amount of the detail to the good judgment of the examiner.

Not enough can be said concerning the importance of following the standardized procedures for administering and scoring specific tests. To the extent that we fail to control the testing situation we reduce the reliability of the test. We also invalidate the meaning which we attach to the test scores by making the normative comparisons questionable. Even small and seemingly unimportant deviations from the set procedure may introduce error which will drastically curtail the utility of a test. Although we do not know the precise effect that many kinds of deviations from procedure have on test scores, it is certain that they can do nothing except introduce inconsistency, and this is to be avoided, if possible. (If a teacher is using a test only once, with one class of students, and if the only score comparisons he wishes to make are *within* that class of students, then standardization of procedures is not important, since all students in the class take the test under the same set of conditions at the same time.) The important thing to note is that the procedures for administering and scoring the test must be the same for obtaining all scores that are to be compared.

Individual and Group Tests

Most tests in use today are *group tests*. That is, they can be administered at the same time and in the same place to more than one individual, by one examiner. Sometimes, if large groups are being tested, a chief examiner will provide the verbal instructions and one or more assistants will distribute and collect test material. Of course, any test that can be administered to a group of examinees can also be administered to only one examinee. On the other hand, some tests *must* be administered to one person at a time. These *individual tests* usually require that the full attention of the examiner be given to the examinee for purposes of presenting the tasks and recording the resulting behavior. Sometimes the sequence of procedures must be varied, depending on the behavior elicited in response to the tasks. Or the administration may require audible communication between the examiner and the examinee, which would be distracting to others attempting to take or administer the test at the same time and in the same place. Most aptitude and achievement tests are group tests; however, some "intelligence" tests must be administered individually —for example, the Stanford-Binet Intelligence Scale,* the Wechsler Adult Intelligence Scale†, and the Wechsler Intelligence Scale for Children†.

Individual tests are, of course, more expensive and time-consuming to use than are group tests. They are, however, especially valuable and even necessary for use with young children who are not able to read or are not able to follow complicated (for them) procedures. In addition, individual tests have the advantage of allowing the examiner an opportunity for close observation of an individual. It is still an open question as to whether the one factor—individual administration—results in any better or more valid test scores than can be obtained from group administrations.

Objective and Essay Tests

Tests can also differ in the amount of subjective judgment required in scoring. Tests that require no more than clerical skill in scoring are known as *objective* tests. These tests usually contain tasks of the "multiple choice" variety, scored by simply counting the predetermined correct responses in order to obtain a summary of success. Subjective tests, on the other hand, contain "essay" or "free response" types of tasks and usually require that considerable subjective judgment be exercised in determining how successfully an examinee performs.

The differences between these two types of tests go beyond scoring procedures. Each has advantages and disadvantages that make them more or less appropriate and useful in different measurement settings. A great deal has been written (sometimes with considerable emotion) concerning the relative merits of each type. Although we do not intend to enter this controversy or to discuss the merits in detail, it does seem appropriate to summarize a few of the main points concerning each.

In the tasks on an objective test the examinee is required to select one appropriate response from among a limited number of alternative responses. The number of possible responses can vary from two (such as in a "true-false" type item) to any number (such as in "matching" type problems). Tasks with four or five possible responses seem to be the most efficient in terms of balancing the extent to which "guessing" plays a part and the time and space necessary to present and respond to the tasks. Since all the examinee needs to do is to read the problem or task and to select the appropriate response, a large number of multiple-choice tasks can be presented in a single test. This means that the test can provide an extensive sampling of knowledge from any field of study and therefore measure with considerable reliability.

In essay tests the examinee is given a topic or an idea and is asked to write a composition about the topic or a discussion of the idea. This requires that the examinee express himself in his own words and in so doing draw upon his own background of experiences and knowledge. This procedure is time-consuming, which usually means that only a few essays can be required in one test. The sampling of

---

* Published by Houghton Mifflin Company, Boston.
† Published by The Psychological Corporation, New York.

knowledge in any field of study is considerably less than with objective tests, and therefore the reliability of essay tests (from the task-sampling point of view) is lower.

Although it is true that essay tests are easier to construct than objective tests, care must be exercised in devising tasks for either type. In both cases the tasks should be presented so that there is *no doubt* in the examinee's mind as to what the task is. In essay tests only a few tasks or topics are required. These must be clearly defined and, while general enough to offer some leeway of response, specific enough that limits are set on the nature of the response. Otherwise, an exceptionally fluent examinee can often avoid discussing important points of which he is unsure. Furthermore, the scoring or grading of a group of essays based on an ill-defined topic is quite difficult, since the essays will probably cover different aspects of the topic and will vary greatly in length, points covered, and general approach. For example, an essay topic such as *"Explain why you think the United Nations has been a success or a failure"* sets almost no limits on student response and provides very few guidelines to help the student know what is wanted in the essay. The following version lends more structure to the topic and, while still allowing the student considerable flexibility, does set some limits on the nature and length of the response:

An important function of the United Nations is to help settle disputes between nations. Describe how one dispute was handled successfully, pointing out how the settlement illustrates a general strength of the United Nations. Describe also how one dispute was handled unsuccessfully, pointing out how this illustrates a general weakness of the United Nations. Your essay should be about 300–400 words in length (2 or 3 pages in long-hand).*

In objective tests many tasks must be devised. These must be constructed so that there is but one correct or appropriate response to the task and so that the other responses maintain some reasonableness as possible answers. Wording must be carefully checked to remove ambiguity and to assure that there is no clue which would "give away" the correct response.

It is a popular conception that objective tests can be used to measure only superficial skills such as recall of factual information or computational skill and that these tasks require little thought, less insight, and no understanding on the part of the examinee. Such is not the case, however. Multiple-choice questions can be devised that will measure the higher levels of thought processes, such as understanding principles, organizing ideas, interpreting materials, drawing inferences and conclusions, integrating knowledge, evaluating information, or interpreting graphs, charts, maps, and tables. Even verbal and language skills, once thought to be exclusively in the measurement domain of essay tests, can be effectively measured through multiple-choice tasks.

To demonstrate the level of reasoning ability that can be measured by objective techniques, the following examples are reproduced from the booklet *Multiple-Choice*

---

* *Making the Classroom Test: A Guide for Teachers.* Princeton: Educational Testing Service, 1959.

Questions: A Close Look.† These examples are drawn from a variety of subject-matter areas such as social studies, English, science, and mathematics. Several are of the type used in tests of general verbal ability and mathematical ability. A portion of the accompanying discussion has been reproduced with each item in order to indicate the higher-level thought processes that are probably necessary to solve the problems or respond to the tasks. Correct answers are indicated by asterisks.

Example 1

In the following questions you are asked to make inferences from the data which are given you on the map of the imaginary country, Serendip. The answers in most instances must be probabilities rather than certainties. The relative size of towns and cities is not shown. To assist you in the location of the places mentioned in the questions, the map is divided into squares lettered vertically from A to E and numbered horizontally from 1 to 5.

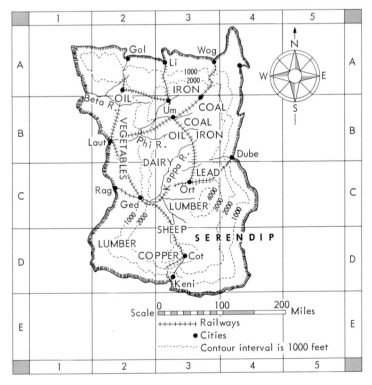

Which of the following cities would be the best location for a steel mill?

(A) Li	(3A)	*(B) Um	(3B)
(C) Cot	(3D)	(D) Dube	(4B)

---

† *Multiple-Choice Questions: A Close Look.* Princeton: Educational Testing Service, 1963. All material reproduced by permission of the publisher.

Discussion. A map of an imaginary country, such as that shown above, offers numerous possibilities for questions which measure important understandings. One could ask several questions requiring an understanding of the symbols used on the map. To determine student comprehension of the meaning of contour lines, for example, one might ask which railroad has the steepest grades to climb. Similar questions can be developed which require knowledge of the factors influencing population distribution, economic activities, and so on.

The question reproduced beneath the map requires knowledge of the natural resources used in producing steel and an awareness of the importance of transportation facilities in bringing these resources together. It was part of a general achievement test given to high school seniors.

Example 2

In the following question you are given a complete sentence to be rephrased according to the directions which follow it. You should rephrase the sentence mentally to save time, although you may make notes in your test book if you wish.

Below the sentence and its directions are listed words or phrases that may occur in your revised sentence. When you have thought out a good sentence, find in the choices A to E the word or entire phrase that is included in your revised sentence. The word or phrase you choose should be the most accurate and most nearly complete of all the choices given.

Although the directions may require you to change the relationship between parts of the sentence or to make slight changes in meaning in other ways, <u>make only those changes that the directions require;</u> that is, keep the meaning the same, or as nearly the same as the directions permit. If you think that more than one good sentence can be made according to the directions, select the sentence that is most exact, effective, and natural in phrasing and construction.

<u>Sentence:</u>   John, shy as he was of girls, still managed to marry one of the most desirable of them.

<u>Directions:</u>   Substitute <u>John's shyness</u> for <u>John, shy.</u>

Your rewritten sentence will contain which of the following?

(A) him being married to

(B) himself married to

*(C) him from marrying

(D) was himself married to

(E) him to have married

Discussion. In developing this type of question the committee of examiners reasoned that most good writers reconstruct sentences to change emphasis, to improve style, to avoid ambiguity, or to eliminate verbosity, and that the good student should be able to make such changes without involving himself in structural faults or grammatical errors. This type of question is designed, therefore, to assess the student's mastery of variety in sentence structure, his ability to make a change within a sentence so that it says what he intends to say more smoothly, concisely, and effectively than the original version may. Furthermore, the committee decided that to test this ability the question should require the student first to construct his new sentence mentally and then to compare his answer with a number of possible answers presented to him. As choices for answers they chose the kinds of expressions which students include in their own writing when they attempt to solve problems of sentence variety and become enmeshed in grammatical incongruities or verbal obscurities.

Example 3

In which of the following centuries was the piece of sculpture shown above most probably produced?
  (A) The fifth century B.C.
  (C) The sixteenth century A.D.
 *(E) The twentieth century A.D.
  (B) The fourteenth century A.D.
  (D) The eighteenth century A.D.

Discussion. This question on art appeared in a test of general background given to college seniors and graduate students. To answer the question, the student must apply his knowledge of the characteristics of various periods in the history of sculpture in order to place the statue within its proper period.

Example 4

Directions: Maintenant, vous allez entendre une conversation entre deux personnes. Attendez la deuxième réplique et ensuite choisissez la réponse qui convient le mieux.

"Henriette, passe-moi cette petite robe légère qui se trouve dans mon armoire à glace."
"Attends un moment; j'ai la bouche pleine de pâte dentifrice. J'aurai fini ma toilette dans un instant."

*(A) Ne te presse pas. Je la chercherai moi-même.
(B) Je l'ai trouvée tout à l'heure.
(C) Quand tu auras fini de te peigner.
(D) Oui, je l'ai repassée hier soir.

Discussion. The testing of a student's ability to understand a foreign language when spoken is a relatively recent development. Students listen to the recorded voices of native speakers in statements, short conversations, and short narrations. Suggested answers to questions based on the spoken material are printed in the students' test books. In listening comprehension tests the foreign language is used throughout, not only in the test questions but also in the directions to students. The sample question given here was part of a test designed for teachers of French in secondary schools. Paraphrased in English it reads:

Directions: Now you will hear a conversation between two people. Wait for the reply of the second speaker and then select the reply which is most appropriate.

Recorded conversation:
"Henrietta, hand me the little summer dress which is in my closet."
"Wait a moment; I have a mouth full of toothpaste. I shall be through in a minute."

Answer choices:
*(A) Don't hurry. I shall get it myself.
(B) I found it just a little while ago.
(C) When you are through doing your hair.
(D) Yes, I ironed it last night.

To select the right answer to this question, the student has to apply his knowledge of French grammar, vocabulary, and idiomatic expression, and his understanding of the French sound system. The students who have grasped the meaning of what they have heard will select (A) as the only choice that makes sense in the context.

Example 5

This question is based on the following situation:

A piece of mineral is placed in a bottle half-filled with a colorless liquid. A two-holed rubber stopper is then placed in the bottle. The system is then sealed by inserting a thermometer and connecting a glass tube to the stoppered bottle and a beaker of lime-water as shown in the accompanying diagram:

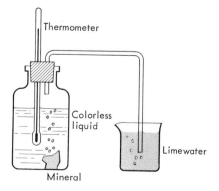

The following series of observations is recorded:

I. Observations during the first few minutes:
   1. Bubbles of a colorless gas rise to the top of the stoppered bottle from the mineral.
   2. Bubbles of colorless gas begin to come out of the glass tube and rise to the surface of the limewater.
   3. The limewater remains colorless throughout this period of time.
   4. The thermometer reads 20°C.

II. Observations at the end of thirty minutes:
   1. Bubbles of colorless gas continue to rise in the stoppered bottle.
   2. The piece of mineral has become noticeably smaller.
   3. There is no apparent change in the level of the colorless liquid in the bottle.
   4. The colorless liquid in the bottle remains colorless.
   5. The thermometer reads 24°C.
   6. The limewater is cloudy.

Which one of the following is the best explanation for the appearance of gas bubbles at the end of the tube in the beaker of limewater?

(A) The pressure exerted by the colorless liquid is greater than that exerted by the limewater.

*(B) The bubbles coming from the mineral cause an increased gas pressure in the stoppered bottle.

(C) The temperature increase at the end of thirty minutes causes an expansion of gas in the stoppered bottle.

(D) The decrease in the size of the piece of mineral causes reduced pressure in the stoppered bottle.

(E) The glass tube serves as a siphon for the flow of gas from the bottle to the beaker.

Discussion. This question is taken from a test designed to be used with a new curriculum in high school chemistry. The question is only one of a series based on the experimental situation described. Questions in the series are grouped in sequence relating to the situation in order to permit the student to think intensively in one setting for an extended period of time. The student is asked to deal with a realistic laboratory situation—one he has not yet encountered in the course at the time the test was given—and to employ scientific problem-solving ability in using the data given to answer the questions.

Example 6

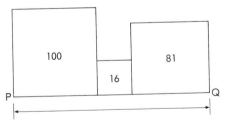

In the figure above, three squares with areas of 100, 16, and 81 lie side by side as shown. By how much must the area of the middle square be reduced in order that the total length PQ of the resulting three squares be 21?

(A) $\sqrt{2}$ (B) 2   (C) 4   (D) 8   *(E) 12

Discussion. This question is similar to those included in tests of mathematical aptitude for high school students. One of the problems surrounding such aptitude questions is the need to avoid familiar textbook material while at the same time restricting the content level to that which was mastered earlier in the junior high school—geometry and simple algebra. If this need is met, then the focus of the aptitude test is where it should be, namely on ingenuity in the solving of novel problems, rather than on the recall of memorized procedures. This ingenuity, or what some like to call "mathematical maturity," probably improves with taking good mathematics courses throughout high school but is not much affected by short-range cramming.

This question involves procedures which the student is extremely unlikely to have encountered in high school textbooks; the content knowledge required is certainly not beyond what is taught in the junior high school.

Example 7

The question below is followed by two statements, labeled (1) and (2), in which certain data are given. In this question you do not actually have to compute an answer, but rather you have to decide whether the data given in the statements are sufficient for answering the question. Using the data given in the statements plus your knowledge of mathematics and everyday facts (such as the number of days in July), you are to select answer

- (A) if statement (1) ALONE is sufficient but statement (2) alone is not sufficient to answer the question asked,
- (B) if statement (2) ALONE is sufficient but statement (1) alone is not sufficient to answer the question asked,
- (C) if both statements (1) and (2) TOGETHER are sufficient to answer the question asked, but NEITHER statement ALONE is sufficient,
- *(D) if EACH statement is sufficient by itself to answer the question asked,
- (E) if statements (1) and (2) TOGETHER are NOT sufficient to answer the question asked and additional data specific to the problem are needed.

If x is a whole number, is it a two-digit number?
- (1) x^2 is a three-digit number.
- (2) $10x$ is a three-digit number.

Discussion. One of the abilities which has been receiving increasing emphasis from the elementary school through college is that of judging the relevancy of data in the solution of problems in mathematics, science, and social studies. Measurement of the extent to which a student has developed this ability near the end of the high school years is believed to be important in predicting scholastic success in college. To accomplish such measurement the type of test question presented here has been designed, validated by research, and is now in use in the College Entrance Examination Board's Scholastic Aptitude Test. This type of question is used in arithmetic, algebra, and geometry. It shifts the emphasis from rote, manipulative skills to higher level judgments and reasoning.

This question shows the very great versatility of this type, for it requires little factual knowledge and the simplest aspects of elementary algebra, but does require a considerable degree of numerical judgment.

The examples just presented should dispel the notion that objective tests are inadequate for measurement of thought and reasoning. However, essay tests can also be used to measure higher-level reasoning processes, and in addition, they provide the most direct way to observe an examinee's ability to write a composition *in his own words*. To the extent that this is valuable behavior to observe, the essay test provides a means of observing it while the objective test does not.

The last essay-objective comparison we shall make (and perhaps the most important) concerns reliability. As we pointed out quite early in this chapter, objective tests can be scored with a high degree of accuracy or consistency, whereas essay or free-response tasks cannot usually be scored with consistency. Suppose, for example, that we are using an essay test as a measure of composition ability. Scorers might look for any of the following characteristics: development of ideas, organization, style, flavor, wording and phrasing, grammar, sentence structure, spelling, neatness, handwriting, punctuation. Depending on what is observed and how important it is considered, different scorers will arrive at different evaluations of the essay. Needless to say, this often introduces considerable inconsistency into the measuring system and results in decreased reliability.

It might be suggested that the problem of inconsistency in scoring would not exist if a single examiner scored the different performances—for example, if a teacher used an essay test with his class and then scored all the papers himself. Numerous studies have revealed, however, that there is considerable variation even in a single individual's evaluations of an essay paper over a period of time. On the whole, this variation is nearly as great as the variation among different scorers.

It is possible, at the cost of considerable time and effort, to develop highly objective procedures for scoring essay tests. However, this requires preliminary training of scorers in order to obtain agreement as to the behaviors to be observed and the relative importance of each, and in most situations it is not economically feasible to conduct such preliminary training activities unless a sizable number of essay tests are to be scored at one time.

Commercial and Locally Prepared Tests

Many tests are informally constructed by individual teachers, research workers, or others, for rather limited purposes and for use in specific local situations. These tests are not made widely available and are usually used only by those who have constructed them. We might call them "locally constructed" tests or "teacher-made" tests, since it is probable that the great majority of them are used in class-room settings.

Other tests, however, come into being through the efforts of organizations that have need of tests for use on large-scale bases or that produce them as marketable products. These organizations may be commercial test publishers, nonprofit educational organizations, or state and national governmental agencies. Tests constructed under these auspices do not usually meet local testing needs as directly as the teacher-made tests. They are produced for relatively widespread use, and may have objectives that are either too specialized or too general for local utility. On the other hand, since the resources of large organizations are behind these tests they are usually produced according to rather formal procedures, and a great deal of time, effort, and money is devoted to improving the quality and utility of the tests. A teacher who is constructing a test can attempt, at least, to approximate the statistical and research procedures which large organizations use in test construction; nevertheless, it is a difficult undertaking for a single individual. Often the incentive to spend the necessary time and effort is not there. Therefore, if appropriate (in terms of test objectives) commercially available tests can be located it is usually advantageous to use them in local situations rather than to attempt local construction.

The number of different teacher-made tests is legion and they come in all varieties. The reader who wishes to find out about constructing his own tests will have no difficulty in locating books on the subject. Similarly, the number and variety of tests produced for large-scale consumption is considerable, and hence again, we will not attempt to describe them in any detail—especially since many of these tests are produced for use with rather specific populations where specialized selection or certification is the aim, so that they are of little general interest. Our attention will, instead, be focused on the tests that are prepared by test publishers and marketed by them for use in local situations. We shall refer to these as "commercial" tests.

When a commercial test is contemplated for use in a local situation, great care must be taken to examine the test's objectives and compare these with the local testing objectives. As we pointed out earlier in this chapter, the name of a test is not a sufficient guide for judging it to be an appropriate tool for evaluation in a local situation. A careful examination of the items in a test is necessary in order to judge its appropriateness.

Most published commercial tests are standardized and objective. For the most part, too, they are aptitude and achievement measures and are used in educational settings. A relatively small number are personality scales, interest inventories, manual skills tests, and the like. Altogether there are over 2000 currently available commercial tests, published or distributed by literally hundreds of organizations. Therefore, although the problems associated with the selection of appropriate tests for use in specific local situations are indeed great, an even more basic problem faces the novice in the field—that of locating information about these many tests. Without this information the problem of selecting appropriate tests becomes academic.

SOURCES OF INFORMATION ABOUT COMMERCIAL TESTS

The most comprehensive reference books on published tests are the *Mental Measurements Yearbooks,* compiled by Oscar K. Buros and published periodically since the 1930's. Nearly every available standardized test in the English language has been categorized and listed in these volumes. In addition to the test title, the *Yearbooks* give descriptions of the groups for which the test is intended, date of publication, types of resulting scores, methods of scoring, forms available, cost (at time of *Yearbook* publication), administration time required, author, and publisher.

To assist test users in evaluating the technical qualities of standardized tests, the *Yearbooks* present one or more critical reviews of each listed test. These reviews, solicited by the editor of the *Yearbooks* from recognized practicing experts in the field of measurement or in subject matter fields, are of considerable value. It should be remembered, however, that each review represents one person's judgment concerning the test. As the editor has pointed out, "Despite our best efforts to insure fairness and balance of opinion, we have undoubtedly published some reviews which lacked fairness because they were either too harsh or too lenient."*

Tests in Print, also edited by Buros, is published as a companion to the *Year-books*. It provides only the factual information about the tests; i.e., it does not contain the critical reviews. However, cross references are provided which enable the test user to locate pertinent reviews in various editions of the *Yearbooks*.

The test publishers themselves constitute a second major source of information about commercial tests. However, there is wide variation in the amount of descriptive and technical information provided and the ways in which it is provided, and it is relatively easy for a test to be misrepresented and misused. Therefore, several professional organizations that are concerned with testing have jointly recommended standards for describing tests. These standards are set forth in a booklet, *Standards for Educational and Psychological Tests and Manuals,* prepared by a joint committee of the American Psychological Association, the American Educational Research Association, and the National Council on Measurement in Education. The purpose of this booklet is to encourage test publishers to provide sufficient information about tests to enable qualified users to make sound judgments regarding the usefulness and interpretation of the tests. Most test publishers attempt to adhere to these recommendations. Some succeed more than others.

Test catalogs are provided free of charge by the major test publishers (see Appendix A). The catalogs vary in the amount of detailed information which they contain. Usually they provide a brief description of each test, an indication of the groups with which the publisher feels it is appropriate to use the test, information on ordering the test (prices, qualifications of purchasers, etc.), and descriptions of services (scoring, reporting, and interpreting) that may be available with the test.

For most tests, the publisher will also make available (usually at a small cost) a specimen set of the test. As with catalogs, specimen sets vary as to their contents. Most will include: a sample copy of the test (perhaps only one form if several are available); a sample answer sheet (if separate answer sheets are used); a manual, usually containing a description of the nature and use of the test, directions for administering the test, interpretative data, relevant research data which the publisher has collected (reliability studies, reports of the relationships between the test scores and various criteria, statistical descriptions of the standardization or norms populations, etc.); and any other material that is intended for use with the test. Specimen sets represent probably the most valuable and useful source of informa-

---

* Oscar K. Buros (ed.), *The Fifth Mental Measurements Yearbook.* Highland Park, N.J.: The Gryphon Press, 1959, p. xxii.

tion on any test, since they not only provide for direct examination of the materials but also permit the test user to make detailed analyses of the items in the test.

It should be noted at this point that most test publishers have placed restrictions on the sale of specimen sets and test copies. The values of using commercial tests could be seriously impaired if the tests were to fall into the hands of students or others who may be taking the tests. Moreover, the administration of some tests requires professional knowledge and training, and a great deal of harm can be done through improper use. In such cases, the purchaser must possess certain qualifications to obtain the tests. Most publishers attempt to adhere to the ethical standards for distribution of tests that have been suggested by the Committee on Ethical Standards of the American Psychological Association, and that were reported in the *American Psychologist* (November, 1950). The committee suggests that distribution be regulated in accordance with classification of tests by levels:

Level A: Tests or aids which can be adequately administered, scored, and interpreted with the aid of the manual and a general orientation to the kind of organization in which one is working.

Level B: Tests or aids which require some technical knowledge of test construction and use, and of supporting psychological and educational subjects such as statistics, individual differences, the psychology of adjustment, personnel psychology, and guidance.

Level C: Tests and aids which require substantial understanding of testing and supporting psychological subjects together with supervised experience in the use of these devices.

Given the existence of restrictions on distribution of most commercial tests, it is usually a good idea to examine the publisher's catalog for conditions of purchase before attempting to place an order for any test.

If the information needed about a specific test is not contained in the catalog, specimen set, or one of the reference books noted above, it may be possible to obtain the information by writing to the publisher or contacting the publisher's area representative. Most publishers welcome inquiries about their tests and will make every effort to supply the requested information if it is available. The area representative of a publisher can be a fruitful and convenient source of information about specific tests, and he can often provide helpful advice concerning their use. Test catalogs provide listings of area, regional, or local representatives, and arrangements can often be made for personal contact with these representatives.

To provide the reader with both an indication of the scope of available educational tests and some readily available information about a number of tests, we have assembled in Appendix B an annotated listing of many commonly used tests, testing programs, and test batteries.* Several points should be made concerning

---

* The writer is indebted to staff members of the Evaluation and Advisory Service of Educational Testing Service for compiling, classifying, and annotating the list of tests in Appendix B.

this listing:

1) The tests listed represent only a small fraction of the currently available tests. They do, however, account for a large percentage of the millions of tests administered in the United States each year. The reader is referred to the *Mental Measurements Yearbooks* and *Tests in Print* for more comprehensive listings.

2) The information given for each entry has been abstracted from the most recent publications and catalogs of the various test publishers and program sponsors.

3) The entries have been classified under three separate headings: National Testing Programs, General Ability Tests (including "intelligence tests"), and Achievement Test Batteries. Although no test is included in more than one category, there are many instances where, for example, a national testing program will include tests of both general ability and achievement.

4) Since it would be impractical to list all the available achievement tests covering a myriad of subject matter areas, we have limited achievement test coverage to the major achievement test batteries, which contain subtests in specific subject matter areas.

REFERENCES

Anastasi, Anne, *Psychological Testing.* New York: Macmillan, 1961

Anastasi, Anne (ed.), *Testing Problems in Perspective.* Washington, D.C.: American Council on Education, 1966

"Aptitude, Intelligence, and Achievement," Test Service Bulletin No. 51, December 1956. New York: The Psychological Corporation, 1956

"Better Than Chance," Test Service Bulletin No. 45, May 1958. New York: The Psychological Corporation, 1958

Bloom, B. S. (ed.), *Taxonomy of Educational Objectives: The Classification of Educational Goals. Handbook I: Cognitive Domain.* New York: Longmans, Green, 1956

Buros, O. K. (ed.), *The Fifth Mental Measurements Yearbook.* Highland Park, N.J.: The Gryphon Press, 1959

Buros, O. K. (ed.), *Tests in Print.* Highland Park, N.J.: The Gryphon Press, 1961

Buros, O. K. (ed.), *The Sixth Mental Measurements Yearbook.* Highland Park, N.J.: The Gryphon Press, 1965

Chase, C. I., and H. G. Ludlow, *Readings in Educational and Psychological Measurement.* Boston: Houghton Mifflin, 1966

Chauncey, H., and J. E. Dobbin, *Testing: Its Place in Education Today.* New York: Harper and Row, 1963

Cronbach, L. J., *Essentials of Psychological Testing.* New York: Harper, 1960

Dressel, P., and C. Nelson, *Questions and Problems in Science.* Princeton: Educational Testing Service, 1956

Ebel, R. L., *Measuring Educational Achievement.* Englewood Cliffs, N.J.: Prentice-Hall, 1965

Flynn, J. T., and H. Garber (eds.), *Assessing Behavior: Readings in Educational and Psychological Measurement*. Reading, Mass.: Addison-Wesley, 1967

French, W., *et al., Behavioral Goals of General Education in High School*. New York: Russell Sage Foundation, 1957

Guilford, J. P., *Psychometric Methods*. New York: McGraw-Hill, 1954

Gulliksen, H., *Theory of Mental Tests*. New York: Wiley, 1950

"How Accurate is a Test Score?," Test Service Bulletin No. 50, June 1956. New York: The Psychological Corporation, 1956

Kearney, N. C., *Elementary School Objectives*. New York: Russell Sage Foundation, 1957

Krathwohl, D. R., B. S. Bloom, and B. B. Masia, *Taxonomy of Educational Objectives: The Classification of Educational Goals. Handbook II: Affective Domain*. New York: David McKay, 1964

Lindquist, E. F. (ed.), *Educational Measurement*. Washington, D.C.: American Council on Education, 1951

Locating Information on Educational Measurement: Sources and References. Princeton: Educational Testing Service, 1965

Making the Classroom Test: A Guide for Teachers. Princeton: Educational Testing Service, 1959

"Methods of Expressing Test Scores," Test Service Bulletin No. 48, January 1955. New York: The Psychological Corporation, 1955

Multiple-Choice Questions: A Close Look. Princeton: Educational Testing Service, 1963

Noll, V. H., *Introduction to Educational Measurement*. Boston: Houghton Mifflin, 1965

"Norms Must Be Relevant," Test Service Bulletin No. 39, May 1950. New York: The Psychological Corporation, 1950

Selecting an Achievement Test: Principles and Procedures. Princeton: Educational Testing Service, 1958

Short-Cut Statistics for Teacher-Made Tests. Princeton: Educational Testing Service, 1960

Standards for Educational and Psychological Tests and Manuals. Washington, D.C.: American Psychological Association, 1966

Thorndike, R. L., and Elizabeth Hagen, *Measurement and Evaluation in Psychology and Education*. New York: John Wiley & Sons, 1961

Wood, Dorothy A., *Test Construction: Development and Interpretation of Achievement Tests*. Columbus, O.: C. E. Merrill, 1960

APPENDIX A: SOURCES OF CATALOGS

Listed below are the names and addresses of publishers in the United States who issue test catalogs.

American Guidance Service, Inc., Publishers' Building, Circle Pines, Minn. 55014

The Bobbs-Merrill Company, Inc., 4300 West 62nd Street, Indianapolis, Ind. 46206

Bureau of Educational Measurements, Kansas State Teachers College, Emporia, Kans. 66801

Bureau of Educational Research and Service, State University of Iowa, Iowa City, Ia. 52240

California Test Bureau, Del Monte Research Park, Monterey, Calif. 93940

Center for Psychological Service, 1835 Eye Street, N.W., Washington, D.C. 20006

Committee on Diagnostic Reading Tests, Inc., Mountain Home, N.C. 28758

Consulting Psychologists Press, Inc., 577 College Avenue, Palo Alto, Calif. 94306

Cooperative Test Division, Educational Testing Service, Princeton, N.J. 08540

Harcourt, Brace & World, Inc., 757 Third Avenue, New York, N.Y. 10017

Houghton Mifflin Company, 110 Tremont Street, Boston, Mass. 02107

Institute for Personality and Ability Testing, 1602 Coronado Drive, Champaign, Ill. 61822

Martin M. Bruce, 340 Oxford Road, New Rochelle, N.Y. 10804

Personnel Press, Inc., 20 Nassau Street, Princeton, N.J. 08540

Personnel Research Institute, Western Reserve University, Cleveland, O. 44106

The Psychological Corporation, 304 East 45th Street, New York, N.Y. 10017

Psychometric Affiliates, 1743 Monterey Avenue, Chicago, Ill. 60643

Scholastic Testing Service, Inc., 480 Meyer Road, Bensenville, Ill. 60106

Science Research Associates, Inc., 259 East Erie Street, Chicago, Ill. 60611

Sheridan Psychological Services, Inc., P. O. Box 837, Beverly Hills, Calif. 90213

C. H. Stoelting Company, 424 North Homan Avenue, Chicago, Ill. 60624

Teachers College Press, Teachers College, Columbia University, New York, N.Y. 10027

Western Psychological Services, Box 775, Beverly Hills, Calif. 90213

APPENDIX B: A SELECTED LIST OF STANDARDIZED TESTS

National Testing Programs

American College Testing Program. P.O. Box 168, Iowa City, Ia. *Level:* Grade 12.

These tests are required for admission to a number of colleges in the United States. Students register to take the examinations on selected administration dates at testing centers. The tests include English, Mathematics, Social Studies Reading, and Natural Sciences Reading. A total score is also obtained.

College Entrance Examination Board Admissions Testing Program. College Entrance Examination Board, 475 Riverside Drive, New York, N.Y. *Level:* Grade 12.

These tests are required for admission to a number of colleges in the United States. Included are the Scholastic Aptitude Test (Verbal and Mathematical), and Achievement Tests in American History and Social Studies, European History and World Cultures, Biology, Chemistry, English Composition, French, German, Latin, Mathematics, Physics, Spanish, Greek, Hebrew, Italian, Russian. In addition, a Writing Sample, and Listening Comprehension Tests in French, German, Italian, Russian, and Spanish are available. The tests are administered on selected dates at testing centers.*

College Board Advanced Placement Examinations. College Entrance Examination Board, 475 Riverside Drive, New York, N.Y. *Level:* Grade 12.

These tests are administered to able students who have done college-level work in secondary school and who wish to demonstrate their readiness for courses more advanced than those usually studied in the freshman year of college. They are used primarily for academic placement and guidance purposes and are administered on selected dates at established centers. The tests include: American History, Biology, Chemistry, English, European History. French, German, Latin, Mathematics, Physics, and Spanish. Also available are Listening Comprehension Tests in French, German, and Spanish.*

College Placement Tests. College Entrance Examination Board, 475 Riverside Drive, New York, N.Y. *Level:* Grade 13.

Through this program, the College Board makes available, on a rental basis, retired forms of its Achievement Tests for local administration by colleges. The tests may be administered only to enrolled students, on any date suitable to the college, and are used primarily for placement and guidance purposes. The following examinations are available: Biology, Chemistry, English Composition, Intermediate Mathematics, Advanced Mathematics, Physics, Spatial Relations. The tests also include Language Reading Tests in French, German, Greek, Hebrew, Italian, Latin, Russian, and Spanish. In addition, Listening Comprehension Tests are available in French, German, Italian, Russian, and Spanish.*

---

* The testing program is administered for the sponsoring organization by Educational Testing Service.

College-Level Examination Program. College Entrance Examination Board, 475 Riverside Drive, New York, N.Y. *Level:* Grades 13–14.

The tests included in this program are designed to measure undergraduate achievement in the liberal arts. The program consists of two groups of tests. The General Examinations are comprehensive measures of achievement in five basic areas; the Subject Examinations are tests in specific subjects commonly taught in the first two years of college. The Subject Examinations, which include optional essay sections, are designed for awarding credit by examination as well as for end-of-course testing. Colleges administer the examinations on dates convenient for them. General Examinations include the following tests: English Composition, Humanities, Mathematics, Natural Sciences, Social Sciences. The following Subject Examinations are currently available: Analysis and Interpretation of Literature, General Chemistry, Introductory Economics, Introductory Calculus, Tests and Measurements, Western Civilization.*

Doppelt Mathematical Reasoning Test. The Psychological Corporation, 304 East 45th Street, New York, N.Y. *Level:* Grade 16.

In educational situations, this high-level measure of numerical reasoning ability is used to help in the selection of graduate students. The test is administered at licensed testing centers which have contracted to examine seniors and college graduates who are required to take the test. It is often used in conjunction with the Miller Analogies Test to obtain measures of verbal and quantitative ability. Scores are reported to graduate admissions officers and faculty advisors.

General Aptitude Test Battery. United States Employment Service, Washington, D.C. *Level:* See comments below.

The GATB was developed for use with older adolescents and adults who are in need of vocational counseling. The revised battery consists of 12 tests as follows: Tool Matching, Computation, Arithmetic Reasoning, Mark-Making, Pegboard (two scores), Name Comparison, Three-Dimensional Space, Vocabulary, Form Matching, Finger Dexterity Board (two scores). The scores on these 12 tests are combined to yield nine additional aptitude scores as follows: Intelligence, Numerical Aptitude, Form Perception, Motor Coordination, Manual Dexterity, Verbal Aptitude, Spatial Aptitude, Clerical Perception, Finger Dexterity. The aptitude scores are used to predict performance in a number of occupational fields. Local United States Employment Service offices are responsible for the test administration.

Graduate Record Examinations: Institutional Testing Program. Educational Testing Service, Princeton, N.J. *Level:* Grades 13–16.

This program is offered to colleges for use in evaluating student performance at various levels. The tests are made available to colleges on a temporary loan basis

---

*The testing program is administered for the sponsoring organization by Educational Testing Service.

for administration to complete groups of enrolled students on dates the colleges select. The tests available in the program are of three different kinds. The Aptitude Test yields two scores, Verbal and Quantitative. The Advanced Tests are available in 22 different subject matter areas. The Area Tests yield three scores—Humanities, Natural Science, and Social Science.

Graduate Record Examinations: National Program for Graduate School Selection. Educational Testing Service, Princeton, N.J. *Level:* Grade 16.

This program is designed to assist graduate school admissions officers in evaluating an applicant's fitness for graduate study. Scores indicate general scholastic ability and thoroughness of comprehension in specific fields. The tests are administered on selected dates at established centers. Ordinarily, the graduate school indicates which tests the applicant should take. The Aptitude Test yields Verbal and Quantitative scores. The Advanced Tests are available in 21 different subject matter areas.

Miller Analogies Test. The Psychological Corporation, 304 East 45th Street, New York, N.Y. *Level:* Grade 16.

This is a test of verbal reasoning ability for use in the admission of students to graduate school. The test is administered under the same conditions as the Doppelt Mathematical Reasoning Test and may be used in conjunction with that test to obtain measures of both verbal and mathematical ability. The publisher licenses testing centers, provides restricted test copies for use at these centers, and maintains a central registry of examinees and test scores.

National Merit Scholarship Qualifying Test. National Merit Scholarship Corporation, 990 Grove Street, Evanston, Ill. *Level:* Grades 11–12.

This program is intended primarily for students who hope to qualify for one of the Merit Scholarships. Secondary schools that wish to participate register their students with Science Research Associates, Chicago, Ill. The test provides scores in English Usage, Mathematics Usage, Social Studies Reading, Natural Sciences Reading, and Word Usage.

National Teacher Examinations. Educational Testing Service, Princeton, N.J. *Level:* Advanced college and professional level.

This testing program is designed to assess prospective teachers' preparation for elementary and secondary school teaching. The test results are used by colleges for evaluative and placement purposes and may be used by school districts in the selection of teachers or by states as a factor in teacher certification. The tests are administered on selected dates at established testing centers. The Common Examinations include the following tests: Psychological Foundations of Education; Societal Foundations of Education; Principles and Practices; Science and Mathematics; Social Studies, Literature, and the Fine Arts; Written English Expression. Teaching Area Examinations are also available in 13 different fields.

Preliminary Scholastic Aptitude Test. College Entrance Examination Board, 475 Riverside Drive, New York, N.Y. *Level:* Grades 11–12.

This test is designed to measure the scholastic ability of college-bound secondary school students, and is used chiefly in the guidance of high school juniors and seniors. It yields Verbal and Mathematical scores. Schools register their students and administer the test each year in October.*

Secondary School Admission Test Program. Secondary School Admission Test Board, Inc., % Loomis School, Windsor, Conn. *Level:* Grades 6–11.

The tests are required by a number of independent secondary schools and are used to assist in the selection of students for admission to grades seven through twelve. Included are a general ability tests and a reading comprehension test.*

Teacher Education Examination Program. Educational Testing Service, Princeton, N.J. *Level:* Grades 15–16.

This program consists of two groups of tests: the General Professional Examinations, designed to measure general knowledge and abilities considered essential for all prospective teachers, and the Teaching Field Tests, designed to be used as an aid in evaluating competence for teaching in specific fields. Institutions offering a program of teacher education may administer these examinations on any date suitable to them. The General Professional Examinations consist of tests in: Child Development and Educational Psychology; Foundations of Education; Guidance and Measurement; Instructional Methods; English; General Culture Part I (History, Literature, and Fine Arts); and General Culture Part II (Mathematics and Science). Teaching Field Tests are available in 13 different areas.

Test of English as a Foreign Language. College Entrance Examination Board, 475 Riverside Drive, New York, N.Y. *Level:* See comments below.

This testing program is designed to measure the English proficiency of foreign students who apply for or are assigned to education or training in countries where English is the common language. The test is administered at centers throughout the world at selected times during the year. The five subtests in the battery are: Auditory Comprehension, Reading Comprehension, Structure, Writing, Vocabulary.*

Tests of General Ability

Academic Promise Tests. The Psychological Corporation, 304 East 45th Street, New York, N.Y. *Level:* Grades 6–9. *Time:* 90 min.

The battery measures four aspects of mental ability: Verbal, Numerical, Abstract Reasoning, and Language Usage. Each test yields a separate score, and the battery provides two combination scores (Verbal and Non-Verbal) plus a Total Score. Percentile band norms for grades 6–9 are provided.

---

*The testing program is administered for the sponsoring organization by Educational Testing Service.

California Test of Mental Maturity. California Test Bureau, Del Monte Research Park, Monterey, Calif. *Level:* Kindergarten–grade 16 and adults. *Time:* Approx. 1 hr. 20 min.

The test provides scores on Language, Non-Language, and Total Test. Mental age scores and IQ's may be obtained.

College Qualification Tests. The Psychological Corporation, 304 East 45th Street, New York, N.Y. *Level:* Grades 11–13. *Time:* 1 hr. 20 min.

The test consists of three subtests, Verbal, Numerical, and Information. The Information subtest includes scores on Science Information, Social Studies Information and Total. Norms are given for freshmen at state universities, private colleges, southern universities, junior colleges, and for six different degree programs.

Cooperative Academic Ability Test. Educational Testing Service, Cooperative Test Division, Princeton, N.J.. *Level:* Grade 12. *Time:* Approx. 40 min.

The test is designed for use with students of superior ability. It yields a Verbal Score, a Mathematical Score, and a Total Score.

Differential Aptitude Tests. The Psychological Corporation, 304 East 45th Street, New York, N.Y. *Level:* Grades 8–12 and adult. *Time:* Approx. 3 hr.

The battery consists of eight tests giving nine scores: Verbal Reasoning, Numerical Ability, Verbal Reasoning plus Numerical Ability, Abstract Reasoning, Space Relations, Mechanical Reasoning, Clerical Speed and Accuracy, Spelling, and Grammar.

Flanagan Aptitude Classification Test. Science Research Associates, Inc., 259 East Erie Street, Chicago, Ill. *Level:* Grades 9–12 and adults. *Time:* 3 half-day sessions.

This battery provides 19 scores: Inspection, Mechanics, Tables, Reasoning, Vocabulary, Assembly, Judgment and Comprehension, Components, Planning, Arithmetic, Ingenuity, Scales, Expression, Precision, Alertness, Coordination, Patterns, Coding, and Memory. The results are used by counselors in guiding high school students in their choice of subjects, selection of post-high school study, and pursuit of job training.

Henmon-Nelson Tests of Mental Ability. Houghton Mifflin Company, 110 Tremont Street, Boston, Mass. *Level:* Grades 3–17. *Time:* 30 min.

These tests furnish Verbal, Quantitative, and Total Scores at the upper levels and IQ's at the lower levels.

Kuhlman-Anderson Measure of Academic Potential (Intelligence Tests). Personnel Press, Inc., 20 Nassau Street, Princeton, N.J. *Level:* Kindergarten–grade 12. *Time:* Approx. 30 min.

In grades K–7 these tests yield an IQ. In grades 7–12 scores include Verbal, Quantitative, and Total.

Lorge-Thorndike Intelligence Tests. Houghton Mifflin Company, 110 Tremont Street, Boston, Mass. *Level:* Kindergarten–grade 13. *Time:* Approx. 1 hr.

The tests provide measurement of nonverbal intelligence in grades K–13 and of verbal intelligence in grades 4–13. IQ, grade equivalent, and age equivalent scores are provided.

Ohio State University Psychological Test. Science Research Associates, Inc., 259 East Erie Street, Chicago, Ill. *Level:* Grades 9–13. *Time:* Approx. 2 hrs.

The test is designed as a measure of verbal aptitude and is composed of three parts: vocabulary, word relationships, and reading comprehension. The test yields a score for each part and a total score.

Otis Quick-Scoring Mental Ability Tests. Harcourt, Brace & World, Inc., 757 Third Avenue, New York, N.Y. *Level:* Grades 1–12. *Time:* Approx. 30 min.

Tests included are the Alpha Test (grades 1–4) giving Non-Verbal, Verbal, and Composite Scores; the Beta Test (grades 4–9) with a single score; and the Gamma Test (grades 9–12), also with a single score. Scores may be converted to mental age equivalents and deviation IQ's.

Pintner General Ability Tests. Harcourt, Brace & World, Inc., 757 Third Avenue, New York, N.Y. *Level:* Kindergarten–grade 12. *Time:* Approx. 50 min. for each series.

These tests consist of a Verbal Series (grades K–12) which measures a variety of aspects of general mental ability; and a Non-Language Series (grades 4–9) which measures general intellectual ability without the use of language. Each series furnishes one score and provides mental age equivalents and deviation IQ's at all levels.

Primary Mental Abilities. Science Research Associates, Inc., 259 East Erie Street, Chicago, Ill. *Level:* Kindergarten–grade 12. *Time:* Approx. 60 min. at each level.

This test is designed to measure separate factors of individual intelligence. Five test batteries are available for use at different grade levels. At most levels separate scores are available on subtests in verbal meaning, number facility, spatial ability, perceptual speed, and reasoning, plus a total intelligence score.

School and College Ability Tests. Educational Testing Service, Cooperative Test Division, Princeton, N.J. *Level:* Grades 4–16. *Time:* 1 hr. 10 min.

These tests yield Verbal, Quantitative, and Total Scores and are designed as measures of academic aptitude.

Terman-McNemar Test of Mental Ability. Harcourt, Brace & World, Inc., 757 Third Avenue, New York, N.Y. *Level:* Grades 7–13. *Time:* 40 min.

The test gives scores on seven subtests: Information, Synonyms, Logical Selection, Classification, Analogies, Opposites, and Best Answer. It stresses verbal components of intelligence and gives age norms for computation of deviation IQ's.

SRA Tests of Educational Ability. Science Research Associates, Inc., 259 East Erie Street, Chicago, Ill. *Level:* Grades 4–12. *Time:* Approx. 30 min.

These tests provide a total score and scores for language, reasoning, and quantitative.

Achievement Test Batteries

California Achievement Tests. California Test Bureau, Del Monte Research Park, Monterey, Calif. *Level:* Grades 1–14. *Time:* Approx. 2–3 hr.

Subtests: Reading Vocabulary, Reading Comprehension, Arithmetic Reasoning, Arithmetic Fundamentals, Mechanics of English, and Spelling.

Essential High School Content Battery. Harcourt, Brace & World, Inc., 757 Third Avenue, New York, N.Y. *Level:* Grades 10–12. *Time:* 3 hr. 25 min.

Subtests: Mathematics, Science, Social Studies, and English.

Iowa Tests of Basic Skills. Houghton Mifflin Company, 110 Tremont Street, Boston, Mass. *Levels:* Grades 3–9. *Time:* 4 hr. 39 min.

Subtests: Vocabulary; Reading Comprehension; Language Skills (Spelling, Capitalization, Punctuation, Usage); Work-Study Skills (Map Reading, Reading Graphs and Tables, Knowledge and Use of Reference Materials); and Arithmetic Skills (Arithmetic Concepts, Arithmetic Problem-Solving).

Iowa Tests of Educational Development. Science Research Associates, Inc., 259 East Erie Street, Chicago, Ill. *Level:* Grades 9–12. *Time* ("full length" version): Approx. two full school days.

Subtests: Understanding of Basic Social Concepts; General Background in the Natural Sciences; Correctness and Appropriateness of Expression; Ability to Think Quantitatively; Ability to Interpret Reading Materials in the Social Studies, in the Natural Sciences, and in Literary Materials; General Vocabulary; and Use of Sources of Information.

Metropolitan Achievement Tests. Harcourt, Brace & World, Inc., 757 Third Avenue, New York, N.Y. *Level:* Grades 1–12. *Time:* Varies from 1 hr. 45 min. to 5 hr. 15 min. for different levels.

Subtests: The subtests vary from level to level but cover at appropriate levels reading, arithmetic, language, study skills, and mastery of science and social studies content.

SRA Achievement Series. Science Research Associates, Inc., 259 East Erie Street, Chicago, Ill. *Level:* Grades 1–9. *Time:* Approx. one full school day.

Subtests: Social Studies, Science, Reading, Language Arts, Arithmetic, and Work Study Skills.

Sequential Tests of Educational Progress. Educational Testing Service, Cooperative Test Division, Princeton, N.J. *Level:* Grades 4–14. *Time:* 1 hr. 10 min. for each test.

Subtests: Reading, Writing, Listening, Science, Mathematics, and Social Studies.

Stanford Achievement Test. Harcourt, Brace & World, Inc., 757 Third Avenue, New York, N.Y. *Level:* Grades 1–12. *Time:* (complete battery): varies from 2 hr. 40 min. to 5 hr. 20 min. for different levels.

Subtests: The subtests vary from level to level but cover, as appropriate, arithmetic, reading, language arts, science, and social studies.

Tests of Academic Progress. Houghton Mifflin Company, 110 Tremont Street, Boston, Mass. *Level:* Grades 9–12. *Time:* 50–60 min. for each test.

Subtests: Social Studies, Composition, Science, Reading, Mathematics, and Literature.

CHAPTER 9

MEASUREMENT OF PERSONALITY

CLIFF W. WING, JR., *Duke University*

INTRODUCTION

The measurement of personality may be said to encompass four ingredients. There is, first, the process or trait, or related conglomerations of processes or traits, which are within the person and can be imagined but not seen. There is, second, the observable behavior of the person, whether that behavior takes the form of speech, writing, measurable physiological response, or inadvertent or purposive action. Third, there is the environment, including the people in it, whose own characteristics and activities affect and are affected by the individual's personality. Finally, there are the selective perceptions of the persons making the measurement and their analysis of what they have perceived.

In a sense, personality is not unlike electricity. We know it is there, although we cannot see it. Behavior is emitted as a result of its force. The kind of behavior varies depending on the conditions. And the interpretations placed upon the behavior—the inferences drawn about the characteristics of the unseeable—depend on the observers' perceptions and analysis.

To the continuing frustration of researchers in personality (and sometimes to their delight) personality is infinitely more complex than electricity. With due respect to the wit of Benjamin Franklin and his successors, it is no wonder that they were able to harness electricity, a relatively simple phenomenon; the parameters of personality still elude positive identification.

Consider for a moment the imposing array of alternatives that confront one who would measure personality. A basic question is, "What aspect or aspects of personality are to be measured?" This matter, in turn, rests largely on the question, "For what purpose is the personality being measured?" Is it with therapy in mind, and with the general purpose of promoting modification of the personality in order to increase "happiness" or better adaptation to the environment? Is it to predict an individual's future behavior on the basis of analysis of his entire personality? Is it an attempt to identify one particular trait, or a group of them, as distinctive from other personality traits, in order to itemize the parts of which personality (or various personalities) may be composed? Is the purpose to root out a cluster of characteristics that are, or are posited to be, the ingredients necessary for the successful performance of a particular task?

A similar list of alternatives may be posed for the specific behavior to be observed. A clinician may deliberately leave himself free to observe any kind of behavior he deems important at the moment. Other approaches to measurement require that the measurer restrict the range of what he observes, but within that restriction may be included anything from a complete case history to a galvanic skin response.

The environment in which the behavior takes place may vary from a real-life situation with on-the-job observation to a classroom where a paper-and-pencil test is administered. The individual whose personality is being measured may be confronted with a familiar situation that seems or is "normal," or he may be presented with artificially produced stresses and strains.

As to the methods of analyzing the data, the range is almost infinite. To begin with, a holistic approach, encouraging the observer to take into account whatever seems pertinent as an interview proceeds, means that each observer will have a different set of data to analyze and a different analysis to make, depending on his own experience and perceptivity and his role as part of the subject's environment. Beyond the clinical approach lie analytic methods which call into play a certain degree of intuitiveness, as well as those methods which are more objective. Even within the realm of the objective, research designs and statistical tools for analysis vary from the simple to the highly sophisticated and complex.

In summary, there is wide diversity in methods of personality measurement. Events and observations considered to yield profitably to examination do not fall neatly into categories. The same event or observation may be approached in different ways. Even when the observation to be made is the same and the method of making the observation is similar, treatment and interpretation of results may vary greatly. But despite the great diversity in what is studied and how, there is also, among students of personality, much overlap of interest and technique. Anything from an intuitively analyzed Rorschach to the pressing of a button may become a part of personality measurement—from whatever viewpoint.

The combination of diversity of approach with overlapping use of specific tools or techniques suggests the difficulty inherent in attempting systematic classification of procedures in personality measurement. Yet, certain distinctions can legitimately be made. If the reader will keep in mind that these distinctions are at best muddy, the writer will proceed to draw them in the hope that contrasting various approaches will increase understanding of all.

APPROACHES TO MEASUREMENT OF PERSONALITY

The discussion that follows will consider approaches to personality under three main headings: (1) clinical observation, (2) experimental manipulation, and (3) statistical manipulation. This division is by no means to be considered as standard or even popular. Other classification systems used by researchers include a simple clinical-versus-experimental dichotomy; a breakdown into clinical, bivariate, and multivariate approaches (Cattell, 1963); and a division that groups clinical and experimental together under one heading, separated from other approaches (Holt, 1962)—to mention only a few combinations. As Sears (1950) points out in his own system of classification, there is apt to be overlapping; categories are not mutually exclusive. In short, then, there is no universally accepted means of classifying ways of measuring personality. Grouping measurement approaches under some set of headings does, however, lend organization to the discussion. The group titles we have chosen contain (we hope) no "loaded" words to prejudice the reader as to the efficacy of any of the approaches; our purpose is to present each method sympathetically. A later section will discuss techniques and problems as they are shared by the three approaches.

Clinical Observation

The clinical method of personality assessment has been labeled by its defenders as "dynamic, global, meaningful, holistic, subtle, sympathetic, configural, patterned, organized, rich, deep, genuine, sensitive, sophisticated, real, living, concrete, natural, true to life, and understanding;" and by its critics as "mystical, transcendent, metaphysical, super-mundane, vague, hazy, subjective, unscientific, unreliable, crude, private, unverifiable, qualitative, primitive, prescientific, sloppy, uncontrolled, careless, verbalistic, intuitive, and muddleheaded" (Meehl, 1954, p. 4). However, clinical assessment is considered even by its most vigorous opponents to be fertile ground for ideas about personality.

The clinical method places major emphasis on the dynamics of behavioral assessment. It is directed toward securing data about factors that underlie motivation, adjustment mechanisms, defenses, and conflicts. The data for analysis may include verbal symbols, free association, word association, dreams, both objective and projective tests, both structured and unstructured interviews, biographical information, and the observation of behavior formally elicited by the clinician as well as behavior informally volunteered by the subject. The clinical method often takes as its focus the development of behavior. Assessment relates the subject's history to the development of patterns of behavior, and attempts to project the current assessment to predict future behavior.

One of the salient features of global assessment is its focus on the individual. Where other approaches are concerned with personality traits as exemplified in groups of people, or with differences among groups, the clinician is usually interested in only one person at a given moment. Where other approaches may attempt to measure only certain parts of personality in a study—and to assess those parts as they exist at a particular time—the clinical approach attempts to assess the entire personality and to take into account not only the current point in time but also the history of the subject. The clinical point of view is that predictions of value concerning an individual can be made only when one has obtained a thorough understanding of that individual. Such understanding cannot be reached solely by comparing the individual's traits with group norms, nor by considering him at a moment in time cut off from his personal history.

The individual focus of global assessment has, from time to time, been referred to as "personological" (Murray, 1938). This viewpoint is perhaps exemplified in the following quote from Allport (1961, p. 20):

To say that 85 in 100 boys having such a background will become delinquent is not to say that Jimmy, who has this background, has 85 in 100 chances of being delinquent . . . Only a complete knowledge of Jimmy will enable us to predict for sure.

A second characteristic of the clinical approach is the interest in theory, or the kind of interest in theory, that accompanies the global view. Garfield (1963, p. 475) puts it thus: "Clinicians are characteristically attracted to theories which postulate internal personality processes and structures only indirectly open to observation." Actually, as will be shown later, all approaches to measuring personality use inference about what is going on inside the person in order to classify, describe, or communicate characteristics or patterns. What may differentiate the clinician from others is a greater emphasis on postulated processes and structures in describing and explaining personality.

Another distinguishing feature of clinical theory is the sheer quantity of concepts—postulated traits or processes—that have emerged from holistic thinking. One need only begin with Freud and his psychoanalytic approach, go through the modifications and alterations of his contemporaries and successors, come upon Murray's needs-press analyses, and enter the current world of clinical publication to obtain an overview of the enormous number of ideas flowing continuously out of clinical work. The words used to express the concepts often have been used in nonclinical approaches to personality assessment, and so have the concepts themselves, expressed perhaps in different words.

Garfield (1963, p. 478) says that

. . . the theoretical framework which the clinician uses as a guide to his observations and formulations about the case at hand is a variable of importance. It is basic to the "cognitive activity of the clinician"—the ingredient which truly distinguishes the clinical method from other methods of studying personality.*

What the clinician elects to perceive about the individual personality is influenced by his theories—by the concepts he thinks are important and by the samples of behavior he thinks are most apt to reflect accurately the significant personality characteristics. In fact, McArthur (1956, p. 169), in his "dynamic model" for clinical prediction, would approach each individual as a new problem, developing theories to suit, in accordance with "the postulate that each individual is entirely consistent within himself."

Although the clinician's perceptivity is doubtless circumscribed in some ways by his own theoretical orientation, he brings to the observation of personality a

---

* S. L. Garfield, "The Clinical Method in Personality Assessment," in J. W. Wepman and R. W. Heine (eds.) *Concepts of Personality* (Chicago: Aldine Publishing Company, 1963). Quoted by permission of the publisher.

kind of flexibility which is absent from more objectively measured approaches to assessment. He is free to observe anything from a handshake to a score on a paper-and-pencil test. Further, an analysis of results on a test is likely to cover not only the score obtained but also other behavior displayed by the subject during the course of taking the test. Informal activity may be just as important as or more important than formally measured responses. The clinician's flexibility touches not only what he perceives about one subject, but also his own receptiveness in approaching each subject according to what seems the most effective route toward comprehensive understanding. In the selection of what is to be measured, the clinician gives priority to the variables he considers important over the availability of precise instruments to measure the variables.

To a very important degree, the investigator in a clinical situation uses himself—his own past experiences, his theoretical biases, his cognitive skills—as a measuring instrument. Even among clinicians themselves, there is divergent opinion about the efficacy of the clinician-instrument, although all seem agreed that the very subjectivity of some of his evaluation requires that the clinician be an instrument. McArthur (1954) sets out vigorously to find out how this clinician-instrument works by analyzing the clinician's processes of arriving at personality assessments. Meehl (1954) reports a number of studies comparing the predictive efficiency of the clinician-instrument with the predictive efficiency of "actuarial" (objective test) instruments. He finds the actuarial instruments generally superior to the clinicians, but goes on to argue (p. 120) that

The kind of episode *during therapy* which gives [clinicians] a conviction of [their] own predictive power may be quite legitimate, but the transition to the straight *prediction problem* involves features which seriously impair an analogy between the two sorts of situation.

Garfield (1963) finds hope in the idea that some clinicians are better predictors than others, and suggests that actuarial methods seem to be more efficient than the clinician partly because the predictions of less acute clinicians often are lumped together with those of more acute clinicians, thereby lowering the average predictive efficiency. It may also be that some clinicians' efficiency depends on the kinds of subjects or environmental situations involved in the predictions to be made. Competition for efficient prediction between the clinical method used exclusively and the actuarial approach used exclusively is likely to continue into the indefinite future among those who embrace only one of the two methods. However, combinations of the two approaches, as we shall see later, may produce more predictive efficiency than either alone. This suggests that there is value in both.

Still another characteristic of the clinical approach is that it tends to be used at times and in situations where the more objective angels fear to tread, for it is the clinician, foolishly or not, who is called upon to rush in when action is necessary. The clinician's obligation is often primarily to provide therapy and only secondarily to do research, and his responsibility to practice as well as to study necessarily influences the scope of his interest. The population of subjects available to him for research ordinarily would include a high proportion of people with pathological personality characteristics. The availabality of subjects who exhibit an intense or extensive amount of some personality trait might be counted as an advantage or a disadvantage for research opportunity.

By and large, specific examples of assessment research conducted by clinicians and reported in journals and books are, in at least some ways, clinical-experimental, rather than purely clinical. This result seems natural in view of two facts. First, the clinician probably seldom finds it worth while to publish his observations, however perceptive, based on one case study. Like the medical practitioner, he is likely to publish when he has a finding to report based on several cases. The results are organized, whether retrospectively or in advance, around some crucial test of observation and have or seem to have an experimental organization to the extent that something has been systematically observed. Second, many clinicians are acutely aware of the contributions that systematic observation—the objective scientific approach—can make to personality assessment. Although they do not accept the limitations imposed by those experimentalists who would rule out subjectivity of judgment, these clinicians are eager to be as objective as the situation permits. They are equally eager to present their results in a way that will induce the interest and perhaps the research participation of experimental researchers in personality assessment.

Examples of clinical studies, with or without experimental overtones, may be found in Kluckhohn and Murray (1950), Louttit (1947), Burton and Harris (1947), and Ferguson (1952), among a myriad of others. Of more recent origin are investigations by Holt (1962), of which the following is a sample (p. 276):

Using many simultaneous methods of measuring personality, one gains security from the overlap of findings. Thus, for example, in a study on reality deprivation Holt and Goldberger (1959) found a pattern of positive adaptation to the unusual experimental demands (mostly, to perceive and do nothing for eight hours) and proceeded to look for its personological correlates. It was correlated with clinical ratings of effeminacy *and* with questionnaire measures of it . . . this experimental measure correlated with esthetic sensitivity as measured in three different ways: by pencil-and-paper instruments . . . by an objective technique . . . and by the clinical ratings.*

Experimental Manipulation

The measurement of personality through the manipulation of the subject or his environment covers an amazingly wide range of materials, terminology, and theoretical points of departure. The materials may be objective tests, projective tests, physiological responses, sets of instructions about how subjects should behave, or experimenter-controlled changes in stimulating conditions, to mention a few possibilities.

---

* R. R. Holt, "A Clinical-Experimental Strategy for Research in Personality," in S. Messick and J. Ross (eds.), *Measurement in Personality and Cognition* (New York: John Wiley & Sons, 1962). Quoted by permission of the publisher.

The subjects themselves may be lower animal forms, such as rats, or humans at various age levels. The terminology and theoretical points of departure may be analytic or strict behaviorist.

What is considered here as unifying these varied pieces of work is their approach to measuring personality. A salient characteristic differentiating the experimental approach from the clinical is the requirement that the behavior to be observed must be stipulated as part of the experimental design, in advance of the observation. There must be a clear statement of what is to be counted, and behavior that has been informally observed is not admitted as evidence for results. Measures are typically made of traits that are defined explicitly or operationally. For example, anxiety may be defined as being present if there is a hand tremor, or palm sweat, or according to scores on a test. Note that as in the clinical approach, inferences are drawn concerning the internal process or trait, but here they are necessarily drawn from behavior that is formally counted or measured.

A second characteristic of experimental studies is that they define with rigor the conditions under which measurement proceeds. If a group of subjects is to be submitted to a frustrating experience, the same experience is provided in the same way to all members of the group. If a Rorschach is given, it is scored the same way for all.

Experimental studies begin with a clear statement of the hypothesis to be tested. The statement is presented in terms of the measurement conditions. As in other examples of the scientific or experimental method in its classical accepted sense, the portion of behavior selected for observation is the dependent variable. The environment, controlled and manipulated by the experimenter, is the independent variable. The results are an analysis of the characteristics of the dependent variable under varying conditions of the independent variable. Depending on the theoretical point of departure of the researcher, the explanation of the behavior (the inferred personality traits or processes) may be called constructs or intervening variables.

As contrasted with the clinician who flexibly approaches each case with an eye and an ear open to what may turn up as relevant, the assessor of personality in the experimental study makes every attempt to minimize or to standardize his role. If he is a part of the subject's environment—for example, in giving instructions—then he seeks to give the instructions the same way each time so that the stimulating conditions remain constant.

Researchers using the experimental approach to measure personality typically limit their interest, in a given study, to assessing changes in one or two responses under various experimental conditions rather than assessing the patterning of many responses. The emphasis is on manipulating one condition and holding the others constant. This restriction of interest to one or two dependent variables at a time has led researchers approaching personality measurement from other viewpoints to label this approach as "bivariate." These same researchers, as will be seen in the next section, call their own research "multivariate."

Three final points will serve to complete a general overview of characteristics of the experimental approach. One is that whereas the clinician frequently uses, as part of his approach, a study of the developmental or longitudinal aspects of personality through attempts to draw out the subject about his past, the experimenter takes the individuals under study at a particular moment in time and studies them at that moment thoroughly. He may be *interested* in or may draw inferences about longitudinal or developmental theory, but the experiment itself limits the time coverage.

Second, experimental manipulation usually involves a number of individuals divided into groups and subjected to different environmental or treatment conditions. Interest is focused on what may be called "normative" behavior—personality traits or characteristics exhibited by many people under the same conditions. Each group studied in an experiment offers opportunity for the observation of the dependent variable under varying controlled manipulations of the independent variable. The effects of the independent variable may be assessed by comparing responses in the different groups.

Third, among researchers who utilize the experimental approach are some who work not on human personality but, from the comparative viewpoint, with the behavior of lower animal forms. Such researchers justify drawing analogies from the behavior of lower animal forms and applying the results of their studies to humans in much the same way that others have justified applying to humans the results of studies of learning in rats or apes or dogs. These latter psychological studies are themselves justified, of course, on the basis of what is known about physiological and structural elements in common among various mammalian species. Moreover, comparative work has indeed served effectively not only in biology and medicine, but also in psychology, where principles of learning established on lower animal forms frequently have been found to have systematic applicability to human learning.

Clearly, a simple and rough listing of procedures used in common is not sufficient defense for grouping in one category researchers starting out with points of view so obviously divergent as that of the Freudian-analytic researcher and that of the comparative-psychologist–learning-theorist. To illustrate why they may be so grouped we present the following summary of two experiments by psychologists starting with entirely different theoretical orientations or interests and using entirely different techniques for measuring.

A study on "masculinity, identification, and father-son relationships" was performed by Mussen and Distler (1959, pp. 350–356). They were interested in shedding light upon three alternative and possibly either conflicting or coordinate hypotheses about how boys become identified with their fathers.

According to psychoanalytic theory, the boy's shift to identification with his father begins during the Oedipal phase of development and is motivated by fears and anxieties related to his hostility toward that parent. . . . This is the defense mechanism that has been called "identification with the aggressor" and "defensive identification." . . . In contrast to this, the developmental hypothesis states that identification with father depends on a positive, affectionate relationship between father and son . . . The two hypothesized identification processes . . . may function together . . . This view is consistent with that of the role theorists . . . [who] maintain that identification, or role-playing, depends on the *power* of the identificand—a combination of his reward value *and* his threat or punishment potential.*

The two experimenters first administered the IT Scale for Children, a projective test of sex-role preference, to 38 kindergarten children. From these, they selected two groups of ten each, matched for socioeconomic background, the same number in each group from each of two kindergarten classes, but divided into high scorers and low scorers on the IT Scale for Children. That is, one group had a high feminine role preference, the other a high masculine role preference.

The researchers then tested each boy in a structured doll-play session with three dolls representing mother, father, and boy-child. The examiners told nine partially completed stories which the children were to finish—for example, "The child wants a certain toy. He can't reach it. He goes into the living room to get help. Both Mommy and Daddy are busy reading. What happens?"

The answers were scored for "Father Nurturance" (number of times Daddy helped), "Mother Nurturance" (Mommy helped), "They Nurturance" (both helped), and Total Nurturance (the total of the first three); and for "Father," "Mother," "They," and "Total Punishment" (the number of punishments). "The total number of stories involving relationships with the father, either nurturant or punitive . . . constituted the Father Power score." The "Mother Power" score was derived in the same way.

The results, according to the authors, lend some support to all three hypotheses. The fact that the boys with high masculine identification also perceived themselves as receiving significantly more Father Nurturance than the low masculinity group supports the developmental identification hypothesis which predicts "that young boys are more likely to identify strongly with their fathers, and thus to acquire masculine interests, if they perceive their fathers as highly nurturant and rewarding." The defensive identification hypothesis was supported in the results showing that the "highly masculine boys tended to attribute more punishment to the fathers in their doll-play stories than" the other group. "The third, or role-taking, hypothesis states that the degree of identification and, consequently, sex-role learning varies with the amount of the child's interaction with the identificand and the degree to which the latter has power over him, i.e., controls both his rewards and his punishments. The data of the present study seem to be fully in accord with this hypothesis, since the low and high masculinity groups differ markedly in Father Power," with the high masculinity group yielding the higher scores.

Note that the researchers for this study followed the procedures outlined as characteristic of the experimental approach. The hypotheses to be tested were

* P. Mussen and L. Distler, "Masculinity, Identification, and Father-Son Relationships." *J. Abnormal Soc. Psychol,* **59** (1959). Quoted by permission of the author and the publisher.

stated. The personality traits under scrutiny were defined operationally (masculinity as measured by scores on the IT Scale). The conditions of measurement were held standard (the same stories offered for completion to each child). It may be safely assumed that the examiners did not intrude upon the experimental conditions by attempting to interact with the subjects. The researchers' interest in responses was limited to answers offered by the children in completing the stories. There was one set of variables, story completion, which may be considered as dependent. Degree of masculinity was the independent variable. Although the experimenters certainly were interested in developmental theory, they took their evidence for or against developmental influences out of a cross section of behavior at a point in time. Finally, there were two groups subjected to differing experimental treatment and the results were presented in normative fashion.

Before reporting another study under the "experimental manipulation" label, it may be appropriate to quote a small part of the opening remarks of Lundin in his book *Personality: An Experimental Approach* (1961, p. 47):

Since the establishment of Darwin's theory of evolution, scientists (including psychologists) have compared and contrasted the behavior of organisms at various levels. The universality of many of the principles is amazing. Because of the greater opportunity for control and precise measurement, animals below man have frequently been employed in order to discover new psychological laws . . . We cannot attribute a principle learned from the study of rats to human conduct until we have also observed it operating in the human species. However, once we have done so, our rat experiment may have given us a more precise understanding of the principle involved because of the more adequate controls imposed.*

We turn now to a summary of a study performed by Skinner and Estes (1959), whose language, theoretical point of view, and measuring tools could hardly differ more than they do from those of Mussen and Distler; yet the approach to personality measurement is experimental manipulation.

Anxiety, state the authors, involves behavior arising in (p. 394)

. . . 'anticipation' of a future event. Since a stimulus which has not yet occurred cannot act as a cause, we must look for a *current* variable. An analogy with the typical conditioning experiment, in which S_1, having in the past been followed by S_2, now leads to an 'anticipatory' response to S_2, puts the matter in good scientific order because it is a current stimulus S_1, not the future occurrence of S_2, which produces the reaction. Past instances of S_2 have played their part in bringing this about, but it is not S_2 which is currently responsible.

Anxiety further involves, the paper goes on, not only possible muscular or autonomic reactions, but, of possibly greater importance, the weakening or strengthening of other responses already in the "current repertoire." Thus the authors designed an experiment to set up an emotional state in "anticipation" of a disturbing

---

* R. W. Lundin, *Personality: An Experimental Approach* (New York: Macmillan, 1961, © 1961 by The Macmillan Company). Quoted by permission of the publisher.

stimulus, and measured the magnitude of the emotion by (p. 395) "its effect upon the strength of certain hunger-motivated behavior, more specifically upon the rate with which a rat makes an arbitrary response which is periodically reinforced with food."

The disturbing stimulus was an electric shock administered to the rat-subjects through the floor of the experimental box. A tone was used as the stimulus preceding the shock, the stimulus ultimately eliciting the anxiety response. The details of the experimental conditions need not concern us for the purposes of this illustration, but they are carefully specified in every regard.

The principal result of this part of the experiment was the conditioning of a state of anxiety to the tone, where the primary index was a reduction in strength of the hunger-motivated lever-pressing behavior. The ratio of the number of responses made during the period of the tone to the average number made during the same fraction of the hour in control experiments was 1.2:1.0 for the first experimental hours; it had dropped to 0.3:1.0 by the eighth. (p. 397)

That is to say, the tone acquired a depressing effect upon the rats' behavior. Another result was

. . . the compensatory increase in periodic rate following the period of depression. . . . Evidently the effect of the emotional state is a temporary depression of the strength of the behavior, the total amount responding during the experimental period . . . remaining the same. Similar compensatory increases have been described under a number of circumstances, including physical restraint of the response.*

Although the four researchers who worked on the two experiments just reported might resent being given the same label, it does seem that there is, for all the difference, a similar interest in establishing the relationship between dependent and independent variables. The fact that the tools for measurement vastly differ, or that the applicability of the results to human behavior might be questioned for either set of results, does not alter the premise that both approaches seem to be experimental manipulation. The reader may well imagine that this label covers not only studies at the two extremes presented here, but also hundreds of studies of an in-between kind, with tools and techniques and theoretical viewpoints varying on a scale at least as broad as the one encompassing rats and kindergartners.

Statistical Manipulation

The third avenue to personality measurement has some features in common with each of the other two, and some that are different. With the clinical approach, the method involving statistical manipulation shares some interests and language. Some concepts common to Freudianism and other analytic approaches find a place here. There is a commitment to observing the personality holistically. At the same time,

---

* B. F. Skinner, *Cumulative Record* (New York: Appleton-Century-Crofts, 1959, © 1959, 1961 by Appleton-Century-Crofts, Inc.). Quoted by permission of the publisher.

studies involving statistical manipulation, like those involving experimental manipulation, proceed under conditions of rigorous, quantitative measurement.

Proponents of the statistical method maintain that the clinical method, although it deals, as it should, with large segments of personality through the utilization of varied observational techniques, depends too greatly on the acuity and memory of the clinician to yield scientifically dependable results, and that environmental manipulation, although it permits precise measurement and evaluation, as it should, fails to deal with enough personality variables at a time to give a meaningful result. Therefore, measurement of an array of activities purported to be indicative of personality should be rigorously made, and statistical devices (predominately, factor analysis) should be employed to analyze the data and cull out patterns of response which fit complex personality traits or processes. The method, in short, seeks to make multifaceted but objective measurements of personality, and to base descriptions and predictions about personality upon statistical manipulation of the data collected. A leading exponent of this approach, Raymond Cattell (1959, 1962, 1963) calls it "multivariate," to contrast it with the univariate or bivariate methods of design employed by experimentalists working with dependent and independent variables.

It may be helpful to continue to compare and contrast the three approaches as we list certain characteristics of statistical manipulation. Of primary consideration is the matter of testing hypotheses. The clinician develops hypotheses out of previous experience and knowledge, but the flexibility of his approach may lead him to modify any given hypothesis in the process of studying an individual's personality. The experimental researcher restricts himself to a fixed hypothesis to be tested; he then collects critical data which either support or refute the hypothesis. The statistical researcher collects data in large quantities and then processes them mathematically to discern patterns which may then form the basis for hypotheses to be tested later, or for replication purposes. That is, the statistical manipulator may or may not have one or more hypotheses when he begins to collect data, except to the extent that he will collect data, obviously, only when he has some reason or hunch for believing that the measures to be made bear some relevance to personality characteristics. But he is certain to have hypotheses after completing the study, assuming the emergence of any patterns of statistically related materials. These hypotheses are derived from what the data themselves indicate, and the patterns and resulting hypotheses may support or verify others or may be entirely new. Research of this kind is frequently said to be hypothesis-generating, as contrasted with hypothesis-testing.

The clinician attempts to develop a great quantity of information, through various channels, about an individual, whereas the experimental manipulator carefully restricts the information to be obtained. The statistical manipulator, like the clinician, opens the door wide to a variety of measures; but the approach is not so flexible as to allow him to include any item of behavior that turns up, as with the clinician. Rather, a whole series of paper-and-pencil tests may be given, a variety of physiological and other objective responses may be measured, and certain verbal responses may be noted. But what is to be measured is planned in advance. And only measurements that can be made with a certain precision are included.

The statistical approach, with its mathematical models as a base and its computers as weapons, naturally encompasses more subjects in each study than most pieces of experimental research, let alone clinical research. The subjects, moreover, are selected to cover the entire range of population—the normal, rather than the abnormal, is the concern of the statistical researcher, and this concern is expressed by taking great care to sample truly representative populations. Further, an interest in developmental personality leads the statistical manipulator to repeat studies over time with the same individuals and also to make the same or closely similar observations among groups at different age levels. Some work has also been done cross-culturally, using American, Australian, British, French, Italian, and Japanese samples (Cattell, 1963, p. 424). The statistical manipulator does not work with lower animal forms.

The role of the statistical researcher is more like that of the experimentalist than of the clinician. He does not use himself as a measurement instrument nor deliberately guide one subject in this direction, another in that. He minimizes or standardizes his role. He does, however, play an important role in the hypothetical deductive analysis that follows treatment of results. From his analytic work stems the generation of hypotheses, mentioned earlier. As these hypotheses rest not only upon a command of the mathematical principles underlying the analyses but also upon verbalizing, relating, and communicating concepts, there is a substantial interpretive and therefore subjective role to be played by the statistical manipulator. In this respect his role resembles the clinician's more than the experimental manipulator's. (The latter interprets data also, of course, although the interpretations often tend to involve fewer assumptions or constructs—possibly because there are fewer variables, and because these variables are removed, for purposes of control, from real-life situations.)

Still left to discuss is what the statistical researcher does with the environment of the subjects whose personality is under investigation. About this matter there is disagreement not only among proponents of different approaches but also among proponents of the "multivariate experiment." Cattell says (1959, p. 45): "The multivariate experimenter, like the clinician, allows life itself to make the experiments, in naturally functioning organic wholes, and then extracts the causal connections by superior statistical analytical procedures." Abelson (1962, p. 241 ff.), another member of the multivariate school, contends that ". . . there has been a rather serious neglect of situational variables . . . *To the extent that response variables are controlled by motivational systems which in turn are subject to environmental arousal, the locus of appropriate factorial investigation should shift from the individual-difference level to the environmental-situations level.*" This, of course, does not suggest a need to manipulate the environment so much as it does the desirability of studying it statistically. To do so, however, would inevitably require that measurements of it be made, to provide a basis for the statistical analysis. Still a third view is expressed by one not a member of the multivariate school. Far from going along with Cattell's description of the conditions for some of his personality observations as (1959, p. 47) "life records of behavior *in situ,*" Tomkins (1962, p. 287) thinks that the factor analytic approach, presumably including its conditions for measurement as well as its statistical orientation, is "as appropriate for the unravelling of a dynamic system as complex as man as a centrifuge might be."

To get an overview of how the statistical manipulation method proceeds from experiment to statistical analysis to hypothesis formation to experiment, and so on in the cycle, it is simplest to turn to Cattell himself for the tracing of the development of one concept, "general inhibition." According to the researcher (1962, p. 254), the work began in 1947 when the factor with the following pattern came to light:

. . . a large loading for mean galvanic skin deflection in response to threat stimuli; a loading on a paper-and-pencil test called "absence of questionable reading preferences," which showed a tendency to choose safe rather than blood-and-thunder titles; a third loading for much slowing of reaction time by complex instructions (we measured the subject's reaction time in a simple situation and then put him in a situation with complex instructions and measured the lengthening of his reaction time); and a fourth loading for slow speed of closure in Gestalt completion, which had been used to mark one of Thurstone's perceptual factors.

Cattell then proceeded to analyze these results and to discern what the tests which load the factor had in common. There seemed to the researcher to be two possibilities—that a "high aspiration" factor was represented, or that a "timidity" factor was represented, with evidence somewhat in favor of the latter. A new series of studies was now launched to determine whether the factor, now called U. I. 17, was high aspiration level, timidity, or a third—high general inhibition from sources other than timidity.

As a test of the aspiration-level hypothesis, we inserted a variety of measures having to do with aspiration and tenacity in reaching goals. As a test of the general inhibition hypothesis, we introduced a number of measures of carefulness of procedure, such as a maze test in which the individual was scored on the number of times he cut across lines and a copying test in which he was measured on the exactness with which he reproduced figures. As a test of the timidity hypothesis, we added a finger-maze test in which the individual first ran his finger, behind a screen, as far as he could through the grooves of a maze, and then did the same thing under conditions in which he would be liable to receive an electric shock for excessive activity. We also introduced a test of the time required to name an object becoming visible through a process of dark adaptation of the eye. We argued that if the slow speed of closure arose from caution rather than from any disability in perceptual skill as such, it would also show up in another sensory test in which the same kind of perceptual ability is not involved. The outcome of the next factorization . . . distinguished pretty sharply between these hypotheses and indicated that the general inhibition hypothesis was the nearest: The factor proved to load quite substantially the reduction of finger-maze activity by shock; it also loaded a measure of carefulness of procedure and a new test of the tendency to see threatening objects in unstructured pictures.*

The foregoing summary by Cattell of a small portion of his own work may illustrate for the reader some of the general character of multivariate research using the statistical manipulation approach. One may note the catholicity of interest evidenced in the number of different techniques for measurement called into play, the hypothesis-generating quality of the approach, and the judgment, as well as the mathematical knowledge, demanded of the experimenter as he endows the various factor loadings with communicable meaning and replicable experimental aims.

TECHNIQUES OF MEASURING PERSONALITY

The clinical, experimental, and statistical approaches to the measurement of personality have several fundamental characteristics in common not only with each other but also with other scientific attempts to study human behavior. As stated in the beginning of this chapter, the internal states or traits or processes which presumably develop over time according to hereditary and environmental factors and which, taken together as "personality," presumably govern some aspects of human behavior, cannot be seen or measured directly. Thus it has been necessary for all researchers, whether clinicians or behaviorists, and whether exponents of the multivariate or bivariate, to make inferences or constructs about the unseeable. These inferences or constructs about personality have been developed to provide some order or system by means of which research may be organized, communicated, and replicated. Some inferences have been restricted in scope and highly particularized; some have been at a more complex level and might be considered general hypotheses or even theories. Since we are concerned here not with theories of personality, but with the measurement of it, let it suffice to say that despite vast differences in the specific words used, there is beginning to emerge some consistent notion of at least a few of the important considerations in personality. Many of these considerations rest in part on inference. None are yet so perfectly delineated as to permit predicting behavior with great accuracy.

Just as all researchers in personality must be concerned with constructed or inferred underlying principles, all must also be concerned with what techniques should be applied to measure or observe behavior, for it is behavior itself—and only behavior—to which we can directly apply our senses. Even those closest to the armchair would venture out occasionally, or have others do so, to test their ideas in the crucible of experience. Thus all roads lead to the necessity of selecting

---

* R. B. Cattell, "Personality Measurement Related to Source Trait Structure," in S. Messick and J. Ross (eds.), *Measurement in Personality and Cognition* (New York: John Wiley & Sons, 1962). Quoted by permission of the publisher.

measuring instruments, and to the immense and varied problems attendant upon that selection.

There is one general problem concerning all techniques of measurement, and that is economy—economy in the sense of the cost of the devices used, the training required of people who administer and score them, and the time and number of subjects necessary. Economy may seem an odd place to start, but its pervasive influence, whether explicitly stated or not, must be recognized if one is alert to the times when testing procedure is changed (shortened) in the interests of practicality. An extreme view of the role of economy in research is exemplified by the following cogent remarks taken from Meehl (1954, p. 128), a clinician himself:

Psychologist *X* gives four or five projective devices, a Shipley, a Wechsler-Bellevue, and an MMPI [Minnesota Multiphasic Personality Inventory], and chews over the results *ad nauseam* when he is functioning in an institutional context. He picks up his semi-monthly check in any event, so the value of time per case, while willingly conceded as important *in abstracto,* is not strikingly called to his attention. We find the battery, and the time spent on interpreting it, undergoes a suspicious shrinkage when our psychologist acts as a consultant to a privately practicing psychiatrist with the latter collecting his fee for him. Lastly, behold him in his own private therapeutic practice, where he *himself* is the evaluator of the therapeutic power conferred by his armamentarium and he himself has to put the financial bite on his client. His enthusiasm for 'advance knowledge through dynamic integration' has now so flagged that we find him slipping the client a quick Bender and sending him home with a group form MMPI to be filled out between sessions. I have a hunch that some profound and terrifying truths are discernible in this psychometric devolution but I shall not press the point.*

Cattell (1962, p. 251), while extolling the greater merit in the multivariate approach, remarks that the only argument he can see on the side of the clinician is that "his subjects usually pay him, whereas the experimentalist often has to pay his subjects." Stern, Stein, and Bloom (1956, p. 123), after using a variety of projective and objective tests and reporting the results of two intensive studies supported by outside sources, maintain that "the small number of cases represented in these two projects, and the high cost of analysis per case in terms of time as well as money, make the limitations of this approach clear. The essential characteristics of the testing techniques employed in these two studies constitute a major cost factor." The authors go on to suggest and to perform research in the hope of finding techniques less costly but equally accurate to use.

The point here is not to raise any question whatsoever about the self-interest of researchers in the field of personality. It is simply to call attention to some indications that the selection of techniques for measurement does not go on in a vacuum, but in real life, where practicing clinicians may have to handle more patients than the kind of testing he would like to do permits; where researchers,

---

* P. E. Meehl, *Clinical Versus Statistical Prediction* (Minneapolis: University of Minnesota Press, 1962). Quoted by permission of the publisher.

supported by universities or governmental agencies or foundations, must decide how to allocate funds; where—and here is the basic point—every investigator must decide which measurements can most efficiently give him enough data to answer the questions asked. Even Cattell, who brandishes mightily the sword of the mathematical models that permit the use of enormous quantities of data, cannot and does not use all the kinds of measuring techniques that are available for use. He, too, must be selective. In a sense, then, every researcher is to some extent affected in his selection of techniques by a search for economy of one sort or another.

Like any other tests, whether of intelligence or the basal metabolism rate, tests of personality must be considered for their reliability and validity. Before considering the types of personality tests in existence, let us summarize some general aspects of their reliability and validity.

The three usual measures of test reliability are the test-retest method, the equivalent-form method, and the split-half method. As Allen (1958) explains, the last of these three methods is usually not appropriate for personality testing. Scales to measure personality do not involve items paired for difficulty, as do intelligence tests. The test-retest method is complicated by the possibility that the subject may simply be recalling what his answer was on the first occasion. The equivalent-form procedure, though difficult to follow, is probably the best method of assessing reliability, according to Allen.

Allen (1958) lists six ways of measuring validity that are in common use in literature concerning the measurement of personality. These are test validity (the extent to which a test measures what it was designed to measure); face validity (based on assumption rather than on any objective validation); content validity (validity by definition); factorial validity (factor analysis used to establish basic elements evaluated by the test); empirical validity (results on test checked against actual performance measured in another situation); and construct validity (validity of the theory underlying the test).

In the literature, the merit of these respective approaches, which are in some cases overlapping, seems to have been argued over the breakfast table. Allen (1958, p. 21) says of factorial validity (which can overlap with construct validity) that "The test factor analyst comes out only with what he has put into the mathematical grinder. An orange will be reduced to orange peel, orange pits, orange juice, and orange pulp. No factor analysis has yet produced grapefruit juice in the factor analysis of an orange." Allport (1958, p. 251), discussing the characteristics of units that hang together in defining factors in some factorial studies, says, "One wonders what to say about them. To me they resemble sausage meat that has failed to pass the pure food and health inspection." By contrast, Loevinger (1957, p. 641) argues that criterion-oriented psychometrics, presumably resting on empirical validity, "contributes no more to the science of psychology than rules for boiling an egg contribute to the science of chemistry. And the number of genuine egg-boiling decisions which clinicians and psychotechnologists face is small compared with the number of situations where a deeper knowledge of psychological theory would be helpful." Loevinger argues that construct validity is most fruitful, and that tests constructed on the basis of it need not utilize test-retest or parallel-form reliability.

While the relative merit of factorial, construct, and empirical validity is clearly a matter of debate, it is almost uniformly agreed that test, face, or content validity, which all overlap in concept, lack sufficient rigor for scientific use. To demonstrate the unimportance of the face validity or content of test items, Berg and Collier (1953), as have others, used abstract designs, had subjects rate how much they liked each design, and obtained results showing that subjects who made extreme choices tended to be anxious, as measured by other devices. The point relevant here to test item content, or face, validity is that a test that works (i.e., discriminates and evidences some validity) may bear no *apparent* relation to the characteristic being tested. It follows that a test whose content *does seem* to relate to the characteristic under study need not necessarily discriminate or evidence validity.

Turning now from the general matters of the economy of tests and means of determining their reliability and validity, let us consider the tests or devices themselves. Personality is currently being assessed in an enormous number of different ways—by physiologic responses; by objectively measured performance on a variety of tasks requiring physical or verbal action; by paper-and-pencil tests whose content varies from questions that are ostensibly directly related to traits like anxiety or aggressiveness or ostensibly related to nothing; by projective tests, including the Rorschach, Murray's TAT (Thematic Apperception Test), paper-and-pencil tests (sentence or picture completion), and situational tests (projective doll play). Efforts have been made to assess personality through observation of body types and through observations of entire cultures or subcultures (Kluckhohn and Murray, 1950), as well as through observations of real-life behavior, for example in some clinical studies, and through reconstructions of past behavior in interviews.

Thorndike and Hagen (1961, p. 318), by way of providing some ordered way of thinking about the great variety of types of tests in use, suggested that

. . . we can see what the individual has to say about himself. Second, we can find out what others say about him. Third, we can see what he actually does, how he behaves in the real world of things or people. Fourth, we can observe how he reacts to the world of fantasy and make-believe.*

These four categories might well be combined into two: what the individual tells you about himself, whether through interviews, paper-and-pencil tests, projective tests, or reports of dreams; and what can be observed about him by others, whether in controlled or laboratory situations or in real-life situations. No matter what kind of measurement it is—whether the observed data originate from the subject or from

---

* R. L. Thorndike and E. Hagen, *Measurement and Evaluation in Psychology and Education* (*2nd ed.*) (New York: John Wiley & Sons, 1961). Quoted by permission of the publisher.

the perception of the observer—the *assessor* of the data is bound to figure importantly in the interpretation of results.

All the approaches—clinical, experimental, and statistical—use data from a variety of sources. But there is a tendency for some approaches to emphasize certain sources and techniques more than others. Thus the clinician emphasizes interviews, case histories, all observable behavior, projective techniques, and certain objectively scored paper-and-pencil tests. The experimentalist emphasizes the contrived environment for observation, objective measures of behavior and physiologic responses, and objectively scored tests. The statistical analyst emphasizes the use of objective tests of various kinds, including self-ratings, the ratings of others, and objectively measured behavioral or physiologic responses. From the immense array of measuring devices in use, we can generalize some basic types for a closer look at particular characteristics.

Projective Techniques

The name "projective technique" was originated by L. K. Frank (1939) and is used to cover a variety of testing instruments, the most famous and researched being the Rorschach (Beck, 1944; Klopfer and Kelly, 1946) and the TAT (Thematic Apperception Test) (Morgan and Murray, 1935; Tomkins, 1947). Whether through inkblots, pictures of people, or sentences or drawings to be completed, the projective technique aims to obtain responses that will reveal something about people's innermost thoughts and feelings, their private worlds, their fantasies.

Proponents of the use of projective tests typically consider that the analytic purposes of the tests are concealed or disguised to a degree that allows subjects to respond freely and without the usual inhibitions, thereby revealing things about themselves that they would not reveal under direct questioning. The stimuli presented to subjects are relatively unstructured or ambiguous, as compared with stimuli in other kinds of tests. The task of telling what is perceived in an inkblot or a picture is, for most subjects, novel. The responses do not directly depend on skills previously acquired, and the subject has little idea of what might be considered a "socially acceptable" story.

As Holtzman (1959, p. 120) puts it, "Given any projective technique where the subject is offered a wide latitude in which to reveal himself, the particular sample of responses obtained is assumed to reflect significant aspects of the subject's personality organization, if only the examiner can find the key to its interpretation." Users of projective tests differ widely in their opinions about how results should be analyzed. Methods range from purely global inspection and intuition on the one hand to complex scoring techniques on the other.

Despite the enormous past and current work being done with projective techniques, much evidence indicates that when they are used in the absence of other corroborating material the results yield information that is neither reliable nor validly predictive. Kelly (1954, p. 288) described the situation as follows: "The curious state of affairs wherein the most widely (and confidently) used techniques are those for which there is little or no evidence of predictive validity is indeed a phenomenon appropriate for study by social psychologists."

Weiss *et al.* (1959) reported that a need achievement score, based on an analysis of TAT-like pictures as suggested by McClelland *et al.* (1953), correlated 0.34 with grades obtained in college. Academic aptitude test scores yielded higher correlations with grades (0.55). When need achievement scores plus academic aptitude test scores were correlated with the criterion, the correlation was 0.63. Correlations of the same order were obtained using paper-and-pencil tests of need achievement.

Munroe (1945) obtained a correlation of -0.49 between a number of signs of maladjustment, scored from an inspection technique designed for use with the Rorschach, and freshman grades at Sarah Lawrence College. Cronbach (1950), however, was not able to achieve useful relationships with the Rorschach in predicting the grades of freshmen at the University of Chicago.

Cronbach (1956, p. 173–174), after reviewing a number of efforts to predict with projective techniques, reached the conclusion that the reason why validation troubles are encountered is that assessors must make "hazardous inferences," meaning that global assessors have ventured "predictions of behavior in unanalyzed situations, using tests whose construct interpretations are dubious and personality theory which has more gaps than solid matter." Another difficulty with using projective techniques lies in the possibility that different assessors may draw different inferences. It has, in fact, been remarked that one can tell more about the psychologist than about the subject from reviewing protocols and assessments based on projective techniques.

Riccuiti (1962), in a review of a good many recent studies of projective techniques, called attention to two important general matters related to the validation of these techniques. One is that situational factors, such as the instructions given subjects in the testing process, have an important effect upon projective responses. (See also Masling, 1960.) Presumably, failure to place these situational factors sufficiently under control has had a deleterious effect on the search for successful validation.

Riccuiti also found fault with the general design of projective test validating studies. Although he admired contributions by Campbell and Fiske (1959) and Maher, Watt, and Campbell (1960), who sought evidence of discriminant validation by using multiple tests and measuring multiple traits, he concluded (p. 74) that "Projective techniques of high construct validity and reliability are not likely to be produced without the simultaneous development of a progressively more valid theory of projection-response behavior."

Still on the merit of projective techniques, Super (1959, pp. 30–31) has remarked:

A few years ago someone suggested that if we were honest we would cease using projective techniques in assessment, since they have not been shown to have predictive validity . . . Although we have considered dropping the skill course in projectives in my own institution, we still require that all clinical, counseling, most people in personnel, and all school psychologists devote a large block of time to acquiring some competence with these projective techniques, the utility of which is unknown . . . We do this for three reasons: 1) . . . such psychologists are expected to have these skills . . . 2) . . . they can learn something useful about clinical interaction by studying these procedures, and, 3) the hope that familiarity with these methods may yet provide psychologists with a basis for some major break-through in the field of personality assessment.*

The foregoing paragraphs have presented an infinitesimal sample of discussion, comment, and studies in which attempts have been made to validate empirically projective technique results, with variable but generally negative findings. One reason for the lack of predictive efficiency, in addition to those listed above, may well be that projective tests measure the behavior response *potential* of individuals under conditions free of the usual social constraints. These conditions may be appropriate for obtaining information about how subjects might typically *like* to behave. But when predictions based on these responses are used to estimate the likelihood of the occurrence of similar responses in a real-life situation, they fall short of accuracy because behavior in the real-life situation is influenced by the environment—social constraints *are* operating. Thus the individual responds in a manner that he has learned for the particular environmental situation, rather than in the way he might like to respond in the abstract.

To Super's reasons favoring the continuing study of projective techniques, quoted above, two more might be added. First, there remains the not-well-documented but still unresolved argument that certain very experienced, perceptive clinicians *can* accurately predict some kinds of behavior. If there is any small hope that this is so, perhaps the key to their greater understanding may some day be found—for example, through studies like those of McArthur (1954). Second, there is some evidence—as will be discussed later in this chapter—to indicate that projective techniques *used in conjunction with other measuring devices* can help to develop an assessment picture that does successfully predict in accordance with a carefully defined outside criterion.

Self-Evaluating Techniques

Techniques of self-evaluation include paper-and-pencil tests, questionnaires, or inventories requesting the subject to rate various statements of interest, attitude, values, or specific examples of behavior. Each statement is rated according to how well it describes the subject, as he sees himself, or according to what he considers to be a desirable value, attitude, interest, or way of behaving. The objective of the personality assessor is to obtain from the subject a description of himself representing his typical behavior or reactions.

---

* D. E. Super, "Theories and Assumptions Underlying Approaches to Personality Assessment," in B. M. Bass and I. A. Berg (eds.), *Objective Approaches to Personality Assessment* (Princeton: D. Van Nostrand, 1959). Quoted by permission of the publisher.

One of the most widely used and researched instruments of this kind is the MMPI (Minnesota Multiphasic Personality Inventory) (Hathaway and McKinley, 1951). Its specific purpose is to differentiate among pathological and normal individuals and, accordingly, it was developed on the basis of responses from persons representing particular pathological patterns. But many other personality questionnaires have been developed on the basis of normal populations. The total number of such paper-and-pencil tests now in existence and on the market has been estimated to be at least 500 (Watson, 1959).

Subjects filling out personality questionnaires are typically asked to give the answer that seems to fit best (best describes their behavior, best tells what they think should be done, etc.), and they are also told that there are no right or wrong answers. They are often given little or no information about what the investigator is investigating. The conditions under which the tests are given are standardized. The situation for the subject is considered to be more highly structured than that in projective tests; that is, the number of answers and range of answers is confined to the alternatives given for each question. At the same time, it is not so highly structured as the situation in certain other types of objective tests where it is clear that there are right and wrong answers to each question and where the subject is encouraged to do his best to select the right answers.

Three techniques may be used in the development of personality inventories (Edwards, 1959). One method has been to use criterion groups, as in the case of the MMPI; in this procedure the content of the item is not so important as its ability to differentiate between members and nonmembers of the criterion group. Cattell and others have used the method of factor analysis, starting with no preconceived idea of which items will have content relevant to others or to any outside criterion or conception of a trait, but factoring the responses in order to determine the loadings and discover patterns of relationship in the data. Edwards and others have used a third technique, which he calls the construct approach, wherein the psychologist starts with some idea of a personality variable that interests him and attempts even in the earliest stages of the questionnaire's development to select items apparently related to the personality variable under study.

There is some difference of opinion about how objective personality questionnaires are, and under what conditions they are or are not considered as sufficiently objective *tests* to be of scientific value. As described in Watson (1959), some consider objectivity as complete independence from examiner effects; others consider objective those tests whose scores would be the same if scored by different but competent people. Cattell (1959, 1963) emphasizes the importance of the subject's not knowing how his answers will be interpreted by the examiner. Edwards (1959), who defines an objective test as one for which the method of scoring is "rigorously defined," has developed a forced-choice pattern wherein, by using independent judges, he develops items equated in "social desirability," so that the individual must in effect choose between two items which seem equally desirable. His opportunity to make selections on the basis of what might make him "look good" is thereby greatly minimized.

The results of attempts to achieve empirical validation of most personality questionnaires or inventories have been, on the whole, disappointing. An analysis of some of the factors involved in self-evaluation instruments may shed some light on possible reasons for the poor reliability and validity findings. Some of the following points have been made by Thorndike and Hagen (1961).

There is, first, the fact that the questionnaires are written. They demand, therefore, a certain level of literacy from the subject. Beyond that, there is the matter of how well the subject understands the question or statement and how he interprets it. Then the subject is asked to analyze his own behavior and decide whether it fits a statement or item this way or that. Assuming every effort on the part of the subject to be honest in his self-assessment, it is hard to imagine that some individuals will not be able to evaluate themselves with more insight than others. Still another point is the willingness of the respondent to say frankly what he feels about himself. He may have a tendency to select the answer he thinks would put him in the best light. Edwards' control for social desirability, or Cattell's condition that subjects must not know how the assessor will score his response, would counteract this objection; but there are many questionnaires in use containing items whose content is obvious in the sense of allowing a socially acceptable response. Finally, there is the point that a subject may give different descriptions of himself depending on the purpose for which he is taking the test or filling out the questionnaire. If he is participating in a research project for experimental purposes, he may answer questions one way; if he is seeking admission to college or trying to get a job, he may answer entirely differently.

Edwards' summary (1959, p. 116) seems appropriate:

Probably all of us who have attempted to develop objective personality inventories are not overly satisfied with the results of our efforts. There is much that remains to be done in the way of research before we will have personality inventories that are judged satisfactory as, let us say, achievement tests.*

Observations of Behavior

The reader will recall that earlier we established two very general sources of information about an individual's personality. One was directly from the person himself, as in the case of projective techniques and self-evaluating schedules of one kind or another. We turn now to the other source of assessment, observations of the individual by others.

Techniques for obtaining information about individual personality on the basis of observation by others has ranged from the collection of anecdotes or recommendations to the construction of "forced-choice" instruments designed to disguise the meaning of the rating to the rater and thereby to control for his tendency to be biased about the person he is rating. The observers (or reporters) have been teachers, peers, or employers asked to give their holistic impressions about "what

---

* A. L. Edwards, "Social Desirability and Test Construction," in B. M. Bass and I. A. Berg (eds.), *Objective Approaches to Personality Assessment* (Princeton: D. Van Nostrand, 1959). Quoted by permission of the publisher.

kind of person this is;" or trained experimental observers recording the number of errors and trials involved in an objectively defined task.

Observations about behavior are recorded differently according to the nature of the research design. Anecdotal reports or ratings involving preferences (Which member of this group would you prefer to lead you out of a dangerous situation?), as well as observations based on selecting which individual being rated best fits a description given, all rest on the observers' synthesis of their reactions to the individual being rated. The observers in effect summarize their impressions, and these impressions are in turn based on the sample of behavior they have been exposed to and on what they have perceived of that behavior.

Counting the frequency or intensity of emitted behavior, or observing categorized responses, involves the selection and definition of responses to be counted by the investigator. What is to be measured is defined with sufficient objectivity so that other researchers could presumably make the same observations and obtain the same frequency or intensity of response, if given the same behavior to record.

Bass (1959) summarizes some of the varied observational techniques (as well as, by the way, self-evaluation techniques) that have been used in the assessment of successful leadership. Among the methods he notes are: behavior check lists beginning with empirical surveys and ending with factored scales of leader behavior; observations of what roles are played by members of a group, according to certain categories—a method said to produce high observer reliability; and observed changes in a group resulting from interaction with others. An example of the latter technique from his own work (1959, p. 156) involves having

. . . a group of subjects privately rank order their initial decisions about the true order of familiarity of five words. Or they may be asked to rank five cities according to size of population . . . Then they carry on a discussion to reach a group decision. Finally, they privately register their own rankings again. Three measures of successful leadership — public, private, and relative — are derived from the correlations between members in opinions before and after discussion.*

Some psychologists have built up entire theories about personality on the basis of observations of both lower animal forms and people (Dollard and Miller, 1950). Other researchers have leaned toward the exclusive use of either *homo sapiens* or the lower animals as subjects. Two examples are presented below, showing the scope in recent literature of the kinds of observations that have been made.

Harlow (1962) set out to study the heterosexual affectional system in monkeys. He measured, among other things, the frequency of threat responses by males and females, the frequency of withdrawal responses by males and females, the percentage of male mounts showing dorsal orientation, the frequency of grooming responses by males and females, the frequency of play-initiations by males and females to

---

* B. M. Bass, "An Approach to the Objective Assessment of Successful Leadership," in B. M. Bass and I. A. Berg (eds.), *Objective Approaches to Personality Assessment* (Princeton: D. Van Nostrand, 1959). Quoted by permission of the publisher.

monkeys of the same and to the other sex, and the frequency of "rough and tumble" play for males and females. Each of these measures was made over many months at regular daily periods of observation, and the frequency of each event was plotted against the chronological age of the monkeys. From the data, Harlow reached the conclusion that male and female infant monkeys show differences in sex behavior from the time they are two months old on. Differences were statistically significant. The author was convinced that the data have generality for man and that they indicate that (p. 6) "sex behaviors differ in large part because of genetic factors." However, the affectional system is also influenced by infantile environmental experiences. The implications of these findings for human personality were by no means lost on the author.

Murray (1963), making an entirely different set of observations on humans, studied the reactions of people subjected to stressful interpersonal disputes. Deliberately manipulating the environment, Murray plunged an unsuspecting subject into discussion with an apparent peer. While the subject was verbally attacked by his opposite (peer) in the experimental environment, Murray measured manifestations of anger. Data were classified into covert manifestations, physiological manifestations (including heart rate and respiration), and overt manifestations, including (p. 32)

(a) physiognomic and motoric phenomena which can be seen in the silent moving picture and analyzed in great detail by means of a perceptoscope projecting one frame at a time; (b) verbal productions of an oppositional, rude, critical, aggressive, or insulting nature which can be read in the typed protocol; (c) vocal qualities, such as louder and more rapid speech which, in conjunction with the verbal productions, can be heard in the playback of the magnetic tape . . . (d) temporal patterns of these motoric, verbal, and vocal manifestations, which can be synchronously seen and heard in the sound movie.

The results suggested, in part, (p. 35) "that individual differences among our subjects in respect to basal heart rate and degree of sensitivity of the neurocardiac system were not so great or influential as to cancel the possibility of demonstrating a consistent relationship between motivation and heart rate under the stressful conditions that existed."

Given the enormous scope of observations that potentially could be made, it is difficult to generalize about the merit of observational approaches to the measurement of personality. The pros and cons, furthermore, range across the full scale of data collected, from what must be considered more "subjective" (as with anecdotes) to what is usually conceded to be more "objective" (as with heart rate). Moreover, even where it may be agreed that the data collected are objective, there is disagreement as to whether the environment in which the observations are made is an appropriate one for collecting information truly revealing about personality. Thus Murray, whose interest is certainly holistic and who uses what might be called projective techniques in conjunction with what we are calling here observations of behavior, *might* be considered by Cattell to have formulated, in the study just reported, an unproductive situation in which to measure behavior. We base this guess on the following quote from Cattell (1959, pp. 44–45):

There are two objections to the manipulative experimental design in the field of personality. The first is that you ought not to do it, and the second is that, if you throw ethics aside and proceed, the artificial insult of the experiment may create a situation quite different from the naturally occurring one.*

Some of Cattell's measuring devices such as finger-mazes presumably squeeze under the wire of his declared aim of allowing (p. 45) "life itself to make the experiments, in naturally functioning organic wholes," by being introduced as only one piece of an enormous array of behavior observations.

In general, it seems safe to say that objectively reported observations of behavior have the following advantages in measuring personality: Because the response to be counted is defined operationally, the observations usually have high reporter reliability. Two investigators will get the same results. The procedure includes making a record of what actually occurs in a setting that may be defined as natural or not, depending on whose side one takes. Observations can be made in situations where verbal communication is either not practical or not appropriate.

Disadvantages or problems seem to be the control of observer bias, especially in ratings of others; the definition of a meaningful segment of behavior to observe and determination of its significance to personality assessment; considerations involving the fact that only a segment of behavior is observed, and that it is observed out of context; and, in the case of observations made in situations involving complex environmental manipulation or requiring complex analyses, the cost of making observations.

DISCUSSION

This chapter began with the statement that the *measurement* of personality encompassed four ingredients: (1) processes or traits imagined but not seen; (2) observable behavior; (3) the environmental context; and (4) the selective perceptions of the observer or measurer. Nowhere in this chapter, however, have we attempted to define personality itself. In declining to present a general definition, we are certainly not alone. Pepinsky (1959, p. 223), who studied and summarized a variety of discussions and measures of personality, stated that "Strangely enough, none of the authors has stopped to define the term, 'personality.'" And Fiske (1963, p. 469), in a recent review of the measurement problem in personality, said, "Closer scrutiny of the problem suggests that, in operational terms, it is meaningless to talk about the way a person usually behaves."

---

* R. B. Cattell, "Foundations of Personality Measurement Theory in Multivariate Experiment," in B. M. Bass and I. A. Berg (eds.), *Objective Approaches to Personality Assessment* (Princeton: D. Van Nostrand, 1959). Quoted by permission of the publisher.

The complex composition of personality makes it difficult to give a single meaningful definition of just what personality is. This difficulty is not very different from that encountered in attempting to define other qualities or traits—such as, for example, intelligence—which we talk about in common speech and measure for a variety of purposes in every day life. However, we *can* define intelligence or personality, or aspects of them, in any given instance where we can specify the *purpose* for which we are measuring. To put it another way, it may be reasonably argued that personality, like beauty, is in the eye of the beholder.

If we leave aside any attempt to develop an overall definition of personality, there are still certain general and unifying statements that may be made about the measurement of personality, and perhaps some suggestions for improving the measurement. That improved measurement is desirable is evident from the liberal sprinkling, in preceding pages, of comment concerning the lack of validity or predictive efficiency for most of the tactics used.

In the course of this chapter, we have discussed many examples of the four ingredients initially enumerated as elements of personality measurement. Internal processes or traits, imagined but not seen, have ranged from a term like "anxiety" to a letter-number label given to a complex of posited traits. Observed behavior of rats, monkeys, kindergartners, and angered men has been reported. Approaches and theories influencing the selective perception of the assessors have been outlined, from the highly flexible to the rigid; and the concern among some that assessors should assess themselves has been voiced. It is about the fourth ingredient, the environmental context, that additional general comment needs to be made, for vague or specific discontent about this matter is increasingly being expressed by researchers in personality measurement. (See, among others, Abelson, 1962; Stern, Stein, and Bloom, 1956; Cronbach, 1956; Riccuiti, 1962; and Masling, 1960.)

In the opinion of this writer, an important key to improving the predictive efficiency, or empirical validity, of many personality measures lies in developing conformity between the measurement environment and the criterion environment. The hypothesis we put forth here is that the greater the similarity between criterion environment and measurement environment, the greater are the chances of achieving high empirical validity.

Personality typically has been observed or measured in one environment, with attempts made to predict how the personality will manifest itself through future behavior in environments that may be similar or dissimilar to the measurement environment. The *continuity or discontinuity of the environmental conditions* for observing and validating behavior ought to be studied intensively. It is expected that predictive efficiency will be greater when measurement and criterion environments are continuous, and lower when they are discontinuous.

The results of a study performed by Sears (1951) may be reinterpreted as an example of the effect of continuity and discontinuity between measurement and criterion environments upon prediction of behavior. Two measures were made of aggressive acts of preschool children, one in a doll-play session, and the other in the environmental context of a nursery school. The relationship between aggressiveness in these two situations was low (0.13). This finding was contrary to what one would hope for if he wished to use aggressive acts in a fantasy environment (the measurement environment) to predict aggressiveness in the school environment (the criterion environment). Sears further analyzed this relationship by dividing the children into three groups (low, medium, and high) on the basis of measures of the punitiveness of the mother in treating aggressive acts in the home. If one assumes that punitive action towards aggressive responses in the home would lead to few aggressive responses by the child in the home and in other environments where sanctions were applied against aggressive acts, then one would expect to find few aggressive responses in the school environment among children from the highly punitive group of mothers.

In the Sears data, this finding was in fact obtained when aggressive responses were compared using the home as the measurement environment and the school as the criterion environment. However, the opposite of these results was obtained when the doll-play sessions were used as the criterion environment. In that case, the highest number of aggressive responses was made by the highly punitive group.

If it is assumed that the school and home environments are relatively continuous in the way they apply sanctions to aggressive behavior, and if punitiveness in the home leads to few aggressive responses in the home, then few aggressive responses at school would be expected, as Sears found. On the other hand, when the environments are discontinuous—as are the home environment and the fantasy doll-play session (in the latter case negative sanctions are not generally applied against aggressive acts)—one might well find the children of highly punitive mothers emitting a high number of aggressive responses, as Sears did find.

In more recent studies, Stern, Stein, and Bloom (1956) and Stein (1963) deliberately and thoroughly studied the criterion environment and created a model for prediction. They were attempting to assess the potential of students for success in certain programs of study. Far from ignoring the criterion environment, they based their predictions on, for example, the degree of conformity between the faculty's conception of the ideal student and a variety of measures of student characteristics. In setting up a hypothetical model for success, they actually created good continuity between measurement and criterion environments.

Using a variety of measures (including interviews, biographical information, objective paper-and-pencil tests, and several projective techniques), the authors obtained high correlations between their predictions and actual student performance. During the course of this chapter, it has been suggested several times that some measures of personality which ordinarily seem to lack empirical validity—notably the projective tests—give evidence of empirical validity when they are used in conjunction with other tests. The work of Stern, Stein, and Bloom (1956) reported here is an instance of the achievement of empirical validity using projective measures of personality in conjunction with other measures. On the basis of our own hypothesis that continuity between measurement and criterion environments may be a necessary condition for validation, it might be fair to add that the private world measured by projective techniques could seldom if ever have sufficient continuity with the public world associated with empirical validation to produce high validity coefficients. Perhaps it is because of the "private world" environment of the projective techniques that other measures must be used in conjunction with them in order to predict accurately to the criterion environment.

Outside the realm of projective techniques, most studies concerning the prediction of college grades show that the high school record is a better predictor of what the college record will be like than are objective tests of scholastic aptitude. This result well may be due in part to the continuity between school and college environments, as contrasted with the discontinuity between the criterion (college) environment and the measurement environment of objective tests. In the school environment, students bring to bear upon their achievement many different kinds of behavior that influence grades in both the school and college environments. Much of this behavior goes unobserved in the objective test environment.

A preliminary and admittedly conjectural piece of research by Wing (1962, 1963) suggests another example of the many possible ways environmental or cultural discontinuity might be studied. He considered the cultural backgrounds (principally, the type of high school, geographical location, urban or rural character of the home, and parents' occupational, educational, and economic backgrounds) of students who were entering a particular university. He found evidence indicating that adjustments might be made in using preentrance test scores for prediction of success in the college course work, the type of adjustments necessary being related to the degree of continuity between the precollege cultural background and the cultural milieu of the university attended. It is at least possible— assuming that the results suggested by this study can be cross-checked and validated in other colleges—that the discontinuity factor may explain some of the error that is now current in the prediction of success in college.

To say that the continuity of measurement and criterion environments needs to be studied in order to improve the empirical validation of personality assessments is to breathe new hope, it seems to the present writer, into the validity potential of some old and standard means of measuring personality. It may be that discontinuity between measurement and criterion environments has had the effect of disguising or masking some relationships that otherwise would have been consistently observable.

SUMMARY

Three general approaches to the measurement of personality have been presented. The first of these was the clinical approach, characterized by attention to the whole individual, developmentally and in all his current personality manifestations. Other salient characteristics of the clinical approach are the importance of the clinician or measurer himself as a tool in the analysis, the flexibility of the clinical observer, the wide range of observations that may be made, and the fertility of the strategy in the production of concepts and hypotheses about personality.

Experimental manipulation was presented as a second strategy for the measurement of personality. An important requirement of that approach is that the behavior to be observed and the environmental conditions for the observation must be stipulated as part of the experimental design. Once the design is set, the observer must adhere rigidly to a specific pattern in the collection of data. The manipulation is designed to test the correctness of hypotheses, explicitly stated, usually in terms of dependent and independent variables. Unlike the clinical approach, experimental manipulation may focus on pieces or parts of personality, one or a few traits at a time. These selected topics of interest may be studied among cross sections of people—or lower animal forms—organized into groups for control in the testing of hypotheses.

The third approach to personality measurement, statistical manipulation, was described as having some features in common with each of the other two, with a commitment to observing the personality holistically, as in the clinical approach, and a commitment to rigorous, countable measurement conditions, as in the experimental approach. The statistical researcher processes large quantities of data mathematically to discern patterns which may then form the basis for hypotheses to be tested. Research of this kind is hypothesis-generating. In his studies, the statistical manipulator utilizes a wide variety of kinds of tests and large numbers of subjects representing cross sections of different age groups or cultures.

Following the description of these general strategies for measuring personality, some specific techniques utilized in the various approaches were discussed. Considerations of the economy, reliability, and validity were touched upon as general background, and then three kinds of techniques were discussed more fully: projective techniques, self-evaluating techniques, and observations of behavior. Some merits and limitations of each group of techniques were presented.

Discussion following these presentations dealt with the fact that most techniques for measuring personality fail to yield evidence of high predictive efficiency. The possible importance of continuity or discontinuity between measurement environments and criterion environments was brought out, and research in environmental continuity was suggested as an area for potentially fruitful work in personality measurement.

REFERENCES

ABELSON, R. P., "Commentary: Situational variables in personality research," in S. Messick and J. Ross (eds.), *Measurement in Personality and Cognition.* New York: John Wiley & Sons, 1962, pp. 241–246

ALLEN, R. M., *Personality Assessment Procedures.* New York: Harper and Brothers, 1958

ALLPORT, G. W., "What units shall we employ?" in G. Lindzey (ed.), *Assessment of Human Motives.* New York: Rinehart, 1958, pp. 239–258

ALLPORT, G. W., *Pattern and Growth in Personality.* New York: Holt, Rinehart and Winston, 1961

BASS, B. M., "An approach to the objective assessment of successful leadership," in B. M. Bass and I. A. Berg (eds.), *Objective Approaches to Personality Assessment.* Princeton: D. Van Nostrand, 1959, pp. 146–168

BECK, S. J., *Rorschach's Test.* New York: Grune and Stratton, 1944

BERG, I. A., and J. S. COLLIER, "Personality and group differences in extreme response sets." *Educ. and Psychol. Meas.* **13,** 164–169 (1953)

BURTON, A., and R. E. HARRIS, *Case Histories in Clinical and Abnormal Psychology.* New York: Harper and Brothers, 1947

CAMPBELL, D. T., and D. W. FISKE, "Convergent and discriminant validation by the multitrait-multimethod matrix." *Psychol. Bull.* **56,** 81–105 (1959)

CATTELL, R. B., "Foundations of personality measurement theory in multivariate experiment," in B. M. Bass and I. A. Berg (eds.), *Objective Approaches to Personality Assessment.* Princeton: D. Van Nostrand, 1959, pp. 42–65

CATTELL, R. B., "Personality measurement related to source trait structure," in S. Messick and J. Ross (eds.), *Measurement in Personality and Cognition.* New York: John Wiley & Sons, 1962, pp. 249–267

CATTELL, R. B., "Concepts of personality growing from multivariate experiment," in J. M. Wepman and R. W. Heine (eds.), *Concepts of Personality.* Chicago: Aldine Publishing Company, 1963, pp. 413–448

CRONBACH, L. J., "Studies of the group Rorschach in relation to success in the college of the University of Chicago." *J. Educ. Psychol.* **41,** 65–82 (1950)

CRONBACH, L. J., "Assessment of individual differences." *Annu. Rev. Psychol.* **7,** 173–196 (1956)

DOLLARD, J., and N. E. MILLER, *Personality and Psychotherapy.* New York: McGraw-Hill, 1950

EDWARDS, A. L., "Social desirability and personality test construction," in B. M. Bass and I. A. Berg (eds.), *Objective Approaches to Personality Assessment.* Princeton: D. Van Nostrand, 1959, pp. 100–118

FERGUSON, L. W., *Personality Measurement.* New York: McGraw-Hill, 1952

FISKE, D. W., "Problems in measuring personality," in J. M. Wepman and R. W. Heine (eds.), *Concepts of Personality.* Chicago: Aldine Publishing Company, 1963, pp. 449–473

FRANK, L. K., "Projective methods for the study of personality." *J. Psychol.* **8,** 389–413 (1939)

GARFIELD, S. L., "The clinical method in personality assessment," in J. M. Wepman and R. W. Heine (eds.), *Concepts of Personality.* Chicago: Aldine Publishing Company, 1963, pp. 474–502

HARLOW, H. F., "The heterosexual affectional system in monkeys." *Amer. Psychol.* **17,** 1–9 (1962)

HATHAWAY, S. R., and J. C. MCKINLEY, *Manual for the Minnesota Multiphasic Personality Inventory (Rev. ed.).* New York: Psychological Corporation, 1951

HOLT, R. R., "A clinical-experimental strategy for research in personality," in S. Messick and J. Ross (eds.), *Measurement in Personality and Cognition.* New York: John Wiley & Sons, 1962, pp. 269–283

HOLTZMAN, W. H., "Objective scoring of projective tests," in B. M. Bass and I. A. Berg (eds.), *Objective Approaches to Personality Assessment.* Princeton: D. Van Nostrand, 1959, pp. 119–145

KELLY, E. L., "Theory and technique of assessment." *Ann. Rev. Psychol.* **5,** 281–311 (1954)

KLOPFER, B., and D. M. KELLEY, *The Rorschach Technique (Rev. Ed.).* New York: World Book Company, 1946

KLUCKHOHN, C., and H. A. MURRAY, *Personality in Nature, Society, and Culture.* New York: Alfred A. Knopf, 1950

LOEVINGER, JANE, "Objective tests as instruments of psychological theory." *Psychological Reports* **3,** Monograph Supplement No. 9 (Missoula, Montana: Box 1441), 1957, 635–694

LOUTTIT, C. M., *Clinical Psychology (Rev. Ed.).* New York: Harper and Brothers, 1947

LUNDIN, R. W., *Personality: An Experimental Approach.* New York: MacMillan Company, 1961

MCARTHUR, C., "Analyzing the clinical process." *J. Counseling Psychol.* **4,** 203–206 (1954)

MCARTHUR, C., "The dynamic model." *J. Counseling Psychol.* **3,** 169–171 (1956)

MAHER, B. A., N. WATT, and D. T. CAMPBELL, "Comparative validity of two projective and two structured attitude tests in a prison population." *J. Applied Psychol.* **44,** 284–288 (1960)

MASLING, J., "The influence of situational and interpersonal variables in projective testing." *Psychol. Bull.* **57,** 65–85 (1960)

MCCLELLAND, D. C., J. W. ATKINSON, R. A. CLARK, and E. L. LOWELL, *The Achievement Motive.* New York: Appleton-Century-Crofts, 1953

MEEHL, P. E., *Clinical Versus Statistical Prediction.* Minneapolis: University of Minnesota Press, 1954

MORGAN, C. D., and H. A. MURRAY, "A method for investigating fantasies: The thematic apperception test." *Archives of Neurology and Psychiatry* **34,** 289–306 (1935)

MUNROE, RUTH L., "Prediction of the adjustment and academic performance of college students by a modification of the Rorschach method." *Applied Psychol. Monographs* **7,** 1–104 (1945)

MURRAY, H. A., *Explorations in Personality.* New York: Oxford University Press, 1938

MURRAY, H. A., "Studies of stressful interpersonal disputations." *Amer. Psychologist* **18,** 28–36 (1963)

Mussen, P., and L. Distler, "Masculinity, identification, and father-son relationships." *J. Abnormal Soc. Psychol.* **59,** 350–356 (1959)

Pepinsky, H. B., "Summary and conclusions," in B. M. Bass and I. A. Berg (eds.), *Objective Approaches to Personality Assessment.* Princeton: D. Van Nostrand, 1959, pp. 217–224

Riccuiti, H., "Development and application of projective techniques of personality." *Rev. Educ. Res.* **32,** 64–77 (1962)

Sears, R. R., "Personality." *Annu. Rev. of Psychol.* **1,** 105–118 (1950)

Sears, R. R., "Social behavior and personality development," in T. Parsons and E. A. Shils (eds.), *Toward a General Theory of Action.* Cambridge: Harvard University Press, 1951, pp. 465–478

Skinner, B. F., *Cumulative Record.* New York: Appleton-Century-Crofts, 1959

Stein, M. I., *Personality Measures in Admissions.* New York: College Entrance Examination Board, 1963

Stern, G. G., M. I. Stein, and B. S. Bloom, *Methods in Personality Assessment.* Glencoe, Ill.: The Free Press, 1956

Super, D. E., "Theories and assumptions underlying approaches to personality assessment," in B. M. Bass and I. A. Berg (eds.), *Objective Approaches to Personality Assessment.* Princeton: D. Van Nostrand, 1959, pp. 24–41

Thorndike, R. L., and E. Hagen, *Measurement and Evaluation in Psychology and Education* (2nd ed.). New York: John Wiley & Sons, 1961

Tomkins, S. S., *The Thematic Apperception Test.* New York: Grune and Stratton, 1947

Tomkins, S. S., "Commentary: The ideology of research strategies," in S. Messick and J. Ross (eds.), *Measurement in Personality and Cognition.* New York: John Wiley & Sons, 1962, pp. 285–294

Watson, R. I., "Historical review of objective personality testing: The search for objectivity," in B. M. Bass and I. A. Berg (eds.), *Objective Approaches to Personality Assessment.* Princeton: D. Van Nostrand, 1959, pp. 1–23

Weiss, P., B. Groesbeck, and M. Wertheimer, "Achievement motivation, academic aptitude, and college grades." *Educ. Psychol. Meas.* **19,** 663–666 (1959)

Wing, C. W., "The use of test data in admissions." *J. Association of College Admissions Counselors* **7,** 25–28 (1962)

Wing, C. W., "Do family finances influence college adjustment?" *J. Association of College Admissions Counselors* **9,** 17–19 (1964)

CHAPTER 10

THE MEASUREMENT OF CREATIVITY

FRANK BARRON, *University of California, Berkeley*

PROBLEMS IN MAKING UP TESTS

A primary strategic consideration in devising tests of creativity derives from the practical need for tests that can be administered to groups of subjects rather than to one subject at a time, that can be scored mechanically without the intermediation of skilled judgment, and that depend on simple enumeration which can yield frequency distributions readily susceptible to statistical analysis.

This set of requirements, however, bumps head-on immediately into the nature of the creative act, which most commonly is quite complex and, if it is to be recognized, must have an observer capable of embracing its complexities. Emerson once declared that the person closest to the thinker of an original thought is he who first recognizes its originality. Thomas Huxley is reputed to have exclaimed, upon first hearing the statement of Darwin's theory of natural selection, "Now why didn't I think of that!" Even though he hadn't thought of it, he recognized immediately its originality and validity. A mechanical scoring system, so far as we know, could not have done the same.

This difficulty applies to the evaluation of any complex symbolic production. Consider the following three examples from the writer's own experience.

1) Graduate students who were serving as subjects in an assessment study were asked to construct a mosaic out of one-inch-square pieces of colored cardboard, each piece being solid-colored, with a dozen or so colors available. The instructions were to build the mosaic design in a defined area, rectangular in shape, the dimensions being 8 inches in height and 10 inches in width. One subject, however, turned the frame around, so that the vertical dimension was 10 inches and the horizontal dimension 8 inches and he then proceeded to construct a question mark in yellow on a light gray background. Another subject selected white as the only color he would use, so that in his mosaic construction there was no definition of figure by colors within the given frame.

2) In another study, a subject was presented with cards of the Rorschach Psychodiagnostic, a set of inkblots of somewhat ambiguous form, and was asked to tell what he saw in each blot. Unlike most subjects, who take the test card and look at the blot straight-on, he proceeded to inspect the card edgewise and even to bend cards in the middle to produce alterations in the area he could see. He gave

responses never before heard of by the examining psychologist, a veteran of several thousand Rorschach testings.

3) A subject in a study of dreaming reported no dreams with visual content; all her dreams were of voices.

In all these cases, the rater or raters were in a quandary as to how to evaluate the response. In the study of dreams, for example, the dreams of 150 subjects had been rated for originality with very high interrater agreement, but this particular subject's dreams were rated either quite high or quite low. The scorer for the Rohrschach test was certain that his subject's responses were "originals," for the test manual defines an original response as one which occurs no more often than once in one hundred examinations; but whether to score the responses O-plus (a "good" original) or O-minus (an original response which does not sufficiently respect the inkblot "reality") was difficult to decide. Artists who rated a large set of colored-paper mosaics gave the "question-mark" a very low rating, feeling that it was simply manneristic and that the subject had not really done the job he was asked to; a group of architects, however, were bemused and diverted by the all-white "non-mosaic" and thought it very clever.

This point is made at such length because of its crucial importance in the evaluation of the creative act. The merely eccentric is not creative even though it is in a statistical sense uncommon. But at the same time one must be wary of dismissing all eccentricity that is tinged with mannerism as "mere eccentricity." As I have written elsewhere (Barron, 1963a) in response to a question put to me by the late Albert Deutsch:

People who think oddly often act and dress oddly as well, although this is by no means always true. As children, creative people frequently realize that in some way they are different from those around them, and this inner difference in perception may readily give rise, intentionally or unintentionally, to outer differences. Sometimes, of course, the outer differences go along hand-in-glove with the inner. It is only when a person *puts on* differences, when he tries self-consciously to act or dress differently, that we begin to wonder whether the eccentricity is superficial and simply an act. In important movements in art, there are usually a certain number of untalented hangers-on who talk, dress, and act like the real artists, and may even be accepted as real artists, but who actually do not create. Frequently, however, the genuine artist or creative scientist is really distinctive in bearing, dress, and manner; therefore it would be a mistake to interpret even consciously adopted eccentricities as pretentious. The unusual individual often feels isolated, and he may be pardoned for flying the flag of his individuality.*

In brief, in scoring tests of creativity in which considerable latitude of interpretation is permitted both the testee and the evaluator or assessor, it is a good policy to be lenient in accepting the "far-out" response. Still, the optimal practical situation is one in which a derivative measure, one not requiring complex evaluation, can be

---

* F. Barron, "Creativity and Genius," in A. Deutsch (ed.), *The Encyclopedia of Mental Health* (New York: Franklin Watts, 1963). Quoted by permission of the publisher.

substituted for the test designed to evoke directly a creative behavior. If careful and complex ratings can be done just once, and then correlates of those ratings discovered in, for example, mechanically scored questionnaires, then such problems as objectivity, replicability, and ease of obtaining large samples will be solved.

With these few examples of some of the difficulties of test construction in mind, consider the following efforts to develop tests that meet the research need.

PERFORMANCE TESTS OF ORIGINALITY AND INGENUITY

If we assume that acts are original only in relation to some specified commonality, then the original must be defined relative to the usual, and the degree of originality must be specified statistically in terms of incidence of occurrence. Thus a first criterion for an original response is that it should have a certain stated uncommonness in the particular group being studied.

A second criterion that should be met if a response is to be called genuinely original, i.e., a new *form,* is that it must correspond to some extent, or be adaptive to, reality. The intent of this requirement is to exclude uncommon responses which are merely random, or which proceed from ignorance or delusion.

A variety of simple tests of originality have been developed. An example of a measure which meets the two criteria just discussed is the originality-scoring of the common test, Anagrams. In one study (Barron, 1957) the test word "generation" was administered to a sample of 100 military officers. The score for originality was a count of the number of uncommon (defined in that instance as one-in-a-hundred) *and correct* anagram solutions to the test word. Many subjects did not hesitate to offer solutions that were incorrect, and that were usually unique. In such instances, the application of the second criterion of originality was straightforward and decisive, consisting only of looking up the given spelling in a standard unabridged dictionary. Thus such solutions as "nation," "rate," and "gene" received scores of 0 because of their commonness, and such proposed solutions as "tanion," "etar," and "nege" received scores of 0 because of their unacceptability, while such comparatively rare and correct solutions as "onager," "argentine," and "ergot" received scores of 1.

A test scored by similar standards, although not by quite so unambiguous an arbiter as the dictionary, is Unusual Uses, one of the tests of the Guilford battery. The following is a hypothetical example, not drawn from the actual Guilford test. The examinee is asked to think of uses other than the common one for such an object as a sugar cube.

One quite common set of responses might be derived from the sugar cube's adaptability to service as a building block. Perhaps a less common response might be that it could be converted into a die and used for gambling. Or it could be conceived of as a water-soluble building block to be used as the base of a soap castle, and to be eroded at a given rate when placed in a pan filled with $\frac{1}{16}$-inch of water, so that the soap castle drops into the water at a specified time—in brief, the trigger of a watery time bomb, if you will. The "building block" type of response would be considered banal and scored 1 or 2 on a five-point scale; the "sugar cubes can be dice" response is a notch or two up on the originality scale, and might be scored 3, or possibly 4; the fanciful idea of a watery time bomb trigger might be scored 5, although on further thought it might be considered too zany or nonsensical to merit such a high score. Some scorers would perhaps be inclined to score it 0. The Unusual Uses test, then, does meet some criteria of desirability quite well, but there remains an area of uncertainty in the scoring.

One way to retain the advantages of a free-response test while yet employing machine-scoring is to make the response a verbal one, preferably a single word, and to offer the examinee, on a multiple-choice answer sheet, several alternative initial letters, only one of which is the initial letter of the response the examiner thinks is right. Flanagan (1963) has employed a version of this technique to advantage in his Ingenuity test, and it has been used in other tests of this sort as well. Here is an illustration provided by Flanagan:

As part of a manufacturing process, the inside lip of a deep cup-shaped casting is machine-threaded. The company found that metal chips produced by the threading operation were difficult to remove from the bottom of the casting without scratching the sides. A design engineer was able to solve this problem by having the operation performed

> A. i-----p h--h
> B. m-----n c--e
> C. f-----r w--l
> D. l-----d b--k
> E. u-----e d--n

The two words intended by the examiner as the correct solution to this problem are "upside down," corresponding to the letters given in choice E.*

There are two shortcomings in this sort of test. One is that the respondent who is clever with words but not ingenious in thinking his way through to physical solutions may arrive at the phrase "upside down" from the gestalt in alternative E, and then, having gotten the words "upside down" recognize that they do provide a good solution to the problem. This might be a sort of use of cleverness, but not the kind of ingenuity the test is seeking to measure.

Another objection is that an ingenious examinee may think of a fine solution which is not represented at all among the alternatives. The truly ingenious person might thus find the test extremely exasperating. Flanagan points out this difficulty, giving as an example in the above problem the possible use of a powerful magnet. He depends on the examinee's being sufficiently test-wise, or perhaps one should say test-broken, to discard the magnet solution and to try to think of other types of solutions.

---

* J. Flanagan, "Definition and Measurement of Ingenuity," in C. W. Taylor and F. Barron (eds.), *Scientific Creativity: Its Recognition and Development* (New York: John Wiley & Sons, 1963). Quoted by permission of the publisher.

An interesting application of this scoring method is provided by the Remote Associates test devised by Mednick (1962). It is a clever modification of one of the tests of the Guilford battery employing a similar scoring method, and it is of interest in this context because of the logic of development, a cross between the free-response methodology and the one-right-answer type of problem. Mednick began with the idea of constructing items from pairs of infrequently occurring response words to the Kent-Rosanoff Word Association test. The published Minnesota norms to the Kent-Rosanoff provided numerous examples of responses that occurred no more often than once-in-a-thousand. Mednick would pair two once-in-a-thousand responses, explain to the examinee how these responses were obtained, and then ask the examinee to reconstruct or recapture the original stimulus word. Suppose (again, as a hypothetical example) that the original stimulus word was "sugar." A quite common response might be "cube"; another might be "salt," another might be "sweet," still another might be "tea." If one combined the two words "cube" and "sweet" and asked the examinee to guess at the original stimulus words, most persons of average intelligence would soon arrive at "sugar." But if the paired words were "money" and "softsnow," both rather derivative associates of sugar as a means of persuasion, the task would be much more difficult. Mednick began with quite difficult items selected on the basis of observed statistical infrequency in the Minnesota norms (p less than 0.001), but found that the test was too hard and did not yield the sorts of distributions of scores he wanted. The present published version of the test employs the same basic idea, but three rather than two response words are given and they occur more frequently in normal associations: the words "pot," "butterflies," and "ulcer," e.g., to the stimulus word "stomach," or the words "brick," "out," and "boat" to the word "house."

One further example of a verbal test might be given, based on the same logic as Unusual Uses but designed to tap a different dimension, viz., capacity for metaphor. In this test (Barron, 1958), the examinee is given a stimulus image and asked to think of another image which is somewhat equivalent to it, or a metaphor for it. The test is scored both for originality and for aptness of metaphor, with the ideas of elegance and fit as two of the criteria. To the stimulus image "empty bookcases," for example, a common response is "an empty mind," or "a desert," or "a deserted room." Applying the scoring scheme for Unusual Uses, these appropriate but common metaphorical responses would receive scores of 1. "An abandoned beehive" is a more original and more apt metaphor, since it implies that the books were once active things as well as residents of their natural chamber. Busy bees, busy books, the product of busy minds; complexity of connotation, the hallmark of poetic metaphor, is at least reached for in this response, and it would be scored 3 or 4. Another uncommon response is "the vacant eyes of an idiot"; this too is an elegant and original equivalent. An empty bookcase is a mindless space; it is not just an empty space, but a vacant one, a space that was meant to be occupied, and perhaps even had earlier been occupied. The vacancy is tragic; an empty bookcase is a waste.

One or two other examples should serve to make the purpose of this test clear. To the stimulus image "sitting alone in a dark room," two common responses are "lying awake at night" and, even more banal, "a bear in a cave." Two uncommon and apt responses are "one letter in a mailbox" and "a coffin in an open grave." To the stimulus image "sound of a foghorn," a common response is "a frog's croak"; an uncommon one is "a public address system announcing disaster."

Just as in tests of intellectual aptitudes in general, there has been some tendency in the development of performance tests of creativity to depend heavily on verbal materials. Nonverbal constructions are certainly of great importance, however, and in such real-life creative activities as architecture, sculpture, painting, music, mathematics, and mechanical invention the chief aptitudes needed for creation are nonverbal. Guilford has properly emphasized this point in his development of a model for the structure of intellect, and he and his associates have gone ahead and developed a variety of nonverbal tests of creativity. Since his work is presented elsewhere in this volume, we shall draw our examples from contributions by other investigators.

The work of Hermann Rorschach (1942), a Swiss psychiatrist, deserves to be mentioned first, for it has had a most important effect on theory both in the psychology of personality as a whole and specifically in theories of perception and imagination. We have mentioned it already in discussing the problems of evaluating the "fit with reality" of a perceptual response which is original in terms of uncommonness, but which must meet the additional criterion of correspondence with the physical stimulus configuration that evoked it if it is to be called an "original-plus" in the Rorschach scoring.

A description of the development of the test may be found in Rorschach's monograph, *Psychodiagnostic: a Diagnostic Test Based on Perception.* The test consists of ten inkblots, some of which contain color while others are black and white. The blots are shown one at a time to the examinee, and he is asked to say what he thinks the blot or portions of the blot might be, or what they remind him of. The great diversity of response one finds to these inkblots—which were chosen by Rorschach after much experimentation, so that they would provide a wide sampling of important perceptual functions—makes the test a good candidate for the discovery of originality in the examinee's responses. Unfortunately, the scoring scheme is almost as ambiguous as the blots themselves, although this of course has not interfered with its popularity among clinical psychologists, since ambiguity at least leaves room for speculation, and if the Rorschach "pigeonholes" anyone it does so quite feebly and need not be taken too seriously or conclusively. An "original" response, then, since it does not have unambiguous denotative meaning, must be evaluated in the same way one evaluates fantasy or works of art. If the examiner himself cannot "see" the form the examinee "sees," he must try to find someone else who *can* see it. If after a reasonable effort in searching, the form still proves elusive, it is considered not to be "there." History furnishes us enough examples of misguided multitudes (fifty million Frenchmen have often been wrong) to make us wary of this sort of consensual verification. The Rorschach, more than any other test we have considered, confronts us with this problem.

The Rorschach has other shortcomings as well, and an effort by the present writer to remedy some of these difficulties in a new inkblot test led by a roundabout way to another measure of originality in inkblot perception. The effort may be worth reviewing as an exercise in test construction.

As users of the Rorschach know, the stimulus and the scoring scheme of the Psychodiagnostic are very complex, and the test does not lend itself well to any attempt to isolate variables and to separate out their correlational components. Although this complexity is important to the test as a vehicle for clinical observation, it contributes to certain psychometric shortcomings and unnecessary difficulties when the verification of theory is the chief concern.

One important difficulty with the scoring scheme is that the number of responses varies widely for different subjects. Productivity is itself an important variable, of course, but the present method of obtaining a measure of it tends to confound the evaluation of other measures which may be equally important. Subjects now cannot be compared in terms of absolute incidence of a given type of response, since this is partly a function of total number of responses. Furthermore, subjects cannot be compared in terms of *relative* incidence, for relative incidence of response in a given category varies in some nonlinear and as yet undetermined fashion with total number of responses. This in turn is dependent to some extent on stimulus properties of the blots; there is clearly a limitation to the number of responses which can be given in any single category, and after a certain point in the production of responses the more limited categories begin to suffer relative to the others.

What is needed, then, is a method of keeping the number of responses more or less constant for all subjects, while yet providing considerable opportunity for the subject's response tendencies to emerge. At the same time, stimulus strength should be weighted properly in evaluating response strength; one difficulty with the Rorschach measure of, for example, *M* tendency, is that it is a simple count of the number of human movement percepts which are verbalized by the subject, without regard for the power of the stimulus to evoke a human movement response in the average person.

Some of the difficulties were met by following these prescriptions: (a) increase the number of blots; (b) score only one response, the first, to each blot; (c) take systematic account of the relationship between stimulus strength and response tendency by employing the conventional experimental index of this relationship, namely, the response threshold; (d) isolate the main Rorschach variables and study them one at a time before attempting to study them all together.

The rationale of these prescriptions is simple and clear. An increase in the number of blots should achieve more representativeness on the stimulus side and more total-score reliability (since reliability may be increased, up to a point, by increasing test length). Scoring of only one response to each blot makes the absolute number of responses in each scoring category comparable from subject to subject, and makes feasible the use of some sort of standard score, such as Z-scores, so that the individual subject's performance may be immediately referred to that of the general population. (It might be pointed out, incidentally, that Rorschach ratios, such as M : Sum C, may be much more meaningful if they are ratios of Z-scores rather than absolute scores; Z-ratios would be free of the often unrecognized and cumbersome assumption underlying absolute score ratios, viz., that the blots themselves present precisely equal opportunity for the two contrasting experience-types, introversive and extratensive, to manifest themselves.) The weighting of stimulus strength in evaluating response strength is essentially a more differentiated way of scoring, comparable to the use of refined rather than crude weights in prediction; the addition of the concept of threshold makes the perceptual phenomenon more assimilable to established knowledge and methods in experimental psychology, which is all to the good so far as Rorschach theory is concerned. Finally, the study of variables in isolation, however unholistic it may seem, may really be the best possible foundation for the understanding of variables in interaction.

Human movement was taken as the first variable to be measured in accord with these prescriptions. The model for the construction of a measure of threshold for perception of human movement was the conventional stimulus series used to determine response thresholds in such sense modalities as the auditory, olfactory, tactile, and the like. Although stimulus strength or intensity is not determinable from physical properties of the stimulus in the case of inkblots, this is no great loss so long as relative frequencies of response can be established in large samples and with some stability. By arranging inkblots of known relative frequency in a regularly graduated series, with p values ranging from 0.00 to 1.00, a measure analagous to the usual perceptual stimulus series is constructed. The subject's threshold for human movement is then the ordinal position of that blot in the series at which he first gives a human movement response.

With these considerations in mind, 150 achromatic inkblots were constructed, using 4- by 6-inch sheets of white paper, which were then mounted on stiff cardboard of the same dimensions. Twenty-six blots were selected from the 150 on the basis of observed frequencies of M response in such a manner as to make a series with graduations of approximately 0.04.

The human movement response on the Rorschach test itself is thought to be a good indicator of imagination, ability to use fantasy constructively, and "inner resources." The threshold index constructed in the manner described does not correlate with such performance measures as the Guilford Unusual Uses test, but there are systematic differences between low and high threshold examinees in the expected direction: Those who react first to M-potentialities are more often described by observers who have watched them for three days in a living-in assessment situation as "intelligent" and "inventive" and possessed of wide interests. Those who are not alert to human forms in the blots are seen as "simple" and "practical"; they are described as dogmatic, rigid, inflexible in thought and action, and narrow in their interests.

The M-threshold blots proved readily adaptable to the scoring scheme already described for the Guilford Unusual Uses test. By tabulating frequencies of types of response to each blot, and then assigning weights of 1 to 5 in terms of "uncommonness" and "appropriateness," the test could be scored for originality.

Again, an example may help to make clear what is taken to be an original response as opposed to a banal one. One of the blots shows an ape-like figure in a crouched position. A common response is simply "an ape," or "a baboon." The crouch is interpretable as being an intermediate position between a squat and the upright, however, and if one imputes lively motion to it and sees the movement as upward, the ape can be seen as leaping up. Moreover, the humanoid face can be interpreted by a bit of charitable looseness as the face of a man. Finally, by an act that can only be called imagination, the entire inkblot can be seen, as one examinee saw it, as "Rodin's Thinker shouting 'Eureka!'" In the absence of the actual inkblot the reader will have to take this on faith if at all, but the response really is a divertingly apt and elegant resolution of the "problem" presented by the ambiguous blot.

The mosaic construction test has already been mentioned. Samples of original and unoriginal responses to it, as well as a reproduction of the inkblot described in the preceding paragraph, may be found in the author's *Scientific American* article "The psychology of imagination" (Barron, 1958). In that article too are presented examples of unoriginal and varying degrees of original response to still another performance test, the Franck Drawing Completion test. In that test, the examinee is presented with a few lines which are to serve as the beginning of a drawing, and he is asked to complete the drawing within a given frame. This free-response test was intended by the test's author, the late Kate Franck, to measure masculinity-femininity in figural expression, but it too, like some of the other tests mentioned, proved readily adaptable to an evaluation scheme for originality.

One other kind of test, derived in large part from the work of the Gestalt psychologists, particularly Wertheimer (1954), should be mentioned. A set of such tests was adapted by R. Crutchfield (1951) of the Institute of Personality Assessment and Research and incorporated into a series known as the Insight Puzzles test. It included such old standbys as the size-weight illusion, pinning the tail on a hidden donkey, and the word "summer" written once in longhand and joined to its mirror-image upside down below it, so that the most compelling gestalt at first glance is a corkscrew-like object. The task is then to "break the gestalt," or to see a simple figure masked in a more complex one, or to get rid of an overriding preconception; in brief, to take the necessary first step in finding a new way of seeing things.

Examples might be multiplied indefinitely, and the creation of new tests of this sort is proceeding apace. In all of the creativity-testing movement there is much activity, and test batteries themselves are so in flux that no single set of measures can be said to have captured the field in the way that some of the older intelligence tests and personality tests were able to do both before and immediately after World War II.

QUESTIONNAIRES AND PREFERENCE INVENTORIES

Simple frequency counts, in company with judicious evaluation of appropriateness, aptness, and elegance, provide the basis of scoring of most of the tests discussed above. A logical next step is to use such tests to provide criteria for the development of still other measures that lend themselves to machine scoring but that depend not on sampling in miniature certain kinds of creative abilities but rather on searching widely for the attitudes, preferences, and motives that are known to stimulate an individual to create.

In this latter kind of search, we are fortunate in having at hand a proven resource of great value in such time-tested item pools as the Strong Vocational Interest Blank (SVIB), the Minnesota Multiphasic Personality Inventory (MMPI), and similar questionnaires. An obvious first step is to use these item pools to discover verbally expressed attitudes that are correlated with measures of creativity.

We shall describe first a study by the present writer, employing the SVIB in this fashion. The group of 100 military officers already referred to had been tested not only with the SVIB but also with eight performance measures that furnish some indication of originality. These included: (1) three of the measures of the Guilford battery (Unusual Uses, Consequences B, and Plot Titles B); (2) two inkblot tests, scored for originality in the manner described above (the Rorschach Psychodiagnostic and the Barron movement-threshold blots); (3) Anagrams, using the test word "generation"; (4) the Thematic Apperception Test rated for originality by two raters working independently of one another; and (5) the Barron Word Synthesis test, rated for originality. (In the latter test, the examinee is given 50 words selected at random from a list of common nouns, adjectives, and adverbs, and told to make up a story that will enable him to use as many as possible of the listed words).

Standard scores on these eight tests were summed for the sample of 100 examinees, giving an overall index of originality (the Originality Composite Score). Scorers in the top 27% of the group were then compared with scorers in the bottom 27% on the Originality Composite Score, in terms of their responses to the SVIB. Significant difference between the groups were found for 85 of the items. The next logical step was to look for another group of subjects against which to cross-validate the 85-item scale so that items that had appeared by chance could be eliminated. The only available group that came close to meeting the necessary requirements was a sample of 243 other military officers who had taken the SVIB as well as the three Guilford measures and the Barron Word Synthesis test. A second criterion made up of these four measures was developed and scored for the 243 officers. Responses for the 85 original items were compared for 28 high scorers and 28 low scorers on the second criterion. Forty-nine of the 85 items continued to show statistically significant (0.05 level) differences, and the final SVIB Originality Scale is composed of these 49 items. Because the second criterion omits the visual perceptual measures, the scale is more accurately called the SVIB Verbal Originality Scale.

Table 1

SVIB #	Item	Scored response	Highs			Lows		
			L	I	D	L	I	D
1	Actor (not movie)	L	44	37	19	22	41	37
5	Artist	L	37	33	30	19	37	44
28	Consul	L	78	11	11	26	52	22
31	Editor	L	59	33	7	30	52	19
32	Electrical engineer	I	48	41	11	70	11	19
35	Factory manager	D	44	41	15	70	26	4
46	Jeweler	D	19	44	37	41	56	4
57	Magazine writer	L, I	52	37	11	26	30	44
61	Mining superintendent	D	33	41	26	59	30	11
62	Musician	L	52	15	33	26	41	33
64	Office clerk	I, D	0	41	59	19	22	59
76	Rancher	D	70	11	19	81	19	0
94	Toolmaker	D	41	22	37	44	41	15
98	Watchmaker	D	15	26	59	41	33	26
99	Wholesaler	I	26	56	19	52	33	15
104	Art	L	41	33	26	19	44	37
106	Botany	L	56	30	15	30	52	19
110	Dramatics	L	54	32	14	19	37	44
112	English composition	L	48	26	26	22	48	30
114	Geology	L	70	30	0	41	48	11
119	Literature	L, I	52	44	4	23	50	27
124	Music	L	48	30	22	22	56	22
126	Philosophy	L	59	37	4	26	59	15
127	Physical training	D	67	15	19	74	26	0
131	Public speaking	L	74	19	7	37	37	26
136	Zoology	L	44	41	15	22	52	26
138	Fishing	I	63	33	4	89	7	4
139	Hunting	I	63	33	4	89	4	7
140	Tennis	L	63	26	11	41	52	7
159	Full-dress affairs	L	37	30	33	4	59	37
167	Symphony concerts	L	44	37	19	22	52	26
185	Making a radio set	D	22	19	59	41	26	33
187	Adjusting a carburetor	I	37	44	19	63	22	15
188	Repairing electrical wiring	I	44	44	11	67	19	15
195	Arguments	L	44	19	37	15	38	46
198	Interviewing clients	L	52	41	7	19	59	22
199	Making a speech	L	59	30	11	22	37	41
200	Organizing a play	L	22	48	30	7	26	67
222	Being pitted against another as in a political or athletic race	L	63	30	7	33	59	7
240	Optimists	L	59	33	7	30	56	15
250	Religious people	I, D	22	63	15	52	44	4

The 49-item scale correlates 0.64 with "Composite Originality" on the first sample of 100 officers and 0.43 with the second composite criterion on the 243-officer sample. Scores on the scale in these samples were normally distributed, with a mean of 18.1 and standard deviation of 6.34.

The actual items are given in Table 1, together with the corresponding SVIB item numbers, the direction of scored response (L—Like, I—Indifferent, D—Dislike), and the response percentages for the 27 highs and the 27 lows in Composite Originality in the sample of 100 officers.

To summarize these results briefly, high scorers in performance tests calling for verbal originality would like (to a significantly greater degree than low scorers) such vocational roles as actor, artist, consul, editor, and musician, and they would either like or be indifferent to the vocation of magazine writing; they would dislike such vocations as electrical engineer, factory manager, jeweler, mining superintendent, rancher, toolmaker, and watchmaker, and they would either dislike or be indifferent to the calling of office clerk (and would be simply indifferent to being a wholesaler). The college subjects they like are Art, Botany, Dramatics, English Composition, Geology, Music, Philosophy, Public Speaking, and Zoology, and they would either like or be indifferent to Literature; they dislike only Physical Training. In sports, they like tennis and are indifferent to fishing and hunting. Socially, they like full-dress affairs and symphony concerts. They are indifferent to such jobs as adjusting a carburetor or repairing electrical wiring, and they would dislike making a radio set, but they like arguments, interviewing clients, making speeches, organizing plays, and being pitted against another person in a race, whether political or athletic. Finally, they like optimists and they are either indifferent to or dislike religious people.

A counterpart to this Verbal Originality Scale on the SVIB was constructed for a pool of items of the true-false variety. In this case, the top and bottom 27% of scorers on the Verbal Originality Composite were compared, using the entire sample of 343 officers for the comparison. The item pool consisted of 957 items, and included the MMPI, the California Psychological Inventory (CPI), and several hundred items written in 1950 by the staff of the Institute of Personality Assessment and Research, known now as the IPAR pool.

Of these 957 items, 150 were found to differentiate significantly (at the 0.05 level) between high and low scorers on the Originality Composite. This is too unwieldy a number to reproduce here, but the interested reader can find a subset drawn only from items of the California Psychological Inventory elsewhere (Gough, 1957), and that scale is representative of the entire set of 150 items. By selecting from the 150 items the ten items having the highest correlation with the performance criterion and the ten having the lowest, we find the following sorts of affirmations for high and low scorers, respectively.

High scorers like to know important people, they've tried their hand at writing poetry, they like to be the center of attention, they read fast and read at least ten books a year, they would like, some time, to fight in a boxing match, they admit they are pretty fair talkers, they are willing to describe themselves as "strong" personalities, they are better talkers than listeners, they would like the work of a schoolteacher, and when they work on a committee they like to take charge of things.

Low scorers affirm these sorts of statements: Their home life was always happy, the members of their family were always very close to one another, they don't usually like to talk much unless they are with people they know very well, it's no business of theirs if some minority groups get rough treatment, a person who lets himself get tricked has no one but himself to blame, when prices are high you can't blame a person for getting all he can while the getting is good, disobedience to the government is never justified, every person ought to be a booster for his own home town, in most ways the poor man is better off than the rich man, young people sometimes get rebellious ideas but as they grow up they ought to get over them and settle down, and, finally, the details of a job are as important as the job itself.

The item-content of this scale for Verbal Originality is similar in some respects to the body of findings emerging from research on the creative personality in general (Barron, 1963b). Certainly one finds here a suggestion that the original person is forceful, self-assertive, fond of conflict and even combat, perhaps a bit self-dramatizing or exhibitionistic, and with a flair for individualistic and distinctive statement. His opposite number counters by being somewhat smugly contented with life at home, and is notably lacking in the sort of sympathy and large-mindedness that one associates with the great givers to humanity.

Our intention here has not been to appraise the validities of the tests we are describing, however, nor even to appraise the knotty problems encountered in establishing real-life criteria of creativity. Suffice it to say that these items have been observed to correlate with original performance in tests calling primarily for verbal expression, and that they seem to merit further exploration as potential predictors of at least one aspect of creativity. Other scales from the same item pool that are relevant to the measurement of personality correlates of creativity are the Complexity Scale and the Independence of Judgment Scale, and the interested reader is referred to the technical articles describing them (Barron, 1953a, b).

A nonverbal preference inventory has been constructed by G. S. Welsh and the present writer (Barron and Welsh, 1952). It consists of 62 line drawings, made in black ink on 3- by 5-inch white cards. The drawings were chosen from the 400-item Welsh Figure Preference test on the basis of their power to discriminate between artists and nonartists when the given task is to separate the drawings into two groups, those *liked* by the respondent and those *disliked*. The resultant scale is called the Barron-Welsh Art Scale, and it has been shown to relate to ratings of originality and creativity both in artists and in scientists.

The essential variable in the Barron-Welsh Art Scale, as revealed both by the stimulus properties of the figures preferred by artists and by observed correlations in the personalities of high and low scorers, appears to be a preference for "complex dynamic asymmetry" as opposed to "simple static symmetry" (Barron, 1953a).

MEASUREMENT OF CREATIVITY IN CHILDREN

Tests similar to those we have described for the measurement of creativity in adults have been used in studies of imagination and originality in children. As long ago as 1900 some investigators were using inkblots in studies with children as well as with adults (Dearborn, 1898). The telling of stories and the composition of essays and poems have long been recognized as behaviors which may be readily appraised for quality of invention and power of perception and imagination (Andrews, 1930). The drawing-completion sort of test is also an old favorite, and fluency, originality, and flexibility were seen as important factors in such productions (Burchard, 1952).

Just as the Guilford group drew extensively upon its predecessors in modifying tests for more efficient use in investigations by the factor analytic method, so too have E. Paul Torrance and his highly productive colleagues, in research with children, borrowed and adapted what they could find and invented what they could not if they thought they needed it. Adaptation of adult tests usually consisted in substituting materials, objects, or situations more familiar to children. The Consequences test, for example, was made to include such items as "What would happen if animals and birds could speak the language of men?" and instead of a Brick Uses test a Tin Can Uses test was employed.

Many tests were made up anew by the Torrance group, again with care to draw upon materials familiar to children. In the Ask-and-Guess test, prints from Mother Goose stories such as "Tom, the Piper's Son," "Ding Dong Bell," and "Little Boy Blue" were used; the task is to ask questions about the picture and to make guesses about what might be happening or might be going to happen. Toys are used in the Product Improvement test; the children are asked to think of things that would make the toy more fun to play with, and of ways they could play with the toy besides the usual way.

To test originality in making up stories, children are given intriguing titles, such as "The Flying Monkey" or "The Lion That Won't Roar," and asked to make up a story to fit the title. Another test is the Just Suppose Test, similar to Consequences; the examiner might ask, for example, "Just suppose that no one ever has to go to school anymore; what would happen?"

Nonverbal tests used with children have included, in addition to inkblots and drawing completions, tasks similar to mosaic constructions. In the Shape test, the child is asked to make up a picture out of many standardized shapes of colored paper. In the Circles test, he is asked to sketch objects or pictures that have a circle as a major part.

An interesting test that may also serve as a training device is the audio-tape test of B. F. Cunnington, described by Torrance (1962). Four unusual sound effects are presented and the children are asked to think of word pictures as they listen. The instructions as the test proceeds include an injunction to the children to "stretch your imagination *further* and *further*" as the sounds are played a second and a third time.

NEEDS FOR NEW TESTS

At a conference on the identification of creative scientific talent held several years ago at the University of Utah (Taylor, 1957), the present writer served as reporter for a subcommittee whose task was to suggest possible new predictors of criteria of creativity in science. The report seems to have aroused little response, but some of the ideas for tests suggested by the committee may yet prove useful. A section of the report listing several possibilities is therefore given here.

Highly creative individuals sometimes get very annoyed when as subjects of study they are asked to take the sorts of tests we have been describing. This need not mean that the tests are no good; persons with high IQ's often are displeased with intelligence tests, just as the best student in a class will often think ill of the course examination. Nevertheless, in this case as in the other two we might do well to heed their objections.

The objections are chiefly on these counts: (1) the tests are too superficial and in no sense do they engage the subject's deepest being, as creative work in the real world certainly does; (2) because they measure creative ability in fragments, as indeed factor analysts take pains to do, they provide no opportunity for what we have called "the integral quality of intellect" to manifest itself; (3) related to these first two objections is the third: that short and closely timed tests do violence to the very essence of the creative process, which goes at its own pace, will not be hurried, is behaviorally silent for long periods of time, and is easily aborted if someone is always blowing a whistle on it.

Practical limitations may make it impossible for the psychologist to meet these objections in the construction of new tests, but still these points may well be kept in mind as we proceed with further measurement efforts. In some research settings it should be possible to present tests which provide an opportunity for a longer gestation period, for example. In one of our own experiments, we sought to measure originality in dreaming by placing the subject in a deep trance for which he was posthypnotically amnesic and implanting a factitious "complex" (by having the operator narrate a set of conflictful events presumably happening to the subject) and then instructing him to have a dream about the events that night while asleep. Subjects differed widely among themselves in the way in which they represented the implanted complex in their dreams, and analysis of the manifest content of the dream left little doubt that events during the rest of the trance day found expression in the dream. In other words, the dreams were "solutions" which were being cooked up outside conscious awareness throughout the day.

The integrative tendency so important in high-level creative work is measured to some extent in several of the tests we have described earlier, but new and better measures can perhaps be devised. The prototype of what is needed is the W (whole blot area) score on the Rorschach, with adequate attention to the distinction between a shallow W and a complex and sharply conceived W. A test is needed that will help us to identify the kind of person that Henry James has enjoined all of us to be: "one on whom nothing is lost." This implies an open perceptual system, sharp not fuzzy, with excellent memory, and an ability to hold many ideas in one's head at once and to keep them open to complex combination with one another.

Perhaps tests of this sort must by their nature be dependent upon the quality of discernment in the rater or scorer. Emerson once remarked that the person next in originality to the thinker of an original thought is he who first appreciates it. Perhaps we shall need a "recognition of originality" test with which to select our scorers.*

To ask for tests of this degree of identity with the creative act itself may be asking too much, however. Life itself is prodigal in generating problems that challenge us to find a creative solution; this is the point at which test and criterion meet.

This chapter has presented various examples of tests designed to measure aspects of creativity. The examples were chosen for their relevance to the problems posed by measurement and research in an area in which the criterion variable is complex and elusive. Measurement of creative performance in nontest situations was not discussed, although the problems there are not unlike the problems of rating products and persons in the sorts of miniature job-samples represented by performance tests. The latter themselves, in fact, can be used as criteria for the development of nonperformance measures of correlated attitudinal and personality traits, and some examples of these were given.

REFERENCES

ANDERSON, H. H., *Creativity and Its Cultivation.* New York: Harper and Brothers, 1959

ANDREWS, E., "Development of imagination in pre-school children." *University of Iowa Studies in Character* **3,** 4 (1930)

BALKAN, E. R., and J. H. MASSERMAN, "Language of phantasy, III." *J. Psychol.* **10,** 75–86 (1940)

BARRON, F., "Complexity-simplicity as a personality dimension." *J. Abnorm. Soc. Psychol.* **68,** 163–172 (1953a)

BARRON, F., "Creativity and genius," in A. Deutsch (ed.), *The Encyclopedia of Mental Health (Vol. II.).* New York: Franklin Watts, 1963a

BARRON, F., *Creativity and Psychological Health.* Princeton: D. Van Nostrand, 1963b

BARRON, F., "Some personality correlates of independence of judgment." *J. Pers.* **21,** 289–297 (1953b)

BARRON, F., "Inventory of personal philosophy." Berkeley: University of California Press, 1952

BARRON, F., "Originality in relation to personality and intellect." *J. Pers.* **25,** 730–742 (1957)

BARRON, F., "The psychology of imagination." *Sci. Amer.* September 1958, 151–166

BARRON, F., "The needs for order and disorder as motives in creative activity," in C. W. Taylor and F. Barron (eds.), *Scientific Creativity: Its Recognition and Development.* New York: John Wiley & Sons, 1963

BARRON, F., "Threshold for the perception of human movement in inkblots." *J. Consult. Psychol.* **19,** 33–38 (1955)

---

* C. W. Taylor, "The Identification of Creative Scientific Talent." *Amer. Psychologist* **14,** 100–102 (1959). Quoted by permission of the publisher.

BARRON, F., M. JARVICK, and S. BUNNELL, "The hallucinogenic drugs." *Sci. Amer.* April 1964, 3–11

BARRON, F., and G. S. WELSH, "Artistic perception as a possible factor in personality style: Its measurement by figure preference test." *J. Psychol.* **33,** 199–203 (1952)

BENNETT, G. K., *A Test of Productive Thinking.* New York: Psychological Corporation, 1947

BERGER, R. M., J. P. GUILFORD, and P. R. CHRISTENSEN, "A factor-analytical study of planning abilities." *Psychol. Monogr.* **71** (Whole No. 435) (1957)

BISCHLER, W., "Intelligence and the higher mental functions." Trans. by P. Winner in *Psych. Quart.* **6,** 277–307 (1937)

BLATT, S. J., and M. T. STEIN, "Some personality, value and cognitive characteristics of the creative person." *Amer. J. Psychol.* **12,** 406 (1957)

BRITTAIN, H. L., "A study of imagination." *Ped. Sem.* **14,** 137–207 (1907)

BRITTAIN, W., and K. BEITTAL, "Analyses of levels of creative performance." *J. Aesth. Art. Crit.* **19,** 83–90 (1960)

BUELL, W. D., "Validity of behavioral rating scale items for assessment of individual creativity." *J. Appl. Psychol.* **44,** 407–412 (1960)

BURCHARD, E., "The use of projective techniques in the analysis of creativity." *J. Prof. Tech.* **16,** 412–427 (1952)

BURKHART, R., "The relation of intelligence to artistic ability." *J. Aesth. Art. Crit.* **12,** 230–241 (1958)

CHRISTENSEN, P. R., and J. P. GUILFORD, "An experimental study of verbal fluency factors." *Brit. J. Stat. Psychol.* **16,** 1–26 (1963)

CLINE, V. B., J. M. RICHARDS, and A. CLIFFORD, "The validity of a battery of creativity tests in a high school sample." *Educ. Psychol. Measmt.* **22,** 781–784 (1962)

CRUTCHFIELD, R. S., "Assessment of persons through a quasi-group interaction technique." *J. Abnorm. Soc. Psychol.* **4,** 577–588 (1951)

DEARBORN, G. V., "A study of imagination." *Amer. J. Psychol.* **5 (9),** 183 (1898)

DREVDAHL, J. E., and R. B. CATTELL, "Personality and creativity in artists and writers." *J. Clin. Psychol.* **14,** 107–111 (1958)

FLANAGAN, J., "Definition and measurement of ingenuity," in C. W. Taylor and F. Barron (eds.), *Scientific Creativity: Its Recognition and Development.* New York: John Wiley & Sons, 1963

FRICK, J. W., J. P. GUILFORD, P. R. CHRISTENSEN, and P. R. MERRIFIELD, "A factor analytic study of creative thinking." *Educ. Psychol. Measmt.* **19,** 469–496 (1959)

GETZELS, J. W., and P. O. JACKSON, *Creativity and Intelligence.* New York: John Wiley & Sons, 1962

GOUGH, H. G., *Manual for the California Psychological Inventory.* Palo Alto: Consulting Psychologists Press, 1957

GRIFFIN, D. P., "Movement responses and creativity." *J. Consult. Psychol.* **22,** 134–136 (1958)

GUILFORD, J. P., "Creativity." *Amer. Psychologist* **5,** 444–454 (1950)

GUILFORD, J. P., "Zero correlations among tests of intellectual abilities." *Psychol. Bull.* **61,** 401–404 (1964c)

HALL, W. B., "The development of a technique for assessing aesthetic predisposition and its application to a sample of research scientists." Paper read Western Psych. Assoc., Monterey, Calif., April 1958. Berkeley: Institute of Personality Assessment and Research, Univer. of California

HARMS, E., "A test for types of formal creativity." *Psychol. Bull.* **36,** 526–527 (1939)

HARRIS, D., "Development and validity of test of creativity in engineering." *J. Appl. Psychol.* **44,** 254–257 (1960)

HELSON, RAVENNA, "Creativity, sex, and mathematics," in D. W. MacKinnon (ed.), *The Creative Person.* Berkeley: University of California Extension, 1961

HUTCHINSON, E. D., "Materials for the study of creative thinking." *Psychol. Bull.* **28,** 392–410 (1931)

JOHNSON, S. R., and E. E. GLAZE, "A critical analysis of psychological treatments of children's drawings and paintings." *J. Aesth. Art. Crit.* **17,** 242–250 (1958)

MACKINNON, D. W., *et al., Proceedings of the Conference on "The Creative Person," University of California Alumni Center, Lake Tahoe, Calif.* Berkeley: University of California Extension, 1961

MACKINNON, D. W., "Fostering creativity in students of engineering." *J. Engng. Educ.* **52,** 129–142 (1961)

MANDELL, M. M., and S. ADAMS, "Measuring originality in physical scientists." *Educ. and Psychol. Measmt.* **8,** 515–582 (1948)

MCGEOCH, J. A., "Relationship between three tests for imagination and their correlation with intelligence." *J. Appl. Psychol.* **8,** 443–459 (1924)

MEDNICK, S., "The associative basis of the creative process." *Psychol. Rev.* **69,** 220–232 (1962)

MEER, B., and M. I. STEIN, "Measures of intelligence and creativity." *J. Psychol.* **39,** 117–126 (1955)

MOSING, L. W., "Development of a multi-media creativity test." *Dist. Abstr.* **19,** 2137 (1959)

MUELLER, R. E., *Inventivity.* New York: John Day, 1963

MURRAY, H. A., *Exploration in Personality.* New York: Oxford University Press, 1938

ROE, ANNE, "A study of imagery in research scientists." *J. Pers.* **19,** 459–470 (1951)

ROE, ANNE, "Psychological tests of research scientists." *J. Consult. Psychol.* 491–495 (1951)

RORSCHACH, H., *Psychodiagnostics.* Bern: Huber (Grune & Stratton, New York, distributors), 1942

RUTHERFORD, J. M., "Personality correlates of creativity." *Diss. Abst.* **20,** 4434 (1960)

STERN, W., "Cloud pictures. A new method for testing imagination." *Charact. and Pers.* **6,** 132–146 (1937)

STRONG, E. K., JR., *The Vocational Interests of Men and Women.* Stanford: Stanford University Press, 1943

TAYLOR, C. W., "The identification of creative scientific talent." *Amer. Psychologist* **14,** 100–102 (1959)

TAYLOR, C. W., and F. BARRON, *Scientific Creativity: Its Recognition and Development.* New York: John Wiley & Sons, 1963

THURSTONE, L. L., "Creative talent." in L. L. Thurstone (ed.), *Applications of Psychology.* New York: Harper and Brothers, 1952

THURSTONE, L. L., "Primary mental abilities." *Psychometric Monogr.* **1** (1938)

TORRANCE, E. P., *Guiding Creative Talent.* Englewood Cliffs, N.J.: Prentice-Hall, 1962

VERNON, P. E., *The Structure of Human Abilities.* New York: John Wiley & Sons, 1950

VINACKE, W. E., "Creative thinking," in W. E. Vinacke (ed.), *The Psychology of Thinking.* New York: McGraw-Hill, 1952, pp. 238–261

WELCH, L., "Recombination of ideas in creative thinking." *J. Appl. Psychol.* **30,** 638–643 (1946)

WERTHEIMER, M., *Productive Thinking.* New York: Harper and Brothers, 1954

WHITING, C. S., *Creative Thinking.* New York: Henry Holt, 1958

WILSON, R. C., J. P. GUILFORD, and P. R. CHRISTENSEN, "The measurement of individual differences in originality." *Psychol. Bull.* **50,** 362–370 (1953)

WILSON, R. N., "Poetic creativity, process and personality." *Psychiat.* **17,** 163–176 (1954)

CHAPTER 11

MEASUREMENT OF INTEREST

RALPH F. BERDIE and DAVID P. CAMPBELL, *University of Minnesota*

Interest measurement is that aspect of personality assessment which emphasizes behaviors or statements of choice: acceptance, rejection, liking, disliking, approach, and avoidance. These actions are the products of interest, and the amount of interest is inferred by observing these behaviors or similar ones related to direct interest manifestations.

The concept of interest, like many other concepts in psychology, is a convenient but not a necessary construct. Observations of behavior can lead directly to predictions of subsequent behaviors without the use of such concepts. If one asked a group of college freshmen to specify their occupational choices and later found that all who said that they were going to be engineers in fact became engineers, accurate predictions could be made without reference to concepts of interest or choice. The concept of interest, however, has led to fruitful ideas and hypotheses concerning behavior and refinement in methods of observation and measurement. It also has greatly facilitated communication between investigators.

The number of specific interests is limited only by the number of activities and objects within the environment. However, almost all research on interest measurement has been devoted to interests classified as either vocational or recreational, i.e., work or play interests. Since the 1940's, most of this research has been devoted to vocational interests.

BROAD METHODS OF ASSESSING INTEREST

Super (1949) has identified four interpretations of interest, all essentially dependent on the method of observation employed. He defined an *expressed interest* as "the verbal profession of interest in an object, activity, task, or occupation." A *manifest interest* is exhibited through participation in an activity or an occupation. A *tested interest* is an interest measured "by objective tests, as differentiated from inventories which are based on subjective self-estimates." *Inventoried interests* are observed through the use of items pertaining to activities, occupations, and objects to which the person responds in terms of liking, preference, or choice. In comparing inventoried and expressed interest, Super says (p. 379),

The essential and all-important difference is that in the case of the inventory each possible response is given an experimentally determined weight, and the weights corresponding to the answers given by the person completing the inventory are added in order to yield a score which represents, not a single subjective estimate as in the case of expressed interests, but a pattern of interests which research has shown to be rather stable.

Expressed interests usually are inferred through responses to a single question or a small number of questions. For example, a student may be asked to express his vocational choice or simply to state his interests. Another may be asked to list 12 books that interest him and from his responses an inference will be made about the strength of his interests in people as compared to his interests in machines. If the list of questions and stimuli is expanded and the method of handling the responses is systemized, one then has *inventoried interests.* Regardless of method, in these cases one is dealing with verbal behavior, expressions that themselves can be related to subsequent behavior.

Manifest interests are inferred through observations of other overt behavior, such as hobbies or studies. If a boy solves mathematical problems for enjoyment and devotes much of his time to this, one can predict on this basis that he probably will engage in future mathematical behavior. No inference of mathematical interests is necessary; one behavior is used to predict the next. While this concept of manifest interest may be useful for predictive purposes, it is relatively powerless for the understanding of behavior.

Super also discussed *tested interest,* which he related to objective measures rather than to subjective self-estimates. A student who does well on a mathematics test and poorly on a history test may be demonstrating greater interest in mathematics than in history. However, tests of this type which attempt to measure interests also measure other confounding variables, particularly general intelligence, in addition to interests. No interest test, as opposed to an interest inventory, has been used extensively.

Almost all research on interest measurement has been concerned with inventoried interests and almost all interest inventories have been concerned with vocational interests; thus this review essentially will center on problems of vocational inventories.

PURPOSES OF INTEREST MEASUREMENT

Methods and problems of interest measurement are related to the uses made of measuring instruments. The requirements imposed on interest inventories depend not only on the behaviors observed and predicted and the concepts utilized, but also on the objectives of such predictions. The primary uses of interest inventories are listed below.

1. *Vocational counseling.* Many students seek help from counselors and teachers as they make educational and vocational decisions. These students are trying to answer two questions, "What can I succeed in?" and "What will I be happy doing?" Interest inventories have been used in counseling on the assumption that they can

help students select occupations where they will feel most comfortable and find greatest satisfaction.

2. *Selection of students.* Professional schools frequently have more applicants with sufficient ability than they can admit. From among these qualified applicants, they wish to select those with the greatest probability of remaining in the professional training program and eventually the profession. They wish to eliminate, before admission, students who may soon discover they do not enjoy the program and leave it, and persons who may move into another occupation after only a few years of practice.

3. *Selection of employees.* The purposes underlying the use of interest measurements in employee selection resemble those for student selection. Employers wish to hire workers who will remain on the job and who will gain sufficient satisfaction from the job to maintain high morale. To this end, interest measurement may be included in the selection procedure. Further, employers are concerned not only with the selection of those who will be satisfied with their work but also with workers who will be productive. Previous work experience, biographical information, tests of abilities, achievement, and personality account for only a portion of the variance explaining job success. To the extent that interest measurements can increase the proportion of good employee selections, employers will find these techniques valuable.

4. *Personality research.* Persons studying personality development, psychopathology, and counseling and clinical psychology are concerned with individual behaviors related to home, school, family, friends, supervisors, and other associates of the individual. Interest measurement provides one method for studying these important relationships, and many questions lend themselves to research with these techniques. For example, relationships between the personality development of children and their parents (Strong, 1957), of identical and fraternal twins (Carter, 1932), and consistency over time within the same individual (Hoyt, 1960), are revealed through interest measurements. Childhood experiences recalled by students and their parents are reflected in scores of interest inventories (Segal, 1954).

Personality research often has been based on vocational interest measurement techniques. One such example is Garman's work on an Anxiety Scale for the Strong Vocational Interest Blank (Garman and Uhr, 1958). Another project, using interest inventories, studied general attitudes of "liking and disliking" that extended far beyond vocational interest (Berdie, 1943). Even progress accompanying psychotherapy has been reflected in changes in interest inventory scores.

CRITERION AND REFERENCE GROUPS

Historically, research in interest measurement has centered around the separation of groups. The early projects, around 1920, attempted to differentiate between sales and design engineers (Moore, 1921), successful and unsuccessful life insurance salesmen (Ream, 1924), or salesmen and engineers (Freyd, 1923).

The exact origin of the brilliant decision to use a group of "men-in-general" as a base for comparing specific occupations is lost in history. In 1926, Miner tried to distinguish between students grouped according to their vocational choices (teaching, engineering, law, or medicine) and a separate group of students chosen randomly. Although he was not successful, probably because the students' choices were too tentative, he did have the glimmerings of the men-in-general approach.

It remained for Strong to see the benefits of such an approach, and about 1926–27 he first collected inventories from men actually engaged in certain occupation, to use in both criterion and men-in-general groups. This comparison of specific occupations with a group of men-in-general provided the foundation for current interest measurement techniques. (Kuder's approach, using homogeneous scales, falls into another category and will be discussed later.)

Development of psychological scales to differentiate groups requires that the groups be defined, and the precise definition has proved to be important in determining the eventual characteristics of the scales. The ultimate nature of a scale is determined by the differences between groups, the heterogeneity of the groups, and the extent to which the groups share common characteristics.

The occupational scales of the Strong Vocational Interest Blank (SVIB) and most of the clinical scales of the Minnesota Multiphasic Personality Inventory (MMPI) provide the two best-known examples of scales based on group differences. In developing the SVIB, Strong compared the responses of men in defined occupations with the responses of a reference group consisting of men-in-general. The MMPI was developed by comparing the responses of persons with specific psychiatric diagnoses to the responses of a group of nonpsychiatric hospital visitors. Thus in both these instances the special groups, one occupational, the other diagnostic, were compared to defined reference groups.

Interest scales based on response differences between groups can be developed without a general reference group, as has been demonstrated by Strong's non-occupational scales, some of the specialized scales on the MMPI, the specialized occupational scales for the SVIB developed by Strong and Tucker (1952), Kreidt (1949), and Dunnette (1957), and particularly by the work of Kuder (1963), who has demonstrated the effectiveness of comparing responses of one group with another to obtain a scale to separate two specific occupations.

Scales based on differences between the responses of several specific groups and a reference group of men-in-general are easily understood, relatively simple to develop, and have demonstrated their effectiveness. Scales developed without the use of a common reference group offer much promise, and eventually interest measurement may be based on analysis of differences between special groups to a far greater extent than it has in the past.

Strong first discovered the complexities of the problem of the general reference group in 1935 in the development of the Vocational Interest Blank for Women. He first used a women-in-general group composed of 586 married women, and developed scales by comparing the responses of these women to responses from women in eight different occupations. These scales had an average intercorrelation of 0.77, suggesting that the interests of women in these eight occupations did not differ. He next developed scales for these same eight occupations using a women-in-general group drawn from 15 occupations plus a group of married women. The intercorrelations of these scales ranged from −0.85 to 0.88, and averaged 0.12. This was a clear demonstration that the relationships between occupational scales depended on the characteristics of the reference group (Strong, 1943).

Strong, for his original men-in-general group, used completed inventories taken from his files—in other words, the group was composed of individuals he happened to have studied previously. Although later history has shown this particular group, chosen rather fortuitously, to be a quite acceptable sampling of men-in-general, at least for the purposes of interest measurement, Strong was understandably uneasy about this sampling method. To obtain a men-in-general group which had greater meaning, he later selected blanks to provide a representative picture of occupations of men between the ages of 18 and 60 years. Using the original men-in-general group, he found that the average intercorrelation between the first eight scales studied was −0.03; the corresponding average for the scales based on the revised men-in-general group was 0.27. Strong commented,

This represented a distinct decrease in differentiation among such occupations as physician, CPA, engineer, lawyer, life insurance salesman, minister, and YMCA secretary. Extensive research for over a year finally convinced us of two things: first, occupations from the upper socio-economic levels could not be as well differentiated using a men-in-general group representative of all men in the United States as by using a men-in-general group representative of the upper socio-economic occupations alone. And, second, occupations from the lower socio-economic levels could not be well differentiated using a men-in-general group representative of the upper socio-economic levels but presumably could be well differentiated by using a men-in-general group representative of their level.*

Strong then developed scales using four men-in-general groups and compared the intercorrelations between scales for each of the four sets. For example, when the original men-in-general group was used in developing the lawyer and accountant scales, the correlation between these two scales was −0.48. The first revised men-in-general group provided a correlation of −0.42. When the two scales were based on the men-in-general group representative of the entire population, they correlated 0.36, and when based on the men-in-general group of skilled, semiskilled, and unskilled workers they correlated 0.61. The mean intercorrelations found among the scales for these four men-in-general groups were 0.01, 0.02, 0.22, and 0.42. Clearly, the nature of the men-in-general group is a crucial variable in the development of scales.

In his report, Strong presented an intriguing explanation of the differences in the intercorrelations. When men in professional occupations are compared to a men-in-general group of equal status, the differences between professional groups

---

*E. K. Strong, *Vocational Interests of Men and Women* (Stanford: Stanford University Press, 1943, p. 555). Quoted by permission of the publisher.

will be more marked than they will be when professional men are compared to a men-in-general group consisting primarily of laboring men. Doctors and lawyers differ in many of the same ways from laboring men, and consequently, when compared with laboring men, they appear quite similar. As the reference (men-in-general) group approaches or becomes more similar to the doctors and lawyers, differences between these two occupations become more apparent and gradually outweigh the similarities that are most apparent when these two occupations are viewed from the more distant point of the laboring men.

This concept is clearly illustrated by the work of Strong (1943) and of Dunnette (1957) in developing scales to differentiate among the interests of different kinds of engineers. Strong developed four scales for engineers, based on comparisons of the men-in-general group and the response of electrical, mechanical, mining, and civil engineers. The four scales intercorrelated between 0.84 and 0.96. Obviously, one kind of engineer greatly resembles another kind of engineer when both are viewed from the reference point of persons who are not engineers at all.

Dunnette, on the other hand, developed scales based on the comparisons of different groups of engineers with a total group of engineers and was able to demonstrate that from this point of reference, the interests of one kind of engineer were quite different from the interests of another kind of engineer. (This study is important for another reason also. Whereas the past studies of engineers have grouped them by content, i.e., civil, electrical, etc., Dunnette has shown that groupings based on function, i.e., sales, research, etc., can also be differentiated.) Similar results were demonstrated by Strong and Tucker when they compared the responses of medical specialists with those of physicians-in-general, for they were able to derive scales that differentiated internists, pathologists, surgeons, and psychiatrists.

These studies have dealt mainly with the question of the level of the reference group, or the extent to which the reference group differs from the occupational groups. More work needs to be done on the heterogeneity of the criterion and men-in-general groups. Will scales based on comparisons of occupational groups with reference groups of great variability be more or less valid and have higher or lower intercorrelations than scales based on homogeneous groups? Because the items to be weighted and weights themselves are selected on the basis of percentage of a given group responding as compared to the percentage in a second group responding, the variability of either group might not affect the scales themselves. If the variability of the standardization groups is related to the variability of scores on the obtained scales, the percentage overlap among groups could be related to the variability of the groups themselves. Scales based on homogeneous occupational and reference groups might provide the most efficient instruments to use with persons resembling these populations. When scales are designed for use with persons varying in age, social and educational background, and other characteristics, then the groups on which the scales are based might better resemble in variability the groups for whom the scales are designed.

EMPIRICAL VERSUS HOMOGENEOUS SCALES

Current interest inventories consist either of empirically derived scales containing items that differentiate between two groups or of homogeneous scales containing items that cluster together. The best-known examples of the first type are the scales for the SVIB. The most familiar examples of the latter type are the scales of the Kuder Preference Record, Vocational. Initially, the advantages and disadvantages of each type of scale seem clear but research has demonstrated that the apparent advantages may not be realized.

Empirically derived keys are more powerful in separating criterion groups from reference groups; they can be constructed relatively easily for specific requirements, and they are more easily understood by counselors and their clients. Much research has demonstrated the characteristics of such scales, and they have proved to consistently measure behaviors of predictive value. On the negative side, empirical scales are specific to a single occupation; thus their use requires the development of many scales and the interpretation of several scores. They also have proved relatively sterile in providing a satisfactory theoretical explanation of the nature of interests.

Homogeneous scaling requires fewer scales, presumably just one for each dimension of interest. The number of variables that the counselor and client have to deal with is reduced and, at least in principle, each scale has a more solid foundation than empirical scales. Thus the use of homogeneous keys should extend knowledge about the theoretical framework of interests, as well as increase understanding of a single individual. Further, an optimally weighted combination of homogeneous scales should predict more accurately than a single empirically derived scale, since this combination would utilize a larger proportion of the variance. This means that a new scale would not be necessary for each occupation but, instead, each occupation would be described with a new set of weights. (It is debatable whether this would really simplify matters much. Several weights for each occupation would be more laborious to deal with than one single scale.)

Clark (1961), with his students Gee (1955) and Norman(1957, 1960), has built both types of scales for the Minnesota Vocational Interest Inventory (MVII), and this important work indicated that the issues are not as clear as originally assumed.

First, the empirical scales and the homogeneous scales were highly correlated, usually in a meaningful fashion, and in a way that would indicate they were tapping the same interest dimensions. For example, Clark's empirical Baker key correlated 0.66 with the homogeneous key dealing with food interests; the IBM Operator key correlated 0.85 with the general clerical scale, and the Mechanic key correlated 0.90 with the homogeneous scale containing mechanical items.

Second, not only were Clark's empirical scales better than any single homogeneous scale in correctly classifying individuals, they were better than the optimally weighted set of homogeneous scales. To add to the confusion, the optimally weighted set of empirical keys was best of all.

Third, the homogeneous scales developed did not correspond to the interest dimensions isolated by factor analysis, and a scanning of item content indicated that the scales were probably factually, if not statistically, complex. As Clark put it, "Factorial simplicity and scale homegeneity are not synonymous" (1961, p. 67).

Then what do the homogeneous scales contribute? As Clark pointed out, they do contribute greatly to our understanding of the interests of various occupations and allow greater understanding of the similarities and differences between occupational groups. One example of how these homogeneous keys can contribute to an increased understanding of the structure of interests is the ranking of correlations between Clark's homogeneous mechanical key and several empirical occupational keys (see Table 1). This listing gives an excellent picture of the varying importance of mechanical interests to these occupations.

Table 1 Correlations between the MVII homogeneous mechanical key and various occupational keys

Occupational keys	Correlation with homogeneous mechanical key (H1)
Mechanic	0.90
Sheet metal worker	0.76
Plumber	0.69
Electrician	0.56
Machinist	0.52
Truck driver	0.46
Carpenter	0.20
Plasterer	0.18
Painter	0.07
Pressman	0.04
Warehouseman	−0.45
Baker	−0.58
Printer	−0.78
IBM operator	−0.79
Milk wagon driver	−0.83
Stock clerk	−0.84
Retail sales clerk	−0.91

Another way of using these homogeneous keys is to look at the correlations between one occupational key and the set of homogeneous keys, particularly for occupations with which counselors are not familiar. For example, most counselors might know (or at least think they know) what mechanics are interested in. But what are the interests of milk wagon drivers? What kind of individuals should consider entering this occupation? Table 2 lists the correlations between Clark's Milk Wagon Driver key and the nine homogeneous keys of the MVII. This ranking clearly gives a better picture of the occupation than is available from empirical keys only.

Table 2 Correlations between Milk Wagon Driver scale and the homogeneous keys of the MVII

Homogeneous key	Correlation
H_3 (General clerical work)	0.62
H7 (Verbal-aesthetics activities)	0.57
H9 ("Clean-hand" activities)	0.50
H5 (Food and menu planning)	0.35
H2 (Medical and hospital service)	0.25
H6 (Carpentry and furniture making)	−0.07
H4 (Radio and electronics)	−0.46
H0 (Athletics and outdoor activities)	−0.55
H1 (Mechanics)	−0.83

The conclusion from the above discussion is that both empirical and homogeneous keys have their place in interest measurement. The empirical keys have more predictive power while the homogeneous keys are more useful in revealing construct validity.

This does not resolve the conflict for the practitioner nor the researcher constructing new scales. Is it still necessary for a counselor to have his client's answer sheet scored on all possible scales before he can advise him carefully? Probably not. As Clark has suggested, empirical and homogeneous keys combined in such a way that the profile covers the broad domain of interests are likely to provide the best information.

Is it necessary to develop a scale for every new occupation? In principle, no, a new scale is not necessary. But it is essential to study the occupation, to collect some data, and to see how that occupation compares with others on the existing scales. Homogeneous scales are not shortcuts; the work of studying each occupation is still essential. In practice, few researchers would go to the work of collecting data from an occupational group without developing a new scale, especially if it appeared that this new scale would contribute considerable information about this new occupation.

SELECTION OF ITEMS

Regardless of whether homogeneous or empirical scales are to be used, the validity of the scales depends largely on their constituent items. Two main issues are involved in the initial selection of items for interest inventories: item format and item content.

Item Format

The two most widely used item formats are the L–I–D and the triad formats. The L–I–D format, used on the SVIB, presents an item and asks the individual to answer whether he Likes it, is Indifferent to it, or Dislikes it. The triad format presents three statements, such as:

(a) Sort mail

(b) Make coffee

(c) Fix a tire

and asks the individual to pick the one liked best and the one liked least. The triad format is used on the Kuder Preference Record and the Minnesota Vocational Interest Inventory.

Some work has been done comparing the two forms, notably by Zuckerman (1952, 1953) and Perry (1955). Zuckerman, comparing an inventory written in the L–I–D form with one containing the same items in forced-choice pairs, found that the two formats were virtually identical in validity and reliability but that the forced-choice inventory required more time to complete; thus he concluded that the L–I–D format was the more powerful. However, he constructed the forced-choice inventory by using each item several times in different pairs, while in the L–I–D form each item appeared only once. The difference in time was probably a function of the specific inventory used, rather than the item format.

Perry (1955), in a well-planned study, compared an inventory of L–I–D items with one using the same items in triad form, using each item once in each inventory. He found no significant difference in the time taken to complete the two forms. The triad format was slightly more valid than the L–I–D, being better in 7 of 10 comparisons with a tie in two other instances. On the average, the overlap was decreased by about 6% when the triad format was used. Perry's conclusion was that ". . . forced-choice interest items are superior to L–I–D items in differentiating groups. The difference is small enough, however, that other considerations may well play a part in selection of item form for interest inventory construction" (Perry, 1955, p. 261).

The other considerations that Perry mentions are factors such as faking, reliability, and resistance of individuals being tested. As the two formats differ very little in terms of validity, these other considerations become paramount.

Faking. Interest inventories can be faked; several studies have clearly established this fact. Moreover, faking is possible with either item format. Kuder has done considerable work on this point and has developed a "verification" scale for his Occupational-Form D that seems to work well in selecting individuals who are trying to make themselves look good on the inventory (Kuder, 1950).

In another study on this subject, Jenson, Dunnette, and Kirchner (1963) have developed two SVIB keys for faking, one by asking individuals with high scores on the Accountant scale to fake like accountants on a second administration, another by using a similar method with the Salesman scale. Both scales worked well in identifying the fakers, and both held up under cross-validation. There were only a few items in common between the two scales; thus it appears that faking may be highly situational and test administrators who wish to detect faking may have to develop a specific key for each situation.

Reliability. Because the individual is asked to make a more subtle distinction in the forced-choice item than in the L–I–D item, his choice may be less reliable. Apparently the only data available on this point are those of Zuckerman's, where he found no difference between the two methods, even though the forced-choice inventory was considerably longer than the L–I–D one.

Resistance of individuals being tested. The reaction of individuals to the items is not the most crucial point in inventory development but it certainly should be considered. Strong has said that even poor items should be considered if they help dispel the idea that filling out the blank is a lot of nonsense. In a guidance situation the student is seeking help and is willing to perform any task asked of him on the slim chance that it might help solve his problems. In selection situations, however, and particularly when researchers are trying to collect data from new criterion groups, the feelings of the individual must be considered.

Answering forced-choice items is more annoying than answering L–I–D items and this annoyance increases when the forced-choice items have been equated for social desirability. Before these methods are adopted completely, their advantages must be firmly established. At this point, forced-choice items in interest measurement do not appear any better psychometrically than those arranged in the L–I–D format.

Although the point has not been studied, a varied item format probably has some advantages. In the SVIB, for example, there are four different types of items: L–I–D, forced-choice pairs, groupings of ten where the individual picks the three best liked and the three least liked (in effect a forced-choice format), and a variation of the L–I–D style where the individual indicates how true a given statement is about himself. This variety of formats may relieve some of the tedium of completing the SVIB, and to the extent that this tedium might develop a response style, its elimination should have the effect of keeping the individual more aware of item content.

Item Content

The second issue of item selection, that of item content, has received little systematic attention, and knowledge is sparse. Two leaders in interest measurement have discussed the point recently, Clark in his book (1961, pp. 13–20), and Strong in a journal article (1962). Both of these discussions are mainly speculation but it is well-informed speculation and current researchers should be aware of this thinking.

Item content should in some way reflect occupational activities. The items in Clark's MVII are clearly concerned with work activities, and they include a substantial number of occupational titles. Kuder states that his Preference Record, Occupational, includes items . . . "found to be related to occupational or job satisfaction," although, he continues, "Occupational titles should be avoided . . . (to keep) obvious vocational significance to a minimum" (Kuder, 1959). Strong has virtually ignored the question of specific content and has instead concentrated on developing criteria to use in judging the value of specific items.

Strong has suggested four standards to use in evaluating items. They are:

1. *Unfamiliarity.* Items pertaining to activities that are unfamiliar to most college students should be avoided, although items pertaining to any activity familiar to various subgroups should be retained. Familiarity makes possible an expression of interest.

2. *Ambiguity.* Items are ambiguous if they can be interpreted in more than one way. Generally, this is related to the length of the item.

3. *Differentiation between criterion groups and men-in-general.* This can be measured in various ways; on the SVIB, percentage differences in responses between groups usually are used. An item that shows a 20% difference is preferable to one with a 16% difference.

4. *Number of scales scored on.* This is related to number 3 above. An item that is scored on 10 scales is usually preferred to one that is scored on only one, even if the latter item does a better job of separating men-in-general from the criterion group on that one scale.

Some knowledge germane to the question of item content can be gathered by studying the different sections of the SVIB. It has eight sections; of these, four are essentially nonoccupational. Some work has been done comparing these sections. Table 3 shows the average number of scales on which items from the various sections appear. No general trend stands out and as the sections differ in format as well as in content, either may be operating to create the various differences.

Table 3   Average number of scales among 32 scales per item in parts I to VIII of the men's blank in terms of 16% weighting

Part	Average
I. Occupations	8.9
II. School subjects	8.4
III. Amusements	4.7
IV. Activities	7.6
V. Peculiarities of people	4.3
VI. Order of preference of activities	8.8
VII. Comparison of interest between two items	6.8
VIII. Rating of present abilities and characteristics	4.8
Total	7.0

Sections VI and VII are forced-choice item formats; the remainder are L–I–D items. No significant trend emerges as a result of comparison of the two formats.

Comparing the stability of items from the various sections, Strong concluded, on the basis of research by Rock, Burnham, Glass, and Seder as well as his own, that the rank order for stability of parts of the blank was: III—School subjects; II—Amusements; V—People; IV—Activities; I—Occupations; VII—Comparison of Items; VIII—Present Abilities; VI—Preference of Activities. He continued,

"There is, however, very little difference in the relative standing of the eight parts. Possibly the first two are superior and the last one inferior to the remainder" (Strong, 1943, p. 669).

(This again suggests that the forced-choice formats, which require the individual to make a more subtle distinction, may be slightly less stable over time than the L–I–D formats.)

The work of Guilford and his associates in factor-analyzing interests has considerable relevance to this question of item content (1954). They first sampled systematically the interest domain of items, then factor analyzed these items. The results gave some indication of the possible dimensions of interests. As a useful further step, they indicated the extent to which some of the current interest inventories sample each of these dimensions. In developing new items, researchers might well use this work as a guide to determine whether all dimensions are sufficiently covered.

WEIGHTING OF ITEMS

After the item format and content have been decided, the next step in the development of an interest scale is the assigning of weights to the individual items. The basic question is: In scoring a given item on an occupational scale, how much weight should be given to that item and how should that weight be determined?

In his 1931 book on the measurement of interests, Fryer summarized the section on item weighting with the comment, "The problem of weights is still an unsolved one in the field of interest measurement." More than three decades later, the issue is still a puzzling one, though considerably more data are available.

Unit Weights versus Multiple Weights

In the earliest inventories, before 1920, weights were developed on an *a priori* basis, usually by reference to some "expert" opinion. In 1919, the publication of Yule's Statistics text provided a framework for dealing with percentage differences and in 1924, Ream began weighting items by using the standard error of the difference between two groups, assigning ± 1 weights when the difference was larger than one standard error. This method was used by many investigators, some modifying it to require two standard errors but all using unit weights.

The next advance was made by Cowdery (1926), working with a formula developed for him by T. L. Kelley. This method weighted *all* differences between groups, adjusting for size by giving larger weights to bigger differences, and was the progenitor of future multiple-weight systems. With a slight modification, this was the first scoring formula used by Strong. It generated weights from $+30$ to -30, and clearly was cumbersome both in practice and in research applications. Several studies were undertaken to determine whether this complex weighting was really necessary, but few of them used adequate criteria. For example, one early study comparing unit and multiple weights used as a criterion the correlation between the interest inventory and intelligence (Jacobsen, 1928).

Strong apparently ended the controversy in 1930 when he found that although unit-weight keys had higher reliabilities, they were inferior to multiple-weight keys in correctly classifying men into occupations. But since he was dealing with a validation, not a cross-validation situation, this still wasn't a crucial trial. Also, his method for selecting items for the unit scales was to give unit weights to all items on the multiple-weight scales. Investigators have since discovered that this is not the best way to develop unit-weight scales.

In the early 40's, Peterson and Dunlap (1941) showed that unit-weight scales correlated highly, usually above 0.95, with multiple-weight scales and thus concluded that one was as good as the other. Strong replied (1943) by showing that scales highly correlated could indeed have differing validities and again concluded that weighted scales were better.

Although maintaining that weights were necessary, Strong made several moves toward reducing the range of weights. When his blank was originally published in 1927, the weights ranged from +30 to −30. In the 1930 revision, the range was reduced to ±15 and in the 1938 revision, it was reduced even further to ±4. On the basis of data to be reported below, it appears that the range will be reduced to ±1 in the near future.

Perhaps the most adequate test of the unit-versus-multiple-weight issue was made by McCornack (1956). Using the SVIB, he compared social workers with men-in-general, using three kinds of keys: the regular Strong key, a 6% key (where all differences between social workers and men-in-general exceeding 6% were scored +1), and an analogous 18% key. The 6% key was clearly inferior (note that Strong's earlier unit-weight keys were in effect 6% keys) but the Strong key and the 18% key were virtually identical, particularly on cross validation. The overlap in the validation group was 16% for the Strong key, 18% for the unit-weight key. On cross-validation, it was 18% and 19%, respectively.

In a study comparing items of differing format, Perry (1955) also compared unit-weight scales where 20% differences were scored ±1 with scales weighted according to the Strong formula, using college students versus Navy yeomen (clerical workers). With criterion and cross validation samples each containing 80–100 persons, Perry found unit-weight items consistently superior to Strong-weighted items, and this was true of both the forced-choice triad and the L–I–D formats.

In his development of the MVII, Clark has done extensive systematic research on the problems of item weights and scale length (Clark, 1961), and has reported that in several comparisons between weighted keys and unit-weight keys, he never found the multiple-weighting system to be superior. For example, comparing unit-weight scales with scales weighted according to the Strong formula in separating electricians from tradesmen-in-general, the overlap for the unit-weight key was 37% and for the multiple-weight key, 53%. The overlap for printers was 40% and 57%, respectively.

Using data collected by Kreidt from psychologists, Clark showed that Strong's multiple-weight system separated the psychologists from professional men-in-general by 3.23 standard deviations while a unit-weight key separated them by 3.71 standard deviations, the latter increasing to 4.03 standard deviations on cross validation (Clark, 1961, p. 28).

Another study by Strong (Strong et al., 1964) compared various scoring methods using a variety of unit and weighted scales on eight of Strong's original occupational groups. The results showed clearly that the weighted scales were slightly superior to the unit-weight scales but, equally clearly, the differences were small and of doubtful practical significance, especially as they were validation rather than cross-validation results, and weighted scales have consistently shown more cross-validation shrinkage.

Taken together, the researches of McCornack, Perry, Clark, and Strong et al. suggest strongly that well-selected unit weights are slightly superior to Strong's original multiple weights. These results do not show, of course, that unit weights are superior to all multiple-weighting systems, but simply that they are better than the Strong system.

A system of weights based on multiple-regression techniques might prove superior to unit weights since it would utilize the correlations between items, which the Strong system does not do. A study pertaining to this problem has recently been completed by Fruchter (1963). Using the Kelley Activity Preference Inventory, he developed scales to predict successful service records among Air Force recruits. Four different keying methods were compared:

1) Items selected by multiple regression, using the multiple-regression weights.

2) Items selected by multiple regression, using unit weights.

3) Items selected by percentage differences, using weights similar to the Strong weights.

4) Items selected by percentage differences, using unit weights.

The results show that although the weighted multiple-regression key did best on the validation group, it was inferior to the unit-weight percentage difference key on the cross-validation group. This unit-weight key was also better than the multiple-weight key containing the same items. Again, the unit-weight key stands out.

Kuder recently has proposed another scoring system based on multiple weights (Kuder, 1963). He developed scales for differentiating one occupation from another, rather than from men-in-general, by giving the items a weight equal to the percentage difference between the two groups on the item responses. This method clearly separated occupations and held up well under cross-validation. As Kuder did not report data using analogous scales with unit weights, it is impossible to tell whether unit weights would do as well.

Configural Scoring

One further type of keying, namely, configural or pattern scoring, has been proposed in an effort to improve discrimination between groups. This method would utilize combinations of responses to increase the discriminating power of the items.

Since it seems intuitively clear that some patterns of responses are more meaningful than those same responses taken singly (Meehl, 1950), configural scoring has a certain appeal. However, in practice the configural methods have failed to perform as well as anticipated.

Clark, whose work on item selection and weighting is perhaps the major contribution in this area, has taken a firm stand on this issue. In 1955 he said, concerning configural scoring, "I have made some efforts in this direction, and do not recommend that anyone do more work in this area . . . Let me make certain that this point is not misunderstood. I see no profit in using the more subtle procedures of configural scoring when we already can do so well in our differentiation of groups with responses to items taken one at a time" (Clark, 1960).

Nevertheless, some investigators have tried. Campbell (1964), using patterns of responses within the triads of the MVII, found that the pattern system was inferior to Clark's item scales. In a study mentioned earlier, Fruchter also tried a pattern-scoring technique for tetrads, and again found this to be inferior to his unit-weight scales.

Kuder, in a comprehensive study using his Preference Record, Occupational, compared several of the keying methods just discussed. He used four basic types: single items with unit weights, single items with multiple weights, patterns of items with unit weights, and patterns of items with multiple weights. Several scales of varying lengths were developed for these methods, and his final comparisons were between eleven different types of scales.

Using a group of psychologists as a criterion group, Kuder developed eleven different keys by which to differentiate between psychologists and a reference group of men-in-general. Cross-validation overlaps ranged from 22% to 28%. The analogous figures for scales based on a criterion group of pharmaceutical salesmen were 38–42%.

There were no discernible trends in these figures between the various methods of keying, and Kuder concluded, "The most remarkable feature of the results is the comparatively small range covered by the validities of the keys . . ." (Kuder, 1957).

In the related area of personality measurement, McQuitty has published a series of articles dealing with the problem of classifying individuals by using a configural scoring approach (see for instance, McQuitty, 1957, 1960a, 1960b, 1960c). Since none of these procedures has yet been proven under cross validation, they must be considered tentative and speculative. In particular, one attempt by Malone to use McQuitty's analysis in developing scales for the SVIB showed this method to be inferior to Strong's regular keys (Malone, 1958).

In sum, research to this point has supported the use of unit weighting of individual items over any other method.

Clark's method of item selection and weighting is simple and straightforward. Only items reflecting a reasonably large difference, usually around 18–22%, between the criterion group and the reference group are used on the scale. Then through an iterative procedure, items highly correlated with each other are thinned out, making the key more heterogeneous in content. One notable feature of Clark's method of selecting items is that seldom is there much cross validation shrinkage, and occasionally the keys actually do better on cross validation. His method evidently minimizes the effects of chance on item selection.

REPORTING OF RESULTS

The items that have been selected and the scales developed with these items result in scores or summary statements descriptive of interests. However, there has been little or no research on how to report these results.

Strong has used two methods simultaneously. First, the raw score is converted to a standard score based on the original criterion group with mean of 50 and standard deviation of 10. These scores are then categorized into letter grades from A to C. Scores above 45 are assigned to the A category, 40–45 to B+, and so forth down to 25. Everything below 25 falls into the C category.

Strong also has attempted to map the domain of interests and his report form reflects this work. Occupations are grouped together according to the intercorrelations between the various occupational scales. For example, in Group II are listed the occupations: Mathematician, Physicist, Engineer, and Chemist. The median intercorrelation between these four is 0.86, higher than any correlation of these occupations with any other occupation outside of the group. This grouping is helpful in interpreting scores to individuals. It is probably more meaningful to a student to be told that the interests he has expressed resemble those of the men in these four occupations than to be told simply that he has interests in the Natural Science area.

One other feature of the Strong profile is the use of a shaded "chance" area. This area was established by using the score from SVIB booklets completed by throwing dice, and corresponds to the sigma range (mean ± 1 S.D.). Strong suggests that this range represents the cutting point between scores similar and dissimilar to the criterion group. Scores falling within the shaded area are to be interpreted as chance scores and ignored as indeterminate. However, Stephenson recently has shown that scores within this range are as stable as scores anywhere else and can't be considered chance scores; hence he questions the use of shaded areas (Stephenson, 1961).

A better method of determining the shaded area might be to use the sigma range of the men-in-general distribution on the scale. This would allow counselors to determine not only how much the individual had in common with the criterion group but also how much he differed from men-in-general on that scale. A profile sheet using this type of shaded area can be found in Campbell (1963).

Kuder has used two methods of reporting results. The first, used on his Vocational, is a profile of percentiles and is similar to Strong's plotting of standard scores. The second, used on his newer Form D (Occupational), is an index for each occupational scale, called the Differentiation Ratio (D.R.). According to Kuder, this ratio lists "the degree of confidence with which one can state that a person making a certain score belongs to that specific occupational group rather than to the norm (reference) group" (Kuder Manual). The size of the D.R. is the ratio of the proportion of the two groups who received the score.

To this point, the only way to choose between these and other methods is by personal choice. There may be no essential difference between these methods but, more likely, each method may have its own advantages and disadvantages. A well-designed research project to objectively describe the effects of using each method would be welcome.

One contribution in the area of understanding the results of the Strong Blank is the work of Darley and Hagenah (1955). They have developed objective methods for categorizing the patterns of scores on the SVIB. Their methods in effect condense the scale scores into a smaller number of more meaningful, easier-to-handle patterns.

VALIDITY

Somewhat different from the effectiveness of the items or parts used in measuring interest is the question of the overall validity of the instrument. The appraisal validity, or the validity of the scores or patterns of scores, provides essential information concerning the effectiveness of measurement, but it does not provide any information about the total value of the instrument as it ultimately is used.

Earlier we described the uses of interest measurement in student selection, personnel selection, counseling, and research in personality psychology. The extent to which interest measurement significantly contributes to the efficiency of these four processes depends on, and in turn reflects, the validity of the measurements, as well as other characteristics of the instruments, such as ease of understanding the results or scope of coverage.

No research publications have been identified that directly bear on validity from this point of view. Such research would require the comparison of selection or counseling procedures including interest inventories to procedures similar in every way except that they do not use such instruments. For example, how would the vocational success and satisfaction of students who received counseling including vocational interest score interpretation compare with the success and satisfaction of students who received similar counseling using no vocational interest measures?

Few attempts have been made to assess the validity of any psychological measuring process against these ultimate criteria and little is known about the contribution of interest measurement to the solution of relevant practical problems.

As is true with the evaluation of the validity of most psychological measurements, the available information concerning the validity of interest measurement depends primarily on the use of intermediate criteria.

The first level of validity of an interest inventory is best indicated by the information concerning the items constituting the inventory or its scales. Rationally, a scale consisting of items of proved validity should provide a score of comparable validity and this usually is the case.

The validity of the scores of the Strong Blank is reviewed in several places. In Fryer's book, a detailed review of much information is provided for many early interest inventories, including the SVIB. Strong's book in 1943 and Super's book in 1949 provided additional information. A later review by Berdie (1960) reported results from 94 publications appearing before 1955 and for the most part after 1950; this latter review summarized validity studies in terms of the concepts of content, concurrent, predictive, and construct validity.

Once the items to be included in an inventory have been devised and selected and the scales assembled, little attention has been given to the concept of content validity in interest measurement. Strong has made some comparisons among different types of items, such as those pertaining to occupation and those pertaining to preferences for personal characteristics, but relatively little is known about the more subtle aspects of the content of items used in interest measurement.

Because it is closely related to the most frequently used method of developing interest scales, concurrent validity has been used often in assessing the accuracy of the scales. The development of the SVIB rests on the fact that the scales obtained differentiate concurrently between groups. A mass of information about differences among occupational groups, curricular groups, and groups defined in other ways supports the original SVIB validity data.

For example, Stone demonstrated such differences for the SVIB journalism scale (1953) when he found that a majority of his sample of 86 newspaper men had primary patterns in Group X, which includes the author-journalist scale. In another representative study, Perry (1955) studied 135 office workers with the SVIB and MVII and found that on the SVIB office worker scale, his Navy office workers (yeomen) and men-in-general overlapped 44% while on the MVII yeomen key the overlap with Navy men-in-general was 52%.

England and Paterson (1958) studied a group of personnel directors and found that among 1398 Air Force officers classified as comptroller, accounting-auditing, personnel director, personnel staff, and personnel officer, SVIB scores reflected the degree of vocational adjustment as implied by their vocational aspirations. Officers with high scores on scales related to their assignments planned to enter related civilian occupations more than did officers with low scores, percentages for comptrollers being 55 and 11, for personnel staff 29 and 12.

Concurrent validity studies have demonstrated relationships between interest scales and other psychological measurements such as the Edwards Personal Preference Schedule. Dunnette, Kirchner, and DeGidio (1958), for example, found the following relationships between the SVIB and the Edwards Personal Preference Schedule: correlations between the means of occupational score included in Group I of the SVIB (artist, physician, etc.) and EPPS autonomy score, 0.26;

SVIB Group II (engineer) and endurance scores, 0.24; Group IV (skilled trades—outdoor) and exhibition, 0.28; Group IX (sales) and exhibition, 0.31; Group X (verbal) and exhibition, 0.35. They reported comparable correlations between the SVIB and the California Psychological Inventory: Group IX (sales) and CPI dominance, 0.39; Group X (verbal) and CPI self-acceptance, 0.44; SVIB production manager and CPI psychological-mindedness, 0.45. A large number of research studies leave little question but that interest inventories can provide descriptive psychological information characterizing groups in a way conforming to reasonable expectations.

The predictive validity of interest scores also has been repeatedly demonstrated, although it is somewhat lower than concurrent validity. Ghei reported the validity of scales on the MVII in predicting success and satisfaction of IBM workers (1960). He found that although satisfactory scales comparing IBM workers and tradesmen-in-general could be developed and cross-validated, better scales resulted from comparing satisfied IBM workers and men-in-general. Kloster studied the extent to which vocational interest scores predicted job satisfaction (1956). He found that among 47 pairs of men given the SVIB as college freshmen about 1940, those whose occupations in 1951 were in close harmony with earlier SVIB scores showed significantly greater job satisfaction and income than those whose SVIB scores were not in harmony with their occupations. For example, for the "well-placed" men the mean income was $7172, the mean Hoppock job satisfaction score, 22.9; for the "poorly-placed" men, means were $5845 and 20.7.

Stordahl reported a prediction study using Strong scores during high school to predict similar scores during the college sophomore year (1954). He found a substantial relationship between SVIB scores obtained for 181 men tested in grade 12 and later as college sophomores. Correlations ranged between 0.45 and 0.87 with most being in the 0.70's. Over one-half of the patterns labeled "primary" on the original test remained so on the retest.

Predictive validity in academic situations is only moderate; usually the correlations between interest scores and grades do not exceed 0.30. Frequently the correlations are large enough to attain statistical significance but seldom are they of any practical value for prediction or selection.

Hannum and Thrall (1955) and Layton (1952) studied the extent to which Strong scores predict success in veterinary medicine education. Hannum and Thrall found that SVIB scores did not predict grades in the veterinary medicine curriculum but they did predict curricular membership. The mean score on the SVIB veterinarian scale for veterinary medicine students was 50, for nonveterinary medicine students, 28. Layton found a correlation of 0.30 between scores on the veterinarian scale and grades in veterinary medicine for 87 freshmen. Hendrix did a similar study for freshmen in accounting and found a correlation of 0.26 between the accountant score and grades in freshman accounting for 95 freshmen at the University of Wyoming. Hewer studied the relationship between the grades of premedical students at the University of Minnesota and their scores on the SVIB and found no correlations. She also found no SVIB differences between successful students and those who dropped out. Melville and Frederiksen studied 93 engineering freshmen at Princeton and found a correlation of 0.32 between the SVIB psychologist scale and grades. With ability held constant, this correlation was 0.37. Correlation between SVIB and chemistry grades was 0.29. Kelly and Fiske (1951), in a study of trainees in clinical psychology, found a a correlation of 0.46 between SVIB psychologist scale and grades received on a comprehensive achievement examination.

Of all long-term prediction studies, the most impressive is the 18-year follow-up study of the SVIB reported by Strong (1955). A group of college students were given the SVIB in the early 1930's and were retested, on the average 18 years later. Test-retest correlations ranged from 0.48 to 0.79 with a median of 0.69. Profile stability over the 18-year period approximated a correlation of 0.80. Former students in an occupation averaged 44 on the early scale appropriate for that occupation as compared to an average of 32 obtained by persons not in that occupation. Strong stated, "In terms of expectancy ratios there are 3.6 chances to one that a man with an A rating will enter that specific occupation and 5.0 chances to one that a man with a C rating will not enter the occupation." (pg. 54)

Scores on scales corresponding to the person's occupation 18 years after taking the test correlated 0.23 to 0.30 with satisfaction ratings. These correlations must be considered in light of the fact that most of the subjects were well satisfied with their occupations.

Interest inventories were devised not only for the purpose of predicting success but are used extensively to predict the individual's satisfaction with an occupation. Strong has assumed that persons who are grossly dissatisfied with their work will not remain in it and that consequently the criterion occupational groups that he has used, groups of people who have remained in their occupations for many years, consist primarily of persons who are at least minimally satisfied. Although some persons remain in an occupation they dislike because conditions prevent a change, essentially Strong's assumptions appear sound.

The studies designed to predict occupational satisfaction from interest scores often provide disappointing results. Occupational satisfaction is difficult to define and even more difficult to measure and the results which are only moderately positive, such as those reported by Strong, may be due to these difficulties. McArthur's (1954) study reveals a complexity that may require the study of carefully selected subgroups if existing relationships are to be identified. He found that the correlation between Strong scores obtained early in college and occupation several years later was much higher for graduates of public schools than for graduates from private schools. The influences determining both occupational choice and satisfaction vary from one group to another and these influences may affect the relationship between interests and satisfaction. One further source of error in these comparisons is the gratifying fact that most people like their jobs. If only a small minority is dissatisfied, the relationship between satisfaction and any other variable is difficult to observe.

Many studies concerning the construct validity of interest measurement are summarized in a paper by Darley (1960). Relationships between interest scores and scores on other personality inventories usually are in the expected direction. Frequently differences in scores of persons in different occupations correspond to information derived through other observations. Most recently the work of Bordin's students even shows correspondence between interest measurement results and results expected on the basis of psychoanalytic theory (Bordin, Nachman, and Segal, 1963).

These studies of the construct validity of the SVIB demonstrate that the concept of interests can be useful in the psychological description and interpretation of behavior and that the measurement of interest provides meaningful and useful results.

CONCLUSION

The measurement of vocational interests has been of practical importance in counseling and selection, has provided relevant and productive hypotheses useful in occupational psychology and personality theory, and has extended the methodology used in personality appraisal. The literature on interest measurement is voluminous and the research imaginative.

New interest-measuring instruments and ingenious methods of appraising interests are beginning to appear. Some of these are based on psychometric assumptions derived from other kinds of psychological measurement directed toward intelligence or emotionality. Some are relatively naive and attempt to provide instruments of immediate usefulness, disregarding the complexities of measurement. A few of the new attempts certainly will be psychometrically and psychologically sound and provide improved means for assessing interests. The next frontier of interest measurement is the problem of how and why individuals develop different interests. New methods and continued creative use of the old ones will, it is hoped, contribute further to our knowledge of this phase of human behavior.

REFERENCES

BERDIE, R. F., "Likes, dislikes, and vocational interests." *J. Appl. Psychol.* **27**, 180–189 (1943)

BERDIE, R. F., "Validities of the Strong Vocational Interest Blank," in W. L. Layton (ed.), *The Strong Vocational Interest Blank: Research and Uses.* Minneapolis: University of Minnesota Press, 1960, pp. 18–61

BLUM, L. P., "A comparative study of students preparing for five selected professions including teaching." *J. Exp. Educ.* **16**, 31–65 (1947)

BORDIN, E. S., B. NACHMAN, and S. J. SEGAL, "An articulated framework for vocational development." *J. Counsel. Psychol.* **10**, 107–117 (1963)

CAMPBELL, D. P., "Chance on the SVIB: Dice or men?" *J. Appl. Psychol.* **47**, 127–129 (1963)

CAMPBELL, D. P., "Another attempt at configural scoring." *Educ. Psychol. Measmt.* **23,** 721–727 (1963)

CARTER, H. D., "Twin similarities in occupational interests." *J. Educ. Psychol.* **23,** 641–655 (1932)

CARTER, H. D., "Case studies of mature identical twins." *J. Genet. Psychol.* **44,** 154–174 (1934)

CLARK, K. E., "Problems of method in interest measurement," in W. L. Layton (ed.), *The Strong Vocational Interest Blank: Research and Uses.* Minneapolis: University of Minnesota Press, 1960, pp. 146–162

CLARK, K. E., *Vocational Interests of Non-Professional Men.* Minneapolis: University of Minnesota Press, 1961

COWDERY, K. M., "Measurement of professional attitudes." *J. Personnel Res.* **5,** 131–141 (1926)

DARLEY, J. G., "The theoretical basis of interests," in W. L. Layton (ed.), *The Strong Vocational Interest Blank: Research and Uses.* Minneapolis: University of Minnesota Press, 1960, pp. 118–145

DARLEY, J. G., and THEDA HAGENAH, *Vocational Interest Measurement.* Minneapolis: University of Minnesota Press, 1955

DUNNETTE, M. D., "Vocational interest differences among engineers employed in different functions." *J. Appl. Psychol.* **41,** 273–278 (1957)

DUNNETTE, M. D., W. K. KIRCHNER, and JoANNE DeGIDIO, "Relations among scores on Edwards Personal Preference Schedule, Calif. Psychol. Inventory, and Strong Vocational Interest Blank for an Industrial sample." *J. Appl. Psychol.* **42,** 178–181 (1958)

ENGLAND, G. W., and D. G. PATERSON, "Relationship between measured interest patterns and satisfactory vocational adjustment for Air Force officers in the comptroller and personnel fields." *J. Appl. Psychol.* **42,** 85–88 (1958)

FREYD, M., "Measurements of interests in vocational selection." *J. Personnel Res.* **1,** 319–328 (1923)

FRUCHTER, B., "Prediction of airman success from responses to items of the Kelley Activity Preference Report, Technical Documentary Report." PRL-TDR-62-9, June 1962

FRYER, D., *The Measurement of Interests.* New York: Holt, Rinehart and Winston, 1931

GARMAN, G. D., and L. UHR, "An anxiety scale for the Strong Vocational Interest Blank: Development, cross-validation, and subsequent tests of validity." *J. Appl. Psychol.* **42,** 241–246 (1958)

GEE, H. H., and K. E. CLARK, "A comparison of empirical and homogeneous keys in interest measurement." Minneapolis: University of Minnesota, Department of Psychology, Technical Report No. 6.1956

GHEI, S., "Vocational interests, achievement, and satisfaction." *J. Counsel. Psychol.* **7,** 132–136 (1960)

GUILFORD, J. P., P. R. CHRISTENSEN, N. A. BOND, JR., and M. A. SUTTON, "A factor analysis study of human interests." *Psychol. Monogr.* **68,** 1–38 (1954)

HANNUM, T. E., and J. B. THRALL, "Use of the Strong Vocational Interest Blank for prediction in veterinary medicine." *J. Appl. Psychol.* **39,** 249–252 (1955)

HENDRIX, D. R., "Predicting success in elementary accounting." *J. Appl. Psychol.* **37,** 75–77 (1953)

HEWER, VIVIAN H., "A comparison of successful and unsuccessful students in the medical school at the University of Minnesota." *J. Appl. Psychol.* **40,** 164–168 (1956)

HOYT, D. P., "Measurement and prediction of the permanence of interests," in W. L. Layton (ed.), *The Strong Vocational Interest Blank: Research and Uses.* Minneapolis: University of Minnesota Press, 1960, pp. 93–103

HUGHES, J. L., and W. J. MCNAMARA, "Limitations on the use of the Strong sales keys for selection and counseling." *J. Appl. Psychol.* **42,** 93–96 (1958)

JACOBSON, M. M., "The quantitative determination of scholastic interests among college students." Unpublished doctoral dissertation, University of Minnesota, 1928

JENSON, P., M. DUNNETTE, and W. KIRCHNER, *Personal Communication.* 1963

KELLY, E. L., and D. W. FISKE, *The Prediction of Permanence in Clinical Psychology.* Ann Arbor: The University of Michigan Press, 1951

KLOSTER, C. G., "The relation between measured vocational interests and job satisfaction." *Dissertation Abstr.* **16,** 1104 (1956) (Abstract)

KREIDT, P. H., "Vocational interests of psychologists." *J. Appl. Psychol.* **33,** 482–488 (1949)

KUDER, G. F., "Identifying the faker." *Personnel Psychol.* **3,** 155–167 (1950)

KUDER, G. F., "A comparative study of some methods of developing occupational keys." *Educ. Psychol. Measmt.* **17,** 105–114 (1957)

KUDER, G. F., *Manual: Kuder Preference Record Occupational Form D.* Chicago: Science Research Associates, 1959

KUDER, G. F., "A rationale for evaluating interests." *Educ. Psychol. Measmt.* **23,** 3–12 (1963)

LAYTON, W. L., "Predicting success of students in veterinary medicine." *J. Appl. Psychol.* **36,** 312–315 (1952)

MCARTHUR, C., "Long-term validity of the Strong Vocational Interest Blank in two subcultures." *J. Appl. Psychol.* **38,** 346–533 (1954)

MCCORNACK, R. L., "Sex differences in the vocational interests of a professional group." Unpublished doctoral dissertation, University of Minnesota, 1954

MCQUITTY, L. L., "Elementary linkage analysis for isolating orthogonal and oblique types and typal relevancies." *Educ. Psychol. Measmt.* **17,** 207–229 (1957)

MCQUITTY, L. L., "Hierarchical linkage analysis for the isolation of types." *Educ. Psychol. Measmt.* **20,** 55–67 (1960a)

MCQUITTY, L. L., "Hierarchical syndrome analysis." *Educ. Psychol. Measmt.* **20,** 293–304 (1960b)

McQuitty, L. L., "Comprehensive hierarchical analysis." *Educ. Psychol. Measmt.* **20,** 805–816 (1960c)

Malone, R. L., "A configural vs. the standard method of scoring the SVIB." Unpublished doctoral dissertation, University of Illinois, 1958

Meehl, P. E., "Configural scoring." *J. Consult. Psychol.* **14,** 165–171 (1950)

Melville, S. D., and N. Frederiksen, "Achievement of freshman Engineering students and the Strong Vocational Interest Blank." *J. Appl. Psychol.* **36,** 169–173 (1952)

Miner, J. B., "A method for evaluating a psychograph for vocational guidance." *J. Educ. Psychol.* **17,** 331–340 (1926)

Moore, B. V., "Some principles and practices of personnel selection, with special reference to graduate engineers." *Psychol. Monogr.* **30,** (Whole No. 138) (1921)

Norman, W. T., "A dispersion analysis of the interests of 115 occupational and reference groups." Doctoral dissertation, University of Minnesota, 1957

Norman, W. T., "A spatial analysis of an interest domain." *Educ. and Psychol. Measmt.* **20,** 347–361 (1960)

Perry, D. K., "Forced choice vs. L–I–D response items in vocational interest measurement." *J. Appl. Psychol.* **39,** 256–262 (1955)

Perry, D. K., "Validities of three vocational interest keys for U.S. Navy yeomen." *J. Appl. Psychol.* **29,** 134–138 (1955)

Peterson, B. M., and J. W. Dunlap, "A simplified method for scoring the Strong Vocational Interest Blank." *J. Consult. Psychol.* **5,** 269–274 (1941)

Ream, M. J., *Ability to Sell.* Baltimore: Williams and Wilkins, 1924

Schletzer, Vera M., "A study of the predictive effectiveness of the Strong Vocational Interest Blank for job satisfaction." Doctoral dissertation, University of Minnesota, 1963

Segal, S. J., "The role of personality factors in vocational choice: A study of accountants and creative writers." Doctoral dissertation, University of Michigan, 1954 (Microfilm abstracts, Vol. XIV, No. 4, 1954, p. 714.)

Stephenson, R. R., "Chance vs. nonchance scores on the SVIB." *J. Appl. Psychol.* **45,** 415–420 (1961)

Stone, C. H., "An objective personnel study of metropolitan newspapermen." *Journ. Quart.* **30,** 448–467 (1953)

Stordahl, K. E., "Permanence of interests and interest maturity." *J. Appl. Psychol.* **38,** 334–340 (1954)

Strong, E. K., *Vocational Interests of Men and Women.* Stanford: Stanford University Press, 1943

Strong, E. K., *Vocational Interests 18 Years After College.* Minneapolis: University of Minnesota Press, 1955

Strong, E. K., "Interests of fathers and sons." *J. Appl. Psychol.* **41,** 284–292 (1957)

Strong, E. K., "Good and poor interest items." *J. Appl. Psychol.* **46,** 269–275 (1962)

STRONG, E. K., D. P. CAMPBELL, R. F. BERDIE, and K. E. CLARK, "Proposed scoring changes for the SVIB." *J. Appl. Psychol.*, **48**, 75–80 (1964)

STRONG, E. K., A. C. TUCKER, "The use of vocational interest scales in planning a medical career." *Psychol. Monogr.* **66, 341,** 1–61 (1952)

SUPER, D. E., *Appraising Vocational Fitness*. New York: Harper and Row, 1949

YULE, G. V., *Introduction to the Theory of Statistics* (5th ed.). London: Charles Griffin, Ltd., 1919

ZUCKERMAN, J. V., "Interest item response arrangement as it affects discrimination between professional groups." *J. Appl. Psychol.* **36**, 79–85 (1952)

CHAPTER 12

MEASUREMENT AND ANALYSIS IN ANTHROPOLOGY*

W. W. HOWELLS, *Harvard University*

INTRODUCTION

Anthropological measurement and assessment might be expected to resemble measurement and assessment in other fields such as intellect, health, or physical adequacy. But there are fundamental differences. Anthropology attempts not to assess qualities, but rather to evaluate variation, from the point of view of genetics, of race, or of evolution. Put another way, whereas the other disciplines dealt with in this book measure performance, physical anthropology studies the organism itself. (Indeed, far from observing performance, anthropologists are all too apt to prefer their organism in the form of an inert body or a skeleton.)

Anthropology attempts, in fact, to comprehend in one system the differences between individuals, between populations, and between the human species and others—differences of all possible kinds, but assessed primarily from the point of view of genetics and function. With these interlocking aspects, anthropology has had to face various ultimate theoretical problems which are far from being solved. In its hundred-year history it has seen methodological changes and theoretical developments of great importance. It has seen, on the one hand, the growth of measurement, the discovery of genetics and of definable genetic traits like blood

---

* This chapter was completed several years ago. Relative to the subjects covered in it, there has in the interval been less rather than more work in body typing; known biochemical variations have continued to multiply, though few new polymorphic systems have appeared; and the availability of computers and of easily applied programs of analysis has expanded very rapidly. I have not attempted to rewrite anything except to complete a few references, since the chapter continues to represent my view of the methodological directions in the study of human variation. It is by no means an attempt to present the whole of physical anthropology, since it does not cover the historical evolutionary side of the subject, nor the relation of man to other primates, nor specific aspects of race and racial history. Human genetics, on the other hand, though commonly regarded as antithetical to anthropometric studies, is actually enmeshed with them in the nature of individual variation; therefore, though not the primary subject, genetics will be prominent in the body of the chapter.

The chapter is also meant to be a compendium, not a full-scale work or reference. I feel I have been miserly with illustrative material, of which there is no end. Many other authors could have been cited on most points, and more works of those I did cite, and thus the list of references is merely a sample for guidance.

I wish to thank my colleagues Albert Damon and Fred Mosteller, who will see, if they read the chapter again, how greatly their comments have helped.

groups, and the development of statistics; and on the other, the progress of evolutionary theory (the roles of selection, mutation, genetic drift) and of population genetics.

Furthermore, method and theory have had important interactions. Physical anthropology, with its general problems and biological basis, should serve as an instructive model for some of the more special kinds of assessment and evaluation in the fields of social science, psychology, education, etc. I should like to deal with the subject by going from the particular to the general. First I shall review attempts to assess the whole physique, or body constitution, of the individual from a non-health point of view, so to speak. Second, I shall consider numerical measurement of particular features, such as measurement of height in the study of growth or of the size variations of adults. Finally I shall deal with the most general aspects, the study of population differences—usually "racial" differences—which have always been at the center of anthropology. These are the aspects which raise real problems of method and theory.

VARIATION AMONG INDIVIDUALS

Constitutional Typing

Doubtless the oldest attempt to assess variation in human beings was by recognition of constitutional type, or body type. This approach has a long and well-known history running back to antiquity, when it was entirely divorced from any study of the human species or of races. Hippocrates, for example, distinguished a phthisic and an apoplectic habitus in the diagnosis of disease, which has been a constant concern of constitutionalists. The body-constitution method has been, throughout its history, an endeavor to classify systematically obvious contrasts in bodily conformation such as may exist even between brothers. Furthermore, it has always been an attempt to classify a man's whole nature, temper as well as form. It is fundamentally a philosophical as much as scientific avowal that men are of different kinds. Writers have seldom failed to epitomize it by citing Shakespeare's Caesar on yon Cassius' lean and hungry look ("Would he were fatter!") :

"He thinks too much . . ."	the lean are introverts,
". . . such men . . ."	they can be typed,
". . . are dangerous."	and predicted.

Commonly, but not always, these systems of typing have set in opposition a slender, linear build and a heavy-set, lateral one. The very obviousness of body differences has tended to make such typing a vulgar science akin to phrenology. To proceed past a long history (see Sheldon *et al.,* 1940, p. 22), we may mention the three best-known systems of modern times, namely those of Viola, Kretschmer, and Sheldon.

In Italy, in the latter part of the nineteenth century, measurement was introduced into constitutional work, thus allowing some study of correlation and variation as well as the objective scaling and classing of individuals. The best-known representative of this school was Viola (1932) who combined various body measurements so as to distinguish major groupings or scales, such as "longilineo" versus "brevilineo" extremes, or microsplanchnic versus macrosplanchnic (referring to relative or absolute size in the trunk). This system, which combined constitutional typing and traditional anthropology, was carefully and fully developed but did not have continuous use.

Kretschmer's classification (1925) was more in the familiar typing tradition than was the work of Viola, although he also took certain measurements by which to contrast his types anthropometrically. His polar types were pyknic, athletic, and asthenic; or heavy-set, muscular, and weak or lightly built, respectively. Kretschmer's interest lay in the associations between physique and certain types of psychosis (manic-depressive, preponderantly associated with the pyknic physique, and schizophrenic, largely associated with the asthenic). He was doubtless the most generally influential constitutionalist just prior to Sheldon.

Sheldon (1940, 1954, 1961) began by considering his immediate forerunners and their methods, simultaneously reviewing a large body of photographic data. These data suggested a mass-versus-surface distinction, with a secondary distribution of mass along a "cuboid-spheroid" axis. There was some resemblance to Kretschmer and others generally in the way Sheldon distinguished muscular and nonmuscular massives from each other, and both together from the spindly asthenic type (also called "respiratory" or "cerebral"). Although the above suggests only two axes, or a two-dimensional representation, his inspections suggested to Sheldon that three distinct factors were involved.

Sheldon differed from his predecessors (the Italians excepted) in introducing scaling into the otherwise unwieldy approach of simple typing. His technical contribution was the development of three independent scales for his factors, each originally of seven steps, so that his types (somatotypes) are not primary categories, as in previous systems, but rather intervals in a continuous three-dimensional space. It is easy to neglect this distinction. Furthermore, Sheldon himself (see especially 1954) obviously tends to view these cells or intervals as discontinuous entities with well-defined attributes; however, it seems advisable to consider Sheldon's system and Sheldon's own interpretations separately from one another.

His scales are ratings of three components:

Endomorphy. Softness and roundness of the body, with mass concentrated essentially in the abdomen, and with short tapering limbs, ham-form in the upper segment. Although the conspicuous tissue is fat, Sheldon emphasizes that by "component" he means a general morphological aspect, and not a specific tissue. This distinction is an important point in critical discussions of body typing.

Mesomorphy. Hardness, ruggedness, and squareness, with bone and muscle heavy and prominent—with chest dominating abdomen; leg and forearm thick and strong, not tapering; neck thick; and head suggesting a cube.

Ectomorphy. Delicacy and linearity of the body, with a brainy-looking head having a narrow face, high nose, and pointed chin. Thigh and upper arm are weak, and leg and forearm are long and slender. There are further distinguishing traits, of skin and hair, but a frequent question from critics has been whether ectomorphy is an essential aspect of the body or simply an impoverished development of fat, muscle, and bone, which is the impression given.

Individual assessment was made from nude photographs, with the subjects in standard poses for front, side, and back. (As may be supposed, the requirement of nudity or near-nudity, the need of a fairly elaborate photographic setup, and the time required to rate photographs have been limiting factors in the use of the system clinically.) Each component was assessed separately and for each of five body regions (head-and-neck, thorax, arms, abdomen, legs), leading to an estimate of somatotype, which is written, for example, 5–2–3 and read "five-two-three." This particular example describes an individual rather strong in the first component, endomorphy, and definitely weak in the second, mesomorphy.

Sheldon thus transformed the variables under scrutiny from discontinuous to continuous, with all the theoretical and statistical advantages such a change would make possible. The least useful results of somatotyping have come from the unsophisticated, who unwittingly try to reverse the change, i.e., semi-serious users in clinical work who speak of "the" endomorph.

Perhaps the greatest amount of effort has been put into constitutional psychology, the end for which the system was devised. Sheldon himself promptly produced (1942) *The Varieties of Temperament,* with a corresponding set of coordinates: viscerotonia, somatotonia, and cerebrotonia. This particular lead of Sheldon's has not been followed, and his further attempt, *The Varieties of Delinquent Youth* (1942) has been roundly denounced as unscientific (see, for example, Sutherland, 1951), because of Sheldon's rather impressionistic treatment of the delinquency aspects.

Others, however, in more prosaic studies, have indeed found associations between mesomorphy and juvenile delinquency (Glueck and Glueck, 1956; Seltzer *et al.,* 1948). Mesomorphy has also been related to a tendency to coronary artery disease (Gertler and White, 1954). Many such correlations have been tested, with results ranging from nil to fairly marked. Parnell (1958) has furnished a general and interesting critique of somatotyping together with a variety of results and applications of his own, including an apparent excess of male babies born to more mesomorphic parents, and a confirmation of Kretschmer's relation of schizophrenia to linear body build. Figures 1 and 2, from Parnell, demonstrate his psychosis associations and illustrate the somatotype distribution chart introduced by Sheldon for such purposes.

Thus, although the possibility of using somatotype assessment for actual individual prediction in physical and mental disease remains in question, the existence of associations in this area can hardly be questioned. Other uses of such typing

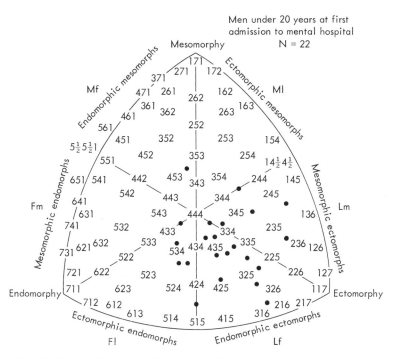

Fig. 1. Distribution of 22 consecutive male schizophrenic patients under the age of 20. (Reproduced by permission of the publisher from R. W. Parnell, *Behavior and Physique: An Introduction to Practical and Applied Anthropometry*. London: Edward Arnold, 1958.)

have not been impressive, perhaps due in part to anthropologists' traditional orientation to the study of populations as a whole rather than to the individual variations within them. Not unexpectedly, high degrees of mesomorphy were found in weight-lifters, average about 3–6½–1 (Eranko and Kervonen, 1955). More interestingly, Japanese *office workers* gave an average type of 3–5.5–1.4, indicating the Japanese norm to be very high in mesomorphy (Kraus, 1951), and tall Nilotic Negroes are extreme in ectomorphy (Roberts and Bainbridge, 1963). These data show that whatever somatotyping might contribute to a knowledge of race differences, racial studies evidently have much light to shed on body-typing, which has so far been essentially restricted to Europeans.

Somatotyping for the most part has not departed far from its original interest, the relation of body form to disease. Sheldon's method, available since 1940, has not spread as far as might have been expected. The chief criticisms and queries have concerned the lack of independence of the three components, the stability of the somatotype with age, and the genetic basis of this kind of variation. Some of these criticisms Sheldon himself has in recent years attempted to cope with by new and only partially published departures from his first formulation (Sheldon, 1961,

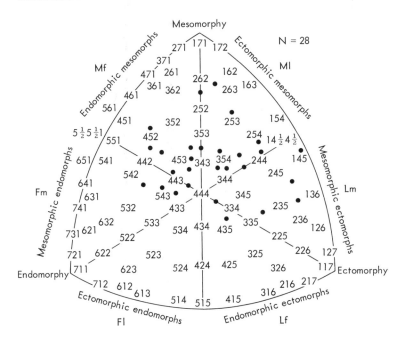

Fig. 2. Distribution of 28 consecutive men patients with primary paranoid disorder, all over 35 years of age. (Reproduced by permission of the publisher from R. W. Parnell, *Behavior and Physique: An Introduction to Practical and Applied Anthropometry.* London: Edward Arnold, 1958.)

1963). The most persistent objection has probably been the lack of objectivity in rating, i.e., the dependence on subjective judgment.

Sheldon, in fact, proposed at the outset (1940) a fairly elaborate analysis of body measurements taken from his photographs, to be used in combination with the visual assessments. This method has been abandoned by all, since the principal workers have shown that, with proper training and attention to criteria, they can consistently approximate one another in their ratings (Tanner, 1954). However, the search for objectivity goes on. Dupertuis (1950) showed that straight anthropometry was useless in differentiating somatotypes. Lindegård (1953) evolved a new set of factors (such as sturdiness, linearity) which *could* be assessed anthropometrically. Parnell developed a chart of distributions having certain basic measures (height, weight, skin folds, some bone breadths and muscle girths) on which an individual's scores can be placed (see Parnell, 1958, p. 21). Such a chart is an anthropometric estimate of fat, muscle, and linearity, to use in place of but corresponding to Sheldon's components. Finally, Damon (Damon and Goldman, 1964) developed multiple regression formulae (which were considered and rejected by Parnell as a method) using eight or nine body measurements to estimate Sheldon's components approximately, but with the same consistency as is possible for a single observer assessing the same photographs on two different occasions.

Factor Analysis

Factor analysis has also been used as an independent method. Sheldon reported (1954) that he used the results of some early trait factor analyses as a guide in formulating his system. Factor analysis of persons was also employed by Howells (1952, 1957b) and Lohr and Fields (1954). This method, creating a "person-space," allows "components" of size and shape to be discovered as the principal axes or factors—that is, as the principal modes of differentiation of the individuals. The advantages here are objectivity and the acceptance of differences in proportion as part of the system of variation studied. (Sheldon's shape differences pertain entirely to the criteria of the components—"roundness," "hamming"; disagreements such as excessive linearity of the legs are termed "dysplasia" and viewed as abnormal and outside the system).

Results of such analysis have readily distinguished factors approximating endomorphy and ectomorphy and, in fact, tend to bring them together at opposite poles of a single factor, thus raising a query as to the actual nature of ectomorphy. A factor representing mesomorphy directly is not found. Instead, other factors have tended to contrast trunk and limb development, and in other ways to reflect such gradients in major proportions (see Damon et al., 1962).

While factor analysis in general is subject to indeterminacy of factors, certain important regularities probably could be found by more work with this particular method, person analysis. New computing facilities make it an obvious method of attack. It offers the possibility of obtaining ratings in the form of factor scores, and of combining anthropometric measurements with physiological and other tests.

Body Composition

It might be expected that constitutional typing, the synthetic approach to physique, would be closely complemented by the analytical approach, i.e., the anatomical and physiological analysis of the body by component tissues: skin, fat, bone, muscle, etc., or water versus fat versus other constituents. Brozek, in fact, pointed out (1953) that Sheldon, in his 1942 book, made statements about specific gravity without adducing supporting data, thus missing the opportunity to link his studies with biophysical and biochemical methods which can be used in analyzing body build.

The straightforward approach in this field would be the careful analysis of cadavers, but the obstacles are overwhelming—the difficulty of the process itself plus that of obtaining an adequate sample of nonemaciated bodies representative of the population. Thus the present energetic research utilizes indirect methods of estimate applied to the living (see Brozek, 1963a). These methods vary from skinfold measurements and X-rays to techniques of helium replacement to obtain volume, underwater weighing for density, and measured dilution of injected substances which are circulated in specific tissues of the body (see Brozek and Henschel, 1961, and Brozek, 1963b, for a full review of these developments). The basic approach is estimate via regression equation.

Table 1   Composition of lean body mass in standard man

Organ or tissue	% of lean body mass
Muscles	47.6
Skin and subcutaneous tissue	13.5
Skeleton	15.9
Blood	8.6
Brain, spinal cord	2.27
Heart	0.56
Lungs	1.51
Alimentary tract	3.65
Liver	2.70
Kidneys	0.48
Spleen	0.24
Pancreas	0.10
Essential fat	0.60
Residual	2.35

A sample result is "the standard man" (see Behnke, 1961, from Lisco), used as reference. This standard man weighs 70 kg, of which 10%, or 7 kg, is excess fat (excluding the essential fat of the bone marrow and the nervous system). The remainder, the "lean body mass," is made up as shown in Table 1.

Since the lean body mass is fairly constant throughout life, the separate estimation of this and of the fat gives an infinitely better idea of the fatness of a person than does gross weight (although, of course, this does not mean goodbye to bathroom scales). Fat may vary from less than 10% of gross weight, in the standard man, up to 50% or more. (For a review of methods of estimating fat by itself from measurements, see Damon and Goldman, 1964). As one means of estimating what the standard weight of an individual (adult male) should be, Brozek (1956) obtained several equations such as the following (measurements taken in centimeters):

Standard weight

= (0.411 × height) + (1.204 × bicristal diameter) + (0.885 × biacromial diameter)

+ (7.342 × corrected upper arm diameter) + (0.220 × age) − 137.510.

This, with an age correction, uses the skeleton to predict what a man *should* weigh, to be compared to what he actually does weigh. It will be seen that the standard tables for height and weight, such as are used on penny scales, are a primitive and inadequate attempt at the same kind of thing, taking no account of variations in body build.

In its type of approach (quantitative analysis of aspects of an individual), the study of body composition probably comes closer to psychological and behavioral measurement than do other fields of anthropology. An interesting point is the unexpected aversion of the proponents of the body-composition method for the constitutionalists and vice versa, essentially one between analysts and synthesists (I am making the contrast rather extreme). To Sheldon, a synthesist, endomorphy is *not* mere tissue (fat); it is a general quality of the body and the personality, involving texture, shape, activity, inclination. Endomorphy has two antagonists, and only two, and these antagonists are qualities of the same order again: mesomorphy is not simply bone and muscle, nor is ectomorphy simply skin and brain. When Hooton evolved a modification of Sheldon's classification, in which endomorphy became simply "fleshiness," mesomorphy "muscularity," and ectomorphy merely the numerical relation of height to weight, he was tampering with Scripture; using the photoscopic method of Sheldon to get the results of the skin-pinchers, his system ended in limbo. The body-composition analysts, on the other hand, make no attempt to synthesize except additively: in their hands a man becomes two dollars' worth of chemicals. Their common ground lies not with the body typers but with the students of growth, who in the most advanced areas must know how growth phenomena proceed in terms of distinct tissues of the body, and not in size and proportion alone.

PRACTICAL ANTHROPOMETRY

A second major division of anthropology is the practical measurement of the living subject for medical, military, or industrial reasons. Here again the basic aim is assessment of an individual relative to norms for his population.

Study of Growth

In the first instance we have the study of growth for the assessment of the developmental status of an individual. In its simplest form, this approach has consisted of the obvious compilation of tables of expected heights and weights, against which anyone could check a child's development. Actually, fifty or sixty years of work by specialists, and the establishment of a number of centers for the study of human growth, have taken matters much further than such tabulations would imply. Students have developed charts of expectancy, such as the Wetzel grid, the Fels Normative Data Chart, or the Tanner-Whitehouse standards for British children. On these an individual child's growth may be plotted over time and changes in later growth observed as well, so that a child may be recognized, let us say, as consistently but not abnormally small for his age, and perhaps also as maturing relatively early. The timing of the adolescent growth spurt is one sign of maturation, along with the appearance of secondary sex characteristics, and of skeletal development; these have also been scaled and standardized for some populations (see Garn and Shamir, 1958). Thus evaluation of normality in growth is now a fairly reliable matter in the hands of competent statisticians. In addition, Tanner (1956) has demonstrated that there is a high correlation of adult stature and other dimensions with the same relative measures in childhood, as early as about three years of age, so that early prediction of eventual body size is possible to some degree. At any rate, he has been able to advise the Royal Ballet School as to how their youngest applicants are likely to develop, and thus to assure the School that a future fawn will not turn out to be an elk instead (Tanner, 1952). Standard prediction tables for ultimate stature are those of Bayley (1946).

The background for this research into basic growth processes involves measurement by several techniques, with strong emphasis on longitudinal observation— following the same child through growth— as opposed to cross-sectional observation, using all children of given age classes. Only by the former method can reliable information on the variation in rates be obtained, since averaging for age groups distorts these changes in cross-sectional data. Indeed, a recognized objection to charts and grids, no matter how sophisticated, is the fact that they blur, on the average, what are sharp spurts or lags in the growth of separate individuals.

Methods and interests in this area converge on those typical of constitutional typing and analysis of body composition. Tanner, for example, follows both general bodily configuration and actual measurement by employing the same photographic methods as Sheldon, with increased emphasis on careful reference scales placed in the picture itself. Biochemical aspects are also an important source of information on growth activity used by Tanner and other workers such as Garn. Both have paid particular attention, too, to changing patterns of fat distribution during growth and aging, by the use both of skinfold calipers and of soft-tissue X-rays. One phenomenon discovered by such methods is the redistribution of subcutaneous fat without change in weight, during adolescence and early maturity, when fat was found to decrease on the limbs and increase on the torso (see Garn, 1956). A general text on growth is Tanner's (1955); a treatment devoted particularly to methods is that of Garn and Shamir (1958).

The field is, of course, a large one involving many other workers; it cannot be more fully reviewed here. It is moving toward means of assessing the developmental status of an individual from a spectrum of indices, rather than from a simple combination of a wall scale and a clinician's eye. A subsidiary field within growth, but a well-advanced one, is that of dental development and the correction of malocclusion, studied both by anthropometric techniques and by cephalometric X-rays. The diagnosis and prognosis of events, and the timing of corrective measures, rests on the accumulated knowledge of eruption and of facial growth. Such work has been prosecuted particularly in this country and in Scandinavia.

Human Engineering

A second general category is the straightforward application of measuring techniques to industrial products or military equipment and supplies. Size distribution of functionally important parts of the human body have been used in the design and procuring of supplies. A classic illustration of its need was the discovery that the steering wheel of a certain make of truck had been so designed that a large proportion of "normal" drivers could not readily shift the leg from the accelerator to the brake pedal. Many other examples of the mechanical engineer's lack of interest in *Homo sapiens* are known. Although by its nature not strongly concerned with theoretical or scientific interest, this field of endeavor, a surprisingly new one, has done much to give comfort, save lives, and win wars. It has also, under the pressure of practicality, enlarged experience and improved instruments in ordinary anthropometry; the presently most useful texts of such measurement are manuals produced by the military (1953, U.S. Air Force WADC TR, No 53–9, WADC TR, No 53–12). Such workers are also well placed for access to large numbers of normal human subjects for study, something which researchers cannot always reach as readily as one might think. A good one-chapter outline of problems and methods is Damon, Stoudt, and McFarland (1963); Table 2, reproduced from this source, shows the presentation of the distribution of stature by percentiles, as an example of measurement data needed by designers. A more complete work on the subject was produced by the same authors (1966). In addition, a limited number of studies have been carried out on the body in action (see papers by Dempster and others in *Count,* 1955; also, Santschi *et al.,* 1963). These may be quite practical, ranging from the limits of reach or the amounts of force a man can apply in given positions to moments of inertia relative to gravity and weightlessness. Or they may relate more to basic mechanics of the skeleton, a matter of interest in evolution. Concern with such investigations and their complex procedures has been strangely foreign to traditional anthropometry.

QUANTITATIVE STUDIES OF POPULATIONS AND VARIATION

Here we come to the original theme of physical anthropology, the metrical study of the variations between individuals of a population, and the distinctions of populations from one another. We recognize this now as one approach to human systematics and evolution. But the first development of methods preceded such a view, and had the simpler aim of describing races, and doubtless of attempting to assign an individual to his proper race.

Anthropometry

It is true that perhaps the earliest important application of measurement rose from "evolutionary" ideas. This was Peter Camper's "facial angle" of 1791, which he devised in order to contrast the profiles of ape and man. His study led him, in that simple day, to find the Negro intermediate (possibly a "hybrid") between European and orangutan. This quantitative demonstration of differences in facial projection in human races not only affected canons of art but also served as a foundation for later anthropology.

Most early measurement, however, was done without regard to views on evolution, simply in order to separate races, to find the differences among them, and if possible to determine their total number. In the eighteenth century Linnaeus had named four races, and Blumenbach, using skin color as his criterion, had added

Table 2* Nude-body height (standing) of male military personnel

Population	Percentiles (in.)					S.D.
	1st	5th	50th	95th	99th	
Air Force personnel[1]	63.5	65.2	69.1	73.1	74.9	2.44
Pilots, multi-engine	64.4	65.9	69.4	73.3	74.9	2.31
Pilots, fighter	63.8	65.2	68.8	72.6	74.2	2.24
Cadets	63.6	65.2	69.2	73.1	74.7	2.45
Bombardiers	63.5	65.2	69.1	73.0	74.5	2.32
Navigators	63.5	65.2	69.2	73.3	75.0	2.46
Observers	63.8	65.4	69.1	72.8	74.2	2.44
Flight engineers	63.1	64.8	69.0	73.2	75.0	2.51
Gunners	62.4	64.2	68.3	72.2	73.7	2.43
Radio Operators	63.0	64.6	68.3	71.8	73.2	2.37
Basic trainees[2]	62.5	64.2	68.6	72.7	74.7	2.61
Army personnel						
Inductees less than 20 yr old[3]	62.4	64.3	68.7	73.1	74.9	2.66
Inductees more than 20 yr old[3]	62.7	64.6	69.0	73.4	75.2	2.65
Separatees, white[4]	62.7	64.3	68.5	72.6	74.5	2.52
Separatees, Negro[5]	62.3	64.0	68.0	72.2	74.0	2.58
Marine Corps personnel[6]	64.4	66.1	69.7	73.5	74.5	2.18
Recruits[7]	63.0	64.6	68.6	72.5	74.1	2.40
Navy personnel[8]	64.1	65.7	69.7	73.5	75.1	2.34
Recruits, 18 yr old[7]	62.8	64.5	68.5	72.6	74.2	2.50
Recruits, 17–25 yr old[9]	62.9	64.6	68.6	72.7	74.4	2.48
Enlisted men, general[10]	63.2	64.8	69.5	73.5	75.5	2.48
Enlisted men, submarine[11]	63.3†	65.0†	69.9†	74.1†	76.1†	
Officers, submarine[11]	63.7†	65.6†	70.8†	74.7†	76.4†	2.80
Pilots, aircraft[12]	64.9	66.3	70.2	74.1	75.9	4.70
Cadets, aviation[10]	65.1	66.6	70.1	73.8	75.2	

[1] Hertzberg, et al., 1954 (except as noted).
[2] Daniels, et al., 1953b.
[3] Damon, 1957.
[4] Newman and White, 1951.
[5] USA, 1946.
[6] USMC, 1949.
† Including shoes (subtract 1 in. for nude height).

[7] USN, 1949b.
[8] King, et al., 1947.
[9] Gibbons, et al., 1953.
[10] USN, 1955.
[11] USN, 1957.
[12] USN, 1959.

another. To these first simple descriptions Anders Retzius (1842) added the cephalic index, with considerable eventual effect. He treated head shape as a ratio of breadth to length, following actual measurement of the two. For example, he stated that among Swedish skulls the proportion of length to breadth was as 1000 to 773, or "almost 9 : 7." Slavs, by contrast, gave a ratio of 1000 : 888, or "about 8 : 7." He also supplied the terms "dolichocephalic" for a long skull and "brachycephalic" for a short one. His breadth ratio thus became the cephalic index, which has been very widely used ever since.

Although we are today little closer to explaining this kind of variation, head form in fact does vary rather constantly within populations, and shows marked differences between populations. The index furnished a new quantitative characteristic to use in description, and thus led to a whole conception of the biometrical description of individuals and groups. It separates shape from size, and may indeed be seen as a simple form of discriminant, since heads of the same size may be distinguished in shape by plotting on a graph the length and breadth simultaneously (a device used effectively in recent times by Twiesselmann and his colleagues (1954; see also Howells, 1965).

Samuel G. Morton (1839) applied measurements to skulls in the United States in order to demonstrate differences between Whites, Negroes, and Indians, as well as the likenesses of the fabled Mound Builders to living Indians. In France, Broca founded the Société d'Anthropologie in Paris in 1859, and with his followers did work on brain weight, body size, etc., from cadaver material. He also fostered the collection of a variety of measurements on peoples of the world (see Topinard, 1875), and published a handbook for the use of travelers. Eastward also measurement burgeoned, reaching its culmination with von Török in Budapest. He recommended taking 5371 measurements, not to mention over 2000 angles, on a single skull (1890). The unruly growth of method, in fact, led to conferences in the interest of standardization, the outstanding one being the so-called Frankfort Agreement of 1882.

By the early twentieth century it was possible for Rudolph Martin in Switzerland to publish the first edition of his well-known work, *Lehrbuch der Anthropologie* (1914). This and the second edition remain valuable for containing the most accepted set of definitions for reference, being sufficiently extensive for many purposes, and reflecting the already long experience with the accumulated techniques involved. The work also contains a large amount of tabulated information collected from various populations of the world, but neither this excellent reference nor any other of the time endeavored to say which measurements might be most meaningful, or what assumptions underlay the taking of measurements at all. Another set of standardizations and definitions was produced by the Galton Laboratory under Karl Pearson, to which the center of gravity now shifted.

Francis Galton provided a major alternative to race as a reason for anthropometric study: quality in man, or "eugenics." He estimated "eminence," he studied its distribution in man, and attempted to relate it to inheritance. It was this kind of motive which led to his "law of ancestral inheritance," for the fractional contributions of one's forebears to one's heritage, and also to his "law of filial regression," according to which the mean of the offspring tends to regress toward the population mean rather than to reproduce the mean of the parents themselves. Galton sought physical as well as psychological evidence for his conclusions, and he needed a measure of the "regression," or incomplete association of parent and child, or of any two continuous variables. Pearson devised the technique for him, in the product-moment correlation coefficient, which he denoted by r, for regression.

There are sound and simple genetic reasons behind Galton's "laws": recombination of parental genes; polygenic inheritance of continuous traits generally, with the additive and substitutive nature of the genes involved so that most immediate antecedents do in fact contribute genes to any individual, and variation does approximate a normal curve. Galton, of course, did not know about this, since it was before Mendel's rediscovery, and long before comprehension of polygenic inheritance. And Pearson, working by mathematical methods in a milieu of continuous traits, could not bring himself to understand Mendelian particulate inheritance, and said so. He became, in fact, an anti-Mendelian. He turned away from the avenue of investigation which would have made Galton's impulse eventually more fruitful, and instead interested himself and the Laboratory purely in the differences between groups, or "races." For this he evolved the measures of difference and dispersion for which he is so well known, and which led to the t-test. Specifically, Pearson devised the "Coefficient of Racial Likeness," long employed with groups of crania (see many volumes of *Biometrika*). This was actually not a measure of likeness or distance, but rather of the significance of differences over a number of measurements. Pearson's methodological contribution was great, but his anthropological approach, a search for differences, was that of the nineteenth century. He understood variation statistically, but not genetically.

It is only fair to say that almost no one else understood variation genetically either. This was an era in which anthropologists, doubtless led on by their simple statistics, tended to equate a central tendency with a type, an ideal form, ignoring the importance of viewing the population as a whole. Those holding such a view in its most pronounced degree—and they were not a minority—in fact saw the variation in a population as caused by the mixture of "types," and they tried to reconstruct history by resolving the group under study into "pure" forms. In their genetic innocence, they did not recognize the supposed mixtures as representing simply random combinations of the genes present in the population, the only possible source of such variations. Boas alone, far ahead of his time, for forty years kept repeating that the within-population variation lay only in family lines, and also that the variation within a group was more important than that between groups. Separately from Pearson (whose work he nevertheless knew well), he developed some mathematical treatment to demonstrate his ideas—approximating, in fact, both analysis of variance and factor analysis (see Howells, 1958, for a review, also Tanner, 1958)—but few anthropologists knew what he meant. Thus by 1940 there had passed a century of technical achievement in measuring. It had produced a methodology, much descriptive material (an inventory of man, as Laughlin, 1960, points out), and a general statistical technique for establishing differences between populations. It had not solved the problems it had set for itself: how many races existed, how they had evolved, or how they might be systematically classified. It could say that two groups were different in such and such a dimension—all else was inference.

Serology

The advent of serology—the study of blood traits—produced a major shift in anthropology. The A B O groups were discovered in 1900, and the M N groups in 1927. Their first attraction was their apparent Mendelian simplicity, in utter contrast to all normal aspects of man previously studied. Their second attraction was their phenotypic fixity; they do not vary under environmental conditions of development, as do most measurable traits of continuous variation. By 1940, and coincidentally with the finding of the Rh groups, so much information had been collected the world over that populations could be described in these terms—either by the proportions of the blood groups in a population, or better, by the relative frequencies of the genes themselves, computed from the actual phenotypes, or groups, present. During the 1950's a series of further independent blood types were found, and more recently other variations in blood serum as well, with known single gene locus control, so that a population may be described in terms of more than twenty such systems.

As a means of description, of relating populations taxonomically, blood groups have had much the same history as measurements. Blood group maps of the world can now be drawn for several of the major systems, giving results coinciding in many ways with the distribution of traditional "races," but displaying certain differences. However, for actual scientific results in this matter of taxonomy, they are like measurements—they are used only to differentiate. The importance of their introduction has been to rivet attention on populations structures and the genetic background of variation, and so to sweep away the misconceptions as to "types" in the old sense of prepotent combinations of skin color, head form, etc., combinations supposed to be "purer" or more typical of a race. Thus blood groups have at last served to establish Mendel's old laws of segregation and independent assortment of characters in place of certain previous fallacious conceptions of human inheritance. Since the actual genes can be identified so exactly, the blood groups further provide potent possibilities for the study of natural selection, genetic drift, etc., in man (see Reed, 1961). While all this does not contribute much toward any kind of identification, assessment, or measurement of individuals or groups, it does more than anything else in anthropology to clarify the nature of the genetic variation which underlies all other kinds of measurement and assessment, and provides the biological justification, in polygenic inheritance, for applying statistics of probability and variation. Quetelet's application was empirical—genetics provides an actual theoretical basis.

Common Considerations

To resume, the anthropological problem of describing and handling human variation has gone through a measuring phase, which ran up against limits both of theory and of method (the inability to see populations in proper perspective, and the inability to handle a number of measured variables together, i.e., the lack of multivariate analyses). It has been for some time in a phase of genetic study in which the actual work on populations has been the counting of blood group frequencies. This approach, too, has encountered limits as a method of population description, although for intrapopulation investigations its resources, like those of measurement, are far from exhausted.

Perhaps the figure who can best be looked on as bridging these phases is R. A. Fisher. To begin with, he was both a statistician and a theoretical geneticist. Many mathematicians may not know of his extraordinary feat of deducing the basic antibody relationships of the Rh blood system—leading to his CDE notation—when only part of the evidence was in, and thus predicting the rest. Together with Sewall Wright, he developed a theory of population genetics, the step in theory from Mendel's single genes to the structure of populations in genetic terms. And unlike Mendel he lived at the right time.

In 1936, he wrote critically of Pearson's Coefficient of Racial Likeness, stressing the need for workers to know the limitations both of such statistics and of their own data. He added that

... the science of craniometry must be in a very primitive condition, if it is still concerned with clarifying its fundamental notions at the stage we have been discussing. It seems, indeed, undoubtedly true that the theoretical concepts developed in the subject have lagged far behind the mass of observational material which has been accumulated. This may be partly due to the sheer magnitude of the programme which the energy of its founders sketched out, partly to an intuitive confidence, widely held in other fields, though everywhere difficult to justify, that, by amassing sufficient statistical material, all difficulties may ultimately be overcome.*

The following year, 1937, he wrote another article implying that the development of statistics had not reached its ultimate with Pearson, and offering practical suggestions, including the following:

Many biological and sociological workers are faced with mathematical difficulties which, for various reasons, they cannot overcome. Most, naturally, prefer to tackle their own problems, but, even when they are sufficiently successful in this, a more expert examination of the problem is often very fruitful. Actually, whole bodies of data, or potential data, lie fallow for lack of the means of interpreting them. A live center of statistical teaching will seek out such cases, both among their colleagues, and in the literature.†

---

* R. A. Fisher, "The 'Coefficient of Racial Likeness' and the Future of Craniometry." *J. Roy. Anthrop. Inst.* **66**, 57–63 (1936). Quoted by permission of the publisher.
† R. A. Fisher, "Professor Karl Pearson and the Method of Moments." *Ann. Eugenics* **7**, 303–318 (1937). Quoted by permission of the publisher.

And he was not merely criticizing. He was at the same time beginning to introduce the discriminant function, having already provided analysis of variance. The history of this and of generalizations of Pearsonian methods made by Hotelling, and the systematizing of multivariate analysis, need no review here (see Tatsuoka and Tiedeman, 1954). Fisher thus not only provides a temporal link from the time of Galton, Pearson, and Boas to the present, he also combined in his own work several important interests of physical anthropology: blood genetics, population genetics, and the multivariate handling of continuous variables. It is well worth remarking that he, like Pearson before him and like some of the factor analysts (e.g., Burt and Thurstone), often used anthropological materials to develop or illustrate a statistical method.

Apart from a few even-minded individuals such as Fisher, different groups of workers have been subject to rather violent swings of opinion as to the values of different approaches as one or another yielded useful returns. It must be emphasized here that a great deal of development is to be looked for in several lines. Rapid progress is being made in the study of biochemical traits, so much so that useful discoveries are being made virtually by accident. Isoniazid inactivation is an example (see Szeinberg *et al.,* 1963). Isoniazid, a drug administered orally to tuberculosis patients, is rapidly metabolized and rendered inactive by some, and slowly by others. A check showed that the difference in reaction is constant and due to a single gene. Thus a valuable one-gene trait and locus were turned up, useful in other studies. (We may well ask, what was the meaning of this trait for man before the creation of isoniazid?) The strictly genetic approach to variation has important possibilities open before it for studies particularly of genetic linkage and mapping, and all that such development implies for the special identification of carriers of other traits.

At the same time, the use of anthropometry has tended to be denigrated. In fact, insofar as anthropometry has been identified with measurement for measurement's sake, without a problem at hand other than the metrical description of a given population sample, it has come in for heavy scorn (Garn, 1962). However, when anthropometry is taken, as it should be, to mean the measurement of human variables generally (i.e., of continuous variables not susceptible to single-gene control and not manifesting two- or three-state phenotypes), then it must be recognized as the study of man in many of his most important aspects. It is the avenue to eventual analysis of multifactorial genetics. It is the key to the study of the response of individuals and groups during growth to different environments or diets (Hulse, 1960), just as changes in gene frequencies of blood groups are a key to microevolutionary changes in a population due to selection. It has the potential to serve in certain general predictions of disease susceptibility (Damon, 1960), just as genealogical records for single genes serve in the individual prediction of certain other diseases.

I stress this approach because it involves the kind of variables related to the interests of educators, behavioral scientists, and others. For example, genetic native intelligence is a matter of compelling concern, and it is only through the same general approach that progress can be made toward useful assessment of it, so that here the paths of psychologists, geneticists, anthropologists, and statisticians all come together. The approach to assessment and analysis via more strictly genetic methods is well covered in Stern (1960).

The time seems ripe for some kind of synthesis of the genetic and anthropometric approaches. Human biology necessarily comprehends all human variation and the forces—genetic, environmental, microevolutionary—which determine it. The relations of the two approaches which I have named are probably not always as explicitly understood as they might be. The theoretical backgrounds, fortunately, are the same, and both aim at and permit the simultaneous handling of populations and individuals. Genetic analysis is precise and incisive because the genes can be pinpointed, counted, mapped, held constant; but, within the population, genes at different loci are, in the sense of demonstrated genetic linkage, uncorrelated, a fact that limits in certain ways the mathematical treatment possible. The aspects approachable by measurement (including *both* head length and heart rate, let us say) have a complex genetic background, and are subject both to genetic variation *and* to environmental lability, which is itself subject to genetic control. Furthermore, such variables are apt to show morphological or other correlation, hence a large group of requirements and of possibilities is introduced into their analysis. The technical developments in genetics are proceeding apace; the technical possibilities in anthropometry (*sensu lato*) are, at the moment, so broad that the training of students is a problem. Both the biological knowledge and the mathematical training involved promise to be considerable. New discoveries may bring both theory and problem into clearer focus, opening the way for the kind of advances already seen in the "genetic" aspects.

SOME FURTHER DEVELOPMENTS

The diversity of anthropological interests in the assessment of variation should now be clear. I wish to mention two more matters as examples of developments which may become important for anthropometry.

Causes of Variation

The first matter relates to the theoretical attempt to identify external causes of variation in human traits. For example, tests have been made of certain zoological principles of body form and heat conservation in warm-blooded animals. These rules relate to the fact that as body size varies, volume varies as the cube, and surface area as the square, of linear dimensions; they relate also to the ability of animals to maintain an optimum rate of dissipation of the heat they produce, by varying in size and form. By Bergmann's rule, of a group of closely related populations, those in colder parts of the occupied range are larger in mean body size, and thus have a lower ratio of surface (the heat-dissipating agent) to mass (the heat-producing agent). Thus size is varied as an adaptation to temperature. By

Allen's rule, form is varied to the same end; in warmer parts of the range, extremities—limbs, nose, ears, tail—tend to be longer, thus presenting more surface for the loss of heat.

Schreider (1950, 1957), Roberts (1953), and Newman (1960) have all marshaled published figures to show that these rules apply to man, a worldwide species, e.g., by using multiple regression to show the relation of such simple measures of body size as stature or weight to external conditions of temperature. Weiner (1954) has similarly indicated the importance of the nasal membranes as an air-dampening agent by relating variations in human nose shape to climatic features: temperature, humidity, and, above all, vapor pressure.

In a series of studies on Army personnel, Baker (1955, 1958) has pushed such inquiries by direct experiment, showing that body size, surface area, and amount of fat are related to resistance to heat stress; he has also shown, using Negro and White subjects carefully paired in size and fat, that race is a factor, Negroes being slightly more heat-tolerant under hot-wet conditions, Whites more so under hot-dry conditions.

Some of the demonstrations have been questioned, and investigation must still be considered in a primitive stage. A beginning has been made in this very important field of the meaning of individual variation in body form, and also of the heritable differences between populations, or races, in the same terms. Here, in fact, is the kind of investigation which alone can determine how much of racial difference is due to historical accident and how much to a working adaptation to the recent environment of different races. Anthropometry—general measurement of form or of fat content—has been the necessary tool thus far, but better understanding of the related biochemistry (including such things as skin color) and practical techniques of measuring such variables will of course fill out the picture as time goes on.

The matter of cause and function, in fact, has this shape at present. Certain single-gene differences have clear effects, or relations to disease, etc., giving them selective values. The sickling gene produces a difference in hemoglobin, rendering it less efficient for its primary oxygen-carrying purpose, which accidentally but importantly also renders it less suitable as a prey for certain malaria parasites. The ABO substances are related less clearly to differential disease resistances; further investigation will eventually satisfy curiosity here and contribute enormously to understanding the underlying processes of predisposition.

On the other side are variations of a polygenic, continuously varying sort: physical and physiological variations of body form, tissue proportions, and levels of maintenance or of excretion of metabolites (though many of these are clearly under single-gene rather than multi-gene control). These are also being analyzed in functional and selective terms; their flexibility, in fact, puts them in a different category. They are to a greater degree responsive *both* to the adaptive needs of the individual during his lifetime *and* to those of the group, changing genetically more readily because the genetic base is broader. In a polygenic system, more genes are available to change their frequencies; genetic recombination, basic in the nature of polygenic traits, is a process of change and variation far more rapid than changes in the gene frequencies of single genes. If this seems like one more digression into genetics, my excuse is its importance in understanding the behavior of continuous traits.

Multivariate analysis

The second matter is the vastly broadened possibilities of statistical analysis that are created by the availability of high speed computers. In anthropology computers should aid in the study of human genetics, where precise tests of linkage and estimation of gene frequencies in the more complex blood systems involve laborious calculations. Their impact, however, will probably be greatest in the field of measurable traits, where correlation among traits is important. Here the striking change has been in the development and generalization of multivariate statistics, heretofore used in anthropology only at the cost of more labor than most workers would care to put in, even when many of them had been devoted to collection of the data.

Multivariate statistics have already been developed and used for practical purposes in such fields as education. In anthropology they take on added significance, forming models for biological and genetic realities. As I have already said, the mathematically derived normal curve of error was long ago found to provide a model for the variation (genetic and other) in a single measured trait in biology. The new statistics will provide the means of fitting more complex models to the variation of many traits and many populations. Let me expand.

With factor analysis, for example, a number of studies in physical anthropology have pointed to factors of size and of bodily linearity versus laterality (see above, e.g., Burt, 1947; Schreider, 1951; Howells, 1951). More specifically, it is clear that limb growth is apt to be distinguishable from trunk growth, that intralimb proportions may be expressed in another factor or so, and that the head constitutes a system or systems apart from the body. (Tanner and Sawin, 1953, using the related method of analysis of covariance have shown that races of rabbits differ in local factors in the spinal column.) Within the head a number of distinctions have emerged (Howells, 1957a; Landauer, 1963; Schwidetzky, 1960), particularly of general size, of relative brain size, of facial length, and of a series of minor distinctions as to forehead breadth, breadth of the skull base, breadth of the upper face, etc., which are doubtless modes of variation both in individual differences in conformation and between racial groups.

Ideally, such factors might be found to correspond to distinguishable (if co-ordinated) events in development, under hormonal or genetic control. If so, scoring a factor for an individual would provide a method of assessment, like a rating for mathematical ability, which in turn should provide a useful weapon in the study of the genetics of physique or in the study of growth processes. Factor analysis suffers, however, from the indeterminacy of factor axes: the biological reality and exact specification of such factors is not yet clear, although it is difficult to doubt their existence. Too little has been done to test the correspondence of factors from different studies. This testing can be done (see Howells, 1957a), and will determine the further usefulness of factor analysis in physical anthropology. Something in the nature of local growth factors must be responsible for a good deal of human differentiation in shape and size, the kind of recognizable differentiation which has never been handled appropriately by direct and simple measurements. The specific genetic relationships of possible factors (see Howells and Slowey, 1957), have not been established although the existence of a genetic component in measured traits has at various times been demonstrated (Osborne and DeGeorge, 1959). This state of affairs is typical in the development of the genetics of human morphology. Only the merest beginnings exist of tests of the nature of genetic control (see, e.g., Tanner, 1953; Tanner et al., 1959; Terada, 1962).

Generalized distance between populations is of particular interest to physical anthropologists, who have always had the problem of simultaneously distinguishing and relating a set of populations by a series of variables. It has, however, been little used. A pioneer study was that of Mahalanobis (Mahalanobis, Majumdar, and Rao, 1949) on tribal groups of the United Provinces of India, a study of interest since canonical variates were also used to find group relationships. Perhaps the most interesting work to date is that of Hiernaux (1956), who used the D-statistic for a number of tribes of the Eastern Congo and the former Ruanda-Urundi. He found a gradient in relationships, running east and west, open to interpretation either as environmental in cause (shade forest versus uplands) or as genetic, meaning that it would be due to the intermixing of different parent stocks with established genetic differences. Since Hiernaux also measured distance by blood groups, using chi-square as the measure, he was able to compare the results from measurements and from blood. In the blood data the differences and the gradient were missing, indicating that the environmental explanation for the measured differences was the correct one. (See also Hiernaux, 1963, and Howells, 1953, for discussions of the problems of measuring environmental and genetic factors on different aspects of physique.)

Multiple discriminant functions have been generalized from the original single function of Fisher, and are readily available for computers (see Cooley and Lohnes, 1962). The original form has been used a number of times, especially for assignment of sex to a skeleton (Thieme and Schull, 1957; Hanihara, 1959; Giles and Elliot, 1963; Howells, 1965). Multiple discrimination, however, though barely used as yet in anthropology, should take over the work of generalized distance and other objectives, since it does several things at once and fits the genetic population model so well. The several functions, as coordinates, provide a distribution space for individuals and populations. The analysis takes account simultaneously of the distribution of the individuals of each population and the distances between centroids of several populations, stating the second in terms of the first. This is an important point, as is the fact that the variables or features significant in differentiating the populations are identified. Both have been problems in anthropology as well as in zoological systematics.

As an example, Crchton (1966) approached the problem, which had been attacked before, of the possible influences of Negro admixture on Egyptian populations of different periods and regions. He used four populations of crania: a Kenya tribe, Upper Egypt Predynastic and Old Kingdom, and Lower Egypt New Kingdom (eight groups, since both sexes were represented). The hypothesis was one of a decrease of Negro genetic influence over time through the order of groups named. He found such a gradient expression in the first function. He also found that this first function clustered the Egyptian groups closely when compared to the Negro tribe; that this function, expressing Egyptian-Negro differences, was more important than the second function, mainly expressing sex. In other words, here is a statement that the cranial distinctions between Egyptians and Negroes are of an order greater than those between two sexes of the same population and that the important features of differentiation were angles of the face and nose, and breadth of the skull and upper face. This last conforms to ordinary observation and has been stated in terms of indvidual means, but has not, by previous methods, been stated in terms of scales, distances, and populations.

Such work is still in early stages. Researchers using these methods of measurement are now faced with finding new and better means of expressing the significant aspects of morphology (or of physiology, etc.) for such studies. Once again physical anthropology is benefiting through method developed in other fields and for possibly less appropriate material. The anthropologists may continue to look for help from others already more sophisticated in analysis. Anthropology may repay this kindness by relating some of the above aspects, through its more tangible materials, to the basic factors in the underlying genetic and biological nature of man.

REFERENCES

BAKER, P. T., "Relationship of desert heat stress to gross morphology." Quartermaster Research and Development Center, Env. Protection Div., Technical Report EP–7 (1955)

BAKER, P. T., "Racial differences in heat tolerance." *Amer. J. Phys. Anthrop.* **16,** 287–305 (1958)

BAYLEY, H., "Tables for predicting adult height from skeletal age and present height." *J. Pediatrics* **28,** 49–64 (1946)

BEHNKE, A. R., "Comment on the determination of whole body density and a resumé of body composition data," in J. Brozek and A. Henschel (eds.), *Techniques for Measuring Body Composition. Proceedings of a Conference, Quartermaster Research and Engineering Center, Natick, Massachusetts, January 22–23, 1959.* Washington: National Academy of Sciences—National Research Council, 1961, p. 121

BROZEK, J., "Measuring nutriture." *Amer. J. Physical Anthrop.* **11,** 147–180 (1953)

BROZEK, J., "Physique and nutritional status of adult men." *Human Biology* **28,** 124–145 (1956)

BROZEK, J. (ed.), "Body composition. Parts I, II." *Ann. N.Y. Acad. Sci.* **110,** 1018 pp. (1963)

BROZEK, J., "Quantitative description of body composition: Physical anthropology's 'fourth' dimension." *Current Anthropology* **4,** 3–39 (1963b)

BROZEK, J., and A. HENSCHEL (eds.), *Techniques for Measuring Body Composition. Proceedings of a Conference, Quartermaster Research and Engineering Center, Natick Massachusetts, January 22–23, 1959.* Washington: National Academy of Sciences—National Research Council, 1961

BURT, C., "Factor analysis and physical types." *Psychometrika* **12,** 171–188 (1947)

COUNT, E. (ed.), "Dynamic anthropometry." *Ann. N.Y. Acad. Sci.* **63,** art. 4 (1955)

CRICHTON, J. M., "A multiple discriminant analysis of Egyptian and African Negro crania." Papers of the Peabody Museum **57,** 47–67 (1966)

DAMON, A., "Host factors in cancer of the breast and uterine cervix and corpus." *J. Nat. Cancer Inst.* **24,** 483–516 (1960)

DAMON, A., "Delineation of the body build variables associated with cardiovascular diseases." *Ann. N.Y. Acad. Sci.* **126,** 711–727 (1965)

DAMON, A., H. K. BLEIBTREU, O. ELLIOT, and E. GILES, "Predicting somatotype from body measurements." *Amer. J. Phys. Anthrop.* **20,** 461–473 (1962)

DAMON, A., and R. F. GOLDMAN, "Predicting fat from body measurements: Densitometric validation of ten anthropometric equations." *Human Biology* **36,** 32–44 (1964)

DAMON, A., H. STOUDT, and R. A. McFARLAND, "Anthropometry," in Clifford T. Morgan *et al.* (eds.), *Human Engineering Guide to Equipment Design.* New York: McGraw-Hill, 1963, Chapter 11

DAMON, A., H. STOUDT, and R. A. McFARLAND, *The Human Body in Equipment Design.* Cambridge: Harvard University Press, 1966

DUPERTUIS, C. W., "Anthropometry of extreme somatotypes." *Amer. J. Phys. Anthrop.* **8,** 367–385 (1950)

ERANKO, O., and M. J. KERVONEN, "Body type of Finnish champion lumberjacks." *Amer. J. Phys. Anthrop.* **13,** 331–343 (1955)

FISHER, R. A., "The 'coefficient of racial likeness' and the future of craniometry." *J. Roy. Anthrop. Inst.* **66,** 57–63 (1936)

FISHER, R. A., "Professor Karl Pearson and the method of moments." *Ann. Eugenics* **7,** 303–318 (1937)

GARN, S. M., "Concurrent fat loss and fat gain." *Amer. J. Phys. Anthrop.* **14,** 497–504 (1956)

GARN, S. M., "The newer physical anthropology." *Am. Anthropologist* **64,** 917–918 (1962)

GARN, S. M., and Z. SHAMIR, *Methods for Research in Human Growth.* Springfield, Ill.: C. C. Thomas, 1958

GERTLER, M. M., and P. O. WHITE, *Coronary Heart Disease in Young Adults: A Multidisciplinary Study.* Cambridge: Harvard University Press, 1954

GILES, E., and O. ELLIOT, "Sex determination by discriminant function analysis of crania." *Amer. J. Phys. Anthrop.* **21,** 53–68 (1963)

GLUECK, S., and E. GLUECK, *Physique and Delinquency.* New York: Harper, 1956

HANIHARA, K., "Sex diagnosis of Japanese skulls and scapulae by means of discriminant function." *Zinruigaku Zassi (J. Anthrop. Soc. of Nippon)* **67,** 191–197 (1959) In Japanese, English summary.

HIERNAUX, J., "Analyse de la variation des caractères physiques humains en une région de l'Afrique Centrale: Ruanda-Urundi et Kivu." *Ann. du Musée Royal du Congo Belge. Série en 8. Sciences de l'Homme, Anthropologie,* Vol. 3, pp. 1–131 (1956)

HIERNAUX, J., "Heredity and environment: Their influence on human morphology. A comparison of two independent lines of study." *Am. J. Phys. Anthrop.* **21,** 575–590 (1963)

HOWELLS, W. W., "Factors of human physique." *Amer. J. Phys. Anthrop.* **9,** 159–192 (1951)

HOWELLS, W. W., "A factorial study of constitutional type." *Amer. J. Phys. Anthrop.* **10,** 91–118 (1952)

HOWELLS, W. W., "Correlations of brothers in factor scores." *Amer. J. Phys. Anthrop.* **11,** 121–140 (1953)

HOWELLS, W. W., "The cranial vault: Factors of size and shape." *Amer. J. Phys. Anthrop.* **15,** 19–48 (1957a)

HOWELLS, W. W., "The variation of external body form in the individual." 116 pp. Dittoed ms. (1957b)

HOWELLS, W. W., "Boas as statistician," in W. Goldschmidt (ed.), *The Anthropology of Franz Boas, Memoirs Am. Anthrop. Assn.* **89,** 112–116 (1958)

HOWELLS, W. W., "Détermination du sexe du bassin par fonction discriminante: Etude du matériel du Dr. Gaillard." *Bulletins et Mémoires de la Soc. d'Anthrop. de Paris,* Vol. 7, Series 11, 95–105 (1965)

HOWELLS, W. W., and A. P. SLOWEY, " 'Linkage studies' in anthropological traits." *Amer. J. Human Genetics* **8,** 154–161 (1957)

HULSE, F. S., "Adaptation, selection, and plasticity in on-going human evolution." *Human Biology* **32,** 63–79 (1960)

KRAUS, B. S., "Male somatotypes among the Japanese of Northern Honshu." *Amer. J. Phys. Anthrop.* **9,** 347–366 (1951)

KRETSCHMER, E., *Physique and Character: An Investigation of the Nature of Constitution and of the Theory of Temperament.* New York: Harcourt, Brace & World, 1925

LANDAUER, C. A., "A factor analysis of the facial skeleton." *Human Biology* **34,** 239–253 (1962)

LAUGHLIN, W. S., "Aspects of current physical anthropology: Method and theory." *Southwestern J. Anthrop.* **16,** 75–92 (1960)

LINDEGARD, B., "Variations in human body-build. A somatometric and X-ray cephalometric investigation of Scandinavian adults." *Acta Psychiatrica et Neurologica, Supplementum 86* (1953)

LOHR, M., and V. FIELDS, "A factorial study of body types." *J. Clinical Psych.* **10,** 182–185 (1954)

MAHALANOBIS, P. C., D. N. MAJUMDAR, and C. R. RAO, "Anthropometric Survey of the United Provinces, 1941: A statistical study." *Sankhya, The Indian Journal of Statistics* **9,** parts 2, 3, pp. 89–324 (1949)

MORTON, S. G., *Crania Americana*. London: Simpkin, Marshall Co., 1839

NEWMAN, M. T., "Adaptations in the physique of American aborigines to nutritional factors." *Human Biology* **32**, 288–313 (1960)

OSBORNE, R. H., and F. V. DEGEORGE, *Genetic Basis of Morphological Variation*. Cambridge: Harvard University Press, 1959

PARNELL, R. W., *Behaviour and Physique. An Introduction to Practical and Applied Anthropometry*. London: Edward Arnold, 1958

REED, T. E., "Polymorphism and natural selection in blood groups." *Proceedings, Conference on Genetic Polymorphisms and Geographic Variations in Disease, Bethesda, Md., 1960*. 80–101

RETZIUS, A., *Om formem af Nordboarnes Cranier. Forhandlingen vid De Skandinaviska Naturforskarnes tredje Mote*. (Translated, 1845, as *Uber die Schadelformen der Nordbewohner, in Archiv fur Anatomie, Physiologie und Wissenschaftliche Medicin*, and reprinted 1864 in *Ethnologische Schriften von Anders Retzius, G. Retzius ed.*)

ROBERTS, D. F., "Body weight, race and climate." *Amer. J. Phys. Anthrop.* **11**, 533–558 (1953)

ROBERTS, D. F., and D. R. BAINBRIDGE, "Nilotic physique." *Amer. J. Phys. Anthrop.* **21**, 341–370 (1963)

SANTSCHI, W. R., J. DUBOIS, and C. OMOTO, "Moments of inertia and centers of gravity of the living human body." *Technical Documentary Report No. AMRL–TDR–63–36*, Behavioral Sciences Laboratory, Aerospace Medical Division, Wright-Patterson Air Force Base, Ohio, 1963. Available OTS, Dept. of Commerce.

SCHREIDER, E., "Les variations raciales et sexualles du tronc humain." *L'Anthropologie* **54**, 67–81 and 228–261

SCHREIDER, E., "Analyse factorielle de quelques charactères susceptibles de définir la structure du corps." *Biotypologie* **12**, 26–32 (1951)

SCHREIDER, E., "Gradients écologiques, régulation thermique et différenciation humaine." *Biotypologie* **18**, 168–183 (1957)

SCHWIDETZKY, I., "Faktoren des Schädelbaus bei der vorspanischen Bevölkerung der Kanarischen Inseln." *Homo* **10**, 237–246 (1960)

SELTZER, C. C., F. L. WELLS, and E. B. MCTERNAN, "A relationship between Sheldonian somatotype and psychotype." *J. Personality* **16**, 431–436 (1948)

SHELDON, W. H., *Varieties of Delinquent Youth*. New York: Harper and Brothers, 1949

SHELDON, W. H., Talk at Children's Hospital Medical Center, March 13, 1961

SHELDON, W. H., "Constitutional variation and mental health," in A. Deutsch (ed.), *The Encyclopedia of Mental Health*. New York: Franklin Watts, 1963

SHELDON, W. H., C. W. DUPERTUIS, and E. MCDERMOTT, *Atlas of Men*. New York: Harper and Brothers, 1954

SHELDON, W. H., and S. S. STEVENS, *Varieties of Temperament*. New York: Harper & Row, 1942

SHELDON, W. H., S. S. STEVENS, and W. B. TUCKER, *The Varieties of Human Physique. An Introduction to Constitutional Psychology*. New York: Harper & Row, 1940

STERN, C., *Principles of Human Genetics* (2nd ed.). San Francisco: W. H. Freeman, 1960

SUTHERLAND, E. H., "Critique of Sheldon's *Varieties of Delinquent Youth.*" *Am. Sociol. Rev.* **16**, 10–13 (1951)

SZEINBERG, A., R. BAR-OR, and C. SHEBA, "Distribution of isoniazid inactivator types in various Jewish groups in Israel." *Proc. 2nd Internat. Cong. Human Genetics,* **1**, 110–112 (1963)

TANNER, J. M., "The evaluation of growth and maturity in children," in F. Gross (ed.), *Protein Metabolism.* Göttingen: Springer, 1952, pp. 361–382

TANNER, J. M., "Inheritance of morphological and physiological traits," Ch. 11 in A. Sorsby (ed.), *Clinical Genetics.* London: Butterworth, 1953

TANNER, J. M., "Reliability of anthroposcopic somatotyping." *Amer. J. Phys. Anthrop.* **12**, 257–265 (1954)

TANNER, J. M., *Growth at Adolescence.* Springfield, Ill.: C. C. Thomas, 1955

TANNER, J. M., "Boas' contributions to knowledge of human growth and form," in W. Goldschmidt (ed.), *The Anthropology of Franz Boas, Memoirs Amer. Anthrop. Assn.* **89**, 76–111 (1958)

TANNER, J. M., M. J. R. HEALY, R. D. LOCKHART, J. D. MACKENZIE, and R. H. WHITE-HOUSE, *Aberdeen Growth Study.* I. The prediction of adult body measurements from measurements taken each year from birth to 5 years. Archive of Diseases in Childhood 31, 372–381 (1956)

TANNER, J. M., A. PRADER, and M. A. FERGUSON-SMITH, "Genes on the Y chromosome influencing rate of maturation in man." *Lancet,* Aug. 22, 1959: 141–144

TANNER, J. M., and P. B. SAWIN, "Morphogenetic studies of the rabbit. XI. Genetic differences in the growth of the vertebral column and their relation to growth and development in man." *J. Anat.* **87**, 54–65 (1953)

TAPPEN, N. C., "An anthropometric and constitutional study of championship weight lifters." *Amer. J. Phys. Anthrop.* **8**, 49–64 (1950)

TATSUOKA, M. M., and D. V. TIEDEMAN, "Discriminant analysis." *Rev. Educ. Res.* **24**, 402–420 (1954)

TERADA, K., "Analysis of resemblance between parents and children: Genetic study on the anthropological measurements." *Zinruigaku Zassi (J. Anthrop. Soc. Nippon)* **70**, 59–78 (1962). In Japanese, English summary.

THIEME, F. P., and W. J. SCHULL, "Sex determination from the skeleton." *Human Biology* **29**, 242–273 (1957)

TOPINARD, P., Eléments d'anthropologie générale. Paris, Delahaye & Lecrosnier, 1875

VON TOROK, A., *Grundzüge einer systematischen Kraniometrie.* Stuttgart: Ferdinand Enke, 1890

TWIESSELMANN, F., "Propos sur l'anthropologie." Volume Jubilaire Victor van Straelen, vol. II, pp. 1065–1098, Brussels (1954)

VIOLA, G., *La Costituzione Individuale.* Bologna: Capelli, 1932, 2 vols.

WEINER, J. S., "Nose shape and climate." *Amer. J. Phys. Anthrop.* **12**, 615–618 (1954)

CHAPTER 13

MEASUREMENT FOR GUIDANCE*

DAVID V. TIEDEMAN, *Harvard University*
FRANK L. FIELD, *University of California, Santa Barbara*

NEEDED: A BASIS FOR CHOICE

Guidance practitioners have always been trained to understand the importance of what is measured as well as the process of measuring. Yet, it is not at all rare to hear counselors or investigators admit that issues underlying the old question "What do we do after we make/improve our predictions?" remain largely unresolved. It is our hope, in this essay, to provide a conceptual structure in which the *use* of prediction can be considered—indeed must be considered—as an integral part of predictive behavioral science. The best of measurements are necessary for ideal guidance, but they are not sufficient. Hence our argument that the guidance counselor's practice must not be defined or delimited solely by the science of measurement, any more than measurement is itself defined solely by the diverse behavioral sciences it serves.

GUIDANCE AS THE CULTIVATION OF PURPOSEFUL ACTION: A PRELIMINARY DEFINITION

We have previously defined guidance as 'the science of purposeful action applied through education' (Tiedeman and Field, 1962). Subsequent developments make it possible now to clarify this definition further (Tiedeman, 1964; Field, 1964; Tyler, 1964). Guidance is a unique professional practice designed to alter behavior. It is unique, first, because it is based on aspects of existing behavioral sciences in a way that affects these sciences—for example, the aforementioned conceptual integration of measurable traits, predicting processes, and the professional uses of such predictions. It is unique, second, because the particular type of application we propose can be made only within the context of education (as opposed to indoctrination, or even to training in some senses of the word). Thus guidance contributes to

* This is No. 31 in the *Harvard Studies in Career Development*. Preparation was supported in part by the Center for Research in Careers under Grant #MH–07308–01 from the National Institute of Mental Health. During 1963–64, when this chapter was drafted, the senior author was a Fellow at the Center for Advanced Study in the Behavioral Sciences, and a Special Fellow at the National Institute of Mental Health; the junior author was teaching at the College of Basic Studies, Boston University.

a freedom in individuals' thinking and acting that might not be useful, or even tolerable, in noneducational contexts where behavior is altered. Military training might be an example of the latter.

Purposeful action on the part of students was the goal we proposed for education, and the outcome we predicted for an educational process involving two complementary functions, guidance and teaching. Very briefly, we now explain this alleged dual need by suggesting that an individual needs two types of information in order to choose his major courses of action with the best chance of reasonable success.* The first type of information is found "outside" the individual student; knowledge of the physical world, of others' conclusions about their experiences, about themselves, and about one another—all such information is available *to* students. A better grasp of it contributes to wiser, more effective personal decisions. But we argue that the very best grasp of this one type of knowledge *cannot by itself assure* the wisest or most effective personal decisions, because a second type of logically necessary information is not found within it.

Equally necessary in order to maximize the chances† of personally effective decisions is a type of information that resides "inside" the individual. Each human being has at any point in time developed a complex set of criteria by which his manifest behavior is selected from among the near-infinite behavioral alternatives (some call this personality). Origins of these selection criteria lie in the parents, in the totality of the individual's experience to date, in the environmental context in which the behavior is planned, elicited, and/or performed, and in factors we are presently forced to treat as random.

It has been well established by behavioral scientists that some of these behavioral determinants take on sufficiently stable patterns within any one individual to be considered information; in other words, when they can be measured they permit more successful prediction regarding the individual's subsequent actions and reactions. To the degree that science (in this case, measurement) can provide scientists and educators with such information, *and can establish the relevance of that information to a particular individual,* any educational process becomes more effective when it increases that student's use of such "inside" information for selecting his behavior. Logically, this is the case regardless of how effectively that educational process already increases the student's use of the information available "outside" himself. Thus the type of individual action we term "purposeful," and propose to make more possible through education, is action consciously selected

---

* An understanding of the concept "information," as introduced by Wiener (e.g., 1950), and used by Miller, Galanter, and Pribram (1960) makes this argument clear. One excellent brief description is available in Floyd Allport (1955).

† We recognize that man lives in a contingent universe where direct cause and effect cannot always be specified. Obviously, no decision could *assure* the best outcome even if this outcome were known. But by definition, the more relevant information (in the mathematical sense) applied to a decision, the more predictable the outcome of that decision. In these terms, we simply hope to bring a relatively untapped source of *relevant* information into more students' decision-making habits.

(hereafter termed chosen) on the basis of both outside and inside information, each in adequate amounts and hence reasonably balanced in effects upon the individual's evaluation of alternative actions or probable outcomes.

At this point it should be clear that teaching—however excellent—is necessary to but not sufficient for education as we have just defined it. Teaching can convey to the student, or even bring the student to seek out, only what the teacher knows or what is available elsewhere but is still outside the student. Learning how to accomplish such communication of outside information in the currently most effective manner for various kinds of students should provide challenge enough for any reasonable educator. And a recognition of this necessary limitation on the professional services of teachers leaves a clear field for the professional practice of guidance, i.e., making inside information more available. Furthermore, if those engaged in the latter practice seek better ways of eliciting and validating the information residing within various kinds of students, they, too, will feel adequately challenged.

New Functions for Measurement Suggested by this Definition

There are several major aspects of the role which measurement would play in the kind of guidance just outlined. Obviously, the basic role is to measure—to indicate how much of what is where. Equally obvious is the fact that this basic measuring task has already been organized, refined, and categorized in terms of content measured, or measuring method, and of reasons for measuring. We all speak of personality assessment, achievement, aptitude, and interest testing, sociological surveying, etc., just as we speak of college admission, employee selection, or course grading. Unfortunately, it is less obvious that many of the refinements in the basic measuring role have been professionally haphazard. Clearly, the interrelationships among the predictive and the applied behavioral sciences are badly in need of examination.

Our present goal is far more modest than the task just outlined. Nevertheless, the goal does represent one step toward a resolution. In this chapter we shall specify the different measurement needs we anticipate for guidance-in-education as it is now taking shape. To accomplish such specification we must first develop a language to describe our overall educational goal, purposeful action. Next, we must differentiate between guidance and teaching as, within education, they can exist as complementary means of achieving this goal. For the time being we are suggesting only a crude distinction between (1) the need for information to be used by others, for decisions about an individual, and (2) the need for information to be used by individuals for their own decision-making. The first type of information may be relevant to a particular individual in terms of a group to which he may or may not belong. The second type, however, is relevant only to the particular individual, and solely in terms of his own idiosyncratic purposes. We now turn to our development of a language to define purposeful action, after which we shall attempt to place the concept into a developmental context.

Purposeful Action: A General Paradigm

At the foundation of all our proposals for applying the behavioral sciences to education lies one deceptively simple concept—purposeful action. Actions can be chosen more effectively if the actor first has some reasonably specific goal in mind. Purposeful action depends on "action at a distance" but must be defined to avoid the teleological fallacies. A useful general definition of such behavior takes the form of a feedback system:

> . . . A goal, if defined as "a desired state," certainly cannot exist in the present. Yet it is quite possible to compare the present state of X with the *concept* of a future state of X, to note the difference, and to choose, develop, modify and perform a series of actions designed to reduce this difference.
> This process is what we mean by the term "purposeful action."*

Purpose, in other words, refers to a contingent "program" which, in the machine data-processing sense, guides the process of choosing certain contingent actions, specifically that series of actions taken in order to guide an individual's "currently experienced situation" toward a "currently held concept of a desired future situation." A diagrammatic representation follows:

CURRENT SITUATION AS EXPERIENCED BY THE INDIVIDUAL	PURPOSEFUL ACTION $\rightarrow$	CURRENTLY HELD CONCEPT OF A MORE DESIRABLE FUTURE SITUATION

Movement from current situation to desired situation is controlled by "feedback":

> For any machine subject to a varied external environment to act effectively it is necessary that information concerning the results of its own action be furnished it as a part of the information on which it must continue to act. . . . This control of a machine on the basis of its *actual* performance rather than its *expected* performance is known as *feedback,* and involves sensory members which are activated by motor members and perform the function of *tell-tales* or *monitors*—that is, of elements which indicate a performance.†

For such a feedback mechanism to work there must first be an "expected performance" to which actual performance can be compared. *This is the key concept on which this entire paradigm is based; the remainder of the paradigm deals*

---

* D. V. Tiedeman and F. L. Field, "Guidance: The Science of Purposeful Action." *Harvard Educ. Rev.* **32** (1962), p. 489. Quoted by permission of the publisher.
† N. Wiener, *The Human Use of Human Beings: Cybernetics and Society* (Boston: Houghton Mifflin, 1950, p. 24). Quoted by permission of the publisher.

only with the origins and evolution of the individual's expected performances. Thus a series of expected performances is nothing more than an established plan or program. A plan is a prediction of the most feasible way to achieve a specified goal. And feedback is a process by which progress toward this goal is assessed and used as a criterion for the selection of actions. Our ideal model for education is no more than a process to enhance the individual's development of information that provides a basis for the feedback.

The paradigm does not suggest how, when, or in what order the various types of information became available to an individual's awareness. Consequently, the next task is to construct a developmental theory describing the individual's evolution of purpose. A paradigm of conceptual differentiation and integration provides the basis on which to construct such a theory. Before turning to this task, however, it is necessary to add two things. First, in order to make the paradigm of purposeful action represent a process there must be a force or source of energy to explain movement. Second, the relevance of this whole elaborate theoretical statement to measurement must be more clearly established.

The Source of Energy

The concept of discontinuity and of human response to the experience of discontinuity is central to the theory of purposeful action (Tiedeman and Field, 1962). A series of discontinuities in experience is ordinarily experienced as a part of civilized life. The arrangements for living in various societies place persons in a sequence of substantially different events from birth to death. To some degree these events are structured; we become involved in various processes—i.e., systems functioning over a period of time—where as individuals we affect and are affected by other individuals (and by other processes). Unless we are entirely oblivious to the structure of any such on-going process, we tend to evolve concepts regarding alternative ways in which the process might develop by some future time. And whether or not we fully realize it, we have varied emotional responses toward each of these conceptualized future alternatives. Thus we prefer some potential outcomes over others, and vice versa. And, still more basic, *we also have an emotional response to the difference between the current state of the process and possible future states that we prefer.*

This latter argument can be considered a partial corollary of Festinger's (1957) theory of cognitive dissonance. He suggests that humans who experience a difference between their real situation and a preferred situation (a) feel discomfort, and (b) tend to reduce this discomfort by *altering their desire* in order to make it congruent with their experience. We concur with (a), but instead of merely observing (b) in others, we would prefer (c) to encourage others to *alter their real state* in order to make it more congruent with their desired state.

In brief, then, we believe that the experience of cognitive dissonance leads to an emotional response: discontent (or agony!). We do not know if there is a basic human drive or a frequently learned human motive to seek self-actualization, but we are comfortable with the premise that people tend to avoid pain and to desire pleasure. And we are assuming that one source of considerable pain/discomfort lies in the awareness of difference between current experience and current desire. This discomfort can be reduced by a form of adaptive behavior we call purposeful action. Others have called it: "goal-directed," "tropistic," "programmed."

Field (1964a) has dealt with this definition operationally as well as logically. Although the entire scheme is not yet fully validated, an empirical study suggested a type of information that appears critical to purposeful action. Thus certain individuals who displayed purpose through structured conversation actually behaved differently from others whose conversation lacked purpose. The most significant difference involved the degree of awareness that one can have some predictable impact on one's more distant future, by choosing among possible actions in the present or in the less distant future. Those who appeared to possess such awareness and to a greater extent to have a "sense of agency" (or to lack an extreme sense of helplessness, pessimism, or fatalism), proved to be far more effective in certain important tasks than did others who displayed the opposite type of belief about themselves.*

Control of This Energy

These preliminary findings are important to our proposed model for guidance—although we are also made more comfortable by White's information concerning the importance of "sensing competence" (White, 1963). All such information suggests reasons: (1) why some individuals appear to deal with discomfort through manifest actions that are more likely to succeed, (2) why others select manifest actions less likely to succeed, and (3) why still others simply try to expunge dissonance-based discomfort mentally, i.e., without acting to alter the course of their lives. Furthermore, these promising reasons appear to us susceptible to modification by certain types of experience, which in turn suggests two basic guidance functions. These are (1) corrective, and (2) additive (and they are too often taken to be the same).

The corrective aspect of the educational process is often used by itself to define guidance. In such cases the practitioner engages in various *re*educative functions that range from out-and-out psychotherapy to the correction of consciously held misinformation. In our proposed conceptual framework this aspect can be described as dealing with individual decision-making in any previously entered process or relationship in which the student is having or has had trouble. It can be part of a broad guidance program, but it is not the basis of our proposed model for guidance-in-education.

---

* This study is currently being refined under a grant from the College Entrance Examination Board. A preliminary report (1964b) is now available.

Additive guidance is quite different in terms of context, though not necessarily in terms of methods.* Instead of revising the information a student has available to consideration when selecting his behavior in on-going personal or social processes, it operates at times when the student is making a transition from one process to another. It is based on a recognition that, for example, effective high school choice-bases are not fully effective in choosing behavior within a college, military, or occupational context. Further, it is based on the assumed importance of a "sense of agency" in determining whether an individual (a) will act successfully, (b) will act in a self-defeating or diffuse fashion, or perhaps (c) will not dare risk acting manifestly at all. Consequently, additive guidance is designed to make certain kinds of logically necessary information more available to students at transitional points. Perhaps, in addition, these are points when students can become most open to necessary changes by discovering, for example, that the mythological "complete" or "automatic" changes that are rumored to happen in college are not essential, desirable, or even humanly possible. In other words, when such realizations occur the student's task as a college freshman becomes humanly possible. Thus we all know that some students fail to act adaptively because they lack the power to act, and we suspect that others fail because they lack an awareness of their power. But perhaps most needless of all (we are suggesting), still others assume they have failed or will fail because they do not understand the tasks, or the criteria for determining human levels of success in meeting the tasks. Additive guidance is defined as a way to minimize the occurrence of such unnecessary (i.e., nonpathological) failure. In this sense, then, we can now clarify our earlier claim that guidance-in-education is neither therapy nor teaching, but something unique.

THE EVOLUTION OF PURPOSE THROUGH DIFFERENTIATION AND INEGTRATION: DEVELOPMENTAL THEORIES

The concept of individual development is well established in the behavioral sciences. In education, and indeed in all of the applied areas, development has become more

---

* There is a third aspect of guidance that might have to be considered educational, although we have not thought it through well as yet, and include it only for your speculative consideration. We have described discontinuities that arise in relatively typical educational experiences, and claimed them as the territory (primarily) of guidance—usually of the additive type. There are, however, intriguing implications if one considers such new concepts as the Job Corps designed to make contributing members out of society's pure consumers who have nothing—or no way —to contribute. By this we mean that one form of corrective guidance might involve a great deal of additive guidance, but operating within an artificially imposed discontinuity; in such contexts as the Job Corps centers, individuals would be placed in situations where their (or their parents' or subculture's) old ways of choosing behavior simply could not be adaptive or satisfying. Clearly there are issues to be resolved before it can be clear how this placing could fit into a context of liberating education. Are there, for example, types of education where we do *not* believe that "Every student has a God-given right to be a damn fool"? We suspect that one is not free who acts foolishly solely from ignorance rather than by choice.

and more central. The changes in a single person over time are as great as the differences between people at birth. Furthermore, the changes we observe frequently take place in relatively discrete steps.

The concept of readiness reflects one source of explanation for these phenomena; reading readiness denotes an individual's degree of physical and intellectual development when the power to read can be acquired; and it would be just as possible to describe such a stage as that suggested by the term "autonomy readiness" (or readiness to assume any of the developmental tasks described by Erikson, 1959). Thus there are steps to be taken (a) that must follow more basic steps, just as (b) they must precede other more advanced steps. Steps that are not taken in sequence tend to have a negative effect on an individual's future development. In the following section, a crude series of logically necessary developmental tasks will be outlined. These are hypothetical descriptions (1) of learning processes, and/or (2) of creative processes by which the information necessary for purposeful action might be acquired or evolved.

Steps in the Evolution of Purpose

The paradigm of purposeful action contains four basic functional aspects:

1) the currently experienced situation (the CE),

2) the (concept of a) currently desired (future) situation (the CD),

3) the planned/expected situations and events lying between, and

4) a feedback mechanism.

The basic premise underlying our proposed program of guidance-in-education is that the amount and quality of information contained in each of these categories will affect the likelihood that the individual will select actions leading to individual adaptive success. To maximize the odds in favor of adaptive success, the following developmental tasks must be reasonably well underway.

1) The CE must become comprehensive and accurate with regard to the states and properties of entities.

2) The CE must then come to include a sense of process, an awareness of the course of events, of changes in states/properties, of sequence, and of time flow.

3) (1) and (2) must then be integrated to form extrapolations (predictions) of alternative future events that are possible.

4) All these alternative future situations must be literally "tried on" by the individual to form various concepts of "self-acting-in-a-future-situation."

5) One or more of these must be selected as likely to be more pleasant (a goal).

6) On the basis of this goal, a plan must be evolved in order to specify "an expected course of events" most likely to lead to achievement of the goal.

7) This prediction of events or situations having the greatest likelihood of leading to the desired goal (a plan), can then provide the basis for a feedback system to operate.

8) This feedback system can serve to affect future events by guiding the individual's current choice of action: actions are chosen continually to reduce the difference between observed events and the previously established expected course of events.

9) To assure (8) requires that all previous informational aspects exist to some degree, and in addition, that the individual be aware that choice of actions in the present can affect the relative likelihood of various future alternatives (i.e., possess a "sense of agency").

Described in terms of what behavior would be like when they are completed, these *ideal* developmental steps serve to define criteria by which an individual's overt actions, or stage of development with regard to (a particular) purpose, can be evaluated or compared with another's. The following are more specific properties of such ideal choice-bases, as derived from the foregoing hypothetical process by which a choosing mechanism is evolved.

   I. A comprehensive and accurate CE would include valid information regarding
      A) current states and properties:
         1) of self,
            a)   positive and negative needs (in the life-or-death sense),
            b)   likes and dislikes (in terms of pleasure-pain),
         2) of one's situation or environment;
      B) the facts of process and time sequence:
         1) the current structure in (and course of) events,
         2) past outcomes of similar courses of events, in situations with similar states and properties.

  II. The information contained in such an ideal CE can be used to predict alternative future events, situations, and personal or environmental states-properties. Such prediction involves extrapolation—the continuation, through abstract thought, of conceptual patterns that represent possible or existing events. Thus
      A) states-properties of the participants in current events can be assessed and categorized as:
         1) unchangeable (gravity, death, taxes),
         2) possibly changeable but by factors not subject to one's control (war, peace, specific economic conditions),
         3) subject to some change if some feasible action were performed;
      B) patterns underlying the current course of events can also be assessed and categorized as:
         1) constant or inevitable (entropy, biological aging),
         2) subject to change by factors not known or controllable (centralization, inflation),
         3) subject to change if some feasible action is performed.

  III. One or more of the predicted alternative future situations can be assessed as
      A) probable in the environment,

B) meeting the probable future requirements of the environment,

C) both adaptive and desirable for the individual in terms of his current nature,

D) adaptive and desirable for the individual in terms of his probable future nature.

This process of extrapolation and selection produces a *goal,* a current concept of a desired future self-in-situation.

IV.   Once a goal (CD) exists in addition to information regarding the present (CE), it is possible to evolve a plan. A plan consists of a series of predicted events that would be likely to result in achievement of the goal. Such events must be

A) inevitable, and/or

B) probable, though beyond control, and/or

C) subject to control by the individual's actions.

V.   Such an expected course of events provides the basis, or plan on which a feedback mechanism can operate to guide the choice of actions:

A) it provides information regarding the current situation and course of events expected to result in progress toward the desired goal;

B) it guides the choice of actions to bring the actual situation closer to the expected/planned situation.

The Paradigm in Terms of Differentiation and Integration

These conceptual steps can be considered as a crude developmental paradigm, a process by which purpose—the capacity to choose action purposefully—*logically* could evolve. Thus it describes a cumulative process by which certain information could become available to an individual's awareness. Once available for his conscious consideration, this information would make it possible for the individual to choose those actions which would have the greatest probability of contributing to maximum individual adaptation. Consequently such actions would fit the ideal definition; they would be purposeful. Unfortunately, they would not resemble many instances of observed human behavior.

If one holds these steps in mind while observing the actions of many people for an extended period, it will become clear that few people consistently behave purposefully. Yet nearly all will display some degree of organization in their behavior. We now believe that an earlier paradigm of differentiation and integration (Tiedeman and O'Hara, 1963) can provide a conceptual framework to order such observations. There appear to be identifiable conditions of conceptualization in the process by which an individual evolves his goal-seeking criteria. In the broadest possible terms these fall into two basic categories, differentiation and integration. Obviously, not all steps are experienced by all people in all the discontinuities they experience. In fact, from the apparent scarcity of purposeful activity it may be that many people never become aware of the possibilities for individual gain which derive from the practice of differentiation and integration in evolving purpose. This scarcity does not necessarily cast doubt upon the proposed paradigm. Rather, it causes concern among those who practice guidance, because they wish to provide all (or at least more) individuals with the adaptive power some individuals display. It is necessary to keep this distinction between the ideal and the observed in mind as one considers the paradigm of differentiation and integration, because the paradigm can represent what is ideally possible, on the one hand, and provide a basis for assessing what is observed on the other.

The onset of rational differentiation and integration is occasioned by the recognition of a need to plan (which results from recognizing a discontinuity). The individual becomes aware that his present situation is unsatisfactory, or is eventually likely to become unsatisfactory—to him, at least. Decisions must be made and implemented. And the problem of deciding may be profitably divided into two aspects, an aspect of anticipation or prediction, and an aspect of implementation or adjustment.

The aspect of anticipation.   Anticipatory behavior may itself profitably be analyzed into subaspects or steps. As noted in Fig. 1, relevant steps are those of exploration, crystallization, choice, and clarification. During exploration, attempts are made to imagine the final state. Various alternative or possible "selves acting in situation" (p_j) are introduced into one's consideration. These, experienced in imaginative ways, make possible the exploration of a "psychological field" (f_j) in relation to each possibility. The full experience of the psychological field likely to be associated with a particular situation gives the individual a means of coming to grips with what he knows about the future, i.e., of discovering (1) which alternatives he is favoring, (2) why he may be favoring some things when he knows little about them, (3) why he may be turning from others either in ignorance of them or in biased or erroneous "knowledge" of such conditions. Thoughts during the exploration step are often somewhat random, rather incomplete, and possibly highly inaccurate.

As the person begins to understand the future emotional, cognitive, or situational conditions which he has the opportunity to achieve by entering the situation under present consideration, he imposes organization (o_j) on the set of $p_j(f_j)$. Organization is a rudiment of crystallization. Inherent in organization is a *contrast* between the current experience of the person and his current conception of a more desired situation. Hence the step of crystallization is considered as a rudimentary aspect of purposeful action.

When the current situation, the alternative possibilities, and the goal are sufficiently understood, the person is capable of entering into the step of behavioral choice. In choice, the organization of predictions achieved through crystallization is invested with some stability, and a plan of action has probably been formed in order to take the person from the currently observed situation into the currently desired situation. Having made a choice, the person becomes intentional along rational lines, but for emotional reasons!

Choice ordinarily occurs some time before it is feasible to undertake the activities required by the plan. The interval of delay is frequently occupied by review

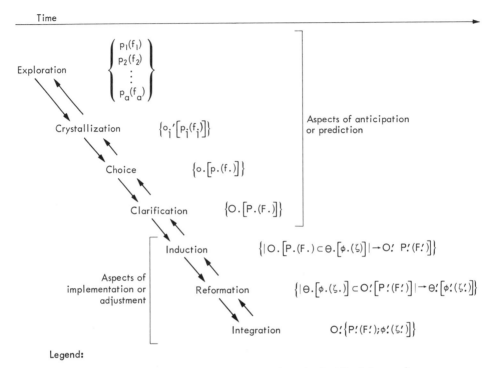

Legend:

p_j , P_j represents possibility when conceived and then clarified ($j = 1, 2, \ldots, n$).

f_j , F_j represents psychological field when conceived and then clarified ($j = 1, 2, \ldots, n$).

  ϕ (the analog of p) represents possibilities the group holds for person.

  ζ (the analog of f) represents the psychological field defined by the group.

o_j , O_j represents organization as conceived and then clarified.

  θ_j represents the analog of O_j in the group, that is, the cumulative effect of the O_j's of the group members.

Fig. 1. A paradigm of the processes of differentiation and integration in problem-solving. (Adapted by permission of the publisher from D. V. Tiedeman and R. P. O'Hara, *Career Development: Choice and Adjustment.* New York: College Entrance Examination Board, 1963.)

of the decision. Doubts arise as further information comes to one's attention, and there may even be a dissolution of the purposeful condition. Such dissolution is in fact possible at any time in the process under consideration. Upon dissolution there is ordinarily return to a more primitive condition of thought and feeling than that involved in the choice. This possibility is noted in Fig. 1 by arrows pointing in opposing directions, with the forward arrow given a longer length in the expectation that the direction of development is generally advancing. Although we have spoken first of the victory of doubt over determination—which is possible in the step of clarification—determination frequently prevails, and the dialogue with doubt frequently clarifies further the crystallization and choice which the person has undergone.

The aspect of implementation. Imaginative concerns meet reality on the day of initiation or implementation; a step of social *induction* into the process or course-of-events begins. Interaction with the environment is a necessary part of implementation. A person with a goal of his own enters a social system which he has previously charted somewhat nebulously. He hesitates; he looks for cues; in short, he is gradually inducted into the social system (unless he is immediately repudiated by it). Superiors and colleagues associated with the person start the process of testing the validity of their expectations for him (symbolized by $\subset$). If the induction process runs its course, the personality organization, $O.\ [P.(F.)]$, of the person is ordinarily modified (often beyond the conceptualized modifications which occurred earlier in clarification). Such modification is suggested in Fig. 1 by the addition of a prime ($'$) to each of the symbols.

Should a person manage to remain on an elected course for a sufficient time, *and be aware of it,* he gains confidence, and begins to discover that he holds power among his colleagues. Upon realization that he is accepted and can to some degree command colleagues, a person frequently enters into a condition of *reformation* which sometimes begins with overreaction. During reformation the primary mode of reaction is no longer just responsive; it becomes somewhat assertive. The object of aggression during reformation may be the group with whom the person is not identified or other groups with which the primary object of identification is in interaction. In either case the effect of reformation is to modify the condition of the *group* as a whole, internally or in a general structure of social relations. This condition of individual effect upon group conditions during reformation is suggested in Fig. 1 by the symbol, $\Theta'[\phi'(\zeta')]$.

The reaction by members of the group or of other groups to the assertiveness of reformation serves to lower the individual's need for proof that assertiveness works. This condition is likely to be further modified through the consideration of goals other than those now being achieved. Both of these conditions ordinarily lead the person into a step of *integration*. Since, in integration, the person now has confidence in his power to move *some* things *some* of the time, the status quo is no longer challenged as automatically as it was in the step of reformation. A form of equilibrium is established between desire and present regard. A new or different problem can now be taken on with more grace than would have been possible in the absence of success in the original situation.

A comment on the length of the process. The above paradigm of differentiation and integration has evolved from study of the process by which choosing operates in career development. In this area, the interval between relevant discontinuities is ordinarily rather long. For instance, the course which is pursued in high school is elected during study in the seventh and eighth grades of junior high school. The discontinuity of transfer from junior high to senior high therefore has a two-year period for the aspect of anticipation, and a four-year period for the aspect of implementation, six years in all. The discontinuity from school to work may have a period for the aspect of anticipation which noticeably appears in Grade 7, and may not give way to the aspect of implementation until completion of the seventeenth year of schooling, an 11-year period of anticipation in its entirety if study is undertaken continuously.

The steps of the paradigm are evident in career development. Furthermore, related aspects are noted in decision patterns when behavior is controlled as in recent experiments (e.g., on the effect of cognitive dissonance on the reactions of members of groups who must interact under variously arranged conditions of dissonance). These latter experiments explore periods of decision of much shorter duration than those periods associated with the experience of discontinuity in career development. Our expectation is that the paradigm also can be applied in such short-term circumstances. What is needed to apply the paradigm here is either a "fore period" for the discontinuity in which some steps of anticipation can occur, or freedom in the aspect of implementation so that purpose can form and/or actions can be modified despite a precipitous entry into the discontinuity.

Our comments on the paradigm of differentiation and integration are intended to widen your consideration of its potential applicability. As you will recall, we have earlier noted that purposeful action can occur in relation to the daily routine of schooling, and in a student's assumption of responsibility for his education. The cultivation of purpose is the business of education. The joint problem of measurement and guidance is to develop schemes whereby this cultivation can be more widespread, more uniform, and still relatively economical.

THE DEVELOPMENT OF PERSONALITY THROUGH CHOOSING

Differentiation and Integration in Personality Development

The major theme of this discourse is the cultivation of purposeful action through a program of guidance organized within the framework of education. The theme has so far been interrupted in order to offer and integrate paradigms (1) of purposeful action and (2) of differentiation and integration. Purposeful action can take place during differentiation and integration if the person is able to foresee his opportunities, his desires, and his capacities while he is involved in anticipation. The organization of such predictions can give rise to a cognitive mapping of a person's beliefs, and to an attitude of confidence which permits a person to embark upon the course elected. The experience obtained, and possibly examined during the aspect of implementation, gives rise to further refinements in the organization of prediction and action. Furthermore, this experience can lead to confidence, to doubt, or to despair.

A person's feelings about his possibilities in life fluctuate. They do so with mood, success, organization contexts, others' actions, roles, etc. One is always in a dynamic condition with regard to the anticipation and implementation aspects of purposeful action. Consider again the step of exploration during anticipation, as defined in the paradigm of differentiation and integration. Exploration was characterized as a condition of considering alternative possibilities in a disorganized emotional way. It was also noted that a psychological field could be imagined (and hence preexperienced) in relation to each predicted alternative. This psychological field is the vehicle of the general condition which hangs together in some organized fashion and thus lends continuity to the behavior of a person even though at the same time some aspects of the field become available for modification in relation to the discontinuity then under consideration.

If the paradigms of purpose and of differentiation and integration are to have generality, we must now think of the psychological field during a discontinuity, and of the (perhaps) new organization which is being imposed upon that field. Figure 1 suggests that in the aspect of anticipation, organization passes through inception during exploration, then into existence during crystallization, and finally, gives rise to choice, clarification of objective, and its likely consequences. During implementation, purpose leads to entry into a discontinuity (during induction) in an attitude of inferiority. This in turn gives way to the assertiveness of superiority during the step of reformation, and possibly becomes more neutralized through the step of integration if presence in the particular process is maintained. Try to amplify the condition of generalization of one organization into the psychological field by thinking in terms of eight discontinuities which are experienced in sequence.

The imagined paradigm of development in personality through differentiation and integration in problem solving must obviously be considered as ideal if it is to be conceived in its entirety. Therefore, suppose that each of the eight discontinuities progresses smoothly through all of its possibilities. Furthermore, imagine one step of each of the eight processes as taking place at any of the eight intervals of time so that the effect in a given time interval is akin to that of a cascade, i.e., integration step of an early process associated with reformation step of the next earliest process, etc. In the personality development of any person, he may not experience all of the steps with regard to some or all of the discontinuities through which he has passed. Furthermore, the person may be on the same step with regard to several discontinuities at the same time. For instance, while in junior high school, a student is likely to be in the step of exploration with regard to the discontinuities of college, major in college, work, etc.

Logically it would appear that for any one person, each stage has its own power relative to the other stages. By power we mean impact on the individual's thought or action. For example, if a student has two or more equally attractive goals that are not necessarily mutually exclusive—say, winning a football letter and obtaining reasonably good high school grades—there is a strong likelihood that one or the other goal may affect the choice of action too much or too little simply because the two discontinuities are at different stages of development. The student may be in junior high, as yet too young and small for the varsity, but already a good student and a fair athlete for his age. The *clearly crystallized* image of self-in-letter-sweater could well affect his behavior more than the *vaguely desirable* notion of pleased parents congratulating an honor student in shirtsleeves. Let us hasten to agree with the reader who objects, "But some kinds of boys couldn't care less about football letters—they study for the pure joy of it." This is precisely our point; personality differences can be discussed in terms of the particular pattern of alternative future situations which various individuals have predicated and chosen to pursue above all else. Of course there are myriad alternatives that could have been given priority! We are trying to equate the term "personality" and the concept of an ever-changing, yet basically consistent, priority system. Then it becomes possible to state that personality (priority) affects all steps in differentiation and integration during problem solving just as it affects the evolution of purpose; both paradigms represent the same process, specifically that by which personality and situation affect behavior.

Although we cannot depict the interrelationship of organization and psychological fields which is implied in the experiencing of these seven steps simultaneously, two analogies come to mind which may still further enlarge your understanding.

The first analogy is that of a union. Seven states exist simultaneously. Their union is what they have in common even though each of the elements has other aspects unique from the aspects of all others. In such a union, the organization of possibility associated with discontinuity 2, in a condition of reformation, has at least one thing in common with the organization of possibility associated with the condition of integration experienced in connection with discontinuity 1. These common things are aspects of personality organization. They are a part of a common organization and psychological field denoted in any one of the steps of the process of differentiation and integration experienced in connection with problem solving.

A second analogy is the process of induction as it is used in mathematics. Imagine a linguistic frame more general than the specifics of the organizations of possibilities as experienced simultaneously in the seven steps of seven different discontinuities. The frame must of course have an internal consistency or else it will not be more general than its specifics. The frame is likely to have structure as noted by Bruner (1962). Such a structure implies that all relevant specifics are contained in a more general concept but that the general concept is not formally defined by the specifics. An act of induction is required for a more general concept to exist. The elements of the structure will be premises and statements of inter-relation among certain of the premises, so that the operation of the premise is also specified. More than one frame may be consistent with a given set of specifics. Furthermore, the alternative explanations may or may not be conceived similarly by the person experiencing the events on the one hand, and an observer conversing with the person on the other hand. This fact will be dealt with in greater detail at a later time. At this time, we simply note a set of basic concepts and the operations which can be performed with these concepts either by the person experiencing the condition or by a second party attempting to assess the condition of the first party.

In considering differentiation and integration in personality development it is useful to consider the discontinuities which a person is experiencing or considering, and to deal with the steps in the process of differentiation and integration of multiple purposes which may yet occur in each instance of problem solving. This is the issue we have just discussed. It is also useful to consider the history of the person with regard to the process of differentiation and integration in problem solving. A history of *success* with each of the seven steps experienced in the interval t_6 is likely to lead to competence and confidence in the meeting of more advanced steps with regard to six of the seven discontinuities active in interval t_7 and in initiating exploration with regard to discontinuity 7. In other words, an experience of integration with regard to discontinuity (0) can help the attainment of integration with regard to discontinuity 7. Similarly, success in reformation with regard to discontinuity 1 can facilitate the attainment of the step of reformation with regard to discontinuity 2. This effect can be traced all the way up the steps in each of the discontinuities imagined in intervals t_6 and t_7. In general, the person's experience with regard to a specific step in all previous discontinuities can bear upon his experience with that step in his meeting of the next discontinuity. Experience of *failure* in earlier problems can have just the opposite effect.

The Development of Personality as an Effect of Second Order

The awareness both of one's urge to find personal advantage through activity, and of one's responsibility to do so within the legal frame of the polity in which one develops has been noted and studied by Erikson (1959, 1961), Maslow (1954), and White (1963). Erikson and White speak of this drive in rather general terms and do not imply its dependence on prior satisfaction of other drive states, although they do place the development of ego within a more general frame without noting any precedence of drives. Maslow, on the other hand, notes that the drive to self-actualization is one of higher order which can find opportunity for expression only after certain minimal satisfaction of other drives (e.g., thirst, hunger). Several of the authors in the collection of essays commissioned by Huxley (1961) also imply some precedence of need satisfaction which must be honored in considering the ideology of improvement of the human condition through social evolution.

We deliberately place differentiation and integration in the center of personality development. We do so because we consider these processes in problem solving to be the proper object of concern in a program of guidance—but also, they provide an *operationally defined* driving force for behavior, i.e., painful awareness of dissonance. Of course, a corollary of this belief is that this is the proper object of measurement in guidance. The purpose of this chapter must be kept in mind; it represents a deliberately placed restraint upon the subject of measurement in guidance.

Although the restraint of placing the paradigm of purposeful action through differentiation and integration in the center of personality development is deliberate, it is not entirely arbitrary. The program in guidance attempts to cultivate differentiation and integration in overall personality development, and it does so by facilitating the student's mastery of the process of differentiation and integration in specific instances of problem solving. Both are processes, and therefore subject to influence while they take place. But both are also highly influenced by the outcome of past attempts by the individual to differentiate and/or integrate. In other words, past and present process outcomes (effects on the person) are cofunctional and covariant. Therefore, it is necessary to place both past and present aspects of differentiation and integration into relation with each other. Furthermore, it is necessary in education to bring one into focus and to make the other more general. This is why we consider personality to be a second-order effect. It is possible to deal with the potential influence of differentiation and integration in problem solving upon personality development. The proper study of guidance requires that these two effects be joined more explicitly than is now accomplished. The two effects interpenetrate. This conclusion is shared by many who write on the subject. The mechanics of the interpenetration are not now highly specific. The purpose of this chapter is to deal with some of the models by which this interpenetration probably can be made more explicit. We first need some general conception of the second-order effects of personality, however.

The subject of personality study is the priority relationship between the desires of a person, and the controls which are imposed upon those desires. These controls may be internal or external. A personality description epitomizes that hierarchical relationship at a specific time.

Since the desires of a person are one aspect of the subject of personality, a lot can be inferred about the condition of desires at various times in life from knowledge of the genetic and other biological conditions of man. For instance, hunger and thirst are desires which appear early and persist continuously. We engage in various efforts to keep them modulated so that they do not reach a condition of acute desire. The desire for sexual relationship also seems to appear early and in forms other than a developed desire for heterosexual relationships. Our purpose here is but to illustrate, not to provide an exhaustive list. The illustrations suggest, however, that experiences of physical modification of the state of the body are potentially precipitating factors in the origin of criteria and priority, and hence in the development of personality or behavioral choice-pattern. These sensations can stimulate reflection and become coupled with myths, or with more reliable explanations that give a person further understanding and sometimes even an appreciation of new capacities. As such, this development has profound influence on the cognitive mapping of a person's control of the world, the effect of particular interest in the program of guidance-in-education.

The introjection of social control into desire is initiated shortly after birth. The attendants and parents of the infant begin the regularization of his (overt) response to his desires. Obviously, this is quite automatic for the infant in the beginning. Nevertheless, he begins interaction with the demands of others and starts the process of experiencing structure and the requirement to adhere to structure. There are other structures of a biological and physical nature which are also experienced at this time. Social, biological, and physical structures all impose restraints on the possibilities for the infant. The person is to grow within restraints without undue error in desiring, pursuing, and evaluating.

One educational problem, the introjection of social control into desire, is that of introducing a gap between impulse and response so that the person has opportunity to assume useful control of his choice among behavioral alternatives. Managing the introduction of rationality (Dewey, 1916) into the choice of behavior is of course arranged through the curriculum of the school. *The major problem is to encourage initiative in goal-setting at the same time that the practice of responsibility in achieving societal goals is both required and cultivated.* The cultivation of responsibility for self-directed activity is pursued by youth, parent, teacher, counselor, cleric, and government official. One position is that the primary authority for supervising this aspect of education should be vested in the counselor, and that he should assign responsibility to his colleagues in accord with their other responsibilities (and possibilities). This is why the counselor must be expert in measurement in the new terms which are being delineated here. This is the source of his information concerning youth's reactions to the educational transitions and processes.

Cultivation of rationality arises from the development of personality within the context of education, but this rationality need not be applied to the students' purposes. In recent years Piaget and his students have contributed to our understanding of the development of capacity for reasoning (e.g., Flavell, 1963). Erikson has advanced a psychosocial framework of the development of ego-identity (Erikson, 1959) and of virtue (Erikson, 1961). Roe (1956) and Super (1957) are constructing a theory of the development of self as attained through the choosing associated with the development of career. Bordin, Nachmann, and Segal (1963) are bridging these two lines of work with theory dealing with the capacity of work to gratify the needs of those engaged in the activity of work. Tiedeman and O'Hara (1963) are attempting to portray the relationship of personality and career as an interpenetration that develops through a sequence of choices of relevance to the making of career. Field (1964b) is developing means for the assessment of individual purpose, as it can be detected in plans for later educational or vocational activity. Weitz (1964) is attempting to deal with these problems of guidance as behavioral change within a general theory of learning. He does not, however, deal explicitly with the cultivation of purposeful action through a program of guidance-in-education. Tyler (1964) is now also engaged in the construction of a psychology of possibility. Her efforts are not yet fully structured, however, although she does offer both clarity and leads in assessment.

It is apparent that there are lines of promise. However, there still seems to be need for greater unification, and sharper focus upon the cultivation of purposeful action. This is the direction which will be attempted, herein.

There are two major problems that must be considered in relation to the cultivation of purposeful action. The first problem is that of presenting information which allows a student to react. The source of this information which we will consider is that of prediction. The second problem is that the person must become capable of assimilating this information so that his initiative to act is unimpaired, yet socially acceptable. It will be necessary to discuss the assessment of initiative both by the person engaged in deciding, and by the person responsible for supervising another's cultivation of purpose. Therein lies the problem of measurement in guidance.

PATTERNS FROM HISTORY

Purpose in Discontinuity

A person encounters discontinuities in the pursuit of self-directed activity. In the aspect of anticipation, preceding the encounter with a discontinuity, a person has an opportunity to engage in the steps of exploration, crystallization, choice, and clarification. It is necessary for the person to inform himself about the particular discontinuity if these steps are to be taken in a rational way. Useful information has to do with the alternative outcomes, their requirements, and personal considerations in relation to each alternative. A considerable effort is expended within the program of guidance-in-education in order to obtain, provide, and transmit this type of information. Yet the major function of measurement in guidance, at the present time, is directed to the provision of reliable and valid information concerning the *external* possibilities which the individual may anticipate. As we will discuss shortly, though, there is relatively little measurement concerned with *internal* personal changes that might also occur, and which might also be predictable.

The provision of statements concerning the possibilities of a student in relation to a set of alternatives under consideration requires an assessment of history in a manner which permits the past to illumine the future. The procedure adopted in psychology is to pose the problem as one of prediction. The past, if first examined systematically in an *a posteriori* fashion, can be used to predict certain *inevitable* later events.

Sometimes the rules for prediction derived in this *a posteriori* fashion are also applied *a priori,* and verification of prediction by actual later events is undertaken. This is the most complete form of prediction and is therefore the model we shall now sketch, because this form must be dealt with in developing a more complete form of measurement for guidance.

Prediction

To predict is to declare which of several possible events will occur before the event or events do occur (or before the outcome is known). A prediction is successful when the prediction coincides with the actual event or events. Systems of prediction vary in their rates of success, and we prefer the prediction system yielding the highest rate of success.

Prediction necessarily occurs in the absence of the event to be predicted. In order to predict, we can therefore designate two time-points within the life experiences of a particular population of people such that the second time-point, t_2 say, always follows the first time-point, t_1, by a specified time interval. t_1 is the time in the lives of members of the population at which we are to predict; t_2 is the time in the lives of these same people at which we are to verify the predicted behavior of the person (or its absence). We shall call the data collected for each member of a population prior to the time t_1 "antecedent information," or, more simply, "antecedents." We shall call the events which will be known at the time t_2 "consequent events," or, more simply, "consequents."

Prediction by the Trait Model

Prediction by the trait model requires specification of a law relating antecedents and consequents in the lives of members of the population. This law is generated by study of a sample of people from the population for whom both antecedents and consequents are known in every case. This law is to be of the following form: when antecedent conditions $X_1, \ldots, X_n$ are evident in the lives of members of this population by time t_1, then consequents $Y_1, \ldots, Y_n$ will be observed at the time t_2.

Generation of this law requires a knowledge of the frequencies with which combinations of antecedents and consequents are found in the population. In order to estimate these frequencies, classes of antecedents and consequents must be established, and the combinations of these two kinds of classes in the sample must be counted. We designate one of a set of mutually exclusive classes of antecedent events as a_i ($i = 1, 2, \ldots, n$) and one of a set of mutually exclusive classes of consequent events as c_j ($j = 1, 2, \ldots, m$). Let us suppose that our counts give the experience indicated in Table 1, where f_{ij} stands for the frequency of the combination (a_i, c_j). In Table 1 the number subscripts simply identify a class; they have no necessary meaning or importance.

Table 1 Frequency of antecedent and consequent combinations

Consequent class	Antecedent class						Total
	a_1	a_2	——	a_i	——	a_n	
c_1	f_{11}	f_{21}	——	f_{i1}	——	f_{n1}	$f_{\cdot 1}$
c_2	f_{12}	f_{22}	——	f_{i2}	——	f_{n2}	$f_{\cdot 2}$
—	—	—	——	—	——	—	—
—	—	—	——	—	——	—	—
c_j	f_{1j}	f_{2j}	——	f_{ij}	——	f_{nj}	$f_{\cdot j}$
—	—	—	——	—	——	—	—
—	—	—	——	—	——	—	—
c_m	f_{1m}	f_{2m}	——	f_{im}	——	f_{nm}	$f_{\cdot m}$
Total	$f_{1\cdot}$	$f_{2\cdot}$	——	$f_{i\cdot}$	——	$f_{n\cdot}$	$f_{\cdot\cdot} = N$

Table 2 Prediction table

Antecedent class	Prediction
a_1	Consequent class associated with the largest f_{1j}
a_2	Consequent class associated with the largest f_{2j}
$\vdots$	$\vdots$
a_i	Consequent class associated with the largest f_{ij}
$\vdots$	$\vdots$
a_n	Consequent class associated with the largest f_{nj}

Provided that the frequencies f_{ij} can be used to make sound estimates of the frequencies of possible combinations of a_i and c_j in the population, a maximum number of coincidences of predictions and consequents results when the prediction made for each antecedent class is that consequent class appearing with greatest frequency in combination with a particular antecedent class. This rule is specified completely in Table 2.

It may be helpful in understanding these tables to note that Table 1 is nothing but the familiar experience table for the case of an ordered antecedent and an ordered consequent variable. In such a case, Table 2 is given directly by a regression equation, provided the modal consequent class for each antecedent class is at the intersection of the regression line and the lines representing each antecedent class. This is only an illustration. Tables 1 and 2 are specified completely generally and need not be conceived solely in terms of regression analysis.

If the greatest frequency of consequent events associated with an antecedent class a_i be designated as f_{ig}, the proportion of successful predictions in the sample—resulting from the rule described in Table 2—will be the sum of the frequencies f_{ig} divided by the total number of cases. This success rate is an estimate of the success rate to be anticipated when applying the prediction rules of Table 2 to any random sample of the population. Short of assuming some specific kind of distribution of antecedent and consequent events in the population, the sample success rate is the greatest that can be achieved by predicting a single consequent event for every class of antecedent events. Predicting sets of alternative consequent events, rather than single consequent events, will raise the success rate of the predictions at the expense of the specificity in the predictions. However, in many problems it is useful to be less sure of the exact consequent event, and to be more sure that the looser predictions of the consequent events will be realized. For instance, we may do a poor job of predicting the actual grade a person will receive, while from the same data we may do better at specifying whether or not his grade will fall in the passing range.

It is obvious from Tables 1 and 2 that the rate of successful prediction increases as the largest frequency in each column of Table 1 approaches the column total for each class of antecedents. The trait model requires delineation of antecedent classes, a_i, which satisfy this condition as closely as possible.

The Isolation of Traits

In a particular group of people we can usually establish, with at least some degree of agreement among judges, that not all members of the group are alike; there are differences among members of the group. We are next able to establish among the judges a common procedure for classifying members of the group into at least two subgroups. In the trait model, we seek that procedure which will result in at least *some* consistency among judges in placing members of the group into subgroups. When we achieve adequate consistency, we refer to the distinctions among members of the various subgroups as traits. Such distinctions ordinarily constitute only a nominal scale, in Stevens' (see Chapter 5 and also 1946) classification of variables. We seek those nominal scales offering the greatest potential association with the consequent events we wish to predict.

In psychology and education it has always been difficult to accumulate experience in sufficient quantity to make stable every frequency or combination of antecedent and consequent events. Consequently, we have invented procedures for studying regularities in the neighborhood of particular cell frequencies. In order to study regularities, it is first necessary to impose order on our nominally scaled variables. Then, if possible, it is desirable to establish systems for numbering those ordered classes of each variable which have the power to designate, through application of regression or discriminant theory, the consequent class appearing with the greatest frequency in combination with a particular antecedent class.

Developing an Experience Table by Means of Regression Analysis

Regression analysis is applicable only for cases in which the complete set of mutually exclusive classes of consequent events can be ordered. Of course, each of the antecedent variables must also be at least an ordinal scale. In linear regression analysis, the linear regression surface is oriented by minimizing the weighted sum of squared deviations from the regression surface of the mean of the consequent class occurring with greatest frequency in combination with the antecedent class. Prediction by the regression equation does have this latter property, however, when the joint distribution of antecedents and consequents is multivariate normal. There probably are more relaxed conditions for specifying the joint distribution of antecedents and consequents, which still maintain the property that the regression surface passes through all consequent classes occurring with greatest frequency in combination with an antecedent class. The distribution would then still portray linear regression but might not be multivariate normal. We cannot currently specify these more relaxed conditions, however.

Several alternative courses of action are available when the antecedent and consequent scales do not meet the assumptions of the linear regression model. The first possibility is to rescale any or all of the scales used so that linearity in regression is better approximated. This alternative is used more frequently; for instance, we do this when we normalize scores. The second alternative is to use the same scales, but to employ a regression model which is nonlinear but still additive. We do this when we fit curved regression lines. This alternative is used infrequently. The third alternative is to employ a nonadditive, or an only partially additive regression model. Product or exponential models would be examples. Travers (1954) has proposed this alternative.

Developing an Experience Table by Means of Discriminant Analysis

If the consequents form only a nominal scale, which cannot be scaled ordinally along a single continuum, the data of the trait model must be analyzed according to discriminant theory. The fundamental purpose of discriminant analysis is precisely that purpose of prediction we outlined previously, namely, the assignment of a consequent event to those antecedent classes with which the consequent is associated with maximum frequency in a given antecedent class. Thus discriminant theory provides Table 2 directly even when the antecedents as well as the consequents are only nominal scales. Use of the system of profile coding, suggested by Hathaway (1947), is an application of discriminant theory in such a situation. Discriminant theory also provides Table 2 directly when the consequent classes can be ordered on a single continuum, while the antecedent classes form only a nominal scale.

When the antecedent data consist of observations of a series of variables, each of which is at least ordinally scaled, and when the assumption of multivariate normality is appropriate for the distributions of antecedent variables for each class of a nominal scale of consequent events, additional techniques of discriminant theory can be used. The additional techniques increase the efficiency with which consequent events are associated with antecedent classes. They also eliminate irregularities due to inadequate specification of frequencies of the antecedent-consequent combinations in the sample. The most important of these techniques, for prediction purposes, is that for specifying boundaries in the space of the antecedent variables which locate the region in that space in which a particular consequent event is most likely to fall (Tatsuoka and Tiedeman, 1954). These boundaries are defined by applying the same logic used to construct a prediction table such as Table 2.

Discriminant theory has evolved from the orientation to prediction which we have presented. For this reason, the techniques of discriminant analysis are completely consistent with the logic of prediction by the trait model as specified herein, provided that the data to which the techniques are applied satisfy the conditions under which the techniques are derived. Choice of the appropriate method hinges both on the purposes of the investigation, and on the distributions of the data. Discriminant theory is most complete for those conditions in which antecedent variables are distributed in a multivariate normal manner for all classes of consequent events.

The Trait Model and the Selection and Classification of Personnel

The trait model has evolved primarily in relation to the responsibility inherent in selecting and classifying personnel. In these processes, an officer is responsible for the admission of an applicant into membership in school, college, business, or armed forces. He may then also become responsible for the allocation of the admitted set of men among the various responsibilities which are vacant in the particular organization. The officer with such responsibilities has been interested in discharging them efficiently. He has therefore ordinarily attempted to improve his effectiveness by studying the history of *his* decisions.

In recent years the responsibilities of admissions or classifications officers have been cast in terms of decision theory (e.g., Cronbach and Gleser, 1957). This theory has placed the responsibilities for selecting and classifying within a framework of two kinds of risks: exclusion of those who might have been effective, and inclusion of those who do not prove to be effective. These conceptions of risk and utility further refine the decision reactions of officers of admission or classification when used in conjunction with information (1) on the predictive efficiency of an experience rule, and (2) on the supply of applicants and the demand for students or employees. In fact, it is possible to regularize some of those decisions which occur frequently to the extent that they can be made mechanically.

Although the use of decision theory in selection has further refined the efficiency of school, business, or military establishment, it should be clearly noted that the procedure is based on the following assumptions.

1) The individual traits used in the decision rule will continue to operate as they have in the past.

2) All the relevant information (a) is contained in the traits, and (b) is preserved during the operations inherent in the decision rule.

3) The decision is best made without the active participation—or even knowledge —of those from whom the acceptable are to be culled.

4) The decision is best made independently of any response by those being selected.

5) The demands of the educational, work, or military setting are assumed to continue operating as in the past.

Thus decision for selection or classification is a procedure in which a decision is made *for* the person; the person is not engaged in it. This is a crucial distinction for measurement for guidance. So is the assumption that what is measured, and the evaluational criteria derived from the reasons for measuring, will both remain unchanged.

The Trait Model in Guidance

The decisions through which purposeful action is to be cultivated through programs of guidance-in-education are those taken *by the students,* not just those which are made for him. The decisions of greatest (potential) interest in guidance therefore differ from those of interest in selection and classification; the individual is responsible for decisions of interest to guidance; the officer of admissions or classification is responsible for the decisions of interest in selection and classification. This distinction has further important implications.* In selection and classification deci-

---

* There are obvious cases where these models overlap; we separate them here for the sake of clarity and also to stress the point that such overlap is far too infrequent.

sions, an array of people (all of whom are presumed to be willing to undertake the responsibilities inherent in acceptance and allocation) are sorted over, and then accepted or rejected. In the decision of concern to guidance, an individual sorts over an array of opportunities, selects those he thinks he will prefer, and sets out to assure their occurrence.

When a group of individuals are each characterized according to a set of measurements, the array of information may be represented as the matrix

$$
\begin{matrix}
x_{11} & x_{12} & \ldots & x_{1j} & \ldots & x_{1m} \\
x_{21} & x_{22} & \ldots & x_{2j} & \ldots & x_{2m} \\
\vdots & & & & & \vdots \\
x_{i1} & x_{i2} & \ldots & x_{ij} & \ldots & x_{im} \\
\vdots & & & & & \vdots \\
x_{n1} & x_{n2} & \ldots & x_{nj} & \ldots & x_{nm}
\end{matrix}
$$

The covariation of the measurements among these individuals is ordinarily represented by the symetrical $m \times m$ matrix of correlations among the pairs of variables. When unpartitioned, this matrix may be investigated in terms of the factor structure of linear components of the original measurements. When partitioned with one of the variables being considered as a criterion, the matrix may be studied in terms of maximum correspondence between (1) a linear composite of the original variables and (2) the criterion. When partitioned in terms of a nominal division of the n subjects, the matrix of dispersion among the resulting subsets of people may be studied in terms of the separation of groups, achieved by linear composites of the original variables. When partitioned so that more than one of the variables is considered to be a criterion, and more than one of the variables is considered to be an independent variable, the matrix may be studied in terms of the maximum correspondence between linear composites of (1) the several dependent and (2) the several independent variables. Each of these possibilities has been considered in greater detail by Tatsuoka and Tiedeman (1963).

When the variables x_j have been standardized for the set of n persons, it is possible to construct an $n \times n$ matrix of intercorrelations between the pairs of people in the matrix. It is possible to treat the $n \times n$ matrix of covariation among individuals according to the same patterns as have been noted for the treatment of the $m \times m$ matrix of correlations among measurements. The usual procedure is to consider the factor analysis of the unpartitioned $n \times n$ matrix of correlations among individuals. This procedure (so-called "inverted factor analysis") has been developed rather fully by Cattell (1952). A variant of the procedure has been introduced by Stephenson (1953), who prefers to deal with the intercorrelations among individuals after each of the persons has created a set of measurements for himself, by designating his opinion of himself in relation to a fixed set of adjectives. This procedure has been termed "Q-methodology." Cronbach and Gleser (1957) have noted the similarity between interperson correlations and the conception of profile similarity. Schweiker (1954) has written a treatise on the interrelation of vectors in test space (intermeasurement matrix of correlations) and in individual space (interindividual matrix of correlations). This treatise deals more with the multivariate techniques than with factor analysis. It is clear from Schweiker's and others' work that, except for Q-methodology, there is a formal mathematical correspondence between the analytic results from the analysis of the $m \times m$ matrix of covariation of measurements and the analysis of the $n \times n$ matrix of covariation of individuals. One set of values may be derived from the other through mathematical transformations which are ascertainable for a particular matrix of scores. This fact is sometimes used (Meehl, 1956) to suggest that there is a purely mathematical transformation which will permit the structure of admissions or classification decisions to be transformed directly into structure for the decisions of an individual. *We do not believe this to be the case.* This will be the issue for examination in the next section. The examination needs to be undertaken in relation to that procedure which has caused people to argue fallaciously that the decision of the individual is the mere obverse of the decision of the organization. But, prior to this examination, there is one further fallacy worthy of note.

The above matrix was introduced on the supposition that the m measures x_j were each of a different trait possessed by one individual. Now let us suppose, as can be done logically, that the m measures x_j represented statements about the same trait of the individual, *each such statement having been observed at a different time.* The $m \times m$ matrix of correlations would *now* give estimates of the reliability of the single measure (assuming that there was no systematic variation of the m measures for any of the n individuals throughout the interval of time required to amass the m measurements on each person). Furthermore, under these conditions a distribution of the m observations of the characteristic of a single individual could be distributed, and the estimates of central tendency and variability provided by the resulting *set* of measurements for an individual could be used to construct estimates of other observations of this same characteristic of the individual which might as yet be untaken. This procedure is valid in any area of a person's life in which observations have the necessary characteristics for actuarial work: namely, (1) events which are occurring in a random manner, without any effect, (2) by observation itself or personal knowledge upon the occurrence of the events themselves.

Again the possibility of the logical analogy which has just been laid out has led some people (e.g., Meehl, 1956) to the generalization that *all* guidance decisions occur in such a context. Obviously this is not the case when the conditions for actuarial estimation no longer apply. However, it is even more inapplicable if the person openly reflects upon the conditions of his decision. Remember, people *do* change. Since such reflection is just what the program of guidance seeks to enhance, it would appear that the procedures of the trait model have limited applicability here, and that a basic problem in measurement for guidance is specification of the limits. This is our next task.

RATIONALITY IN PERSONAL DECISIONS

In Fig. 1 we have schematized a process of evolving purpose. The paradigm suggests that in a state of anticipation, it is possible to embark upon the steps of exploration, crystallization, choice, and clarification. If these conceptual steps are completed a person seeks his goal purposefully, having developed a plan for achieving what he desires. Purpose will evolve from the prediction and pre-experiencing of possibilities, their consequences, their desirability, the reasons for the seeming undesirability of some, and from the organization of such information into a more comprehensive whole, providing an expected course of events—or plan—against which to measure actual progress. This procedure makes the chosen alternatives tropistic, because their absence leads to the awareness of dissonance. During the usual wait prior to entry into an impending process, the person can reflect further upon the instrumental actions which the attainment of his purpose will require him to display in the newly predicted situations. Rehearsing these required actions can further clarify the decision of the person, and give him a more detailed plan for the pursuit of his goal (or grounds on which to revise it).

The trait model and its derivative decision procedure, applied by an officer of admission or classification, *can* be of use to an individual engaged in the formation of purpose, in the following ways.

1) It can help delineate alternative possibilities.

2) It can indicate the effects of various behavior displayed in the past, and their likelihood in the future if the individual were to operate in a behaviorally uninformed manner as did those who went before him.

3) It can indicate the conditions of entry into a given process, and what admissions officers consider desirable and/or demand.

However, the trait model *cannot* illumine the individual's problem of decision any more than has just been set out. The model can delineate possibilities, present statements concerning requirements and the seeming importance of prior accomplishments. Still, the model cannot substitute for personal decision. In personal decision it is necessary to reflect upon possibility, desirability, capability, requirement, and personal power. The consistent continuation of the past course of events is illumined by the trait model. In this manner the expectations of those with whom the person will come in contact can be known in some detail. Yet it is still necessary for the person to organize these data, and to effect a purpose and a plan which will allow *him* to enter into the process—and in such a way that the personal advantage he seeks has some likelihood of being achieved. Consequently the individual's plan must include the possibility—indeed the likelihood—of *his* changing during the process. And this the trait model cannot greatly accommodate.

Decision in the Aspect of Anticipation

We have so far tried to specify a role for the trait model in the *anticipation* stage of personal decisions. We have also noted that this role is subject to the restraint imposed by reflection—when reflection leads to change. Considerations of this nature are the proper object of concern for a program of guidance. Quite obviously, it is necessary that such thinking possess some general characteristics which can be made more definite, and hence cultivated through the processes of guidance. Furthermore, it is necessary that the guidance program assume the obligation to pursue this goal in efficient ways. Hence the needs for measurement designed for these new guidance purposes.

We can now specify the general characteristics of the desired conceptual pattern in only vague terms, because the goal which we have expressed here is rather new. The general characteristics needed seem to involve:

1) the acquisition of concepts necessary for rational decisions;
2) the habitual use of differentiation and integration in problem-solving;
3) the demonstration of competent applications of various techniques upon reasonable demand, such demonstration being accompanied by
   a) a reasonable set of alternatives under consideration,
   b) a reasonable knowledge of each alternative, and of likely personal response to such a situation,
   c) a behavioral organization which can be explained and justified to a reasonable degree,
   d) a plan which is reasonably matured, and
   e) display of knowledge which has been gained from the experiencing of former discontinuities and of the application of this knowledge further to improve the present decision and its effect on one's personality.

Operations with Decisions in the Aspect of Anticipation

The characteristics of purposeful behavior can now be described in more simple terms, i.e., in terms of information the individual must possess and use for maximal selection of goal-directed actions.

Current experience

He must know what he absolutely needs (and needs to avoid).
He must know what he likes (and dislikes).
He must know what the immediate situation absolutely requires (and prevents).
He must know what the immediate situation permits (and resists).
He must be aware of events:

that they take place as processes,

that they are organized to varying degrees,

that common patterns of organization underlay many past events, and

that these patterns provide bases for better-than-chance predictions of future events and situations.

Current desire

He must predict his needs and likes, the requirements and pressures of the environment, and use these to select one favorable alternative system as his goal.

Plan

He must develop the concept of a series of future events

that *will* occur, and/or

that *will probably* occur, and/or

that *he can bring about,*

and these events must be likely to result in achievement of his established goal.

Feedback

He must continually assess what is actually taking place.
He must compare this observed pattern with the planned or expected pattern.
He must choose actions to reduce the difference, or
He must revise the plan and/or the goal.

The foregoing list of necessary information suggests certain underlying characteristics—in effect, the beginnings of a simple evaluational scheme applicable to specific individual's choices. For example, a particular individual's current experience, current goal, and/or plan might be

comprehensive or narrow in scope,

full or fragmentary with regard to idiosyncratic detail,

accurate or inaccurate,

focused on states and properties, or on processes, or on both.

In addition to these commonsense characteristics, however, there are more complex dimensions of information suggested by the paradigm. The individual's reports or actions might reflect over- or underemphasis on

past, present, or future

self-structure, environmental structure, or their overall relationship

what is expected with some certainty, what is only hoped for or feared (passively or helplessly), or what can be caused or prevented (by feasible actions).

Field has engaged in a first effort to apply some of these dimensions. His thesis (1964a) sets out 18 such dimensions which proved usable in connection with the assessment of purposeful action as noted in an interview concerning the occupational choice of male students while juniors in high school. A replication of this study plus a check on reliability is currently underway.

Actually, the objective of the program of guidance-in-education is not simply that a person report (or even engage in) purposeful action once, but rather that he develop the capacity to engage in purposeful action in response to all the numerous opportunities which he will encounter from day to day as he assumes responsibility for the management of his life. The cultivation of such a capacity demands a program of action which is not yet highly developed, but is beginning to take rudimentary form (e.g., Tiedeman, 1964). The rudiments have to do with a problem which complicates measurement in guidance and will be considered next.

Review of Decisions in the Aspect of Anticipation

The ultimate goal of guidance is to encourage in each student a developed capacity for purposeful action. The sign of failure is not the absence of purpose whenever it might seem possible to a second party. Instead, the sign of failure is: (1) the absence of purpose when a goal is desired by the person who might have been purposeful, or (2) the erroneous ascription of blame by that person to others when application of purpose was not made and a goal was lost. The fact that failure can be denoted in terms of missing *information* means that a process of cultivation of purposeful action *by adding information* can be developed. Such a process must be designed to provide guides for the reduction of failures, by applying procedures which reduce the input of behavioral choice criteria from others. This science of behavioral change poses several problems which, however, are generally not faced squarely in the delineation of measurement for guidance.

The first major problem lies in the essentially reactive, remedial aspect of guidance made possible by applying the trait model. The model provides an "ideal" concept of human performance that is too average to be ideal. The golden mean, getting by smoothly, minimum variance from the norm—these were the goals the trait model offered for professional application. As a result, guidance techniques have had to be reactive and remedial, to combat established individual errors in assessing past or present experiences, in choosing among existing goals, or in selecting instrumental actions. The most positive contribution such guidance could offer those who were already getting by nicely was to state, from the trait model, "People with your measured characteristics have tended to perform at X level in Y subject, school, job, etc."

This is obviously useful, but we object to the limitations it has imposed. To begin with it provides no positive contribution to the education of all students; it is less universal than arithmetic. But worse, it discourages—or at least does nothing to encourage—individual initiative. It *necessarily* deals solely with mass or societal goals because of its essentially normative basis in the trait model.

The attainment of the purpose in specific discontinuities can never be specified completely by a second party without destruction of what was to have been aided: the student's responsibility.

A second anomaly of guidance, as herein defined, is that the activities must be practiced as supervision, not as training. This condition is a corollary of the fact that the object of guidance is to get students to accept personal responsibility in all of its frightening, yet exhilarating, ramifications. In order to make supervision possible, it is necessary that the program in guidance:

1) provide the students with opportunity to set their own goals;

2) create sufficient opportunity for each student to engage in instrumental action which is more adaptive/rewarding when it is also purposeful;

3) encourage each student to engage in these opportunities with some comfort regarding the risk of failure; and

4) supervise the student's consideration of his actual versus his expected performances.

The concept of supervision is worthy of specific discussion in this context. In supervision:

1) responsibility for action is placed squarely upon the shoulders of the student;

2) observation of the student's action occurs; and

3) discussion of the student's activities occurs within a reasonably short interval following the observation, so that the experience is still within the memory of participant and observer.

It should be clear that in supervision, then, it is possible to note for the student the operation and/or failure of purpose as the student was engaged in action. The supervisor truly stands in relation to the student as his collaborator. In supervision of this nature, it is likely that the student may become discouraged. Furthermore, it may be that he attributes knowledge to the counselor which supposedly could have been imparted to him (the student) so that he could have avoided failure. It is possible to illumine partially the way ahead for those who are to be supervised, but it is not helpful for such illumination to replace action. Confidence in the power to act purposefully can only come through experience, *preferably in collaboration with those respected for their understanding of what constitutes success and with a respect for the power of others.* If this realization were only to be accepted, we could eliminate much in the way of teaching youth to be purposeful, and get down to the serious educational task of designing opportunities for the student to confront the need for purpose under collaborative supervision.

A third anomaly of guidance is that the supervisor must deliberately review the changing experiences obtained while observing others develop purpose. In such a review, of course, the data become a part of two people's thinking. Interaction of these two systems of thought is to take place so that the collaborative action first initiated in supervision later gives way to independent action on the part of the student. These conditions suggest many possibilities not now of concern in the study of measurement *in* guidance. For instance:

1) there undoubtedly are ways of making the concepts required for purposeful action more understandable to the students who eventually are to be users of those concepts;

2) there undoubtedly are different ways in which the student's oversight of elements of purpose can be pointed out during supervision; and

3) there undoubtedly is some sort of sequence through which the capacity to act purposefully develops, e.g., (a) no thought, no action; (b) some thought, no action; (c) all thought, no action; (d) thought, some action; (e) thought, improved action; . . . ; (z) integrated, easy application of a habitual technique.

Study of these problems is an obligation which those responsible for guidance must accept, if they want to form and further develop the science on which their practice is grounded.

There are two aspects of this third anomaly which are of interest with regard to the issues frequently debated, i.e., those concerning the power of clinical discernment in the assessment of personality (e.g., Meehl, 1954; Meehl, Tiedeman, McArthur, 1956). One of these issues has already been referred to, namely the source of purpose. In fact, it has been emphasized that *only* the person can be the source, if purpose is to remain individual (as it must be, by definition). This organization contains most of the information relevant to the supervision of individual action during an interval of time, i.e., until the organization is modified, and implementation begins to occur. Furthermore, the organization contains clues of importance to speculation about the quality of action likely to appear during implementation of a plan of purpose.

In supervising the cultivation of purposeful action by students, a counselor attempts to enter collaboratively into the examination of conceptual organizations. Because he has knowledge of these organizations, the counselor (the clinician) is in a position to possess a reasonable amount of the same information the student has concerning his directions and possible accomplishments in the near future. In this context the following comment by McArthur (1956) becomes highly credible in underscoring this second aspect of our above third anomaly:

Perhaps this is the place to underline one basic difference between the Trait Model and the Dynamic Model. This difference is in the size and complexity of the piece of antecedent information a_1. In the Dynamic Model, a_1 is nothing less than a theoretical structure of the whole person. In the Trait Model, a_1 is a part, often a very small part, of the person, very often merely a single measurement made on him. It is, in the word's more special psychological meaning, 'a trait.'

Table 2′   Dynamic prediction table

Antecedent construct	Predictions			
a_{11}	Corollaries of this construct: c_{11}	c_{12}	$\ldots$	c_{1j}
a_{21}	Corollaries of this construct: c_{21}	c_{22}	$\ldots$	c_{2j}
$\vdots$	$\vdots$			
a_{n1}	Corollaries of this construct: c_{n1}	c_{n2}	$\ldots$	c_{nj}

(McArthur, 1956, pp. 169–170.)

Not only is the antecedent information of a different sort in the two models but the models differ as to the means by which antecedent information is made to generate predictions. In Table 2, the bond between antecedent a_1 and consequent prediction c_1 is a frequency relation: these two have occurred together very often in the past. This is the rationale of the Trait Model. In the Dynamic Model, the relationship is a logical one: the prediction c_1 follows as a necessary corollary of the theory a_1 from the overriding premise that John Jones will at any time of his life go right on being consistent with himself.

Another difference between the Trait Model and the Dynamic Model is that in the Dynamic Model there can be only one antecedent datum per person—clinical constructs are distributed one to a customer—but the number of consequent predictions per person may be very large. It is true, of course, that a dynamic construct may be built for a second person, creating a new antecedent condition, since the dynamic understanding of each person must start *de novo,* and from this new antecedent there may be derived a new swarm of predictions, applying to the new person under study. For the Dynamic Model we have, then, Table 2', the appropriate revision of Table 2 [p. 440]. In Table 2' the first subscript represents the persons—the case numbers, if you will—and the second subscript represents the number of the datum or the prediction within that individual case. Subscripts of antecedent data must all end in 1, there being but one antecedent to a person. Subscripts of predictions can become large. Table 2' summarizes schematically the main features of the Dynamic Model. A comparison between Tables 2 and 2' shows up most of the important contrasts between the Dynamic and the Trait Models.*

The game of science is to create and then to resolve doubts. It does seem, however, that we play illogically when we contrast the predictive efficiencies of trait and dynamic models as Meehl (1954) has done. The counselor is interested in the student's incorporation of information from the trait model into the organizations of his, the student's, decisions. In the study of this subject it is necessary to make explicit the degree to which the student has attained the ideal conception we have noted above. This new linguistic frame should be used to create a process by which the evolution of purpose is enhanced. It will be necessary to deal with the actions which the supervisor (the counselor) undertakes to enhance the process for those students within his jurisdiction. These actions, and their potential effects, will have to be made more explicit. As the consequences become more explicit, it will be possible to act more wisely: (1) in developing the organizations necessary for supervision, and (2) in supervision itself. The effect desired, however, is a mastery of the concept of purpose. Such mastery can lead to its use at will. This is the effect we will have to learn to obtain more efficiently through the supervision of students expected to become purposeful through education. We will not obtain what we want if we do not provide an opportunity for the student to become confident in his use of purpose for his own ends. Of course, we are not sure that we will secure this effect even when we supervise. We are only sure that it can occur only spontaneously, for a few, until we try to cultivate it for others.

"A WORD TO THE WISE . . ."

We have attempted in this chapter a reorientation of the concept of measurement *for* guidance. We have made this attempt by trying to present the codependent roles of tests, statistics, and supervision in education. We have tried to make clear the interdependence of these tools. Furthermore, we have tried to stress that the stu-

---

* C. McArthur, "The Dynamic Model." *J. Counseling Psychol.* **3** (1956), pp. 169–170. Quoted by permission of the publisher.

dent being helped to mastery of purpose must come to effective use of each of these tools by himself, and for himself, too. Only in this way can he profit from acquiring structure from the past, and knowledge of the expectations of those he will meet subsequently in the pursuit of his purpose. This knowledge is not alone sufficient to complete the process. He must use these tools in his own interests. All is to no avail without the easy use of these procedures, whenever such use is appropriate. This is the condition of integration which is to be sought.

The credibility of this position depends upon an appreciation of a number of concepts which are used in this argument without much explanation. The decision to take this course in the chapter was predicated on the knowledge that much of the data on tests, and much of the theory of procedure in statistics, are to be found in other parts of this handbook. The effort here has been to present a schema for the further study of measurement but as focused on those aspects of human functioning which are involved in purpose, and the adoption of an attitude toward purpose which involves appreciation rather than dread. We consider it obvious that the needed technique is now embryonic. There are leads, however. Some of these have been set out in Tatsuoka and Tiedeman (1954, 1963), Tiedeman and O'Hara (1963), Field (1964a, b), Miller, Galanter, and Pribram (1960), and Tomkins and Messick (1963). The student of measurement for guidance would do well to advance his understanding beyond this chapter, through pursuit of these references and of those noted in the introductory section of this chapter.

REFERENCES

ALLPORT, F., *Theories of Perception and the Concept of Structure.* New York: John Wiley & Sons, 1955

BORDIN, E. S., BARBARA NACHMANN, and S. J. SEGAL, "An articulated framework for vocational development." *J. Counseling Psychol.* **10,** 107–116 (1963)

BRUNER, J. S., *On Knowing.* Cambridge: Harvard University Press, 1962

CATTELL, R. B., *Factor Analysis.* New York: Harper, 1952

CRONBACH, L. J., and GOLDINE C. GLESER, *Psychological Tests and Personnel Decisions.* Urbana, Ill.: University of Illinois Press, 1957

DEWEY, J., *Democracy and Education.* New York: Macmillan, 1916

ERIKSON, E. H., "Identity and the life cycle." *Psychol. Issues* **1,** Monograph 1 (1959)

ERIKSON, E. H., "The roots of virtue," in J. Huxley (ed.), *The Humanist Frame.* New York: Harper, 1961, pp. 147–165

FESTINGER, L., *A Theory of Cognitive Dissonance.* Evanston, Ill.: Row, Peterson, 1957

FIELD, F. L., *An Investigation of Decision-Making in Educational-Vocational Context with Implications for Guidance.* Unpublished doctoral dissertation, Harvard Graduate School of Education, 1964a

FIELD, F. L., *Toward an Operational Goal for Guidance-in-Education.* Santa Barbara, Calif.: The author, University of California at Santa Barbara (duplicated), 1964b

FLAVELL, J. H., *The Developmental Psychology of Jean Piaget.* Princeton: D. Van Nostrand, 1963

HATHAWAY, S. R., "A coding system for MMPI Profile Classification." *J. Consulting Psychol.* **11,** 334–337 (1947)

HUXLEY, J. (ed.), *The Humanist Frame.* New York: Harper, 1961

MASLOW, A., *Motivation and Personality.* New York: Harper, 1954

MCARTHUR, C., "The dynamic model." *J. Counseling Psychol.* **3,** 168–171 (1956)

MEEHL, P. E., *Clinical Versus Statistical Prediction.* Minneapolis, Minn.: University of Minnesota Press, 1954

MEEHL, P. E., "Comment on the McArthur and Tiedeman papers." *J. Counseling Psychol.* **3,** 171–173 (1956)

MEEHL, P. E., D. V. TIEDEMAN, and C. MCARTHUR, "Symposium on clinical and statistical prediction." *J. Counseling Psychol.* **3,** 163–173 (1956)

MILLER, G., E. GALANTER, and K. H. PRIBRAM, *Plans and the Structure of Behavior.* New York: Holt, Rinehart, and Winston, 1960

ROE, ANNE, *The Psychology of Occupations.* New York: John Wiley & Sons, 1956

SCHWEIKER, R. F., *Individual Space Models of Certain Statistics.* Unpublished doctoral dissertation, Harvard Graduate School of Education, 1954

STEPHENSON, W., *The Study of Behavior: Q-Technique and Its Methodology.* Chicago: University of Chicago Press, 1953

STEVENS, S. S., "On the theory of scales of measurement." *Science* **103,** 677–680 (1946)

SUPER, D. E., *The Psychology of Careers.* New York: Harper, 1957

TATSUOKA, M. M., and D. V. TIEDEMAN, "Discriminant analysis." *Rev. Educ. Res.* **24,** 402–420 (1954)

TATSUOKA, M. M., and D. V. TIEDEMAN, "Statistics as an aspect of scientific method in research on teaching," in N. L. Gage (ed.), *Handbook of Research on Teaching.* Chicago: Rand McNally, 1963, pp. 142–170

TIEDEMAN, D. V., "Purposing through education: The further delineation of goal and program for guidance," in E. Landy and P. A. Perry (eds.), *Guidance in American Education: Background and Prospects.* Cambridge: Harvard University Press, 1964, pp. 162–172

TIEDEMAN, D. V., and F. L. FIELD, "Guidance: The science of purposeful action applied through education." *Harvard Educ. Rev.* **32,** 483–501 (1962)

TIEDEMAN, D. V., and R. P. O'HARA, *Career Development: Choice and Adjustment.* New York: College Entrance Examination Board, 1963

TOMKINS, S. S., and S. MESSICK, *Computer Simulation of Personality.* New York: John Wiley & Sons, 1963

TRAVERS, R. M. W., *An Inquiry into the Problem of Predicting Achievement.* San Antonio, Texas: Air Force Personnel and Training Research Center, Lackland Air Force Base, Research Bulletin AFPTRC–TR–54–93, 1954

TYLER, LEONA, "The methods and processes of appraisal and counseling," in A. S. Thompson and D. E. Super, *The Professional Preparation of Counseling Psychologists*. New York: Bureau of Publications, Teachers College, Columbia University, 1964, pp. 76–89

WEITZ, H., *Behavior Change through Guidance*. New York: John Wiley & Sons, 1964

WHITE, R. W., "Ego and reality in psychoanalytic theory." *Psychol. Issues* **3,** Monograph 11 (1963)

WIENER, N., *The Human Use of Human Beings: Cybernetics and Society*. Boston: Houghton Mifflin, 1950

CHAPTER 14

EVALUATION OF DECISION MAKING:
A STUDY OF COLLEGE ADMISSIONS

DEAN K. WHITLA, *Harvard University*

The crucible of admissions serves as an excellent laboratory for explorations using psychological, sociological, and statistical tools. In this respect it is, in fact, a rare institutional phenomenon—it can be separated clearly enough from the macrocosm of the college to permit separate analysis; large quantities of data are collected for the execution of the decisions; and the process cycles annually, providing automatic replication. Furthermore, it is dynamic, reality-oriented, and meets a highly significant institutional need: the selection of new members of the social system.

Only after the second world war did college admissions become selective in the sense that a number of colleges began to have more qualified applicants than they could accommodate. Up to this time, the primary orientation had been not toward selection but toward recruitment, and even that was conducted lackadaisically. As the opportunities for selection have become real—that is, as larger and larger numbers of qualified candidates have been applying—increasingly there has grown an interest in the nature of the selection process. Which students should be selected from the group of applicants? What kinds of students should be gathered together at a college for the best educational effects?

Within the general framework of admissions, there has always been great concern that decisions about individual candidates be made in response to their particular qualities. That concern has tended to result in two very different approaches to the admissions process. On one hand, there has evolved a very humanistic and individual approach, where each case is handled on its private merits, and all data-processing techniques are foreign, even antagonistic, to the operation. Proponents of the contrasting approach maintain that since each person is so individual, and our methods of assessments are so subjective and so limited, it is necessary to use *only* specifiable and quantifiable criteria for selection, in order not to do an injustice to any particular individual because of personal preferences and biases.

Neither of these viewpoints lends itself easily and naturally to the extensive analyses, including statistical investigations, that could lead to an understanding of this decision process and its effects on individuals, institutions, and the larger society.

Among college admissions officers, a particular concern has been prediction of academic success. We have acquired, through various work done in colleges as well as that sponsored by such organizations as the College Entrance Examination

Board and the American College Testing program, a great number of prediction equations designed to help admissions committees decide whether a particular individual is academically capable of handling the college, and what kind of academic record he is likely to compile. A simple prediction equation, however, is not sufficient when the number of applicants predicted to do satisfactory work far exceeds the number of available spaces. The new set of problems presented by the wider selection available to many colleges has forced into existence new dimensions in research programs and styles of investigation. These recent concerns have led to the application of a number of assessment methods; an example of such research will form the body of this chapter.

PREDICTION OF GRADES: THE REGRESSION EQUATION

One of the most important uses we make of test scores is the prediction of grades. In estimating a given applicant's capabilities, admissions personnel rely on a combination of the student's College Board test scores and his secondary school rank-in-class, with the elements weighted in such a manner as to yield the best prediction of his academic standing.

Perhaps the best way to explain a predicted grade average is to say that it is based on an equation that is, in a fundamental sense, abstracted from the academic climate of the college, and that it describes the way any particular student would be likely to respond to and perform in this environment. The equation is derived from the interrelationships that have been found to exist among selected independent variables (the College Board scores, both aptitude and achievement, rank in secondary school, and type of secondary school) and the dependent variable (college achievement). With a statistical representation of past performance of students in the college, it is possible to take the same objective data on applicants and predict how well the applicants will perform academically. The combination of scores and grades represented in the prediction equation gives an index which is, for example, almost twice as effective as grades in secondary school alone, in predicting Harvard College grades. Table 1 shows how well the prediction worked for the class that entered Harvard College in the fall of 1963.

Table 1 Predicted rank list vs. freshman rank list for Class of 1967

Predicted Rank List	Rank List							
	VII	VI	V	IV	III	II	I	Total
1.5–2.4	1	0	4	9	24	35	23	96
2.5–3.4	5	1	30	75	161	88	16	376
3.5–4.4	24	1	67	126	107	22	5	352
4.5–5.4	12	3	49	48	17	—	—	129
5.5–6.0	2	1	10	4	—	—	—	17
	44	6	160	262	309	145	44	970

Rank List (like Predicted Rank List) is essentially a grade average in which I = A, III = B, V = C, VII = Unsatisfactory. Ninety-four percent of the freshmen at Harvard earn a Rank List that does not differ from the Predicted Rank List by more than one rank, yet only 43% earn their actual PRL. Several factors operate to produce a relationship with this latitude.

The first of these is simply that the original applicant-group distributions of scores and secondary school rank have been restricted by the very process of admission (that is, lower-scoring applicants tend to be rejected), leaving a more homogeneous group. This reduces the effectiveness of the predictor variables.* Actually, half of the predictive ability of the PRL is being used up in the critical process of admitting and rejecting, and in a very real sense that is just as it should be.

As a brief overview of the magnitude of correlations that have been found in research (Olsen, 1957†; French, 1960‡; Olsen and Schrader, 1954§; plus compilations by Dyer and Pasanella, and by Whitla‖), summaries are provided in Table 2.

From the table it can be seen that the SAT-Verbal was in general a better predictor of liberal arts college grades than was the SAT-Mathematical score, while the reverse was true for engineering colleges. When comparing the effectiveness of the SAT-V and M with the high school record we find them to be of comparable predictive power for the men's colleges (liberal arts and engineering) but of somewhat less value than secondary school record for women's colleges. When these three variables were combined, they improved the prediction of grades over that of the SAT-V and M or secondary school record alone. There was also an improvement in predictive power when achievement test scores were added as a fourth predictor variable.

This table was compiled to give an index of the order of magnitude of the validity of scores for predicting college grades. The fact that three hours of paper-and-pencil aptitude testing are almost as powerful a predictor of college achievement as is the high school record, and that aptitude test scores add to the value of the latter as a predictor, testifies to the validity of the tests. That such a phenomenon continues to hold over long experience with the CEEB tests supports claims of their relevance as assessors of the educational process.#

A second factor operating to reduce the size of the relationship between Predicted Rank List and Freshman Rank List is the nature of the course programs

---

* The correlation between PRL and four-year grades, were we to admit randomly from the total applicant group, would be 0.78 rather than the obtained correlation of 0.62.
† The SAT scores used in this study came from tests administered in the winter or spring of 1957.
‡ The SAT scores used in this study came from tests administered in the winter or spring of 1960.
§ The testing for this study was carried out in the fall of 1954.
‖ Whitla, D. K., compilations from analyses run for colleges attending Harvard–CEEB Summer Institute in College Admissions.
For further discussion of this topic, see the writer's review in O. Buros (ed.), *Mental Measurement Yearbook,* 6th ed. Highland Park, N.J.: The Gryphon Press, 1959.

Table 2   The validity of independent variables as predictors of college grades

	Men—L.A.	Women—L.A.	Men—Engineering
Max. r_{vg}	0.67	0.66	0.46
Mdn. r_{vg}	0.36	0.37	0.22
Min. r_{vg}	0.05	0.12	0.01
N	125	124	30
Max. r_{mg}	0.53	0.62	0.52
Mdn. r_{mg}	0.31	0.28	0.30
Min. r_{mg}	0.09	0.04	0.10
N	125	124	30
Max. R_{vmg}	0.68	0.71	0.61
Mdn. R_{vmg}	0.45	0.39	0.35
Min. R_{vmg}	0.10	0.16	0.15
N	105	97	25
Max. r_{hg}	0.73	0.78	0.64
Mdn. r_{hg}	0.46	0.52	0.37
Min. r_{hg}	0.20	0.19	0.21
N	103	115	27
Max. R_{vmhg}	0.78	0.82	0.73
Mdn. R_{vmhg}	0.55	0.65	0.55
Min. R_{vmhg}	0.28	0.27	0.29
N	78	100	17
Max. R_{vmhag}	0.80	0.84	0.78
Mdn. R_{vmhag}	0.61	0.68	0.58
Min. R_{vmhag}	0.47	0.38	0.41
N	15	17	14

Key for variables:

g = college grade average	h = high school record
v = SAT-V score	a = achievement test scores
m = SAT-M score	N = number of colleges represented

taken by freshmen. For our statistics an A is an A is an A; yet we know that if these three A's are given in mathematics courses at three different levels, they represent different kinds of achievement and knowledge. However, it is difficult to arrive at a reasonable weighting system, and so any given grade in any of the 1600 courses offered receives equal value in the grade average, with the consequence that average grade becomes a difficult criterion to predict.

Paul Burnham of Yale has effectively emphasized the heterogeneity of the grade measure by reporting that 30 years ago Yale freshman enrollment would have been limited to approximately 20 courses in 12 to 15 departments; now the freshman class is enrolled in 148 courses in 39 departments. Those of us who have been engaged in institutional research have always been plagued by the concept of the "grade average" (Is a man who receives A grades and C grades similar to the man who receives only B grades?), by the unreliability of the grading system, and by the lack of an equal-interval scale. If we add to this list of measurement problems the heterogeneity of courses and then attempt to summarize the quality of a student's work on the single dimension, understandably the demands on our independent variables are many and their predictive power will not be large.

Thus, in attempting to assess student development over the college years, we are faced with the need for an adequate criterion. The search for this criterion pervades much of the work described in this chapter. Post-college activities and achievements have in a few cases been used as the standard, but most studies are limited to data on the college years and accept college grades or some corollary (i.e., graduation standing, satisfactory-unsatisfactory records, retention or dropout rate) as a criterion. Prediction of college grades using objective measures has received more attention than any other area of institutional research.

While grade predictions have been used primarily in the admissions process, they are also useful in placement and counseling; they provide a good index of how the college grading system is functioning, a summary of the relative academic strength of students by department, a method of finding pockets of strength that are overlooked, and even feedback for admissions policy.

In college advising, a prediction of grades is helpful mainly in the sense that it (with the test scores) gives information on how a student looks in terms of the rest of the college population; in addition, it provides some idea, as the year goes on, of how his record compares with his potential.

A grade prediction also helps to give us information about the environment of a college: for example, is grading becoming "tougher"? Since the equation is derived from an earlier population, it is incorporating a partial definition of the climate by translating into quantitative terms what level of grade and achievement we would generally expect of a student with a particular set of academic qualifications. However, since the college climate is constantly changing, we frequently examine and readjust the prediction equation. Comparing statistics, we do arrive at some understanding of the academic climate.

Use of the Regression Equation

With both the CEEB and ACT providing computational services for obtaining regression equations, all institutions should have results from this kind of analysis available for continuing use. The actual grade predictions can be made for each applicant for admissions by means of a desk calculator or a small computer.*

---

* Simple and relatively accurate methods have also been devised for approximating the prediction (contact Warren Willingham, director of research of the College Board staff in New York).

Prediction power. The first point to examine upon receipt of such analysis is the degree of power the variables possess for predicting grades at the college. The multiple correlation coefficient provides this information. If the multiple correlation is less than 0.41, there is no point in attempting to predict grades using a formula, for the errors in the prediction will be so large that little will have been gained from the operation. We can interpret the square of the correlation as the proportion of the total variance of the criterion which is predictable from the independent variables. (The proportion of variance that is due to other causes is $1 - r^2$.) A correlation of the magnitude of 0.40 would account for only 16% of the criterion, hence the recommendation that no formal prediction system be used. Attention should, instead, be directed to an examination of the data, to determine a reason for the low predictive power of the equation. In all the cases on which we have worked there has been a very reasonable explanation. In one dramatic case a correlation of 0.20 was found between secondary school grades, aptitude and achievement scores, and college grades for one division of a university. An examination of the data revealed that there was a normal distribution of scores and grades and that the mathematics of the solution was correct. Therefore, it was concluded, there was a problem somewhere in the institution. Discussions with the students indicated that grades were being given primarily for the efficient handling of trivia—for handing papers in on time, with the correct number of pages, for success on examinations full of questions about material in footnotes, and above all, for attendance and punctuality. The Dean of the division, armed with this information, made his own investigation; procedures were then changed and the correlations rose markedly the following year.

Another way to look at the power of the equation is to examine the range of error that will be found in the predictions. The measure of this range, called the standard error of estimate, is calculated as follows:

$$\sigma_{est} = \sigma_{crit} \sqrt{1 - r^2},$$

where r = simple or multiple correlation with the criterion variable. For example, if the multiple correlation is 0.60, and the sigma of the 4–0 grading scale equals 1.00, then the standard error of estimate is 0.80. For a student with a prediction of 2.8 we would expect grades to fall within the range of 2.8 ±0.8, or 2.0 to 3.6, approximately two-thirds of the time. The value of the radical, which has been labeled the *coefficient of alienation,* gives the magnitude of the error remaining in the prediction. From Table 3 it can be seen that in our example, a correlation of 0.60 makes only a 20% reduction in the standard error of estimate. In fact, a correlation of 0.87 is required to reduce the error by 50%.

The similarity between the variance interpretation of correlation and the coefficient-of-alienation interpretation is simply a function of the square. The amount of variance unaccounted for was $1 - r^2$, while the coefficient of alienation was $\sqrt{1 - r^2}$. These two expressions are equivalent because they are interpreted in

Table 3 Corresponding correlation coefficients and coefficients of alienation

r	$\sqrt{1-r^2}$	r	$\sqrt{1-r^2}$
0.00	1.00	0.60	0.80
0.10	0.99	0.70	0.71
0.20	0.98	0.80	0.60
0.30	0.95	0.90	0.44
0.40	0.92	1.00	0.00

association with the variance and sigma values, respectively. The variance is, of course, the square of the sigma. Therefore, we may discuss the power of the correlation either as a function of the variance we can explain or as the reduction in the sigma; the former is more common, the latter more demanding and conservative; both are proper.

Weighting of the independent variables. Second, one should examine the beta coefficients, for they are the weights given each of the independent variables to obtain the maximum prediction. The beta weight for the verbal aptitude score might be twice as large as that for the mathematical aptitude score, hence the oft-used formula $2V + M$. Probably the most heavily weighted factor will be the rank-in-class or grade average (whichever is used as a measure of secondary school performance).

For predicting grades at Harvard College there are two equations: one computed for students prepared in independent schools and a second for those from public schools. Historically, the weights in these two equations were vastly different. At one time rank-in-class (RIC) and SAT-V were the two most heavily weighted items in the equation for public school students, while achievement scores were by far the most heavily weighted for independent school students.

A favorite hypothesis used to be that RIC served the same psychological function for those from public schools as did achievement scores for the private school students. The differences in the respective beta weights gave support to Charles McArthur's statements that as a measure of excellence, in public school one "beat his peers" while in independent school one "beat the tests." More recently, the differences in weights have largely disappeared. There has been a decrease in the RIC beta weight in the public school equation; however, the greatest shift has been in the Achievement and RIC weights for the private school students, the former decreasing and the latter increasing. As David Riesman has said, the college is now owned by the public school man. The qualities ascribed to the independent school man are not in themselves sufficient to assure him of a place in the professions. This new world of the meritocracy seems to be reflected by the change in beta weights found in the predictive equations at Harvard College (see Table 4).

Table 4 Beta weights for predicting grades at Harvard College

Year	School	Independent Variables		
		SAT-V	ACH	RIC
1957	Public	0.182	0.232	0.423
	Private	0.091	0.428	0.224
1967	Public	0.184	0.228	0.370
	Private	0.099	0.144	0.385

Another example of the usefulness of beta weights in interpreting the academic climate of the college was found at an agricultural college of a university system. The beta weights were very small for secondary school RIC in the agricultural college, whereas they were large for the other colleges of the system. The SAT-V beta was sizable and the SAT-M beta was large. The power of the predictive equation was again comparable to that of the other colleges:

RIC	SAT-V	SAT-M	R
0.035	0.376	0.537	0.57

Discussion of these facts led to an easily interpretable finding. Students entering the agricultural college had their secondary school preparation in vocational-agricultural programs where excellence was measured more by care and feeding of animals than by achievement in science courses, but after they entered the college the roles were reversed, for there the program consisted of agronomy, biochemistry, etc. Consequently, there was little correspondence between high school grades and college grades but considerable correlation between SAT scores and college performance. This information was useful in pinpointing student-faculty problems in the College of Agriculture—it accounted for the considerable unrest the students showed over grading practices, for expectations play a large part in the degree of equanimity with which grades are received. The information was also most useful to the admissions office, since it gave the office a clear mandate from the faculty about the type of student in which they were interested, in terms of dimensions that admissions personnel could use.

One problem that can occur in the interpretation of beta weights is the negative coefficient. The most frequent approach to this problem is to dismiss it by calling it a suppressor variable. More specifically, the term suppressor variable (see McNemar, 1963, p. 186) was derived to explain the paradox of the multiple correlation that is increased by a variable which has a zero correlation with the criterion. Normally we find that variables which contribute to the multiple correlation have stronger relationships with the criterion than with the other independent variables. Hence the paradox. McNemar provides a good illustration as follows. Where

$$r_{12} = 0.400, \qquad r_{13} = 0.000, \qquad \text{and} \qquad r_{23} = 0.707$$

(1 designates the criterion variable, 2 and 3 designate the independent variables), the regresson equation would be

$$\beta_2 = 0.800, \qquad \beta_3 = 0.566, \qquad R \ 0.566.$$

Thus, McNemar continues, it is seen that when variable 3 is combined with variable 2, an appreciable gain in prediction occurs even though, when taken alone, variable 3 is worthless as a predictor of the criterion—variable 1. As an explanation for this phenomenon, it is proposed that the variables be thought of as composed of various numbers of elements which could be represented diagrammatically as shown below.

Criterion

x_1 _____ x_3

$a\,a\,a\,a\,a\,b\,b\,b\,b\,c\,d\,d\,d\,d\,d$

x_2

The elements found in x_2 which are not found in the criterion x_1 lower the correlation between these two variables; however, since a majority of the elements which are unique to x_2 are found in variable x_3, they can be "suppressed" by the use of this variable. Consequently, the relationship between x_1 and x_2 increases because they have in common a higher percentage of elements.

McNemar warns that such situations are "hard to realize in practice." In fact, however, their occurrence in regression equations based on admissions data is not so rare as he surmises. Frequently there *will* be negative beta weights and unfortunately, an admissions committee finds it difficult to accept the explanation that some variables have in common certain elements which through suppressant qualities increase the basic predictive power of the other variables. To be explicit, a negative beta weight was obtained for the SAT-M with data on Radcliffe College. Now, it would not be easy to convince Mrs. Bunting—a natural scientist, as well as president of the College—that the poorer the score a girl made on the mathematical aptitude test (other variables being the same), the higher her grade prediction would be. Certainly, the explanation could not be conducted gracefully in terms of McNemar's concept of common elements. What we did was to examine the data further; we found that the girls with the higher SAT-M scores were the ones who were more likely to take courses in the natural sciences, the area in which the girls received the poorest grades.* The magnitude of the SAT-M score was functioning as a course selector and because of this factor became a grade predictor. Since

---

* This finding has been corroborated at several colleges, among them Duke, Tulane, and Pomona (personal correspondence J. E. Sanders and Cliff Wing).

Radcliffe already had few enough natural science concentrators and the use of this equation would have tended to reduce the number, the pragmatic recommendation was simple: remove the SAT-M score from the matrix and recalculate the predictive equation even though the resulting multiple correlation was slightly reduced. In fact, the Radcliffe admissions committee operates so effectively that it seems to have an internalized regression equation which closely approximates a derived solution.

Beta weights are indices of the relative importance of the independent variable to the prediction equation; therefore, before they can be used to compute the grade prediction for a student, they must be adjusted to compensate for the differences in the scaling of the variables. Examples of differences in scaling of secondary school grades and scores are self-evident. To automatically compensate for these differences and the scale used for college grades, the beta weights are converted to b-weights. The magnitude of change from beta to b-weights is illustrated by the comparison given in Table 5.

Table 5   Beta weights and corresponding b-weights, Harvard College public school population

	SAT-V	ACH	RIC	Constant
Beta weights	0.184	0.232	0.372	—
b-weights	0.039	0.039	0.187	26.24

The Regression Phenomenon

It is useful in exploring prediction problems to be familiar with the concept underlying the regression equation. The fundamental properties of this measure were discovered by Francis Galton and presented during the period 1877 to 1888. Galton's investigations centered on the inheritance of traits, which was suggested by the work of his even more illustrious cousin Charles Darwin. Among his many explorations were investigations of the relationship of parents' to offspring's height. Female heights were multiplied by 1.08 to make them comparable to male heights, and the parents' heights were averaged and plotted against those of their children. A plot of the means of the arrays shows the "reversion" of the offspring height compared to the height of the "mid-parent". In Fig. 1 it can be seen that if the parents' height is 2.50 inches above average, the offspring's height will be only 1.25 inches above average. Galton first used the symbol r for the reversion he found; later he used the terms "regression," "co-relation," and "index of co-relation." Edgworth, in 1892, gave the name "coefficient of correlation" to this relationship, which has continued to be designated by r.

Galton, after years of collecting data and analyzing the materials, carried his conclusions to Dickson, a mathematician, who wrote the equation to represent the correlation surface described to him in probability terms by Galton. Upon receiving Dickson's solution, Galton wrote, "I may be permitted to say that I never felt such

		X_2										
		−4½	−3½	−2½	−1½	−½	½	1½	2½	3½	4½	f
Parent Heights	3½						1	2	2	2	1	8
	2½				2	4	5	5	4	3	1	24
	1½	1	2	3	5	8	9	9	8	5	3	53
	½	2	3	6	10	12	12	12	10	6	3	76
	−½	3	7	11	13	14	13	10	7	3	1	82
	−1½	3	6	8	11	11	8	6	3	1		57
	−2½	2	3	4	6	4	3	2				24
	f	11	21	32	47	53	51	46	34	20	9	324 = N

Fig. 1. Correlation between heights of midparents and offspring, based on data of Sir Francis Galton. Heights of adult offspring are expressed as deviations from the mean height of 68¼ in.

a glow of loyalty and respect towards the sovereignty and magnificent sway of mathematical analysis as when this answer reached me, confirming, by purely mathematical reasoning, my various and laborious statistical conclusions with far more minuteness than I had dared to hope, for the original data ran somewhat roughly, and I had to smooth them with tender caution" (Pearson, 1920, quoted in Kelley, 1947).

Galton's procedures of using medians and quartile deviations have given way to Karl Pearson's more accurate product-moment formula based on means and sigmas. Using Galton's data (Fig. 1), we obtained the correlation of 0.3897 between mid-parent and offspring height and the regression equation of $y = 27.76 + 0.5923x$, a classic case.

What is of especial interest to us is that the predictive equation so often referred to is in fact a regression equation and was so entitled because of the reversive qualities which were found in the data. The regressive quality is as present in admissions predictive equations as it was in Galton's original data. According to the grades predictions based on the formula, few if any admitted students would either earn an A record or fail—yet clearly, a certain number do both. However, A's and failures account for only a small proportion of the results, and the independent variables are not sufficiently sensitive to select them. The prediction with the highest probability of occurrence is the mean of the array, as illustrated in Fig. 1. The degree to which the line connecting these means differs from the major diagonal of the ellipse is dependent on the correlation between the two (or more) variables. When the correlation is 1.00 the major diagonal and the regression line will be identical; when the correlation is 0.00 the regression line will be parallel to the abscissa and all predictions will be equal to the mean of the predicted variable.*

---

* The angle of the regression lines is the tangent where $h = r(\sigma y/\sigma x)$.

The regression concept predicts regression toward the mean and frequently the only cited evidence, as in Galton's work, is a discussion of cases above the mean; obviously, however, it holds equally for cases below the mean. It is the regression phenomenon which makes it possible for tutoring schools to appear to be as successful as they are in the improvement of aptitude scores. Their tutees are primarily those who have low scores, so that the regression phenomenon alone will raise their scores on a second testing. If a student had a score of 300 on the SAT-V, he would be predicted to gain approximately 25 points because of the regression effect alone; the same phenomenon would take place for the student who scores 700—because of the regression effect, he would probably lose 25 points on the second sitting for the examination. We often hear discussed the effect of practice (equated to 25 points) and the effect of growth (at 3 points a month), but seldom regression, for the practice and growth aspects tend to cloak the effect of regression.

The experimental work that has been conducted supports these remarks (CEEB, 1965). In one particular experiment there were significant increases in post-test scores on the CEEB aptitude tests for both the tutored and control groups; however, there was no difference between the groups. Practice, growth, and regression effect were much more powerful influences in changing scores than was the tutoring experience. This was also true for those cases of large score changes (12% increased scores more than 100 points), for even these were equally likely in the tutored and untutored groups.

The "Oscillating Beta" Problem

Since regression equations are constructed to give optimal* predictions for a college,** the equations should be revised whenever the parameters have shifted significantly, i.e., when there are higher scores for the class, fewer failures, etc. However, there are inherent dangers in the revision process. One of these can be called the "oscillating beta" problem. The name is suggested by the pendulous change in values that occurs when regression equations are computed over time. To anyone who examines the sequence during which a regression equation is used, the phenomenon becomes evident. The predicted grades are computed for candidates by applying to one set of data formulae derived from a preceding set. In doing so we assume that it is appropriate to use the same weights because of the similarity in type of applicants, the way their secondary schools are grading them, the meaning of test scores, and the grades our faculty will give them; thus in a very real sense we imply, by using a regression equation, that "history will repeat itself."

In the process of admissions there is a pronounced tendency to admit candidates with high predictions, hence the grade predictions of the admitted candidates are higher and more homogeneous than those of the applicant group. Simultaneously, however, we have truncated the variables in the regression equation,

---

* In the linear, least-square sense.
** The CEEB experience in the state of Indiana indicated that a large percentage of the colleges could be grouped under a small number of equations.

especially those with the greater weight. Suppose, for example, that secondary school grades are most heavily weighted in the equation; then the admissions process automatically truncates this variable, so that admitted students are relatively more homogeneous on grades than on scores. When we recalculate the regression equation, we find that the beta value for the verbal score has increased; conversely, the beta weight for high school grades is markedly reduced. Our tendency is to interpret these findings as a reflection of a drastic change in the college environment—it appears that the faculty members are now rewarding verbal competency and ability to deal with symbolic concepts more than they are the aggressive pursuit of grades. Suppose, however, that we devise a new equation in which the verbal score is heavily weighted. Now the process truncates most severely the verbal score. A reanalysis of the data would show that secondary school grades are again the variable with the largest beta weight. Has our faculty reversed itself again and is it rewarding the secondary school achiever rather than the student with verbal competency? The more likely answer is that we have an oscillating phenomenon produced by the effect of truncation. Clearly, the restriction in range that is inherent in the selection process can cause marked changes in the magnitude of the correlation which in turn are reflected in the beta weights. Unfortunately, such occurrences are not rare, nor are misinterpretations of such statistical artifacts.

For those confronted with the realities of producing grade prediction, a powerful, albeit pragmatic, solution is never to use the exact weights derived by the multiple regression equation, but to make some adjustment, by estimating the weights that would be most appropriate for the actual prediction. One could accumulate experience simply by watching the equation over a period of time without making adjustments, and discovering the magnitude of the oscillation; however, such a rational procedure is time-consuming. If on the second set of calculations there has been a marked shift in the weights, it would be expedient to estimate the size of the correlations using Pearson's formula Case I (which compensates for changes in sigma) and recalculating the beta weights; these data will make it possible to reduce the size of the oscillation. Such adjustments will have two positive effects: first, to give information for better interpretation of beta weights, making possible a more accurate estimation of the effect of college environment on grades; and second, to provide a better basis for estimating grades at the time of selection.

Willingham (1965) of the College Board recently explored theoretically the problem of oscillating beta coefficients. Basing his work on the assumption that grades would be given on an absolute scale—for example, from the results of an achievement test—he found that beta weights changed in magnitude as a reflection of the truncation; even more interestingly, he also found that the b-weights remained constant. These findings do make good sense, for if the grading standards stay the same, students should receive the same grade prediction regardless of the associates with whom they are grouped when the formula is derived. Hence the b-weights must be constant, and since the sigmas have changed the beta weights must necessarily also have changed. At times in the past, beta weights were thought to be

Table 6 Beta weights, public school equation 1940–64

Year	SAT-V	ACH	RIC
1935	0.108	0.298*	0.304
1940	—	0.391*	0.355
1955	0.182	0.232	0.423
1960	0.189	0.234	0.333
1964	0.184	0.228	0.370

* At this time achievement tests were of essay form and readers scored them on a percentage scale.

stable beyond the specific sample, while the *b*-weights, known to be subject to the vicissitudes of sample variance, were assumed to be the fluctuating members of the association. Both empirical and theoretical works now question this interpretation. Granting Willingham's assumption, we know in fact that the opposite is true. Using the more common situation of relative grading standards, we find that both beta and *b*-weights are subject to fluctuation. Fortunately, these fluctuations can be anticipated and compensations can be made for them. The beta weights available over a period of time from Harvard College prediction equations have only limited usefulness in illustrating the oscillating phenomenon, for the process of adjustment has been used for several years. However, an examination of available sets of beta weights (Table 6) does illustrate that the magnitude of the oscillation has decreased.

RESTRICTION IN RANGE

A complicating and frequently ignored aspect of statistical interpretations is the effect of restriction in range, which we mentioned briefly in the preceding section. Most of the research deals not with random samples of the population but with strata which are self-selected or homogeneous within an institution. Such restriction, if not acknowledged in the interpretation, can lead to highly erroneous conclusions. College grade prediction provides the simplest illustration of this effect. For example, if the correlation between grades in college and predicted grades is 0.60 and the sigma of the predicted grades of the admitted groups is half that of the candidate group (in other words, the grade prediction index was an important criterion in the admission decision), then the correlation between predicted grades and actual grades would be 0.85 if the admitted group had been selected at random from the candidates. The equation is written

$$R_{12} = \frac{r_{12}\Sigma/\sigma}{1 - r_{12}^2 + r_{12}^2(\Sigma/\sigma)^2}$$

$$= \frac{0.60\,(2)}{1 - 0.36 + 0.36 \cdot 4} = 0.85,$$

where Σ is the sigma of the unrestricted sample, σ the sigma of the restricted sample, r the correlation of the restricted sample, and R the correlation of the unrestricted sample.

Pearson provided formulas for three cases of restriction in range. Case I (illustrated above) is the most frequently encountered: One wishes to estimate the unrestricted correlation between variables x and y, where the variable x has been restricted and the sigma of x is known both for the restricted and unrestricted groups. Case II is similar in that the restriction is on variable x but the sigmas known are for y under both restricted and unrestricted conditions. Case III is for the conditions that restriction is on z, and the sigmas of z restricted and unrestricted are known, as are r_{xy}, r_{xz}, r_{zy}. With this information it is possible to estimate r_{xy} under unrestricted conditions.

Extensive use of Pearson's formulas can be found in early psychological literature; however, these formulas seem to have fallen into general disfavor. Possibly this occurred because they were grouped under the general rubric of prophecy formulas, a group which generally lost favor because if the assumptions underlying the use of a given formula are not satisfied, the results can be highly spurious,—and such assumptions are often hard to meet.

Should such reservations be raised about Pearson's formulas for correcting for restriction in range? To investigate the appropriateness of Pearson's work, this investigator with the assistance of two colleagues, Miles McPeek and Marshal Smith, determined the conditions under which Pearson's formulas would provide a reasonable approximation of the underlying relationship. Using a series of bivariate distributions having correlations from 1.00 to 0.20, we truncated the distribution by 0.1 sigma units on one variate, and estimated the correlation for the population from that obtained with the restricted sample. We also introduced skewness into the original bivariate distribution to determine the degree to which normality was an essential element of accurate estimates.

In general, the errors introduced by using Pearson's formulas are negligible over the normal range of application. However, the magnitude of errors did increase when the population correlation was less than 0.30 and the sample from which the correlation was estimated was restricted to the range positive one sigma to positive three sigmas. Under such restrictions the errors in the estimates of the population correlation were as large as 0.24 when N was as small as 30. In cases where severe skewness was introduced into the distribution and the sample was restricted to the range positive one sigma to positive three sigma, the estimates of correlation for the population were likely to be biased and high. If ρ was less than 0.50 the estimates of ρ were 0.20 to 0.35 too large. If ρ was large (0.65 or higher) and/or the restricted range of the distribution covered as much as three sigmas of the population, the estimates of ρ were never found to be more than 0.1 in error.

The following illustration demonstrates the havoc that truncation can play with the interpretation of statistical findings. One of the problems in college admissions is that of trying to validate any of the assessments that are not primarily academic in nature. Such an attempt was a study of ratings given scholarship winners who during scholarship renewals were reevaluated along the same scales used in admissions. Correlations were obtained between ratings given at admissions and at the end of the junior year (see Table 7).

One could conclude, upon presentation of the original correlations of 0.62 and 0.18, that the committee was a far better judge of athletic ability than of personal qualities. However, this interpretation is an oversimplification of the problem of the measurements and the way these ratings are used in admissions. The sigmas are much larger for the athletic rating than for personal rating, for the former is less important as an admission criterion than the latter. Second, for athletic ratings made at the end of the junior year there was an excellent criterion scale available; students could be rated in clear cut categories—those earning varsity letters, playing junior varsity, etc., all the way to those displaying an aversion to the shouts of the crowds or the smell of perspiration. Such an explicit criterion scale is not available in rating personal qualities. Personal references for scholarship holders are usually written by professors who are far more knowledgeable about intellectual capabilities than about personal qualities, for they have seen student performance in an academic setting rather than in extracurricular or house functions. Therefore, the ratings cluster around the middle of the scale.

Table 7 Correlation between admission ratings and junior year ratings for scholarship students ($N = 267$)

	Original correlations	Adjusted correlations
Athletic rating	0.62	—
Personal rating	0.18	0.74

Clearly, the correlation between the two sets of personal ratings is based on a different set of conditions than those on which the athletic ratings correlation was made. The restriction in range that was imposed by the admissions decisions would markedly decrease the computed relationship. In an attempt to remove the restriction so that more equatable comparison could be made between the measures of personal and athletic strength, we estimated the magnitude of the correlation, assuming that the admission process had had an equal impact on the range of both variables. By making the sigmas of personal ratings comparable to those of the athletic ratings we found that the correlation between personal ratings increased from 0.18 to 0.74, which is larger than that of 0.62 for the athletic ratings. This does force a reconsideration of the original conclusions. We do not have evidence that the admissions staff could obtain a 0.74 correlation if the sigmas of the admission and junior ratings were increased. Nevertheless, if they were as capable under those conditions as they are under these restricted conditions, they would in fact be able to explain half of the variance in the junior year personal ratings. The other half would be attributed to unreliability of the measures or lack of validity, and/or change during the college years.

However, in examining the existing relationships we should keep in mind that such variables, even athletic rating, are not simple and unitary. Athletic ratings, of 1 for example, are given for outstanding achievement at the respective level (allstate in secondary school or varsity in college); ratings of 2 are given for conference stars or JV men, and ratings of 3 for high school lettermen or intramural participants. Beyond this point, ratings must be assigned only on the basis of attitudes, i.e., 4 for men who would like to play the big sports but can't take the gaff; 5 for a man who shares Mark Twain's attitude that when the thought of exercise comes over him he lies down until it goes away; and 6 for one who gets nauseous at the thought of physical contact. Since those responsible for the ratings base their top three ratings on athletic behavior, the able schoolboy athlete who chooses not to play varsity sports reduces the correlations. This happens frequently enough that some observers have exaggerated the point by saying that a top intramural team would beat the varsity.

The upshot of this discourse on the athletic ratings is that the behavioral style of assessment used at the top of the scale would tend to reduce the apparent relationship (admission versus junior rating) from its true value, because students possessing abundant athletic talent as seen in secondary school, and who then go on to play only intramural college sports (rather than the varsity sports they are qualified for), would add to the error variance.

To understand the personal rating is even more difficult. The concept is as simple as Whitehead's statement that an education makes it possible for you to tell a good man when you see one. But the contrasts in viewpoint about the personal rating (what qualities make a man outstanding?) and the fact that there are many composites which merit outstanding ratings, make the assessment process difficult. "A touch of greatness," was what one counselor ascribed to an applicant, "the simple charm of ingenuousness," "the organized effective energy and the irascibility of a Henry Ford." We examined the materials available to the rater to determine which of the sources he uses is weighted most heavily in his evaluation; they were counselor's report, teachers' reports, autobiographical description, and interview by staff and/or by alumni. Obviously, the weights can vary for applicants because the assessment represents an evaluation made by the reader of the folder, and only the overall assessment is quantified.

If we consider the stability of personality—how unmalleable it is, in fact, even in psychotherapy—then a correlation of 0.74 between two assessments made four years apart appears to be a commentary on the reliability of the assessments and on the consistency of definition regardless of its complexity. If we choose to interpret the 0.74 as a reliability coefficient of clinical judgment we are neither embarrassed nor gratified; if we consider the coefficient as an attenuated measure of validity in the sense that we are rating some functional and viable quality of personality, we are quietly delighted; if we consider it as a finding which is indicative of the readers' ability to reflect the integration of ego strength, we are audacious.

Because the ways the ratings in admissions are determined and the manner in which they are used in the admissions process gave rise to a serious question about our ability to make decisions on this basis, a study was made of original ratings versus similar assessments made four years later. The first interpretation of these data supported the latent fears of the committee—that the assessments of personal strengths were either invalid, unreliable, or both. However, further examination proved that these findings were an artifact of the admissions and assessment process. Adjusting for these effects made it apparent that given the constraints of assessment in college admissions, ratings of personal qualities were as viable a variable as an athletic rating, from the viewpoint of validity. Unfortunately and needlessly, the problem of restriction in range constitutes one of the most frequent sources of misinterpretation of data found in the literature.

STATISTICAL STUDIES OF ADMISSIONS POLICY

The data on applicants to Harvard College provided an opportunity for extensive analyses of admissions policy. Since the credentials of each applicant are extracted from the folders in rating form before committee action is taken, we had available elaborate data with which to work.*

Correlations and Tabulations

One method of examining the change in policy over the last decade is to consider the changes that have taken place in the correlations between a number of variables used in the decision process and the criterion of admit-reject. To simplify this inspection, coefficients for five selected variables are given in Table 8. From these figures we can see that the SAT-V, admit-reject correlation decreased monotonically at a rather consistent rate, starting at 0.63 for the Class of 1958 and declining to 0.25 for the Class of 1968. A similar but less consistent and spectacular decline was also true for the PRL—it ranged from a high of 0.66 with the Class of 1958 to a low of 0.35 with the Class of 1968. The correlation for the personal rating rose from 0.54 to 0.65 over this decade, while principals' ratings carried virtually the same influence over this period. The preliminary overall rating did play the part of a summary rating and the correlations with the admissions decision ranged from a low of 0.86 to a high of 0.90.

---

* Using a six-point scale, the staff members assign ratings to the teachers' reports, the principals' or counselors' report, the alumni and/or staff interview reports, and along other dimensions consisting of academic, extracurricular, athletic, and personal qualities. Each reader then summarizes this information into an overall evaluation and overall scholarship evaluation if the latter is appropriate. A majority of the folders receive three readings, though during the final harried week of folder readings some cases are read only twice and a few only once. Normally, the third reader, who is the Director of Admissions for regular candidates and the Director of Freshman Scholarships for financial aid candidates, gives his own independent assessments as well as summarizing all of the data into a final set of ratings—which can consist of an averaging, but need not be so. The original ratings of the readers are retained in the folder and the discrepancies among them at times form part of the committee discussions.

Table 8 Biserial correlations between admit-reject and selected independent variables, data from Harvard College Classes 1958–1968

Independent variable	1958	1959	1964	1966	1968	1968 adj.
SAT-V	0.63	0.52	0.45	0.33	0.25	0.51
PRL	0.66	0.58	0.63	0.45	0.35	0.35
Personal rating	0.54	0.58	0.58	0.63	0.65	0.81
Principal's rating	0.62	0.65	0.62	0.62	0.61	0.68
Preliminary overall rating	—	0.86	0.90	0.89	0.88	0.92

The changes in the table of means of these variables indicated that the qualities of the applicant group had improved. It is difficult to make definitive remarks about the cause of the small shift in the mean of the principals' ratings, from 3.17 to 3.02 (1 being the desirable end of the scale). Were much better men applying, but tougher staff ratings being given the reports, in order to keep some useful range in the scale? (This is clearly the way the staff would assess the change.) Or, were slightly higher ratings being given principals' reports for similar men? The CEEB scores, tied to an immovable 1941–1945 base, provide a helpful benchmark. During this period the SAT-V medians of the applicants increased about one sigma, while the number of applicants also increased dramatically (see Table 9).

Table 9 Median SAT scores of the applicant group for selected years

Applicants to Class of	SAT Median	N
1958	560	2608
1959	570	3102
1964	632	5048
1966	650	4910
1968	654	5643

An examination of the changes in the distribution of the sigmas of these six variables seemed at first glance unimpressive. The SAT-V sigma dropped over the decade by 10%, from 94.7 to 84.1. The largest shift was in the standard deviation of the personal rating, which dropped from 0.92 to 0.71 on the six-point scale—a decrease of over 20%. We did wish to explore the impact of the change of these sigmas on the relationships presented in Table 8. The coefficients listed under the 1968 adjusted column exhibit these changes; here the sigmas for 1968 were equated to those of 1958. The correlation for SAT-V with admit-reject jumped with this adjustment from 0.25 to 0.51, which means that on 1958 standards, 1968 verbal scores and admission decisions had 25% of their variance in common, as compared to 40% for 1958 and 6% in 1968 (without adjustment for sigma shift). The PRL correlation did not change. We should bear in mind that procedures are used to adjust the PRL to the standards of college grading as much as to the quality of the applicant group; possibly the statistical manipulations that keep the mean and sigma steady also result in the lack of change between raw and adjusted 1968 coefficients. The personal rating, which had shown substantial increase in its unadjusted form, made a striking jump. The principal's rating has over the long period played a strong role in the decision process and is now larger than it was in any of the other years. The preliminary overall rating, as has been mentioned, is a summary rating, and as such plays a commanding part in the decision process.

Clearly, these correlations reveal a shift in the admissions policy of Harvard College. There has been a move away from the objective-academic qualities as important criteria to those of subjective-personal nature. This change has been consistently evolving over the last decade, along with the equally important trend toward an increase in numbers and quality of applicants.

As this change in admissions policy became evident, we compiled some tabulations comparing the admitted and rejected candidates on the various dimensions so that it was unnecessary to have an understanding of correlation coefficients to see easily the shift in the bases of the decisions. Since these compilations have been made more recently than the original analyses, data for the Classes of 1958 and 1959 are not available. The tabulations for the SAT-V and personal ratings are found in Table 10.

Table 10 Comparative summaries of admissions ratings for admitted and rejected candidates

SAT-V	Class of '64			Class of '66			Class of '68		
	Adm.	Rej.	% Adm.	Adm.	Rej.	% Adm.	Adm.	Rej.	% Adm.
750–800	84	36	70.0	177	184	49.0	126	174	42.1
700–749	410	356	53.5	360	497	42.0	380	659	36.5
650–699	445	735	37.7	330	698	32.1	370	966	27.6
600–649	305	828	26.9	267	669	28.5	262	723	26.6
550–599	152	582	20.7	162	442	26.8	153	529	22.4
500–549	335	410	7.9	84	304	21.6	76	351	17.8
Below 500	12	421	2.8	27	306	8.8	32	296	10.8

Personal rating	Class of '64			Class of '66			Class of '68		
	Adm.	Rej.	% Adm.	Adm.	Rej.	% Adm.	Adm.	Rej.	% Adm.
1	80	11	87.9	36	4	90.0	38	1	97.5
2	611	333	64.7	620	227	61.0	737	345	68.3
3	650	1846	26.0	649	1915	25.3	612	2715	18.4
4	116	1181	8.9	44	964	4.4	21	966	2.1
5	5	105	4.5	2	106	1.8	1	103	1.0
6	0	12	0.0	0	9	0.0	0	13	0.0

One graphical method of presenting information such as this so that direct comparisons can be made is to use, for the abscissa, the cumulative percentage and for the ordinate, scores or ratings, the intervals of which are proportional to the frequency of cases. The perfect relationship between the two variables with an infinite number of categories would be a straight line running diagonally across the graph. If a finite number of categories is used, the function consists of a series of steps. Visual evaluation of the degree of discrepancy from the ideal diagonal line makes comparison of the relative power of the relationships easy to evaluate. It is patently apparent that these data across the years 1964, 1966, and 1968 would provide a fallacious comparison, for the percentage admitted over this period has changed. However, by wading through the numbers of men admitted and rejected by score or rating over the three years that are presented, one can see that although the numbers of candidates with high scores increased and the numbers with low scores decreased, the committee action was relatively more stable. An exception to this statement would be at the lower end of the SAT-V scale, where in the Class of 1966 there was a marked increase in number admitted, which was continued in 1968. The numbers of applicants given high personal ratings showed a decline from 1964 to 1968; however, the degree to which the committee seemed to follow this rating in their decisions certainly increased. For example, while fewer recent applicants were given low personal rating, in 1964 there were 121 with poor ratings admitted compared with 22 in the Class of 1968. If we had had 1958 data, these findings would have been more pronounced.

Factor Analyses

Since 1955 we have been using techniques of factor analysis to analyze the admissions committee's decisions, for we have found these procedures helpful in summarizing how the committee "sees" the data given on the admissions docket and how the members use this information to evaluate candidates. Factor analysis in no way puts an evaluation judgment on the admissions process or the policy which is enacted. The power of the factor analysis lies in its summarizing quality. It forces us to examine all candidates simultaneously rather than to risk the bias toward a particular point of view which might result from a sample of selected cases. It enables us to see how the various scores and ratings are related to each other; in factor terms, we are talking of how closely they are associated with each other, or how similarly they are loaded on a given factor.

The original data subjected to the factor routine were from applicants to the Class of 1958. Since this original analysis was made, we have run factor analyses of the data on applicants to the Classes of 1959, 1964, 1966, and 1968. For each of these classes we have run at least four factor analyses and as many as fifteen or more associated rotations. The results of these five series of analyses, covering a decade, provide provocative comparisons.

For all of the solutions, there emerged a factor of the quality of secondary school male seniors as seen through the eyes of an admissions committee. Factor I accounts for 60–70% of the information that is found in these variables. The most heavily loaded variables on the first factor are the PRL, personal rating, principal's rating, staff interview rating, and the admissions decision. There is a pronounced tendency for the committee to see certain characteristics as a cluster; men who do well in school, are personable in their encounters, receive support from the school, and are admitted to Harvard College. The factor solution tells us nothing of the cause-and-effect relationship; however, it illustrates for us that the admissions decision is associated with these other variables in a strong positive fashion.

Factor II, which accounts for 20–30% of the information found in these matrices, is a bipolar variable with positive loadings for personal strengths and negative loadings for intellectual abilities. The positive loadings are found for the variables of personal rating, staff interview, athletic rating, alumni rating, and extracurricular rating; the negative loadings are found for PRL, SAT-V, achievement scores, and RIC. The loading of admit-reject has shifted markedly on Factor II; it was only 0.03 on the 1958 data and is 0.40 on the 1968 material.

If we force the examination of 6000 applicants for admission into a factor analysis format, we find that the most pronounced feature of this mathematical summary is the existence of a *G* factor, a general factor of excellence, and this summary is effective in extracting 60–70% of the information about this group of candidates. The next 20–30% of the information emerges as a bipolar personal-intellectual factor which over the decade of analyses appears to become more associated with the decision itself. The remaining information seems to be so idiosyncratic and elusive that it by and large escapes capture in a factor model.

While the privilege of examining factor output conducted on one problem for over a decade seemed like an opportunity, it was curiously mixed with pitfalls. It was impossible, for example, to interpret the sequentially derived factor output and the associated series of rotations in the normal fashion and do so with any validity. For a simple illustration, we shall consider the problem of percent of trace* and examine the relative magnitude of the latent roots. The percentage of the trace explained by the first two factors (the only two which were significant) in the 1958 factor solution was 91.4; this amount decreased slowly and consistently to the middle seventies over the series of analyses, while the numbers of variables in the factor solution increased from 11 to 21. Similarly, since each latent root is a representation of the relative variance contained in that factor, we considered the comparison of latent roots for this variety of solutions. Latent roots of the first factor were as small as 3.80 for the 1958 data and as large as 8.27 for 1968. To examine the comparability of the solutions, we reanalyzed the 1968 data using only the eleven variables used originally with the 1958 analyses. A comparison of the results of these analyses are found in Table 11. The 1968 percentage trace and latent roots are very similar to those of 1958 when the same variables are selected for analysis. The small differences that exist between these results could be as much a function of the truncation effect as the change in the perception and use of the

---

* "Trace" is the sum of the diagonal elements or estimates of communality in the matrix to be factored.

variables by the admissions committee. These findings illustrate that the overt percentage of variance explained, and the size of the latent roots, are highly dependent on the conditions established for the factor analysis.

We next examined the factor structure to see if it, too, was a function of the differences in the solutions. A continued examination of the 1958 and 1968 data

Table 11 Comparison of factor solutions, 1958 and 1968 data

| | Subgroup not interviewed by staff | | | Subgroup interviewed by staff | | | |
| | | Latent roots | | | Latent roots | | |
	% Trace	1	2	% Trace	1	2	3
Class of 1958	91.4	3.80	1.70	88.2	4.50	1.95	
Class of 1968 (11 variables)	88.6	3.37	1.54	86.9	3.56	2.41	
Class of 1968 (21 variables)	75.7	6.37	2.62	83.9	7.13	3.55	1.16

Table 12 Factor loadings based on data for Classes of 1958 and 1968

| | Factor I | | | Factor II | | |
	1958	1968 (11 var.)	1968 (21 var.)	1958	1968 (11 var.)	1968 (21 var.)
SAT-V	0.57	0.58	0.49	−0.54	−0.53	−0.61
SAT-M	0.53	0.49	0.42	−0.44	−0.39	−0.48
PRL	0.74	0.74	0.64	−0.57	−0.55	−0.66
RIC	0.61	0.61	0.51	−0.36	−0.49	−0.57
Extracurricular	0.49	0.43	0.43	0.35	0.20	0.11
Athletic	0.15	0.05	0.11	0.55	0.51	0.49
Personal	0.67	0.46	0.55	0.57	0.67	0.57
Principal	0.72	0.74	0.73	0.03	0.08	−0.07
Staff interview	0.79	0.69	0.73	0.36	0.33	0.22
Alumni interview	0.59	0.56	0.61	0.35	0.24	0.19
Admit-reject	0.87	0.75	0.88	0.03	0.49	0.40
Regular scholarship			0.11			−0.12
Average achievement			0.51			−0.61
Prel. overall rating			0.92			0.25
Prel. schol. rating			0.86			0.30
Academic			0.71			−0.50
Teacher rating			0.66			−0.02
Public-private			−0.00			0.31
Staff personal			0.53			0.50
Alumni personal			0.46			0.37
Harvard son			0.003			0.28

was useful for this purpose (see Table 12). It was seen that much stability did exist among these solutions and especially between the loadings found for the two 1968 analyses. Most of the loadings changed less than 0.10; the largest change was for Admit-reject, which was from 0.75 to 0.88, or a change of 0.13. The addition of the extra variables did not distort the 1968 (21-variable) factor solution. The fact that the stable variables SAT-V, SAT-M, and RIC retained their same position in the factor structure made it apparent that they had played the role of marker variables and that it was legitimate to make chronological comparisons among the solutions.

Factor Rotation. Having established that the structure of the factor solutions has remained essentially invariant over the sequence of the analyses, we examined the results of a series of oblimin rotations (see Table 13). The choice of oblimin procedure was made because it seems to be the best of the oblique rotational pro-

Table 13   Rotated factor loadings based on data for Classes of 1958 and 1968

	Factor I			Factor II		
	1958	1968 (11 var.)	1968 (21 var.)	1958	1968 (11 var.)	1968 (21 var.)
Sat-V	−0.15	0.04	−0.21	0.76	0.77	0.77
SAT-M	−0.09	0.07	−0.14	0.66	0.61	0.62
PRL	−0.08	0.13	−0.15	0.87	0.89	0.88
RIC	0.02	0.03	−0.16	0.63	0.76	0.74
Extracurricular	0.55	0.45	0.35	−0.03	0.10	0.09
Athletic	0.55	0.40	0.46	−0.38	−0.38	−0.39
Personal	0.85	0.80	0.79	−0.13	−0.26	−0.27
Principal	0.41	0.58	0.38	0.36	0.39	0.39
Staff interview	0.73	0.73	0.61	0.12	0.15	0.12
Alumni interview	0.61	0.56	0.52	0.02	0.15	0.10
Admit-reject	0.49	0.88	0.84	0.44	0.07	0.03
Regular scholarship			−0.03			0.16
Average achievement			−0.19			0.78
Prel. overall rating			0.74			0.18
Prel. schol. rating			0.75			0.11
Academic			0.02			0.76
Teacher rating			0.38			0.31
Public-private			0.25			−0.28
Staff personal			0.72			−0.22
Alumni personal			0.61			−0.12
Harvard son			0.23			−0.25

Factor Intercorrelations
1958   0.43
1968 (11 var.) 0.43
1968 (21 var.) 0.46

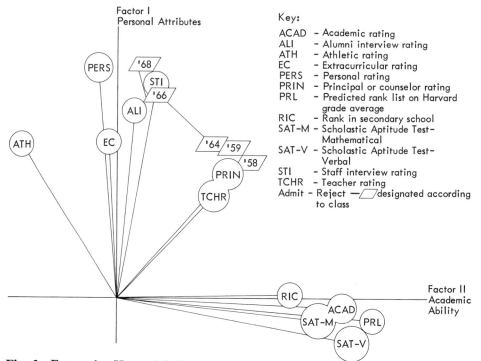

Fig. 2. Factor plot, Harvard College admissions data.

cedures (see Cooley and Lohnes, 1962, p. 211). Since an orthogonal rotation of a two-factor solution would be trivial and since so little in nature is really orthogonal, restricting the position of the axes seemed to impose a severe (albeit at times a useful) limitation.

The oblimin rotations produced two factors, clearly distinguishable as personal attributes and academic ability. The personal attributes factor was defined by the personal rating, the staff interview, the alumni rating, and the extracurricular rating. The variables with high loadings on the academic ability factor were PRL, SAT-V, RIC, academic rating, achievement scores, and SAT-M. The constancy of these rotated loadings is demonstrated in Fig. 2, where we have plotted findings from analyses of all five classes. Two of the variables functioned as singletons; the principal's rating fell halfway between the two major factors and held that position with great consistency over the years. The principals seem to be trying to tell the committee about both personal and academic strengths and this dual role was effectively accomplished in the reports, for principals' ratings had strong loadings on both factors. The second singleton was the athletic rating, which had a negative loading on the academic ability factor and a positive loading on the personal attributes factor, but fell beyond the general area of the factors. The admissions decision, a variable of special interest in admissions policy, is the only variable for

Table 14 Relationship of the admissions decision to personal attributes and academic ability*

Applicants to the Class of	Admissions decision loadings	
	Personal factor	Academic factor
1958	0.47	0.44
1959	0.53	0.41
1964	0.58	0.31
1966	0.74	0.08
1968	0.78	0.06

* Correlation between personal and academic factors, 0.46.

which there has been a consistent and marked shift over this period. The weights, presented in Table 14, show that the decision had loadings of equal magnitude in the Class of 1958 data and that these loadings shifted toward a heavy loading on personal attributes while decreasing on the academic ability factor.

While the interpretation of the admissions policy based on the rotated solutions does seem more dramatic than that based on the factor structure, essentially both of these solutions are reformulations which we can recognize analytically as well as know mathematically as equivalent. The apparent shift in the loading of the admissions variable toward the personal attributes factor must be evaluated with due acknowledgment of the correlation between the two factors, which was virtually constant with $r = 0.46$. To obtain this degree of minimax loading of the variables the factors had to be highly interrelated; this is simply another way of restructuring the same information. In the factor solution, where the change in admission loading was not dramatic, the factors were independent; where the change in the loading was startling, the dimensions were highly interrelated.

Complexity of Factor Structure. These factor analyses have provided a more subtle way in which to examine some of the complexity in decision making. In the 1966 analysis we found that for certain subgroups of candidates, a statistically significant third factor appeared. The third factor was even more prominent in the results from the 1968 data. This, as we discussed, could not be interpreted as a change in the admissions process, for as we have noted, the increased size of the latent roots was a function of the increased number of variables in the factor matrix. However, this third factor gave additional information about the process. We found that three significant factors emerged from the analysis of certain subgroups of the candidate population, and that the different subgroups themselves gave more understanding of this dimension than did the variables with significant loadings. In four of these fifteen subgroups, the two original factors contained the significant variance. These four groups were: (1) applicants not interviewed by the staff, (2) the public school candidates, (3) the scholarship candidates, and (4) the public school group not interviewed by the staff. These groups include about 70% of our candidates. One can understand how public school scholarship applicants who are not interviewed compose a group that is seen in fewer dimensions when decisions are made, as contrasted with candidates who come from schools which are known, and where the data are richer; in the latter case, the committee is induced to use more dimensions in the decision process. The current analyses essentially tell us only that the third factor seems to be conditional; i.e., by and large the significant variables shift, depending on the subgroup being analyzed.

Contribution of Factors to the Admissions Decision. We have seen the influence of the variables separately on the admissions process, we have seen the factors that the committee used in their deliberations and the way that the decision is loaded or correlated with these factors; now we wish to look at how well these variables and factors in combination predict the committee action.

To determine the collective importance of the variables presented to the admissions committee in their decision process we obtained multiple correlations using admit-reject as a criterion. We have chosen to exhibit two equations: those cases where the candidates were interviewed by the staff, and those cases where candidates were not interviewed. The multiple correlations from these regression equations, found in Table 15, are extraordinarily high. Since each of these correlations is the result of an independent solution, there is no indication as to the degree to which the equations would serve as good predictors of future committee action. We did, however, cross-validate the Class of 1959 findings with the Class of 1960 data. The correlations obtained between a predicted admissibility index and committee action were 0.92 and 0.98 for interviewed and noninterviewed candidates.

Table 15 tells us that the multiple correlations for interviewed candidates increased from 0.90 to 0.98 during the decade; this must be contrasted with the decrease in the multiple correlations for candidates not interviewed by the staff, which fell from 0.94 to 0.71. Until the Class of 1966 the predictions were higher for cases where staff interview information was not available. An explanation for this relationship seemed reasonably apparent to one attending the committee meet-

Table 15 Multiple correlations obtained using admission variables to predict the admissions decision

| Class | Multiple correlations | |
	Candidates interviewed by staff	Candidates not interviewed by staff
1958	0.904	0.940
1959	0.902	0.978
1966	0.944	0.925
1968	0.982	0.709

ings. When the staff had not interviewed the men, all of the evidence for presentation at the meetings had to be found in the folder; the action consequently was consistent with the ratings that had been given during the readings of the folder. For interviewed men, however, the staff could personalize the report by describing the candidate with much more color and detail than had been recorded previously. The results of this private information could markedly influence the decisions. Since these data were not found in the folder or in the ratings, their influence would appear as error variance in the multiple correlations.

Now that we have the 1966 and 1968 results we must extend this explanation. The relative contribution of the two factors and two singletons to admissions decisions is shown in Table 16. For the Class of 1958, when staff interview information was present, there was a great tendency to emphasize personal qualities in the decisions; however, in the absence of the staff interview the academic ability measures were given great weight. In other words, in the absence of the "personalized" personal information the committee tended to use other qualities as a basis for assessment, namely, the academic ability factor and the principal's report.

The previous discussion about the equal importance of academic and personal factors in Class of 1958 decisions must be elaborated; the weights used in making decisions were dependent on the type of information which the committee had available. Keeping in mind this extension of the 1958 findings, we can use this perspective to examine the Class of 1968 results. First, consider the case of the interviewed candidates: for these men the weight given personal attributes has increased; not only has this information been drawn upon more heavily by the committee, but it has become formalized and is considered public and reliable information. In support of this position, decisions relying heavily on these variables are very consistent with the original reader ratings; the resulting multiple correlation for 1968 is 0.98. The case for the noninterviewed candidates has changed over this decade. Most pronounced has been the shift in weights given the academic and personal factors, which have changed from 51% and 28% to 23% and 51%, respectively. The committee, as evidenced in their actions, had in fact heeded and extended the suggestions given in the first report on this analysis which was prepared

Table 16 Contribution of factors to the admissions decisions

Factors	Candidates interviewed by staff		Candidates not interviewed by staff	
	Class of 1958	Class of 1968	Class of 1958	Class of 1968
Academic ability	33%	16%	51%	23%
Personal attributes	52%	60%	28%	51%
Principal's report	14%	21%	20%	24%
Athletics	1%	3%	1%	2%
Total	100%	100%	100%	100%

in 1956. The report indicated that there was considerable difference in the criteria established for admissions in cases where the staff interview was available, and suggested that if the committee wished to continue to stress personal attributes, it would have to continue as an integral part of its operational procedure to increase the number of candidates interviewed by staff members. Although a larger number of men are, in fact, interviewed now than in that period, it has been impossible for the staff to increase the percentage of applicants interviewed because of the burgeoning pool. What has been happening is that the committee has changed the weights in the decision process so that the same qualities are serving as criteria regardless of the availability of staff interview information. Since these criteria are based not on objective assessments but on clinical judgments of the individual cases, and all of the information about the cases is universally accessible, the discrepancies between the docket information and the committee decisions have increased.

Because of the magnitude of decrease in the multiple correlation, we ran the correlations on the Classes of 1967, 1969, and 1970 and found that 1968 results were part of a continuing pattern of change; they indicated that the decisions made without staff interview ratings available were less predictable than those where such information was available.

In summary, we have explored a number of ways of examining the variables used in the admissions decisions. The general trend of giving less weight to assessments of academic ability and more weight to personal attributes was documented in a variety of fashions—by simple tabulations, by simple correlations, by factor analysis, by rotated factor solutions, and by regression equations. While each style of analysis had merit and all pointed in the same direction, the more elegant solutions supplied material for richer interpretations; in fact, these abstractions were useful in inducing us to reformulate some hypotheses.

We should also make explicit that the abstract nature of a factor solution, by freeing data from the context of a real-life situation, and by permitting us to explore the interrelations among the variables, is a strength of this method; conversely, it is also one of the limitations of the factor analytic approach. Because the dimensions produced by the system are "detached" from the actual admissions process, we must tie them to the parameters of action that we know, through experience, do exist.

We shall attempt to place these findings in the context of actual admissions policy, for only by this interplay of the abstract and the actual can we really understand the situation. The stress on personal attributes should be construed as evidence not of an antiintellectual emphasis, but rather of a broad base of academic strength in the applicant group, one which enables the committee to expand expectations of quality to include personal characteristics that add diversity and style to the undergraduate body. From a statistical vantage point, the very fact that the personal and academic factors are correlated 0.46 illustrates that these two dimensions do have some common properties.

EXPLORATIONS IN VALIDATION

There are two methodological approaches by which to test the validity of a changing admissions policy. The first is to compare the performance of students admitted over the decade and establish which classes admitted under which policy compiled the best record. The second is to determine whether the independent variables are predictive of subsequent performance. Because of the problems of student inter-action, the former method would certainly be preferable if we had a control college to juxtapose against the experimental model.* However, as we shall see, the absence of controls makes this style of the evaluation elusive, even impossible. Examining the relation of the independent variables to the variety of criteria involves the difficult problem of determining whether relationships are causative or associative. This problem, as old as research, recalls to mind how Lazarsfeld, by showing the high r between fire losses and the number of fire engines at a fire, illustrates that correlation does not necessarily do a superb job of revealing a cause-and-effect relationship.

Let us use the data from admissions to exemplify these two approaches, their strengths, weaknesses, and most importantly, the findings.

Table 17   Percentage of students on dean's list and unsatisfactory in freshman year

Class	1958	1959	1964	1966	1968
% on Dean's List	40.9	41.8	46.1	47.3	51.8
% Unsatisfactory	10.6	10.3	9.7	5.5	4.8

The Class of 1958, during its freshmen year, had 40.9% on Dean's List as compared with 51.8% for the Class of 1968. Similarly, 10.6% of the Class of 1958 were unsatisfactory, as compared with 4.8% for the Class of 1968. We have commented briefly on the change in the prediction equation which seemed to reflect the changes in the attitudes of the public and private school students toward educa-tion—were these in turn a reflection of the admissions policy, or of the changing times far beyond the microcosm of the college? As we can see from Table 17, academic performance has been consistently improving. To imply that this was primarily a function of the admissions policy, or more specifically, the result of the emphasis on personal attributes, would be to distort many realities of the college during this decade and to ignore the instructional and administrative changes that have taken place during the period. Most notable of these probably have been the improvement in the freshman advising system, the development of a freshman seminar program, and the recognition and implementation of advanced placement and advanced standing programs. Such an interpretation would also ignore the

---

* Equally important would be followup of the rejected applicants; however, even such evalua-tion is fraught with methodological hazards.

Table 18   SAT-V score versus graduation standing, Classes of 1962 and 1964

SAT-V	Graduated on schedule, %		Total Class of 1962 graduated as of 1964, %	Graduated on schedule with honors, %		Graduated on schedule *magna* or better, %	
	1962	1964		1962	1964	1962	1964
700–800	77.3	73.0	90.5	55.9	60.1	28.4	29.0
600–699	73.0	75.5	87.5	48.3	49.6	18.6	19.2
500–599	81.0	74.3	90.0	37.2	34.0	7.1	10.2
Below 500	84.2	77.8	87.0	26.3	22.2	5.3	11.1
Total	76.3	74.5	88.9	46.8	51.2	18.4	21.4

fact that even though the scores were deemphasized as selection criteria, because of the increased score strength of the applicant pool the score median of the class rose during the period of Classes 1958 to 1963. Without any control model against which comparison can be made, these results permit little comment on the validity of admissions procedures, especially at the subtle level which we have been exploring. The fact that the variable admit-reject has moved closer over this decade to the location of the athletic rating may be the reason why we have seen more winning teams. Student activities in social service, drama, and music (see the President's report, 1963–64, for special comment) have never seemed as pronounced as recently, but again no comparative information is available.

An interesting set of relationships are those among ratings, scores, and graduation performance of students. During the early part of the decade there was a sizable relation between the SAT-V score and degree completion (see Table 18); however, this has disappeared and, in fact, for several recent years there has actually been a small negative relationship. A positive relationship still exists between scores and graduation standing, most notably for those students graduating *magna cum laude* or higher. However, decreased effectiveness of the scores as predictors of graduation standing or graduation on schedule tends overtly to substantiate the committee's policy of placing less emphasis on the academic ability measures.

Added to this shift in score and graduation relationships are some interesting personal ratings and graduation standing findings. Table 19 shows the performance of the Classes of 1962 and 1964 as related to their personal ratings. In terms of graduating on schedule and with honors, those students with high personal ratings do somewhat better than their classmates. In view of the admissions policy which we have been analyzing, a most logical hypothesis would be that these variables (personal ratings and graduation standing) have an inverse relationship. (For more extensive discussion of these points see Glimp and Whitla, 1964.) The reason for such a hypothesis is that students who have low personal ratings are generally admitted only if they possess outstanding academic strengths, while those

Table 19   Personal ratings versus graduation standing, Classes of 1962 and 1964

Personal rating	Graduated on schedule, %		Graduated with honors, %		Graduated *magna* or better, %	
	1962	1964	1962	1964	1962	1964
1	86.3	72.7	57.0	50.0	33.3	24.2
2	77.3	76.8	47.3	50.3	17.6	19.7
3	75.7	76.1	46.6	53.6	17.3	22.0
4	72.1	60.6	48.4	46.8	20.5	25.5
5	68.8	40.0	18.8	40.0	12.5	00.0
Total	75.5	74.7	46.2	51.4	18.4	21.4

with high personal ratings are admitted if they are thought to possess sufficient ability to survive academically. Hence those with high personal ratings will have, on the average, less academic strength than will those of low personal ratings;* consequently, we would expect higher academic performance from those who had low personal ratings. However, as we have seen, a small positive relation does exist between personal ratings and academic performance. Therefore, personal strengths seem to be relevant to the intellectual life of the college. Henry Dyer proposed the hypothesis that the committee takes special care in admitting those men who are predicted to do poorly, and that this care is effective in selecting those who can do better than their predictions—which is remarkable, considering that the predictions are already regressed. Willingham (1964) documented the fact that those men predicted to do poorly at Georgia Institute of Technology also do better than predicted, though he could find no special reason to explain their behavior. If we, for lack of a better hypothesis, assume that the committee does have the ability to improve the predictions through its clinical wisdom† then we can effectively extend this argument to explain the reduction in SAT-V graduation standing correlation. Quite simply, the more men with low academic prediction who are admitted by the committee and who do in fact beat their prediction, the smaller will be the relationship between scores and graduation standing. Clearly, the phenomena on which these speculations are based do occur; the analyses show that personal attributes are weighted much more heavily in the decision process and that the score-graduation standing relationship has decreased.

We can extend the argument one more stage: If all (or nearly all) students were selected on the basis of personal attributes, since this appears to be a measure of effectiveness, then the correlation between scores and graduation performance would increase. We have some evidence that the correlation between scores and

---

* The references to a positive relationship between personal and academic strengths was for the candidate group; for the admitted candidates a small negative relationship exists.
† There is little evidence currently in the literature to support this position; see especially Meehl, 1954, Chap. 8.

graduation performance on most recently tabulated classes has increased slightly; however, we shall have to have several more years to document this occurrence as part of a trend.

Although the data that we have mesh with these speculations, there are undoubtedly many other theories which have equal or even more validity. Nevertheless, as we sift ideas that might explain these relationships, the thinking outlined above seems to be most plausible to those engaged in admissions.

To introduce nonacademic external criteria by which to judge our decisions, we have in process a series of studies to try to relate admissions information to styles of collegiate and life performance. We would like to be able to compare the evaluations of men given at the time of admission on the basis of a paper portfolio with their subsequent activities and performance in college. We can't help asking ourselves questions: In the process of reading admissions folders, do we read with a precision and validity that yield us a true sense of the kind of man represented by the available information? Do certain types of men respond in a certain way to the Harvard environment? Following up on this tendency to advocate diversity, we have instituted a typology study to see whether we can evaluate the relationship between the personal and intellectual style of the candidate at the time of admission on the one hand, and his development in college on the other. The admissions staff has used a series of prepared definitions to classify descriptively the members of several recent classes as the staff saw these candidates at admission time. We have also gathered from freshman advisers information about these men to compare against the original descriptions.

A few findings from our work to date show that the advisers and proctors tended to see the men during the freshman year as they were seen through the admissions folder. They also gave the highest overall assessment to freshmen classified by the staff at admission as "scholars," and liked best (as did the staff) the group of "all-American" boys (so classified on the basis of their all-around school participation and personal strengths).

We are also using admissions and college variables as predictors of life styles of our graduates, examining the relationships which exist among various experiences, background characteristics, abilities, and attitudes of graduates.

In our society, the minimum educational experience necessary for entry into a large number of occupations is a college education. The tacit assumption has been made that the baccalaureate degree provides the entry into a vocational role and hence is itself an index of success. Now this conception of the criterion has been extended from degree completion to college grades and degree of honors. The adoption of grades as a criterion has, however, been accepted with little validation.* The tendency to base studies on grade and degree completion criteria, however, has been encouraged by difficulty in getting ultimate criteria.

---

* With one exception, namely, the self-fulfilling hypothesis that grades have validity in admissions to graduate schools. Recently, several studies demonstrating the superficiality of college grades as the "gold standard" were conducted by NSF. It was found that those who became contributors in science were not identified by college grades or scores but by references.

The broad acceptance of the proposition that "the good life" is available to the college graduate and that a college education is an economically valuable product both for the individual and for the nation has expanded the pool from which we draw our college group to include a much larger population than that of the upper and upper-middle classes of the past. The broadened base, both in numbers and in variety of types of individuals applying to college (in conjunction with increased financial aid), has given those in admissions choices that were previously unavailable. Only since the end of World War II have colleges had the fiscal freedom that gave them the privilege of rejecting the affluent applicant. For the first time the admissions officer has reason to make serious inquiry into the relationships that may exist between the different forms of excellence exhibited by candidates for admission and the contributions to the world at large made by different types of graduates. Out of such inquiry we are coming to the realization that styles of output are a legitimate admissions concern.

Only recently, too, has a methodology been created that is sufficiently audacious and eclectic to undertake such a task of evaluation. The subtleties and complexities of education as viewed by Henry Adams would not have permitted such group examination, nor would the psychology of William James.

In our concern with the life style of a person, we are attempting, first, to gain a better perspective on the characteristics which affect him as an individual in a particular social structure, and we are thus concerned with the impact of a person's family background both as it affects his achievement in the college setting and as it affects his occupational choice and subsequent development. Second, we hope to learn whether traditional college admissions criteria predict the life style which an individual develops in his post-college years.

Several of our precollege and college variables were effective as predictors of occupational choice. The most effective predictor was graduation standing, followed by predicted college grade average, College Board SAT verbal score, father's occupation, and secondary school rank in class. We have also found a tendency for sons of professional fathers to enter professional occupations regardless of graduation standing, a fact suggesting that the family must have created expectations about occupational choice which influenced these men. Interestingly, there did not seem to be such family expectations of those from blue-collar backgrounds; from this point of view, these people seem to have a wider range of real possibilities in terms of occupational choice.

Our initial exploration produced no significant relationships between our predictor variables and "grades in life." This nonfinding, if indeed it can be validated, has great significance, for it demonstrates that the Harvard experience is a powerful agent in reducing the normal effect of socioeconomic background. As McClelland has stated, the "simple assumption that a son will achieve the same level of success as his father" is a tough one to beat. Yet our data demonstrate that this assumption doesn't hold true for graduates of Harvard College.

In summary, we have been trying to illustrate the kinds of research useful on the complex problems of admissions and the valuable information that systematic analyses can provide to those responsible for admission decisions. For example, it has been possible to demonstrate rather effectively that criteria for admission to Harvard College have been changing, and to point to reasons that have made this change possible. When a group of applicants does become sufficiently able academically, then a college has the opportunity of emphasizing any of several admissions criteria. This committee has chosen to emphasize diversity of personal and academic strengths. We must now continue to explore what happens to this variety of types in the college climate and in later life. With a fuller understanding of the variables we use and the interrelationships among these variables, we shall also come to know more about the development of men in the educational environment of our society.

REFERENCES

"Effects of coaching on scholastic aptitude test scores." New York: College Entrance Examination Board, 1965

COOLEY, W. W., and P. R. LOHNES, *Multivariate Procedures for the Behavioral Sciences.* New York: John Wiley & Sons, 1962

FRENCH, J., "The validity of new tests for the performance of college students with high-level aptitude." *ETS Research Bulletin 63–7,* 1960

GLIMP, F. L., and D. K. WHITLA, "Admissions and performance in the college." *Harvard Alumni Bulletin,* January 1964

McNEMAR, Q. *Psychological Statistics.* New York: John Wiley & Sons, 1963.

MEEHL, P. H., *Statistical Versus Clinical Prediction.* Minneapolis: University of Minnesota Press, 1954, Chapter 8

OLSEN, M., and SCHRADER, B., "The predictive effectiveness of four part scores composed of scholastic aptitude test item types." *ETS Statistical Report 57–18,* 1954

OLSEN, MARJORIE, "Summary of main findings on the validity of the CEEB tests of developed ability as predictors of college grades." *ETS Statistical Report 57–41,* 1957

PEARSON, K., "Notes," 1920, in T. L. Kelley, *Fundamentals of Statistics.* Cambridge: Harvard University Press, 1947, pp. 332–395

WILLINGHAM, W. W., *E. S. Memorandum #67.* Georgia Institute of Technology, May 1964

WILLINGHAM, W. W., Mimeographed paper, College Entrance Examination Board (8 pages), 1965

AUTHOR INDEX

491

SUBJECT INDEX

ABCDE698